To
Dory, Allan, and John,
who have the courage
of my convictions

In the fields of observation,
chance favors only the
prepared mind.

LOUIS PASTEUR

JERRY A. BELL, *Editor*

CHEMICAL PRINCIPLES IN PRACTICE

ADDISON-WESLEY PUBLISHING COMPANY

READING, MASSACHUSETTS

PALO ALTO

LONDON

DON MILLS, ONTARIO

This book is in the

ADDISON-WESLEY SERIES IN CHEMISTRY

FRANCIS T. BONNER, *Consulting Editor*

PREFACE

PRINCIPLES

I have assumed that you, both students and instructors, enjoy independent discovery. Your extended library and laboratory investigations give you opportunities to develop your critical faculties. To develop them efficiently and well, however, remember Pasteur's statement: "In the fields of observation, chance favors only the prepared mind."*

What are the characteristics of a "prepared mind"? Knowledge and activity are the most significant attributes. Preparation must certainly involve learning the skills and techniques of your particular calling. The laboratory problems in this book are intended in part to give you practice in techniques—not just those usually considered to be the techniques of chemistry, but also those of mathematics, an indispensable scientific tool. However, simply attaining such skills is not enough to ensure that your mind will be prepared; it must also be active. An "active" mind exhibits the priceless habit of carefully weighing experience. You can become a questioning observer if you are now only a passive one. All your faculties improve with practice, and thinking is no exception. If you learn nothing else from this book except to apply your mind well to the experiences which accost it at every moment of the day, your time will have been well spent.

---

* Pasteur here gives us a succinct definition of serendipity—what some people incorrectly call "luck." The etymology of the term "serendipity" is entertainingly outlined in the introduction to a translation of the fable which inspired Horace Walpole's original definition, *Serendipity and the Three Princes; From the Peregrinaggio of 1557*, ed. by T. G. Remer, Norman, Okla., University of Oklahoma Press, 1965.

PRACTICE

Traditionally, the authors of textbooks wish their users a smooth journey through the text; my fondest hope is that courses that use this textbook will not run smoothly. The main path I suggest is free of deliberate roadblocks, but I hope you will be tempted to stray often enough from the straight and narrow to make trouble for yourself. If there are no taxing situations, no places for students and instructors to learn together, then neither of you will really have much fun.

There are many places in the text where you can and must exercise your imagination and creativity. When an experiment involves a great deal of new technique, the procedure is given in detail so that you will not have to waste your time groping. On the other hand, in some sections of the book there is very little technical detail and you must devise your own approach. You will find questions posed on nearly every page; the text will seem to be much more alive (as will you) if you tackle these questions when they arise. At the end of almost every experiment there are suggestions for experimental problems that go beyond those presented in detail. To answer these questions, conceptual and experimental, you must recall the ideas you have taken from lectures, homework, collateral reading, discussion, and laboratory work, which you have examined and made your own.

Your imagination may—and, I hope, will—lead to improvements and refinements on the material presented. You may find a much improved method of data reduction for an experiment; you may develop a way to answer one of the experimental problems that is much better than the one presented; you may find that a proposed experiment leads nowhere. I would like very much to hear about any interesting ideas.

You, instructors especially, might like to know how the material presented here has been and will be used. You will be able to use the text most creatively if you allow plenty of time for each problem undertaken. My own classes do about one-half the experiments in a full year general chemistry course with two three-hour laboratory sessions each week.* Toward the end of the course we provide some "free-choice" laboratory time so that each student can choose an unassigned experiment that intrigues him, refine an experiment already done, or develop his own ideas. This material, supplemented by several of the myriad specialized paperbacks available, could be used as the skeleton upon which to build both the laboratory and lecture portions of a course. I hope that you also will write to me if you have any suggestions for possible new experiments, for extensions of the ones presented, or for unconventional uses for the book.

---

* Many of the experiments are useful for second and third year courses following a relatively traditional introductory course.

ACKNOWLEDGMENTS

The structure and philosophy of this text owe much to two laboratory texts, each excellent in its own way: Jürg Waser's *Quantitative Chemistry* (revised edition, W. A. Benjamin, New York, 1964) and Jay A. Young's *Practice in Thinking* (Prentice-Hall, Englewood Cliffs, N. J., 1958).

I owe a substantial debt, in all of the best parts of the text, to Leonard Nash's influence as teacher, colleague, and friend. Grateful and hearty thanks also go to all the contributors to this volume, listed in the table of contents with their experiments, without whom it would not have been possible. If the text is at all understandable and readable, it is due to the patient and constant help of my wife. All the obscurities and impediments left are my own.

Riverside, California   J.A.B.
April, 1967

CONTENTS

LABORATORY RULES

1) *Safety glasses or prescription glasses are mandatory at all times.*

2) Any injury, however slight, must be reported at once to the instructor.

3) Unassigned work is permitted, in fact, encouraged, but it must not be undertaken without previous consultation with the instructor.

4) All data are to be taken in a *bound* laboratory notebook with numbered pages. Taking data on loose scraps of paper will not be tolerated.

1 TOOLS, TECHNIQUES, TOTEMS, AND TABOOS

"Observation with me is second nature."

Sherlock Holmes in "A Study in Scarlet," A. CONAN DOYLE

1–1 QUANTITATIVE THINKING

Why was it that Sherlock Holmes was always able to pick out the details that solved the case, but Dr. Watson and Inspector Lestrade were left in the dark? Holmes had schooled himself in a certain way of thinking and observing. The ability to think and observe quantitatively is as essential to success in science as it is to the art of detection perfected by Holmes.

This text is designed to help you develop the skill of quantitative thinking, but it will require active participation on your part. A pencil and paper are the first essential tools necessary in preparing for and carrying out the laboratory work discussed. Before you even set foot in the laboratory, there will be background material and principles to be read, thought about, and digested. You should read actively. Does the text pose a problem or an illustrative example? Try your hand at solving the problem before reading the printed solution. Allow yourself time to think about the material you have read. What don't you understand? It is not necessary or expected that you will understand everything the first or even the second time through. Mark the sections that give you trouble and come back to them later. Will some secondary reading from the reference list at the end of the chapter help? Ask your instructor for his recommendations about collateral reading and about material you don't understand. Develop these study habits and you will soon find that you comprehend the points being made much more quickly and more clearly.

The laboratory instructions for each experiment are not recipes. In all cases there is quantitative thinking for you to do before coming to the laboratory. Sometimes your thinking will be guided by questions and instructions as you read the experiment; you will have to do other planning on your own. An outline of the operations you expect to carry out in the laboratory during a particular laboratory period will be very useful and will help you make economical use of your time. Do all the necessary calculations for an experiment before coming to the laboratory. Try to understand the reason for each of the operations you are to perform. Does a procedure call for the addition of 10 ml of a critical reagent to give the correct concentration? Calculate what concentration would be produced under the conditions of the experiment to see whether this volume is indeed correct. If you add too little or too much of the reagent, what effect will this have? Calculations on points like this will help you to gain insight concerning which parts of a procedure are most critical and what the effect of an error would be. Often such preliminary calculations can help you save an experiment by appropriate changes in procedure if you make a mistake at first.

Once in the laboratory, your quantitative thinking is reinforced by physical confrontation with quantities. Is 1 gm of a reagent the amount held on the tip of your spatula or a heaping spatulaful? Does your test tube contain 5 ml or 15 ml of reagent? The ability to answer such questions is a matter of practice and observation. Developing this ability is essential for efficient laboratory work. As a result of the habits developed during your preparation for the laboratory work, an extension of your quantitative thinking should not be difficult.

The ultimate goal of all your work is an appreciation for the direction and the order of magnitude of effects. For example, for the experiments discussed in this textbook, weighing errors on the analytical balance are said to be "negligible." "Negligible with respect to what?" should be your immediate response to such a statement.

1

If the substance weighed has a mass of 1 gm, the weighing error is about one part in 10,000 (0.1 mg) and can be neglected if other errors are much larger, as they usually are. On the other hand, if 10 mg is weighed, the error is one part in 100 and can probably no longer be neglected. "Negligible" is, therefore, a relative term, as are other adjectives expressing value judgments, like "fast," "hot," and "small." A good rule of thumb is always to search for a quantitative qualifier for any such adjective. As you get more and more in the habit of quantitative thinking, this response will become automatic.

As you use this textbook, during the first stages of your development, many of the pitfalls will be worked out of the experiments for you. As you go on, however, it will become your responsibility to plan and carry out your own experiments, and the role of quantitative thinking will become paramount. You need to learn the limitations of your equipment and of the techniques available. You must ascertain whether it is feasible to obtain the effect that you wish or whether some change in your system during the experiment will completely swamp the effect of interest. The experimenter who has learned to question quantitatively in all situations can save hours, days, or even years of labor on a fruitless experiment.

1-2 THE LIBRARY

Your knowledge of the library is an important tool for successful work in chemistry (and in all other areas). A few moments spent in the library will often eliminate hours of frustrating and fruitless laboratory time. Here are a few guidelines for library use:

1) Find out what the cataloging system is and how the catalog numbers are arranged on the shelves. With this information you can use the card catalog to find the call number of a topic and will immediately know where to go to find the books you wish.

2) Learn the locations of the periodicals which you might consult most often. In this text you will be advised to look at periodicals such as *Scientific American*, The *Journal of Chemical Education* (*J. Chem. Ed.*), and The *Journal of the American Chemical Society* (*J. Amer. Chem. Soc.*). To find some specific piece of information somewhere in the chemistry periodical literature, your best starting point is *Chemical Abstracts*. The librarian or your instructor can show you how to use it.

3) Spend a little time familiarizing yourself with the reference and reserve books that are available. As a relative novice to the fascinating field of chemistry you may feel that much of the content of the chemistry collection will be unfathomable to you. But how can you say this before you try? The following quotation,

which is taken somewhat out of context from Companion's text *Chemical Bonding* (McGraw-Hill, New York, 1964), is quite *apropos*:

Frequently a student's inability to grasp a difficult concept is due not to his innate impenetrability but rather to a particular author's lack of "penetrating power." ... However, early in the game it is useful to learn to scan difficult treatises in search of a clarifying paragraph, sentence, word or picture—and then pounce on it! It is a rare scientific work which is completely comprehensible to the average reader on its first reading.

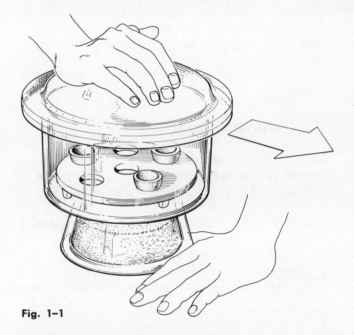

Fig. 1-1

1-3 THE DESICCATOR

Desiccators (Fig. 1-1) are chambers with airtight lids, usually made of glass but sometimes of plastic or metal. The seal between the lid and the body of a glass desiccator is made by a flat ground-glass flange which is lightly greased to increase airtightness. To open the desiccator, slide the lid aside *slowly*, as indicated in Fig. 1-1. This is a precaution to avoid any rapid rush of air into the desiccator which could blow particles of sample out of their containers. Inside the desiccator is a plate pierced with holes, to hold crucibles and weighing bottles steady if the desiccator is moved.

The purpose of the desiccator is to keep objects dry, not to dry them in the first place.* To maintain a dry atmosphere, a desiccant is placed in the bottom part of

---

* At room temperature, with air in the desiccator to impede the diffusion of water molecules, it would take months or years to achieve the drying results of an hour or so in an oven at 120°C.

the desiccator. Anhydrous calcium sulfate (Drierite®) and anhydrous calcium chloride are usually used for routine work because they are much safer than other more potent drying agents like phosphorus pentoxide and concentrated sulfuric acid. Obviously, desiccators will function best if they are kept closed as much as possible.

If a desiccator needs to be recharged with drying agent, open it and move the samples to another desiccator. Remove the desiccator plate, wipe the old grease off the rim and the lid, discard the used desiccant, and wipe out the desiccator with a dry cloth. Apply a light film of stopcock grease to the rim and the lid and press them together to make a good seal and to press the grease into an even film. Remove the lid carefully and use a rolled paper cone as a funnel to add new desiccant to the bottom part of the desiccator. This procedure prevents desiccant "dust" from coating the upper part of the desiccator, where it could contaminate samples, and from getting into the grease on the rim, where it would prevent a good seal. Replace the desiccator plate and the samples and put on the lid.

1-4 THE THERMOMETER

The most common type of thermometer is a bulb of mercury attached to a fine graduated glass capillary. The length of the mercury thread in the capillary is proportional to the temperature, since mercury, like all substances, changes its volume as the temperature changes.

To assign numbers to the graduation marks, a temperature scale is first defined, for instance by choosing the ice point of water at atmospheric pressure as zero and the steam point of water at atmospheric pressure as 100.* A mercury thermometer without any calibration marks is placed in an ice bath and the position of the mercury column is marked. Next, this thermometer is placed in a steam bath and the new position of the mercury column is marked. The distance between the two marks labeled 0 and 100 is measured and divided by 100. The result is the size of the "degree" expressed as a length along the mercury column. Beginning at the zero mark, we now make marks a "degree length" apart along the whole column, assigning to each one a number which we call a temperature. Each "degree length" can be further subdivided into tenths, hundredths, etc., of "degrees." (There are many hidden assumptions in the procedure. Which ones can you find?)

® Drierite is a registered trademark of W. A. Hammond Drierite Co.
* This is no longer the standard definition of temperature (see Section 2–1) but it is close enough to the standard to be valid for our purposes.

Actually, thermometers are not individually calibrated as indicated in the last paragraph. They are made in a standard way from precision bore capillaries, and the same scale is put on each thermometer on the assumption that the manufacturing process is accurate. Before using any thermometer, you should test this assumption on at least one temperature; the most convenient point is 0°C. Make a mixture of ice and distilled water in a beaker and stir it for about a minute with the thermometer to be tested. Read the thermometer and record this reading. If you assume that the whole scale calibration is off by exactly the same amount, you can correct all the temperatures read with this thermometer as follows:

$$t_c = t_a - t_0, \tag{1-1}$$

where t_c is the corrected value of the temperature, t_a is the apparent temperature read on the thermometer, and t_0 is the thermometer reading in the 0°C bath; the subtraction is made algebraically.

Illustrative Example: A thermometer reads -0.2°C in an ice bath. It is used to measure the temperature of a solution and reads 35.3°C. What is the true (corrected) temperature of the solution?

$$t_c = 35.3 - (-0.2) = 35.5°C.$$

You can check the assumption that the thermometer correction is the same along the whole scale by checking the thermometer at other reference temperatures with other constant temperature baths. A list of other reference temperatures is given in most handbooks.

Sometimes you will find it necessary to measure the temperature of two solutions simultaneously, in which case it is advantageous to calibrate one thermometer relative to the other. Label the thermometers A and B and let A be the reference thermometer. Place the thermometers next to each other in the same beaker of water and, after waiting a few minutes to ensure temperature equilibrium, read the thermometers. Call these temperature readings t_{A1} and t_{B1}. To adjust a temperature read on thermometer B, t_B, to the temperature which would be read by thermometer A in the same situation, t_{BA}, use the formula

$$t_{BA} = t_B + (t_{A1} - t_{B1}). \tag{1-2}$$

1-5 THE BURNER

The two major uses for the laboratory gas burner are heating solutions and working glass. Often in experimental work electrical heat could be substituted for gas. However, since gas burners are far more economical, they are commonly used in all cases where inflammable substances are not being heated. In glassworking there is no substitute for a flame.

A common type of laboratory burner is shown in Fig. 1–2. The fuel gas flow is regulated by the gas valve, to which your burner is attached by a length of thin-walled rubber or plastic tubing. Check this tubing periodically to make sure that it has not sprung any leaks that might allow gas to escape into the room forming a potentially explosive gas-air mixture. Although the particular arrangement shown in Fig. 1–2 is not universal, all burners have some means of controlling the intake of air. When the burner is in use, the fuel (which in most laboratories is natural gas, consisting mostly of methane, CH_4, with smaller amounts of other hydrocarbons) mixes with air in the barrel of the burner and burns at the top of the barrel, as indicated in the figure.

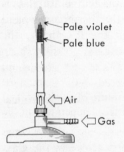

Pale violet
Pale blue

Air

Gas

Fig. 1–2. The laboratory burner.

The first step in using your burner is to shut off the air intake; then turn on the gas and light the flame. The flame will be quite luminous, yellow, and probably smoky. Water will condense on a cold glass held over the flame for a moment, and soot (largely carbon particles formed from partially burned fuel gas) will also be deposited. The carbon is not completely oxidized because when the air intake is closed, there is an insufficient supply of oxygen to the flame. For the gas to be oxidized at all, oxygen from the air must diffuse into the flame; therefore most of the combustion takes place at the surface of the flame, where the fuel and the oxidant first meet. The more flame surface there is, the better the chance that combustion can occur, and the flame is usually quite large. Because the combustion is incomplete and the release of energy is spread over such a large area, this type of flame is relatively cool.

Now, by slowly opening the air intake, you can admit air to the gas stream before it reaches the top of the barrel producing an almost invisible blue-violet flame. In this way the supply of oxidant is intimately mixed with the fuel, and combustion can occur throughout the flame. Since its surface is no longer so important, the flame contracts and can be adjusted as shown in the figure to form a well-shaped cone with two distinct conical regions. The inner pale blue region contains mostly hot unburned fuel and air. The inner cone is called the *reducing region* of the flame because the hot fuel can react here to reduce materials. This is the coolest area of the flame. At the surface between the two cones there is a bright luminous region in which most of the combustion occurs. The oxygen diffusing in from the surrounding air and the oxygen within the gas-air mixture combine here to provide very favorable conditions for complete oxidation of the fuel. This is the hottest region of the flame; the best place to hold objects to be heated is just above this inner cone. The outer, pale violet cone, consisting mostly of hot combustion products and air, is called the *oxidizing region* of the flame because the hot oxidized products and oxygen can oxidize materials placed here.

If the air intake is opened too much, an unstable flame will be produced which often separates from the top of the burner and hangs suspended above it. Usually this flame is so unstable that it simply blows out, whereupon you should shut off the air intake and try the whole operation again. More seriously, however, sometimes this sort of flame will "flash back"; the flame will travel down the barrel of the burner and burn at the jet where the fuel is admitted to the barrel. If this happens and you do not realize that the flame is still burning at the bottom of the barrel and rapidly heating up the burner, your first warning that something has gone wrong will be the strong odor of charring rubber or plastic as the fuel line begins to melt. Turn off the fuel supply at the gas valve immediately. When the burner has cooled enough so that you can touch it to adjust the air intake, relight it, and be careful not to open the air intake quite so far in the future. When you have finished using your burner, shut it off by closing the gas valve.

1–6   GLASSWORKING

Much of the equipment used in chemical laboratories is made of glass. Glass has a number of advantages for this purpose: it is almost completely impervious to chemical attack, quite easy to form into intricate shapes, easy to seal to itself without "glue" or connectors, and transparent (an advantage that is often overlooked). Glass used in the laboratory can usually be classified into two categories: soft glass and hard glass. Soft glass can be bent and worked in the temperature range 600 to 800°C. It has a high coefficient of thermal expansion and is unsuitable for making complex apparatus, since relatively small differences in temperature between the parts can cause the glass to crack. Hard glass (such as Pyrex®, Kimax®, etc.) has a working temperature in the range 800 to 1100°C. It has a much lower coefficient of

---

® Pyrex is a registered trademark of Corning Glass Works.
® Kimax is a registered trademark of Owens-Illinois.

thermal expansion and is ideal for construction of laboratory apparatus. Hard glass, moreover, is attacked less readily by strongly basic solutions than is soft glass. As a result, almost all laboratory glassware is made of hard glass.

For our purposes, hard glass has one important disadvantage; it requires a higher working temperature than is attainable with the gas-air burner that you have (a gas-oxygen torch would be needed). Therefore, we shall discuss how to perform some simple but useful operations on soft-glass tubing and rods which can be worked at the temperature of your burner.

The word *practice* will appear numerous times in this discussion. Glassworking (and glassblowing) is a craft, and good glassblowers are skilled artisans, who developed their skills by patience and practice. You too can become a skilled glassworker if you take pride in your workmanship.

Cutting, Fire-Polishing, and Annealing

To cut a piece of glass tubing or rod, first make a scratch on the piece of glass at the place where you wish to cut it. A sharp triangular file (or "glass knife") is used to make the scratch. Hold the file so that the piece of glass can be grasped firmly between the file and your thumb with the file at right angles to the piece of glass (Fig. 1–3). Grasp the free end of the glass with your other hand,

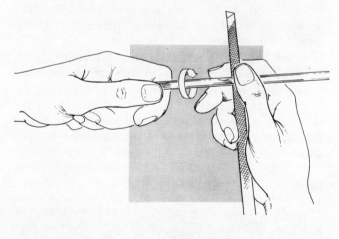

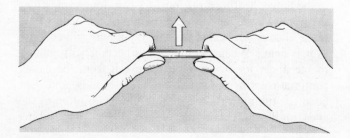

Fig. 1–3. Cutting glass tubing.

and rotate the glass and the file in opposite directions so that you make a scratch about one-quarter to one-third of the way around the glass. (It is a good idea to protect your thumb with a towel while making a scratch.) If this operation is done with dispatch and firmness, there will be no need to repeat it. In any case, do not "saw" at the glass with the file, as this will dull the file and probably shatter the glass and wound you.

Hold the piece of glass with the scratch away from you, with your two thumbs opposite the scratch. Gently but firmly "bend" the glass with your thumbs and, at the same time, pull the two ends apart. You should be rewarded by a sharp "click" and two pieces of glass with relatively square ends where the cut was made. Again, it is a wise idea to protect your hands with a towel during this operation. If the cut end of the glass is jagged, it can be smoothed by briskly stroking a piece of wire gauze against it.

All freshly cut pieces of glass have dangerously sharp edges which must be fire-polished. To fire-polish the end of the tube or rod you have just cut, hold the glass horizontally with one hand and place the end in the hottest part of a blue flame. Rotate the piece continuously so the end is evenly heated. The flame should soon become bright yellow as some of the sodium atoms in the glass are "boiled out" emitting the characteristic yellow sodium D-lines. The glass will begin to soften and the sharp edges will be smoothed. Remove the glass from the flame before it begins to flow or the ends of rods will become bulbous and the ends of tubing will collapse.

At this point, when you have finished working your glass, the glass has been heated to its softening point. Usually this heating has not been uniform enough to prevent strains from developing within the glass. Therefore the strains need to be annealed out. Annealing is accomplished by heating the glass in a flame that is cool enough so the glass will not soften, but hot enough so that an internal flow will heal the strains. The luminous yellow burner flame that results when the air intake is nearly closed is at the right temperature. Rotate the piece of glass that you wish to anneal in this flame until it is evenly covered with soot and then allow it to cool slowly. This uniform heating and slow cooling helps to ensure that the strains are relieved and that new ones are not created in the cooling process.

The precautions mentioned below (Section 1–7) concerning heated containers of solution apply to hot pieces of worked glass as well. Do not place them directly on a laboratory bench. Not only is this bad for benches, particularly painted wooden ones, but the sudden cooling might crack the glass. A piece of asbestos or a wire screen acts as a good support. Remember the old adage: *Hot glass looks the same as cold glass.* Burned fingers and broken glass usually reward forgetfulness.

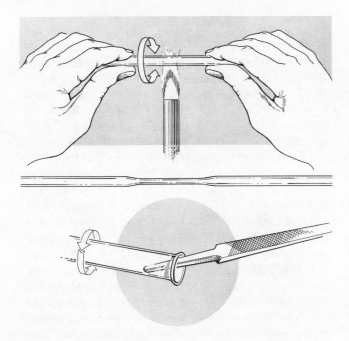

Fig. 1–4. Two of the operations in making a dropper.

Droppers

It is convenient to have a few droppers with varying orifice sizes for delivering different sized drops of reagents. A long dropper is handy for getting solutions from the bottom of deep narrow containers like test tubes.

Making droppers will give you practice in one of the most important glassworking operations: rotating a piece of glass in the flame. If the glass is not rotated in the flame, it will sag, thicken, and become nonuniform. Even after the glass is removed from the flame, it should be rotated as long as it is soft to prevent sagging. Practice rotating a piece of glass without heating it before you try to do any glassworking. Hold the piece of glass with both hands and rotate it, using your thumbs, index, and middle fingers. Use the ring finger of one hand as a support for the glass. For most people this operation is easiest with both palms down (Fig. 1–4) but this is a matter of preference and you should develop a technique which is comfortable for you. Practice until your motion is smooth and uniform.

For the real test, select a piece of 6 mm (outside diameter) soft glass tubing about 25 cm long and rotate it in the hottest part of a blue flame so that the middle 1 to 2 cm are uniformly heated. This will require some lateral motion. Do not allow the tubing to bend and do not pull on the ends, as this will cause the tube to become thin where it is heated. The whole operation requires good coordination of your hand movements, since when the glass is soft you can twist it and move the tube ends independently, creating glass pretzels

rather than a uniformly heated straight glass tube. You should allow the tube walls to thicken slightly, as they do naturally as a result of their own surface tension. When the tube is soft and slightly thickened, remove it from the flame (keep rotating it), wait about three seconds, and *gently* pull the two ends straight away from each other. The heated portion of the tube will be drawn down and constricted (Fig. 1–4). The farther you separate the ends, the smaller the constriction will be. Allow the glass to cool and cut the tube at the middle of the constriction. (Be careful. The walls may be thin and fragile.) Annealing and fire-polishing should be done carefully since it is easy to collapse and bend this drawn tubing.

The dropper bulb will fit better if you flare the bulb end of the dropper. To do this, heat the end of the tubing as for fire-polishing, but allow it to get softer. Remove it from the flame and use the warmed handle of the file, as shown in Fig. 1–4, to form a lip while you rotate the tube. (Do not make the lip any larger than is necessary for the bulb to fit snugly.) Then anneal.

Stirring Rods

Glass rods with diameters of about 3 to 4 mm with fire-polished ends are useful for stirring, guiding liquids when pouring, etc. For special purposes like crushing lumps of precipitate, shaped ends are sometimes convenient. To make an end which is a glass disk perpendicular to the rod, heat the end until it has thickened to about one-and-one-half times its original diameter and then press the rod perpendicularly against a flat surface (e.g., a heated knife blade, a sheet of Transite®, etc.). Heat the glass just enough to smooth out any imperfections and anneal. A paddle shape may be made in the same way except that the soft end is flattened parallel to the axis of the rod by squeezing it between two heated flat surfaces, such as the jaws of crucible tongs. Heat to smooth out imperfections and anneal.

Bends

To make a bend, you will have to heat a relatively long section of tubing, so attach the flame spreader to your burner before lighting it (Fig. 1–5). Rotate the tubing in the flame, heating a section 3 to 4 cm long centered at the point where you wish the middle of the bend to be. If the glass is not heated enough, the tubing will collapse as it is bent. When the tubing has become soft enough to sag under its own weight, remove it from the flame, continue rotating it for two or three seconds, and then bend the tubing with one smooth upward motion of the ends until you obtain the desired angle. The tubing

---

® Transite is a registered trademark of Johns-Manville Co.

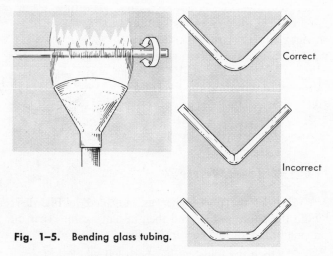

Fig. 1-5. Bending glass tubing.

should all be in one plane. The bend is made with the bent part of the tube down so that the downward flow of the glass under the influence of gravity will help to maintain the round cross section of the tubing. Hold the tubing until it is cool enough not to deform under its own weight and anneal. Reheating to "fix" a bad bend is not an easy task, since it is next to impossible to rotate bent tubing (Fig. 1-5). Practice until you can make bends correctly the first time.

Inserting Tubing into Stoppers

Although this is not strictly a glassworking technique, many of your first efforts will finally involve the insertion of a piece of tubing through a rubber stopper. Make sure that both the stopper hole and the tubing are well wetted and keep them wet throughout the operation or you will have great difficulty. Work the tubing into the stopper with a rotational motion. *Protect your hands with a towel and grasp the tubing very close to the stopper* as you work it in. Working without protection and/or holding the tubing far away from the stopper invites disaster.

1-7   HEATING SOLUTIONS

Solutions may be heated either in containers supported over the flame by a ring stand and wire gauze or in containers held "by hand" directly over the flame. The containers should *never* be held with the fingers (unless you happen to have asbestos skin) because when they get hot you are likely to drop an important solution or to raise large blisters on your hand. The more pleasant alternative is to use a test-tube holder or a handle made of stiff paper, as shown in Fig. 1-6. Do not use crucible tongs or forceps to hold containers over the flame. These are awkward to handle and can crush thin-walled flasks and test tubes.

Flasks and test tubes are the best containers to use for heating solutions, since they are easy to handle when hot. Beakers must sometimes be used, especially when precipitations are to be made and the precipitates transferred to a filter. (In this case, cover the beaker with a watch glass to reduce the chance of your losing solution.)

"Bumping" will be the greatest hazard to you, your experiment, and your classmates when you heat a solution. Bumping occurs when a small region of the liquid becomes superheated and suddenly vaporizes, creating a large bubble that makes the liquid "bump" sending some drops flying out of the container. Containers held directly over the flame should be continuously swirled or shaken to prevent the buildup of superheated regions. The chances of superheating a liquid in a container supported over a flame may be greatly diminished by placing a stirring rod in the container and applying the heat directly under the spot where the rod rests on the bottom. The stirring rod serves to distribute the heat more evenly, and the imperfections on its surface promote the formation of small bubbles of vapor. If it is at all feasible, you should use boiling chips when heating solutions. These are either chips of porcelain or small bits of carborundum, both of which have jagged edges to promote the formation of small bubbles of vapor. (Boiling chips cannot be used, for example, if you plan to weigh a solid that is precipitated from the solution.)

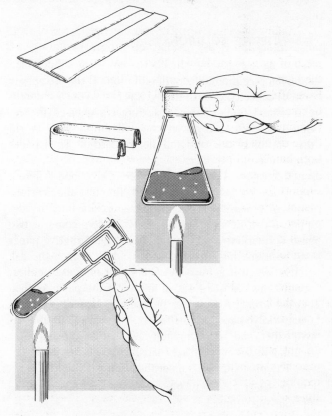

Fig. 1-6. Heating solutions.

When heating solutions in test tubes some special precautions are necessary. Do not hold the test tube straight up and down, but incline it slightly, as shown in Fig. 1–6. Do not heat the liquid at the bottom of the test tube. Rather, heat it near the top surface so that no large bubbles are formed. Never look directly into the mouth of a test tube that you are heating and *never point the open end of a test tube that you are heating toward anyone, including yourself.*

None of the above precautions is a foolproof method of preventing the loss of a solution by bumping or spattering when it is heated. The best advice is simply to be very careful to heat solutions slowly, using a flame that is as small as practicable for the particular heating job you are doing. For safe and efficient heating, containers should never be very full. One-quarter full for test tubes and one-half full for flasks and beakers are satisfactory upper limits. However, smaller fractions are preferable.

After heating a solution, you should set down the hot container on wire gauze, a sheet of asbestos or Transite®, an *un*painted and *un*varnished piece of wood, or a clay triangle; hot test tubes may be placed in wooden test-tube racks. Do not set hot containers of liquid directly on a bench top. They will probably char the finish, harming the bench and allowing messy bits of burned paint to come off on the containers.

1-8 FILTERING SOLUTIONS

Solutions are usually filtered to remove a solid which has been precipitated from the solution. If the precipitate is to be collected quantitatively, it is best to use a sintered-glass filter crucible; this procedure is discussed in Section 3–3. Often, however, you will simply want to rid the solution of the solid and then discard it. Filter paper is very useful in these cases.

Filter papers are made in different sizes and different porosities to suit different-sized funnels and various kinds of precipitates. A medium-porosity filter is adequate for most separations. Filter papers come in two grades, qualitative and quantitative. Quantitative paper has been specially treated with acid to reduce the ash content when it is burned. This paper is used to collect precipitates for quantitative analyses; the paper is then burned away so that the precipitates can be weighed. Quantitative paper is much more expensive than qualitative paper, and you can readily see that for our purposes qualitative paper is entirely satisfactory.

The procedure for paper filtration is as follows.

1) Select a piece of filter paper of the correct size to fit your filter funnel.

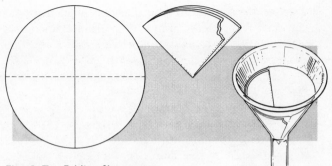

Fig. 1–7. Folding filter paper.

2) Fold the filter paper as indicated in Fig. 1–7: Fold the paper in half and then in half again. Tear off a small piece of one corner, leaving a ragged edge.

3) Open the fold that has been left whole to form a cone. Place this cone in your funnel.

4) Dampen the paper with distilled water and press it firmly against the glass to form a seal. The torn corner allows a "bevelled edge" where the thicker part of the cone begins.

5) Add just enough distilled water to fill the stem of the funnel. If a good seal has been made, this water will fill the stem and create a partial vacuum under the filter which will speed up filtration.

6) Filter the solution by pouring the solution through the filter. Filter by decantation (Section 3–3) to avoid clogging the pores of the paper.

1-9 CLEANING GLASSWARE

Clean glassware is necessary to obtain meaningful, quantitative results in the laboratory. Use a good laboratory cleanser (these are usually rather strong detergents), hot water, and a bottle brush to clean your glassware. For some stubborn jobs you may wish to soak the piece in hot detergent solution for some time. To fill pipets and burets safely with hot or corrosive cleansing agents, clamp them vertically (burets upside down) with their lower ends in a beaker of the cleansing solution and use the suction from an aspirator to draw the liquid up. Do not suck liquid into the aspirator. Close the buret valve or clamp the suction tubing if you wish to let the piece soak.* After washing, copious rinsing is imperative to get rid of all the detergent that clings to the surface of the glass. Use tap water, not distilled water for these operations. Test the glassware for cleanliness by filling it with water and emptying it. If the water drains evenly without forming streaks or

---

* Use hot detergent solutions sparingly on volumetric glassware, since the glass is slowly attacked.

droplets, the surface is clean. Only at this point should you rinse with distilled water. Use distilled water sparingly: *Do not rinse glassware at the distilled water tap. Dispense distilled water from a wash bottle.*

Clean glassware should be thoroughly drained of its final distilled-water rinse and allowed to dry in the air by evaporation. Do not wipe the inside of clean glassware with paper or cloth towels, which will leave lint on the glass. Blowing compressed air into the glassware to speed up drying will simply coat the once-clean glassware with oil vapors that are always present in laboratory compressed air. If a glassware drying oven is available, use it, but do not put wet glassware into ovens that are being used for drying samples. There are only a few instances where you will ever need dry glassware, so drying is usually not a problem.

Form the habit of cleaning glassware immediately after you have finished using it; it is usually a good deal easier to do then.

"Cleaning solution," a very concentrated chromic acid solution, is *not* recommended for this course. It is highly corrosive to skin, clothes, and benches, among other things, and it is almost impossible to remove the last traces of the acid from glassware by simply rinsing it. Stains that do not surrender to detergent washing might yield to hydrochloric acid, which cleans by its acidity and the ion-complexing ability of the chloride. Beyond this, consult your instructor.

1–10 *DISPENSING AND MEASURING SOLIDS*

Dispensing

Solids are almost always dispensed from wide-mouth screw-cap or glass-stoppered bottles. The first step in obtaining the desired compound is to READ THE LABELS on the bottles available; $K_2Cr_2O_7$ is not K_2CrO_4, calcium sulfate is not calcium sulfite, and if a procedure calls for cupric sulfate pentahydrate, that bottle of Cu_2SO_4 in your hand is wrong on two counts. These are imaginary examples; you will not create actual ones of your own if you read the labels carefully and know what you need.

Next, with the cap still in place, make certain that the solid in the bottle is loose and pourable. If it is not, shake the bottle or roll it in your hands to promote pulverization of the solid. *Under no circumstances are you to try to break up a caked solid by poking at it with a spatula or a stirring rod.* This is a task strictly for the instructor.

Now, rotate and tap the bottle so that the solid is ready to pour out. To dispense the solid, follow the procedure outlined below.

1) Remove the cap (or stopper) and pour into it the amount of solid you think you need. Form the habit of taking the smallest possible amounts of reagents. Not only is this economical, but it means less cleanup for you and necessitates thinking ahead, a habit with widespread rewards.

2) Pour the solid from the cap into the container which you have brought from your desk. *Never take stock bottles of reagents to your desk* and do not use a spatula or other implement to remove reagent from the bottle or the cap. If you need both hands for something else, put the cap back on the bottle. If you accidentally pour too much solid into the cap, you may return it to the bottle. Once the reagent has been in your beaker or the piece of paper you brought to weigh it on, it may not be returned to the stock bottle. (If you have extra reagent which you may not return to the stock bottle, ask the other students if one of them needs it.)

3) Replace the cap.

4) Return the bottle to its proper location on the reagent shelf. Even if you did not find it where it belonged, you want it to be there for the next person.

Rough Weighing

Solid reagents are always measured by weight. There will usually be a balance near the reagent shelf for these measurements. In this section we will discuss weighings that only have to be made within 0.1 gm or, perhaps, 0.01 gm. The balances used for these weighings are of two types, the platform balance and the triple-beam balance.* Platform balances usually have a capacity between 200 and 1000 gm. Their range can often be extended by adding supplementary weights to the balance arm, but the extended range is almost never needed. The precision of these balances is about 0.1 gm, which is the smallest division on the scale. The triple-beam balance usually has a 100-gm capacity and a precision of 0.01 gm, again the smallest division on the scale. Both balances have masses that slide on the lever arms, where the scales are marked. The masses are moved to balance the object on the pan; the weight of the object is read from the numbers on the scales beneath the sliding pointers.

The following procedure is for weighing out a quantity of reagent on the rough balance.

1) Place the container or weighing paper that you are going to use to hold the sample on the sample pan and balance the scale. Record this weight.

---

* Using an analytical balance for weighings such as this is poor technique and indicates that you have a lack of understanding of the tools at your disposal. Rough balances are not enclosed and are ruggedly constructed for quick weighings of low precision. They should be used as they were intended.

2) Add the weight of reagent you wish to the weight of the container. Set the sliders to this total weight.

3) Add the reagent slowly from the container in which you are keeping it or from the cap of the reagent bottle. When you near the correct amount, the balance pointer will begin to move and will warn you that you are almost through. Carefully add the last bit to restore the balance and you will have weighed out the amount you desire. There is no point in trying to estimate the weight of your sample any closer than to the nearest smallest scale division; the balance is only that accurate.

In all your measurements, develop a feeling for quantity and quantitative thinking. How full is your 50-ml beaker when you have 20 gm of a solid in it? When you have 15 gm in it? How big a mound does 3 gm make? Is a full spatula tip 1 gm, 0.1 gm or 0.01 gm? With practice, you will soon be estimating closely the amount of material needed, and the time you spend weighing and making other measurements will be greatly reduced.

Analytical Samples: Drying and Weighing by Difference

The principles and operation of the analytical balance are discussed in Appendix C. In this section we shall discuss only drying and weighing by difference. The latter technique is applicable to any balance, but the procedure will be given specifically for making the high-precision weighings that are used for analytical samples and standards.

The precision of a weight measurement will be greatest if as much as possible of the total mass on the pan is the substance of interest, and as little as possible is its container.* Containers for analytical samples should have lids to protect the samples from contamination. A closable container which is also light in weight is the weighing bottle (Figs. 1-8 and 1-9). It is made of very thin-walled glass.

For most analytical purposes, the sample should be dried before weighing to remove surface-adsorbed moisture and, in some cases, waters of crystallization. Place the minimum amount necessary (estimated by eye or a rough weighing) of the pulverized, free-flowing sample in a weighing bottle, mark the bottle for identification, using a pencil on the ground glass spot provided, put the bottle and cap in a beaker that is protected as indicated in Fig. 1-8, and heat them in an oven for the time required by your procedure. Remove the beaker from the oven and carefully transfer the weighing bottle and its cover to a desiccator. (*Never put the cover on a hot*

* This is not necessarily the case for single-pan, constant load balances.

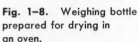
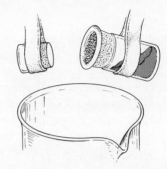

Fig. 1-8. Weighing bottle prepared for drying in an oven.

Fig. 1-9. Transferring a solid from a weighing bottle into a beaker.

weighing bottle.) Do not touch the bottle or the cap with your fingers during this transfer; strips of stiff paper (or a piece of paper folded a few times) make good handles (Fig. 1-9).

When the weighing bottle and the sample have cooled, open the desiccator, place the cover on the bottle (without handling it with your fingers), and weigh the bottle, its cover, and the contents on the analytical balance, recording the weight. Unless your procedure indicates otherwise, repeat the drying, cooling, and weighing procedures until two consecutive weighings agree within the precision that you are seeking.

To weigh by difference use the procedure outlined below.

1) Record the weight of the container and sample: the weighing bottle, its cover, and the contents, in this case.

2) Subtract from this weight the weight of the sample you desire and set the weights on the balance to a value 10 mg or 20 mg higher than the result. On a double-pan balance you will remove some of the weights; on a single-pan balance, you will set the dial to read the new value. Naturally, you will arrest the balance during this operation.

3) Use paper handles to remove the weighing bottle from the balance. Hold it directly over and as close as possible to the mouth of the container (preferably a beaker) to which you are going to transfer the known amount of solid. Use another paper handle to remove the cover carefully so that no drafts will be created in the bottle which could sweep small particles out. Tip the bottle and use a gentle rolling and rocking motion to pour out the necessary amount of solid. Replace the cover and put the bottle back on the balance pan.

4) Semirelease the balance. If the bottle is heavier than the new balance setting, more sample will have to be transferred. Ascertain what weight has already been transferred by balancing the scale. This need not

be done accurately, but it will give you some idea of how much more sample must be transferred. Repeat the transfer and the weighing.

If the bottle is lighter than the balance setting, balance the scale. If you have been skillful, you have probably added about the correct amount of solid. (Remember, you set the weight a bit too high to give yourself some leeway.) If you have overshot the margin by too much, get another beaker and try again.

When you have transferred the desired amount of solid, weigh accurately and record the weight of the weighing bottle and its diminished contents. Subtracting this value from the initial weight, you obtain the weight of sample that was transferred to the container.

Usually you desire to know exactly how much solid you have transferred but you are satisfied if this value is within 10 mg or so of the desired weight. Transferring an exact, predetermined weight of solid will never be required for the experiments in this text. You will be wasting your laboratory time and exhibiting poor technique if you practice such a tedious procedure.

1-11 DISPENSING AND MEASURING LIQUIDS

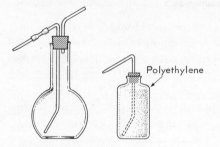

Polyethylene

Fig. 1-10

The Wash Bottle

Wash bottles are used to aim fine streams of water or other wash solutions for use in rinsing down the walls of a container, washing precipitates, transferring precipitates to filters, and, in general, for any task where a small amount of wash liquid is needed. Using a wash bottle is a much more economical way to dispense liquids than pouring them from some container. This is important if you desire to keep the amount of liquid used to a minimum.

Two types of wash bottle (Fig. 1-10) are common. The construction of each is obvious, and making one is a good exercise in glassworking. The glass version is lung-powered, with a movable delivery tip so that you can vary the direction of the wash stream without doing contortions. The polyethylene version is squeeze-powered and is a great deal more convenient, though you

must be careful when you wash precipitates not to squeeze it so hard that the stream spatters the precipitate. Wash bottles made entirely of polyethylene are also commercially available.

Pouring

At your desk, when you pour liquids from one container into another, you should use a stirring rod to direct the flow of the liquid (Fig. 3-3) to minimize splashing. Use either a clean stirring rod or one that is wet with the liquid to be transferred.

At the stock shelf, the first step in obtaining a liquid reagent from its stoppered or capped stock bottle is exactly the same as that in obtaining a solid reagent: make sure you are selecting the correct bottle. Choosing the correct concentration of a reagent in solution often causes confusion. If you desire a standard solution of $AgNO_3$ made up accurately to 0.100 M, and instead you take a solution which is roughly 0.2 M, your experiment will be ruined. Conversely, if you use the accurately made solution when it is not necessary, you are wasting the time and effort of the person who made it. If the reagent bottle is dusty, coated with the ubiquitous white film of ammonium salts associated with chemistry laboratories, or encrusted with solid residue around the stopper, wipe it off and, if necessary, rinse and dry the area around the stopper with distilled water from your wash bottle.

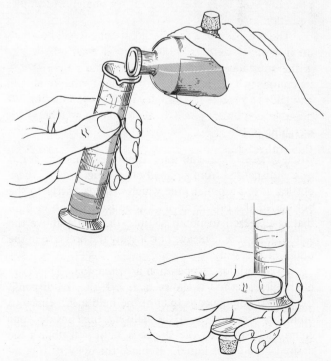

Fig. 1-11. Two ways of holding a glass stopper while pouring a liquid.

Next, remove the stopper or cap and retain it in your hand while you pour the liquid slowly down the inside wall of the container you have brought to the reagent shelf. Two convenient methods of holding glass stoppers while pouring are illustrated in Fig. 1–11. Do not use a stirring rod, dropper, pipet, or other implement to direct the flow or to remove liquids from stock bottles, since they could contaminate the liquids.

Liquids tend to flow along glass surfaces that are already wet. This can make pouring from a glass-stoppered bottle a bit easier. Before removing the glass stopper, tip the bottle to wet the stopper. Use the drops of liquid adhering to the stopper to wet the inside of the neck and that part of the lip of the bottle over which the liquid will flow.

Finally, restopper the bottle, wipe off any dribbles, and return it to its proper place on the reagent shelf. If you spill any liquid, wipe it up immediately. Strong acid that is spilled may first be neutralized with sodium bicarbonate and strong bases with boric acid so they will be safer to wipe up.

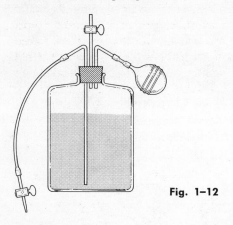

Fig. 1–12

Siphon Bottles

Often large stock quantities of liquid reagents are stored in and dispensed from siphon bottles (Fig. 1–12). These bottles have an outlet tube which extends nearly to the bottom of the bottle, an inlet tube with a siphon bulb that is squeezed to pump air into the bottle above the solution, and some means of releasing the pressure in the bottle, if necessary.

Two methods of operation are common. The setup of the first method is shown in Fig. 1–12. To dispense the liquid, you squeeze (pump) the bulb a few times to build up pressure, hold the delivery tube inside your container, and open the stopcock until you obtain the desired amount of liquid. Replace the delivery tube in whatever holder has been arranged for it so that it will be protected from contamination. Note that once flow has started in this setup, it will continue by siphon action as long as the delivery tube is below the intake to the outlet tube. The solution is put under pressure only to speed up the delivery.

For the second method, the setup shown in Fig. 1–12 is modified to eliminate the flexible delivery tubing and stopcock. You must exercise care in using this arrangement. Hold your container under the outlet tube and pump the siphon bulb carefully. As the pressure builds up in the bottle, the liquid will begin to flow. Pump the bulb just enough to keep the liquid flowing. When you have almost enough of the liquid, open the pressure release. Usually a few more milliliters of liquid will flow out before the pressure in the bottle drops to atmospheric pressure. If you have been overenthusiastic with the siphon bulb, a large amount of extra liquid may be dispensed, since the pressure will take longer to drop. With this setup, liquid will not siphon out of the bottle unless the pressure on it is increased.

Liquid from the container will be siphoned back into the second type of stock bottle if you have inadvertently let the outlet tube dip below the surface of the liquid in your container as you released the pressure in the bottle. Avoid this, since it could cause contamination of the bulk of the solution.

Rough Volume Measurements

Graduated cylinders are the usual tool for making volume measurements with a precision of a few percent. The amount of liquid in the graduate is read from the *bottom* of the liquid meniscus (the curve at the top of the liquid column) on the graduate scale. (This rule holds for relatively transparent liquids which form concave menis-cuses; if the liquid is opaque or forms a convex meniscus, read the position of the top of the meniscus.) Make sure that your line of sight across the point to be read on the scale is perpendicular to the scale (Fig. 1–13) to avoid false readings due to parallax. To give you reference points on both sides of the glass for checking your line of sight, at least some of the scale graduations on gradu-ated glassware are etched completely around the glass.

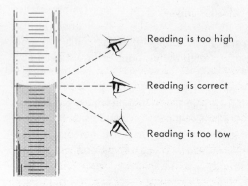

Reading is too high

Reading is correct

Reading is too low

Fig. 1–13. Parallax.

The recent introduction of "graduated" beakers and flasks is an aid to quick, very rough, volume measurements. The graduation marks usually come at intervals of one-fifth of the total capacity. With this glassware it is quite easy to estimate within 5 or 10% the volume of liquid in the containers.

Dispensing 1 or 2 ml of a liquid is much more conveniently done with a *calibrated dropper* than with a larger piece of graduated glassware. Make your droppers as described in Section 1–6. Test each dropper for delivery rate by drawing 1 ml of water into it and then counting how many drops are produced when this water is discharged. (Hold the dropper vertically when discharging liquid; note that the number of drops is different if the dropper is held at an angle.) Droppers with a delivery rate between 20 and 30 drops per milliliter are satisfactory. You can alter the delivery rate of unsatisfactory droppers by adjusting the size of the tip.

To calibrate satisfactory droppers use the following procedure.

1) Fill a small graduated cylinder with water to one of the major graduations. (Adjust the level accurately by adding or removing water with a dropper.)

2) Draw 0.5 ml of the water into the dropper to be calibrated. (Naturally the graduate reading must be taken without the dropper in the solution.)

3) With a file, make a fine scratch on the dropper at the 0.5-ml level.

4) Discard the water in the dropper and repeat the procedure for 1.0 ml, 1.5 ml, etc., until you have a dropper with a capacity of 3 to 5 ml calibrated in 0.5-ml divisions.

The major danger with droppers is that the solution will become contaminated if it touches the rubber bulb. Do not overfill your droppers or turn them upside down when they have liquid in them, and you will avoid this problem.

Precise Volume Measurements

Precise volume measurements are made with volumetric glassware: pipets, burets, and volumetric flasks. All volumetric glassware must be scrupulously clean to give accurate results. Droplets adhering to the inside of the neck of volumetric flasks make measurements of liquids contained in the flasks inaccurate; droplets adhering to pipets and burets indicate that they will not deliver the volume of liquid marked. When pipets and burets are stored, their delivery tips should be protected with a short length of rubber or plastic tubing, or a rubber "policeman" slipped over the end.

Pipets and Pipetting. *Transfer pipets* are cylinders drawn out at both ends into narrow tubes. One tube is more constricted to serve as the delivery tip; the other, the stem, is marked with a calibration line. A transfer pipet will *deliver* its stated volume of water at the temperature marked on it when it is drained as indicated below.

Measuring pipets are narrow tubes that are marked off with a scale and drawn down to a delivery tip at one end. They are used to deliver variable volumes of liquid. The volume delivered is calculated by subtracting the initial reading from the final reading. Do not make the mistake of assuming that the volume of the total contents of the pipet is given by the largest volume on its scale; the volume contained between the last graduation and the delivery tip is not included in the volume calibration.

A *pipet bulb* is a rubber suction bulb which is mandatory for pipetting *all* liquids in the laboratory. Never pipet by mouth. A pipet bulb will protect both you from contamination by the liquid, and the liquid from contamination by you. To draw a liquid into the pipet, squeeze the pipet bulb just enough to create sufficient suction when it is released to draw up the desired amount of liquid. (Do this before bringing the bulb and the pipet together so that any contaminant that might be forced out of the bulb will not be blown into the pipet.) Hold the bulb firmly against the end of the stem, making an airtight seal (Fig. 1–14). It is neither necessary nor desirable to attach the bulb to the stem because this would make subsequent manipulations more difficult. Release the bulb to draw liquid into the pipet.

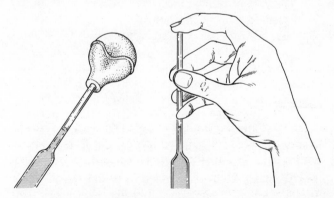

Fig. 1–14. Operation of a pipet.

Before doing the actual pipetting, rinse the pipet with the liquid to be pipetted to make certain that any liquid on the walls is the liquid of interest. Draw 2 or 3 ml (less for 10 ml and smaller pipets) of the liquid into the pipet from a small amount in a clean dry beaker. (Pipets should never be used to draw liquids directly out of stock bottles.) Rotate and rock the pipet so that the whole inner surface comes in contact with the rinse solution. Repeat the rinsing twice.

When rinsing is complete, put enough of the liquid into the beaker to fill the pipet. (A few excess milliliters are desirable so you will not be in danger of sucking up air.) Submerge the tip of the pipet in the liquid to be pipetted and gently release the pipet bulb so that the liquid rises slowly in the pipet. (More violent action will cause bubbles in the liquid and/or the liquid's rising into the pipet bulb (which must be assumed to be contaminated). Either alternative means that you have to start over.) Let the liquid rise 1 or 2 cm above the calibration mark and then quickly remove the pipet bulb and close the end of the stem with your index finger (Fig. 1–14). Wipe the pipet tip with a piece of laboratory tissue or filter paper. Touch the tip of the pipet to the wall of the container holding the solution. Incline the container, if necessary, so that the pipet can be held vertically. To bring the liquid meniscus into exact coincidence with the calibration mark, allow liquid to flow out slowly by manipulating your index finger so that air enters the stem. Now, touch the tip of the pipet to the wall of the container into which the liquid is to be delivered. (The tip of the pipet should be well inside the container.) Allow the liquid to flow freely down the wall from the vertical pipet. Keep the pipet in contact with the wall for *fifteen seconds* after free flow has ceased so that the pipet walls will have a chance to drain. Remove the pipet without disturbing the small amount of liquid still left in the tip. This liquid has been taken into account in the pipet calibration and should not be shaken or blown out with the rest of the contents.

The volume of liquid delivered by a pipet (or buret) is, to some extent, a function of the length of time of delivery. During delivery the rapid flow of the bulk of the solution is accompanied by slow draining from the wet walls. The time (counting from the time you start to deliver the liquid) of draining will be the same regardless of how rapidly the bulk is delivered (if, of course, the bulk is not delivered in more time than it would take the walls to drain naturally). How then can we be sure that fifteen seconds of final drainage is enough? In 1941 the National Bureau of Standards, recognizing this problem, set up standards for the amount of time it should take pipets and burets to deliver the bulk of their liquid (Table 1–1). Pipets which conform to these standards, called Class A pipets (and usually so marked), will drain completely in fifteen seconds after free flow ceases.

Table 1–1
FREE OUTFLOW TIME FOR PIPETS

Capacity of pipet, ml (up to and including)	5	10	50	100	200
Minimum free outflow time, sec	15	20	30	40	50
Maximum free outflow time, sec	60	60	60	60	60

Burets.   Burets are long graduated glass cylinders of uniform bore with a delivery tip at one end and a valve for controlling the flow (a stopcock, flexible tube and clamp, or other device). Burets are used for delivering variable measured amounts of liquid. The most common laboratory burets have a total capacity of 25 or 50 ml with graduations every 0.1 ml. All the graduation marks extend at least halfway around the cylinder to minimize reading error due to parallax. A convenient aid for reading a buret is illustrated in Fig. 1–15; the reflection of the dark portion of the card in the meniscus makes the meniscus stand out more clearly.

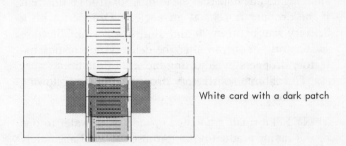

White card with a dark patch

Fig. 1–15.   Buret reading aid.

Burets, like all volumetric glassware, must be absolutely clean to give accurate results. If you have a buret with a glass stopcock, remove the plug of the stopcock and clean all the old grease out of the bore and off the plug before using the buret. Make certain that the narrow portions of the tubing and the delivery tip are also free of grease and other obstructions. Grease trapped in these places is best removed by replacing the stopcock (without grease), filling the buret with water, and releasing this water while the tip and other portions containing grease are immersed in a beaker of boiling water. Carefully clean the buret until it drains without the formation of droplets on the walls. Dry the stopcock bore and the plug. Apply a very light film of stopcock grease around the plug on either side of the hole. Insert the plug into the bore, press firmly, and rotate the plug slowly a few times to lubricate the entire plug and form a good seal. If you use too much grease or get it too close to the hole, grease will be forced into the tip and you will have to remove the plug, clean out the grease, and try again. Many burets now in use have Teflon® stopcocks which need no grease and therefore eliminate the problems of contamination and clogging.

A clean well-draining buret should never be allowed to dry. When not in use, store the buret full of distilled water with a cork stopper to prevent spillage.

® Teflon is a registered trademark of E. I. du Pont de Nemours and Co.

To fill the buret, clamp it vertically and fill it with liquid poured from a beaker; use a small funnel to avoid spillage. (Some burets are flared at the top for ease in filling.) Let liquid into the delivery tip and force out any air bubbles trapped there by letting the liquid flow while gently tapping the tip. If necessary, add more liquid to bring the level just above the zero calibration mark; remove the funnel. Open the valve slightly, letting the liquid flow out slowly until the meniscus is about 0.02 ml above the zero mark. Stop, wait thirty seconds for drainage, and then adjust the meniscus level exactly to the zero mark. (It is not necessary that delivery from a buret be begun at exactly zero, but the exact initial position of the meniscus must be known.)

Test your buret for correct outflow time by filling it with water and noting the time it takes to deliver the water with the valve completely open. The standards for outflow time are given in Table 1-2. Burets that meet these standards will drain completely and will give constant readings thirty seconds after the bulk flow ceases.

Table 1-2
FREE OUTFLOW TIME FOR BURETS

Length graduated, cm	70	60	50	40	30	20
Minimum free outflow time, sec	160	120	90	70	50	35
Maximum free outflow time, sec	180	180	180	180	180	180

Test your buret for leakage by filling it with water at room temperature and reading the meniscus level every five minutes for fifteen minutes. The readings should be constant. If they are not, clean and regrease the stopcock. If this does no good, check with the instructor; a leaky buret is useless.

Quantitatively delivering a standard aqueous solution from a buret is a basic technique in titrating, the major use for the buret. The principles of titration are discussed in Chapter 4; here we shall discuss only the technique of using the buret itself. The buret must be clean and freshly rinsed with distilled water. It is then rinsed with the solution to be used, just as with the pipet. Add 3 to 5 ml of the solution to the empty buret, hold it almost horizontal, and rotate it slowly around its long axis. This way the rinse solution will be spread out over the whole length of the buret and will come in contact with the entire inside surface. Open the valve to release the rinse solution. Repeat this procedure twice more and then pour the solution into the buret. After getting rid of air bubbles in the delivery tip, wipe it off with a piece of filter paper or laboratory tissue. Set the meniscus at some convenient starting level. Remove any

drop adhering to the exit of the delivery tip by touching the tip with a clean stirring rod. Incline the container into which solution is to be delivered so that the tip of the buret touches the wall of the container. This procedure minimizes splashing and ensures that no hanging drops will be left on the buret tip to spoil the volume measurement. Deliver the desired amount of solution by opening the valve carefully. Subtract the starting level from the final level to calculate the volume delivered. (Some further pointers on carrying out titrations are given in Section 4-5.)

Volumetric Flasks. Volumetric flasks are flat-bottomed flasks with long narrow necks. A line is etched on the neck so that when the flask is filled with water to that level the flask *contains* a precise volume of water. Read volumetric flasks the same way as graduated cylinders. The volume contained is given on the flask, along with the temperature at which this calibration was made.

Calibrating Volumetric Glassware

The calibration of volumetric glassware may be tested by weighing the amount of water delivered by pipets and burets or held by volumetric flasks. At first you may think it odd that the mass of the water is measured. This is not at all strange if you consider the definition of the unit of volume in the metric system (Chapter 2): one liter (l) is defined as the volume occupied by a *mass* of one kilogram of water at 3.98°C (the temperature of maximum density of water) and one-atmosphere pressure.* Because the density (mass per unit volume) of water changes as temperature changes, we will have to take this into account when testing the calibration of volumetric glassware.

Testing the calibration of a transfer pipet demonstrates all the principles involved in calibration; the slight changes needed for calibrating other volumetric glassware are given on page 16. To calibrate a transfer pipet use the following procedure.

1) Weigh on the analytical balance to a precision of 0.001 gm a small flask (large enough to hold the water delivered by the pipet) with a small watch glass or cork

---

* Since volumes are lengths cubed, you might suppose that some metric length cubed would be the logical unit of volume. Indeed, it was originally intended that the liter would equal the cubic decimeter. Unfortunately, the difficulties of measurement were such that the definitions do not exactly coincide: one liter actually equals 1.000028 cubic decimeters. For most purposes this difference (one part in 35,000) is negligible and the liter and the cubic decimeter, or more commonly the milliliter and the cubic centimeter, are used interchangeably. Since the international standard of volume is the liter, we shall use liters and milliliters for liquid volume measurements throughout the text.

for a cap. Record the weight. The flask should be clean and dry on the outside but need not be dry on the inside. After it is weighed do not touch it with your fingers or put it down on a bare bench; use a paper handle and a clean piece of paper for the flask to rest on.

2) Fill the pipet which you are testing to the mark with room-temperature distilled water. The exact temperature of the water should be measured and recorded. (It is a good idea to allow the water and the pipet to stand in the same place, out of drafts and sunlight, for an hour or so before filling the pipet so they will come to the same temperature.)

3) Deliver the water to the weighed flask. Remember to hold the pipet vertically and to allow fifteen seconds for drainage.

4) Reweigh the capped flask to 0.001 gm. Calculate the volume of liquid delivered by the pipet by the procedure given below.

5) Repeat the calibration until the agreement is within 0.02 ml. If you cannot attain this, either the pipet is dirty or you are being careless in your technique.

There are three corrections you might think of that have to be made to compare your calibration with the one made by the manufacturer at 20°C: 1) a correction for the thermal expansion or contraction of the glass, 2) a correction for the buoyancy of the water compared with that of the balance weights in the sea of air in which both are immersed, and 3) a correction for the variation of the density of water with temperature, which was probably not 20°C in your calibration.

1) The thermal expansion or contraction of glass containers changes their volume by about 0.003% per degree change at temperatures around 20°C. Since this is only one part in 35,000, its effect on the calibration can be neglected.

2) The correction for the buoyancy difference between water and the metal used for the balance weights is given by the equation

$$M_0 = W\left(1 + \frac{\rho_a}{\rho} - \frac{\rho_a}{\rho_w}\right)$$

from Appendix C, Section C–8. In the equation M_0 is the true mass of the water *in vacuo*, W is the mass of the weights *in vacuo*, ρ_a is the density of air = 0.0012 gm/cc, ρ is the density of the water (It is sufficiently accurate to say that $\rho = 1.00$ gm/ml.), ρ_w = density of the balance weights, and the approximation discussed in the appendix has been made.

3) The volume of the water delivered is calculated by dividing the true mass of the water found by correc-

tion 2 by its density at the temperature of the calibration test, i.e., volume (ml) = mass (gm)/density (gm/ml). The easiest way to obtain the density at a given temperature is to look it up in a table. Table 1–3 is a short list of the density of water (relative to a mass of unity for 1 ml of water at 3.98°C) at different temperatures; more extensive lists are given in most physics and chemistry handbooks.

Table 1–3

THE RELATIVE DENSITY OF WATER AS A FUNCTION OF TEMPERATURE

t, °C	ρ	t, °C	ρ	t, °C	ρ
15	0.99913	20	0.99823	25	0.99707
16	0.99897	21	0.99802	26	0.99681
17	0.99880	22	0.99780	27	0.99654
18	0.99862	23	0.99756	28	0.99626
19	0.99843	24	0.99732	29	0.99597
				30	0.99567

Illustrative Example: A 25-ml pipet delivered a volume of water at a temperature of 24°C that weighed 24.882 gm on a balance with steel weights, density = 7.8 gm/cm. What volume does the pipet deliver?

The true mass of the water is

$$M_0 = 24.882\left(1 + \frac{0.0012}{1.00} - \frac{0.0012}{7.8}\right)$$
$$= 24.882\,(1 + 0.0012 - 0.00015) = 24.882 \times 1.00135$$
$$= 24.9156 \text{ gm.}$$

(Note that we have retained more significant figures in this calculation than are justified by the precision of the constants; it is a good idea to do this and to drop the insignificant figures only in the final result.)

The volume is then

$$V = \frac{24.9156 \text{ gm}}{0.99732 \text{ gm/ml}} = 24.98 \text{ ml.}$$

This volume differs from the marked volume by 0.02 ml. Since Class A pipets of this size may have a maximum error of 0.03 ml from the marked volume, this pipet meets the specified tolerance.

Here are some questions about pipetting technique for which you might try to find experimental answers: What volume is delivered from a pipet inclined at 45° from the vertical? Is it reproducible? What volume is delivered if no drainage time is allowed? Is it reproducible? What volume is delivered from a pipet if the last remaining bit of water in the tip is shaken or blown out with the rest? Is it reproducible?

Calibrating other volumetric glassware requires some differences in technique. Burets are usually calibrated at 5 or 10 ml intervals. This may be done either by delivering the first 5 ml, weighing, refilling the buret, delivering the first 10 ml, weighing, refilling the buret, etc., or by working with successive volumes, delivering the first 5 ml, weighing, delivering the second 5 ml, etc. The second way is faster and the first is more accurate.

Volumetric flasks are calibrated by weighing the dry empty flask and then reweighing the flask filled to the mark with water at a known temperature (preferably room temperature). From these data you calculate the volume delivered by the buret or contained by the flask just as explained above.

REFERENCES

WILSON, E. B., JR., *An Introduction to Scientific Research*, McGraw-Hill, New York, 1952. A superb book written in a lively style, but not to be taken lightly. Become acquainted with it early to learn some of the pitfalls (and ways to avoid them) of experimental work.

PROBLEMS

1. Why might there be a partial vacuum in a desiccator that could cause a rush of air on opening it?

2. Derive Eq. (1–2),

$$t_{BA} = t_B + (t_{A1} - t_{B1}).$$

Show that Eq. (1–1),

$$t_c = t_a - t_0,$$

can be considered to be a special case of Eq. (1–2), if the other thermometer is a standard thermometer.

3. It is possible to construct a glassblowing torch out of glass with the design shown in Fig. 1–16. Gas is admitted at one inlet and oxygen at the other. Is A or B the oxygen inlet? Explain why.

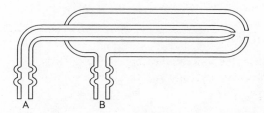

A   B   Fig. 1–16

4. Why should the cover not be placed on a hot weighing bottle?

5. A buret was tested for leakage. The water level in the buret initially was at the 0.50-ml mark. Three more readings after 5, 10, and 15 minutes were 0.48, 0.47, and 0.47 ml, respectively. What cause (or causes) can you think of for this apparent *increase* in the volume of the water in the buret?

6. State in your own words why the National Bureau of Standards set up standards for free flow time of pipets and burets.

7. Will a pipet deliver its stated volume of alcohol instead of water? Why or why not?

2 NAMES AND NAMING

How would you ad-dress a Cat?
So first, your memory I'll jog,
And say: A CAT IS NOT A DOG.
. . .
Again I must remind you that
A Dog's a Dog—A CAT'S A CAT.

T. S. ELIOT, *Old Possum's Book of Practical Cats.*

In the period of alchemy and the search for the philosopher's stone, symbols representing chemicals were used as ciphers to prevent others from understanding one's experiments. Today we use symbols as a shorthand method of accurately conveying our results and ideas to others. However, unless we are all familiar with the definitions of the terms used, we are reduced almost to the state of Babel, like the alchemists. Unfortunately, some terms have changed meaning somewhat in their evolution, and their usage is not universal. This chapter discusses the usage of this textbook.

2–1 UNITS OF MEASUREMENT

We will need measuring units for length, mass, volume, time, and temperature: the meter (m), the gram (gm), the liter (l), the second (sec), and the degree (deg). Often the primary standards for these quantities are of inconvenient size, and it is less burdensome to use multiples or fractions of the basic units. The most commonly used multiple is 10^3, and the unit so formed is the basic unit with the prefix kilo, e.g., 1 kilometer (km) = 10^3 meter (m).* Fractions of the basic units are again the basic units with prefixes: deci, 10^{-1}; centi, 10^{-2}; milli, 10^{-3}; micro, 10^{-6}; nano, 10^{-9}; pico, 10^{-12}. Examples of fractional units are the decimeter (dm), the centimeter (cm), the milliliter (ml), and the microsecond (microsec, μsec).

_____

* In this atomic era the prefix mega, 10^6, is becoming all too common, e.g., megaton.

Length

The primary standard of length is the meter, which is defined as 1,650,763.73 times the wavelength of the orange-red light emitted by the krypton isotope of mass 86 when it is stimulated under controlled conditions. The meter was formerly defined as the distance between two scratches on a platinum-iridium bar, the International Prototype Meter, which is located at the International Bureau of Weights and Measures in Sèvres, France. The present definition is identical, within experimental error which is very small, with the old, and it is not dependent on the preservation of one special piece of matter. For most common laboratory purposes the more convenient unit of length is the centimeter (cm), 10^{-2} meter (m).

Mass

The primary standard of mass is the International Prototype Kilogram, which is defined and discussed in Appendix C. As you read in the Appendix, it was originally intended that the kilogram be the mass of exactly one cubic decimeter of water at 3.98°C, the temperature of maximum density of water. However, because of experimental errors, the Prototype Kilogram is actually equal to the mass of 1.000028 cubic decimeters of water. For most purposes it is the gram (gm), 10^{-3} kilogram (kg), which is the more convenient unit.

Volume

The primary standard of volume is the liter, which is equal to the volume of one kilogram of water at the temperature of maximum density of water, 3.98°C. (See the footnote on page 15.) Usually volumes used in the laboratory are more conveniently expressed in milliliters (ml), 10^{-3} liters (l), although the volume concentration units discussed in Section 2–3 are defined in terms of amount per liter.

Time

The primary standard of time is the mean solar second, which is $\frac{1}{86400}$ of a mean solar day. This standard is quite difficult to use, so clocks are used as secondary standards. Soon the primary standard will probably be changed to a definition in terms of one of the "atomic clocks" now available so that the standard can be used for direct comparison calibrations. Since mechanical devices such as clocks, watches, and timers can be made with high precision, it is usually assumed that they are more accurate than any other part of an experiment; thus only reading errors will produce uncertainties in timing.

Temperature

Temperature is defined in terms of the variations in pressure of the constant-volume hydrogen-gas thermometer. The unit of temperature is the degree. The scale is defined so that the size of the Celsius (centigrade) degree is 1/273.16 of the temperature difference between absolute zero and the triple point of water (the point at which solid, liquid, and gaseous water are in equilibrium: about 0.01°C above the ice point). The difference between the size of the degree defined in that way and the older definition, $\frac{1}{100}$ of the temperature difference between the ice point and steam point of water, is not detectable on the usual mercury-in-glass thermometer, so the change of definition is of little concern for most work. (However, it does facilitate the work of cryoscopists, who study the effects of temperatures near absolute zero, by making absolute zero a fixed point on the temperature scale.)

2–2   CHEMICAL UNITS

The Mole

The mole is the fundamental unit of quantity in chemistry. The standard definition states

> one mole is the amount of a substance which contains Avogadro's number of particles of that substance. Avogadro's number, N_0, is defined as the number of carbon atoms in exactly 12 gm of carbon-12,

$$N_0 = 6.02296 \times 10^{23}.$$

The definition emphasizes that *the mole is based on a fixed number of any type of particles.* Thus we may speak of a mole of oxygen atoms, O, or a mole of hydrogen ions, H^+. Specifying the type of particle is very important. When you speak of a mole of C_6H_6, you are referring to Avogadro's number of the molecular units C_6H_6; but it would not be correct for you to refer to a mole of oxygen, since you have not specified whether the unit is atomic oxygen, O, or molecular oxygen, O_2. Anything that we can say about *relative numbers of atoms or molecules* we can also say about *relative numbers of moles.*

Atomic, Molecular, and Formula Weights

Atomic Weight. The atomic weight of an element is defined by the following equation:

$$\frac{\text{Mass of the element containing } N_0 \text{ atoms}}{\text{Mass of carbon-12 containing } N_0 \text{ atoms (12 gm)}} = \frac{\text{Atomic weight}}{12}.$$

The atomic weight is, therefore, a pure number which has no units. The *gram-atomic weight* is the mass of the element in grams that contains N_0 atoms. (It should be evident that the numbers associated with the atomic weight and the gram-atomic weight of an element are the same.) From this definition and from that of the mole, we see that a mole of atoms is the same as one gram-atomic weight of atoms.

Molecular Weight. The molecular weight of a compound is the sum of the atomic weights of all the atoms of which the molecule of the compound is composed. Thus the molecular weight of pyridine, C_5H_5N, is

$$5(12.011) + 5(1.008) + 14.007 = 79.102.$$

Formula Weight. What is the molecular weight of potassium chloride, KCl? This question is impossible to answer for solid or liquid KCl, because the compound is ionic, so that a particular chloride ion in the crystal or liquid does not belong to one single potassium ion and thus there are no true molecules. A solution for this difficulty is to define the *formula weight* of a compound as the sum of the atomic weights of the atoms that enter into the formula of the compound. Thus the formula weight of KCl is

$$39.102 + 35.453 = 74.555.$$

Gram-molecular weights and gram-formula weights are defined in the same way as molecular and atomic weights except that gram-atomic weights are used instead of atomic weights.

Another way to avoid the impasse created by non-molecular compounds is to go back to the fundamental unit, *the mole*. It is not at all incorrect to talk about a mole of KCl, since we mean Avogadro's number of KCl units, i.e., N_0 potassium ions and N_0 chloride ions. In exactly the same way, we speak of a mole of pyridine, C_5H_5N, and understand that this is N_0 pyridine molecules. In this textbook we shall use definitions based on the mole to avoid any confusion between molecular and formula weights.

Equivalents

Another unit sometimes used is the *gram-equivalent*. Its definition, which is best presented in terms of an example, is based on the reactions of the compound of interest. Consider two reactions of H_2SO_4. In the reaction

$$2NaOH + H_2SO_4 \rightarrow 2H_2O + Na_2SO_4,$$

one mole of sulfuric acid, H_2SO_4, is stoichiometrically equivalent to (i.e., reacts with) two moles of sodium hydroxide, NaOH. Thus one mole of H_2SO_4 is two equivalents of H_2SO_4 in this reaction with NaOH. But in the reaction

$$BaCl_2 + H_2SO_4 \rightarrow BaSO_4 + 2HCl,$$

one mole of H_2SO_4 reacts with one mole of $BaCl_2$, so that one mole of H_2SO_4 is one equivalent of H_2SO_4 in this reaction with $BaCl_2$. The obvious disadvantage of the equivalent as a unit is apparent from these examples; the number of equivalents depends on the reaction being considered and is not an absolute unit, as is the mole.

2–3 UNITS FOR CONCENTRATIONS OF SOLUTIONS

Volume Concentrations

The fastest way to dispense accurately known amounts of reagents is to dissolve them in a suitable solvent and work with appropriate volumes of the solution. To use this method, we must know the amount of reagent in a given volume of solution.

Molarity. The molarity, M, of a solution is defined as the number of moles of the substance being considered contained in one liter *of solution*. Solutions of known solute molarity are easy to prepare. The relationship between the mass and the number of moles of the substance is known from the definition above, so it is an easy matter to weigh out the appropriate mass of the solute, dissolve it in the solvent, and bring the total volume of the solution to the previously determined value so that the number of moles contained per liter of solution is correct.

Illustrative Example: How many grams of KCl are required to make 100.0 ml of an aqueous solution that is 0.0500 M in KCl?

0.0500 M KCl is 0.0500 moles of KCl per liter of solution, or

0.0500 mole/liter $\times$ 79.10 gm/mole = 3.955 gm/liter.

Since we only require 100 ml of solution, we must multiply this result by

$$\frac{100.0 \text{ ml}}{1000 \text{ ml/liter}} = 10^{-1} \text{ liter}$$

to obtain the mass of KCl required. Thus

3.955 gm/liter $\times$ 10^{-1} liter = 0.396 gm of KCl

are required to make 100.0 ml of an 0.0500 M KCl solution.

Formality. Some authors use the volume concentration unit *formality*, F. The formality is defined as the number of gram-formula weights of the substance of interest contained in one liter of solution. This definition was originally introduced to avoid any implication concerning the molecular formula of the added solute either before or after it was put into solution, but the standard definition of the mole makes the definition unnecessary. Speaking of a 1 M KCl solution does not imply, at all, the state of the KCl "units" in the solution, only that an Avogadro's number of potassium and of chlorine atoms are present in some state in each liter of solution. In like manner, "a 1 M Na$_2$SO$_4$ solution" means a solution which contains two moles of sodium atoms, one mole of sulfur atoms, and four moles of oxygen atoms per liter of solution, with no implication about their state in the solution or out of it.* Therefore we shall use molarity as the volume concentration unit for reagent solutions throughout this text. (See below, Section 2–4, for further symbology relating specifically to the state of substances in solution.)

Normality. Normality, N, is defined as the number of gram-equivalents of the substance of interest contained in one liter of solution. Since units of normality have the same drawbacks as gram-equivalents, they will not be used in this text.

Weight Concentrations

A major advantage of weight concentrations is that they are temperature-independent. Weight concentrations are very important in the study of colligative properties

---

* Of course our knowledge of solution chemistry, at least of aqueous solutions, tells us that KCl exists as potassium and chloride ions both in solution and in the crystalline solid. We also know that the unit SO$_4$ usually remains essentially intact with the loss of two electrons to form the sulfate ion, SO$_4^=$.

of solutions because weight ratios are easily converted to mole ratios, the necessary concentration parameters for this application.

Molality.   The molality, m, is defined as the number of moles of the substance of interest dissolved in 1000 gm *of solvent*.   For dilute aqueous solutions the molality and the molarity are very nearly the same, but this is certainly not true of solutions in solvents whose density is much different from 1 gm/ml.   For example, a 1 m solution of solute S in benzene, with density = 0.88 gm/ml at 20°C, contains one mole of S in

$$\frac{1000 \text{ gm}}{0.88 \text{ gm/ml}} = 1137 \text{ ml of benzene.}$$

Neglecting the volume change produced by adding the solute, we can calculate that the molarity of this solution is

$$\frac{1 \text{ mole } S}{1.137 \text{ liter}} = 0.88 \ M,$$

which is a difference of 12 parts per 100 between the molality and the molarity.

Mole Fraction.   The mole fraction of a substance in a solution is defined as the ratio of the number of moles of the substance to the sum of the moles of all other substances present (including the solvent).   For a solution of two components, the solute (species A) and the solvent (species B), we obtain

$$X_A = \text{Mole fraction } A = \frac{\text{Moles } A}{\text{Moles } A + \text{moles } B},$$

$$X_B = \text{Mole fraction } B = \frac{\text{Moles } B}{\text{Moles } A + \text{moles } B}.$$

Note that the mole fraction has no units but is simply a number (always less than 1 by definition).   The *sum* of all the mole fractions in a particular solution is 1:

$$X_A + X_B = \frac{\text{Moles } A}{\text{Moles } A + \text{moles } B}$$
$$+ \frac{\text{Moles } B}{\text{Moles } A + \text{moles } B}$$
$$= \frac{\text{Moles } A + \text{moles } B}{\text{Moles } A + \text{moles } B} = 1.$$

Weight Percent.   The weight percent of a substance in a solution is defined as

$$\text{Weight percent } A = \frac{\text{Mass of } A \text{ in solution}}{\text{Mass of the solution}} \times 100.$$

Weight percent solutions are very common in the older literature which was written when atomic weights and molecular formulas were still somewhat uncertain. Usually, they are only reported now when very concentrated solutions are made and the masses of the solute and the solvent are comparable.

2–4 SYMBOLOGY

Chemical Formulas

Each chemical element is assigned a symbol, a letter or pair of letters, to make references to it more concise and to make molecular formulas compact and easy to read. *Molecular formulas* contain the same number of symbols for each particular atom as there are atoms of that particular kind in the molecule's structure.   For species that have no true molecular structure (e.g., ionic compounds like KCl) we use *empirical formulas* to represent the *ratios* of the numbers of atoms which make up the compound.   Sometimes, most often with organic compounds, the molecular formulas are written to suggest the way that the atoms are joined together in the compound; e.g., acetic acid, which has the molecular formula $C_2H_4O_2$, is often given the symbol CH_3COOH to indicate that the oxygen atoms are both associated with the same carbon atom.

Chemical Equations

Equations.   A chemical reaction is simply a process in which atoms change state (e.g., a change in bonding, a change in oxidation number, etc.).   To symbolize what is going on, we use chemical equations.   For example,

$$BaSO_4(s) + CO_3^=(aq) = BaCO_3(s) + SO_4^=(aq)$$

indicates that some barium, sulfur, oxygen, and carbon atoms in a particular juxtaposition to each other are changed to a different arrangement.   As written, we have as reactants an aqueous (aq) solution of carbonate ion ($CO_3^=$) in contact with solid (s) barium sulfate ($BaSO_4$); the products of the reaction are aqueous sulfate ion ($SO_4^=$) and solid barium carbonate ($BaCO_3$).

Note that the state of the species in the reaction is given by symbols: solid (s), species in aqueous solution (aq), liquid (l), gaseous (g), etc.   This allows us, for example, to avoid the interesting and controversial question of the state of molecular aggregation of the hydrated proton, $H^+(aq)$, and makes equations containing this acid easier to write than if we had to use species such as H_3O^+ and $H_9O_4^+$.

We try to represent as accurately as possible the actual species involved in a reaction without sacrificing the brevity of the symbology.   In the above example, $HCO_3^-(aq)$, $H_2CO_3(aq)$, and $HSO_4^-(aq)$ are also present in the solution but, since in a moderately concentrated solution of the carbonate ion (0.1 M) at least 95% of the carbonate is present as $CO_3^=(aq)$, it would be needlessly complex to include all the possible species in the equation unless there were some specific reason for doing so.

To make chemical equations as concise as possible, we omit species in the solution that remain unchanged. Suppose that in our example we obtained the $CO_3^=(aq)$ solution by adding Na_2CO_3 to water; then $Na^+(aq)$ would be present, but because it remains unchanged it is not included in the equation for the reaction.

Several different symbols are used to connect the two sides of equations. The $=$ sign is used to emphasize the stoichiometric relationship of the reactants and products. (It is not to be read as "equals," but rather as "yields." The two sides of the "equation" are equal only in the sense that the same number of atoms of each kind appear on each side.) To emphasize that a set of reactants gives a certain set of products, we use an arrow:

$$2NO_2(g) \rightarrow N_2O_4(g),$$

$$N_2O_4(g) \rightarrow 2NO_2(g).$$

To emphasize that a reaction is at equilibrium and that an equilibrium is a dynamic situation, we use two arrows pointing in opposite directions:

$$N_2O_2(g) \rightleftharpoons 2NO_2(g).$$

Stoichiometry. The stoichiometric coefficients which appear before the formulas in a chemical equation represent the quantitative aspect of the reaction. When we are discussing collections of molecules, they represent the *relative numbers* of molecules that enter into the reaction. For example, both the following equations,

$$2Na(s) + Cl_2(g) = 2NaCl(s),$$

and

$$Na(s) + \tfrac{1}{2}Cl_2(g) = NaCl(s),$$

tell us that in the reaction of sodium with gaseous chlorine, the number of units of sodium chloride produced is the same as the number of sodium atoms used and is twice the number of chlorine molecules used. In this case the atomic and molecular symbols represent collections of atoms and molecules.

Often, however, we wish to discuss the behavior of individual atoms and molecules; then the stoichiometric coefficients represent the *actual numbers* of atoms or molecules that enter into the reaction. (This usage is particularly desirable when we are discussing the actual physical mechanism of the reaction.) For example, if we wish to discuss the way in which molecules of nitrogen dioxide combine to form nitrogen tetroxide, it is incorrect to write

$$NO_2(g) \rightarrow \tfrac{1}{2}N_2O_4(g)$$

because half-molecules are an absurdity. The correct formulation is

$$2NO_2(g) \rightarrow N_2O_4(g).$$

Concentrations in Solution. The units used for concentrations are those discussed in Section 2–3. Brackets [ ] are placed around chemical symbols to represent the *actual molar concentration of a particular species.* For example, $[SO_4^=(aq)] = 10^{-2}\ M$ means "the concentration of the ion $SO_4^=$ in an aqueous solution is 10^{-2} mole/liter." (Often, to make the symbolism less cumbersome, the state of the species in question is left out, if it is clearly understood from the context.) It must be realized that the molar concentrations of the species that actually exist in a particular situation may bear little resemblance to the molarity of the overall system. As an example, $0.01\ M\ H_2SO_4$ solution does not contain 0.01 mole/liter of $H_2SO_4(aq)$. In fact, since H_2SO_4 is a strong acid, there is almost no $H_2SO_4(aq)$ at all in this solution. When the equilibria set up in the solution are taken into account we can calculate

$$[SO_4^=] = 4.1 \times 10^{-3}\ M,$$

$$[HSO_4^-] = 5.9 \times 10^{-3}\ M.$$

Thus the total number of moles of sulfur-containing species present in a liter of solution ($4.1 \times 10^{-3} + 5.9 \times 10^{-3} = 1.0 \times 10^{-2}$) is equal to the number of moles per liter of sulfur-containing species put into the solution (10^{-2} mole/liter of H_2SO_4) but the reactions that occur in solution must be taken into account in determining the actual molar concentrations of the species present.

There are no universal symbols for actual molal or mole-fraction concentrations. Inside the parentheses, where the state of the solution is given, a notation indicating its concentration is sometimes placed, e.g., $SO_4^=(aq; 0.024\ m)$. When mole fractions are used, the species is usually indicated by a subscript to the symbol for the mole fraction, X, for example, $X_{C_{10}H_8} = 0.208$.

Activity. There are many chemical effects that are due to the number of solute molecules or ions present in the system. It is almost always found (universally in ionic solutions) that as the molar concentration of the solute is increased, the effects increase, but not linearly. Also, the addition of "inert" species to a system often changes the effects, although there appears to be no direct interaction between the inert and the active species. The direction of change differs in different systems; in some cases the effective concentrations of the solutes appear to be lower than the calculated molarities and in other cases they appear to be higher. Even in the same system, the direction of the changes may vary from one concentration range to another.

All these effects are usually lumped together under the heading of activity changes. The *activity* of a species in solution is its *effective concentration*. The activity is always defined as a ratio, so it has no units. The conventions used to define activities are too varied to discuss here, so we shall state, without proving it, that the numerical value of the activity of a species in dilute aqueous solution is very nearly equal to its molarity or molality. If you are interested in reading further about definitions of activity, consult any of the physical chemistry textbooks listed in the references at the end of the chapter.

It is easy to see why ionic species should have different effective concentrations at low and at high concentration. At low concentration in aqueous solution, the ions are widely separated and experience very little interaction with other ions. As the concentration of the solution is increased, there is more and more interionic interaction, since the ions are forced closer together on the average. Positive ions tend to gather negative ions about them and vice versa, so that the ions become slightly more "shielded" from possible reactants and their effective concentration is decreased (see Chapter 9). From time to time as you read this text you will be reminded that we should use activities instead of the usual molarities to express concentrations. However, with the exception of Experiments 15 and 17, we shall assume that the solutions we are working with are dilute enough so that the difference between activity and molarity can be neglected.

We shall use a as the symbol for activity and denote activities of specific species by a with a subscript, e.g., $a_{CH_3COO^-} = 0.023$. Other authors use braces $\{ \}$ around the chemical symbol for the species to represent its activity, but these can be too easily confused with the square brackets used for molarity.

REFERENCES

GUGGENHEIM, E. A., *et al.*, *J. Chem. Ed.* **38**, 86, 549, 551, 554, 555 (1961). This is a series of articles and letters, prompted by the first article, by Guggenheim, on the definition of the mole and other physical quantities dependent on this definition.

HART, C. S., "Use of Activities in Student Calculations," *J. Chem. Ed.* **32**, 314 (1955) includes a number of examples of the use of activities.

HUNTOON, R. D., "Status of the National Standards for Physical Measurement," *Science* **150**, 169 (1965) is a very interesting article on the present standards and future possibilities for standards.

KIEFFER, W., *The Mole Concept in Chemistry*, Reinhold, New York, 1962.

MAHAN, B. H., *Elementary Chemical Thermodynamics*, W. A. Benjamin, New York, 1963. pp. 8–11.

MILLS, A. P., "Derivation of Equations for the Interconversion of Concentration Units," *J. Chem. Ed.* **42**, 314 (1965).

NASH, L. K., *Stoichiometry*, Addison-Wesley, Reading, Mass., 1965.

Some useful, although sometimes difficult, discussions of the activity concept may be found in the following sources:

BARROW, G. M., *Physical Chemistry*, McGraw-Hill, New York, 1961.

BREY, W. S., JR., *Principles of Physical Chemistry*, Appleton-Century-Crofts, New York, 1958.

COLE, R. H., and J. S. COLES, *Physical Principles of Chemistry*, Freeman, San Francisco, 1964.

DANIELS, F., and R. A. ALBERTY, *Physical Chemistry*, 2nd ed. John Wiley & Sons, New York, 1961.

3 GRAVIMETRIC ANALYSIS

Ex Pondere et Numero Veritas

Motto of *Textbook of Quantitative Inorganic
Analysis*, I. M. KOLTHOFF and E. B. SANDELL

The fundamental question in chemical analysis is, "How much of substance X is contained in a given quantity of a particular sample?" You may express "how much" and "a given quantity" in any convenient units such as grams, pounds, moles, weight percent, volume fraction, etc., but you can ultimately trace all these units back to a measurement of weight.* The most common direct technique used in such determinations is to precipitate some insoluble compound of X from a solution containing a known weight of the sample, separate the precipitate by filtration, and weigh the insoluble compound. At first such a technique seems to be almost trivial, but if you stop to think for a moment about this description and consider the definitions of terms such as "insoluble," questions and difficulties should immediately arise. Before continuing to read, jot down some of these questions, and look for their answers in the following discussion or in the references.

3–1 FACTORS AFFECTING PRECIPITATION ANALYSIS

In the description above you read that an *insoluble* compound of X should be formed. How insoluble must this compound be? What factors affect its solubility? Will more than one insoluble compound be formed?

You also read that this insoluble compound was to be weighed; this certainly means that the precipitate, not any extraneous solvent or adsorbed species, is to be weighed. How, then, should we prepare the precipitate for weighing?

---

* It should not, then, be surprising to find that the determination of the weight of X in a given weight of a sample has played a very fundamental role in the development of chemistry as a science.

Will *any* insoluble compound of X be suitable? What properties must the insoluble compound have so that it will yield an accurate analysis for X?

(These problems are, of course, interrelated, since a compound that is suitably insoluble but cannot be prepared to give reproducible weight is obviously useless.)

Solubility and Solubility Product

Ideally, precipitating the compound containing X should remove *all* X from the solution. However, this is not necessary in practice, since the rest of the analysis is not infinitely precise. The usual analytical balances are not sensitive to better than 0.1 mg so that the loss of 0.1 mg of the precipitate will not affect the precision of most analyses. In normal practice a precipitation procedure in which 0.1 mg or less of the precipitate is lost is said to be *quantitative*. Sometimes limits even less stringent will suffice. For example, if a quantitative procedure would produce 1 gm of a precipitate and the necessary precision in the final result is only 1%, a simpler or faster procedure which would lose 5 mg of precipitate would still yield a result with the desired precision.

It is fortunate that it is not necessary to remove *all* of a substance for its quantitative determination since, in practice, solubility equilibria are established which make it impossible to remove all of any substance from a solution by the procedure we are discussing. As a concrete instance of such an equilibrium, let us consider the precipitation of strontium ion as strontium chromate. When a solution containing chromate ion, $CrO_4^=$, is added to a solution containing strontium ion, Sr^{++}, a precipitation reaction occurs,

$$Sr^{++}(aq) + CrO_4^=(aq) \rightarrow SrCrO_4(s). \qquad (3-1)$$

If, on the other hand, solid strontium chromate is shaken with pure water, some of the solid will dissolve into the solution in predominantly ionic form,

$$SrCrO_4(s) \rightarrow Sr^{++}(aq) + CrO_4^{=}(aq). \qquad (3-2)$$

As soon as solid is produced in the precipitation reaction, (3–1), it will begin to redissolve as indicated by reaction (3–2). When equilibrium is attained, the tendency to precipitate will be just balanced by the tendency to dissolve; we symbolize this by writing

$$Sr^{++}(aq) + CrO_4^{=}(aq) \rightleftarrows SrCrO_4(s), \qquad (3-3)$$

which, of course, can also be written

$$SrCrO_4(s) \rightleftarrows Sr^{++}(aq) + CrO_4^{=}(aq). \qquad (3-4)$$

Experimentally it is found that when equilibrium is reached, the following relationship holds:

$$[Sr^{++}][CrO_4^{=}] = K_{sp} = 3 \times 10^{-5} \, M^2. \qquad (3-5)$$

The *solubility product*, K_{sp}, is approximately a constant at constant temperature. [Some variation in the solubility product appears because we should use *activities* instead of *molarities* (or *formalities*) as concentration units. In the present discussion we will neglect the variation of K_{sp} as expressed in Eq. (3–5).] The solubility product, as all equilibrium constants, is temperature dependent, e.g., the value is 3×10^{-5} for strontium chloride at a temperature of 25°C. The solubility product has units; in this case the units are moles^2/liter^2.

We can use solubility products to determine the solubility of solid compounds ($SrCrO_4$ in this case) under different conditions. Let us first calculate what happens when an excess* of solid $SrCrO_4$ is shaken with one liter of pure water. From Eq. (3–2) it is evident that for every Sr^{++} that goes into solution there will also be a $CrO_4^{=}$. Hence $[Sr^{++}] = [CrO_4^{=}]$ throughout the process. We can substitute this relationship into Eq. (3–5) to discover what the concentrations will be *when equilibrium is established*:

$$[Sr^{++}][CrO_4^{=}] = [Sr^{++}][Sr^{++}] = 3 \times 10^{-5} \, M^2,$$
$$[Sr^{++}] = 5.5 \times 10^{-3} \, M,$$
$$[CrO_4^{=}] = 5.5 \times 10^{-3} \, M.$$

At equilibrium, then, the solution contains 5.5×10^{-3} mole (since we have one liter of solution) of both Sr^{++} and $CrO_4^{=}$ ions. In other words, we say that 5.5×10^{-3} mole of $SrCrO_4$ (or 5.5×10^{-3} mole $\times$ 201.6 gm/mole $SrCrO_4$ = 1.1 gm $SrCrO_4$) has dissolved.

* An excess of the solid is necessary since the solubility-product relationship is valid *only* if there is solid compound in contact with the solution containing the ions of that compound.

The Common Ion Effect

Now let us calculate what happens when an excess of $SrCrO_4$ is shaken with one liter of water which is 0.1 M in $CrO_4^{=}$. In this case, as the solid dissolves, $CrO_4^{=}$ is added to the solution, but the total $[CrO_4^{=}]$ is no longer equivalent to $[Sr^{++}]$ because the original solution contained some $CrO_4^{=}$. The total $[CrO_4^{=}]$ is made up of two terms,

$$[CrO_4^{=}] = [CrO_4^{=}] + [CrO_4^{=}],$$
$$\text{Initially} \quad \text{Added by}$$
$$\text{present} \quad \text{solution}$$
$$\text{of SrCrO}_4$$

$$[CrO_4^{=}] = 0.1 \, M,$$
$$\text{Initially}$$
$$\text{present}$$

and, from the relationship embodied in reaction (3–2),

$$[CrO_4^{=}] = [Sr^{++}].$$
$$\text{Added by}$$
$$\text{solution}$$
$$\text{of SrCrO}_4$$

Once more we substitute in Eq. (3–5):

$$[Sr^{++}][CrO_4^{=}] = [Sr^{++}](0.1 + [Sr^{++}])$$
$$= 3 \times 10^{-5}. \qquad (3-6)$$

Rather than solve this quadratic equation directly, let us use a little chemical and mathematical intuition to simplify the task. We shall begin by rearranging Eq. (3–5) to give

$$[Sr^{++}] = \frac{K_{sp}}{[CrO_4^{=}]} = \frac{3 \times 10^{-5}}{[CrO_4^{=}]}. \qquad (3-7)$$

Our original calculation showed that dissolving $SrCrO_4$ in pure water gives $[CrO_4^{=}] = 5.5 \times 10^{-3} \, M$. In the present case we started with $[CrO_4^{=}] = 0.1 \, M$ and increased it. From Eq. (3–7) we can easily see that a larger value for $[CrO_4^{=}]$ means a smaller value for $[Sr^{++}]$. Thus $[Sr^{++}]$ will surely be less than 5.5×10^{-3} in this case, when $[CrO_4^{=}]$ is at least 0.1 M. As an approximation then, we can neglect $[Sr^{++}]$ in the term $(0.1 + [Sr^{++}])$, so that Eq. (3–6) becomes

$$[Sr^{++}] \times 0.1 = 3 \times 10^{-5}, \quad [Sr^{++}] = 3 \times 10^{-4}.$$

In effect this approximation neglects the $CrO_4^{=}$ furnished by the solution of solid $SrCrO_4$. Is this justifiable?†

† We can check our approximation (as one must always check approximations) by noting that

$$[CrO_4^{=}] = (0.1 + [Sr^{++}]) = 0.1 + 0.0003 = 0.1003$$

and that we have made only about 0.3% error. Since solubility products themselves are usually only known to about 5%, such an error is completely insignificant and our approximation is justified.

Now we can compare the solubility of $SrCrO_4$ in pure water with its solubility in water already containing $0.1\ M\ CrO_4^=$:

$$3 \times 10^{-4}\ \text{mole} \times 201.6\ \text{gm/mole}\ SrCrO_4$$
$$= 0.060\ \text{gm}\ SrCrO_4$$

dissolves in a solution $0.1\ M$ in $CrO_4^=$, compared with 1.1 gm in pure water. Another calculation would show that a similar reduction in solubility of the $SrCrO_4$ is brought about if the solid is dissolved in one liter of a solution originally $0.1\ M$ in Sr^{++}. This lowering of solubility, the *common ion effect*, is directly calculable from the solubility-product relationship, Eq. (3–5).

Illustrative Example: 100 ml of a solution is known to contain about 100 mg of Sr^{++}. What amount of solid K_2CrO_4 must be added to determine the amount of Sr^{++} present within 1%, provided that no other reactions of $CrO_4^=$ occur except the precipitation of $SrCrO_4$?

We can break this problem into two parts by *imagining* that reaction (3–1) goes to completion and that the solid $SrCrO_4$ thus formed partially redissolves and reaches the solubility equilibrium represented by Eq. (3–5). In the first step of this process, enough $CrO_4^=$ must be added to the solution to react with all the Sr^{++} present, 100 mg in this case. In the second step of the process we need to add enough extra $CrO_4^=$ to the solution so that its concentration is high enough to prevent more than 1% of the Sr^{++} from reentering the solution.

To begin with, we find that the number of moles of Sr^{++} initially present in the solution is

$$\text{Moles}\ Sr^{++} = \frac{0.1\ \text{gm}}{87.6\ \text{gm/mole}} = 1.1 \times 10^{-3}.$$

We shall need an equivalent number of moles of $CrO_4^=$ (or K_2CrO_4) to react with all the strontium ion.

Furthermore, when the $SrCrO_4$ partially redissolves, we want to keep the amount of Sr^{++} in solution to a maximum of 1 mg, 1% of 100 mg. This corresponds to

$$[Sr^{++}] = \frac{10^{-3}\ \text{gm}}{87.6\ \text{gm/mole}} \times \frac{1000\ \text{ml/liter}}{100\ \text{ml}}$$
$$= 1.1 \times 10^{-4}\ M.$$

The concentration of $CrO_4^=$ which will be needed to maintain this $[Sr^{++}]$ when solubility equilibrium is attained can be calculated from Eq. (3–5):

$$[Sr^{++}][CrO_4^=] = 1.1 \times 10^{-4}[CrO_4^=] = 3 \times 10^{-5},$$
$$[CrO_4^=] = \frac{3 \times 10^{-5}}{1.1 \times 10^{-4}} = 2.7 \times 10^{-1}\ M.$$

This concentration may be converted to moles of $CrO_4^=$ by multiplying the concentration in moles per liter by the volume in liters:

$$\text{Moles}\ CrO_4^= = [CrO_4^=] \times \frac{100\ \text{ml}}{1000\ \text{ml/liter}}$$
$$= 2.7 \times 10^{-2}\ \text{mole}.$$

This much $CrO_4^=$ will have to be added to the solution in excess of that already added to react with the Sr^{++}. Therefore, the total amount of $CrO_4^=$ necessary is

$$\text{Moles}\ CrO_4^= = 1.1 \times 10^{-3} + 2.7 \times 10^{-2}$$
$$= 2.8 \times 10^{-2}\ \text{mole},$$
or
$$K_2CrO_4 = 2.8 \times 10^{-2}\ \text{mole} \times 194.2\ \text{gm/mole}$$
$$= 5.4\ \text{gm}.$$

Complexing Equilibria

On the basis of the foregoing discussion and example, you might think that increasing the addition of a common precipitating ion could only help to make an analysis "more quantitative." In certain cases this is true, but in other cases as more of the common ion is added, the solubility of the solid precipitate actually increases. Cuprous chloride, CuCl, is an example:

$$[Cu^+][Cl^-] = K_{sp} = 1.85 \times 10^{-7}.$$

Because the solubility product is small, we might expect to be able to precipitate Cu^+ quantitatively from solution by adding Cl^-. In the same way that we calculated the solubility of $SrCrO_4$ in a $0.1\ M\ CrO_4^=$ solution, we can calculate the solubility of CuCl in, for example, a $0.01\ M\ Cl^-$ solution:

$$[Cu^+][Cl^-] = [Cu^+](0.01 + [Cu^+]) = 1.85 \times 10^{-7},$$
$$(0.01 + [Cu^+]) \approx 0.01,^*$$
$$[Cu^+] = \frac{1.85 \times 10^{-7}}{0.01} = 1.85 \times 10^{-5}\ M.$$

Thus we have calculated that the number of moles of CuCl that dissolve per liter is 1.85×10^{-5}, but the measured solubility of CuCl in a $0.01\ M\ Cl^-$ solution is, in fact, 7.8×10^{-4} mole/liter, or about 40 times higher than we predicted from the solubility-product relationship. Why? Because in this case, as in many others, *complexing equilibria* become important and ionic species other than those considered in the solubility product are formed in the solution. In the present instance the following complexing equilibria are also established:

$$Cu^+(aq) + 2Cl^-(aq) \rightleftarrows CuCl_2^-(aq),$$
$$CuCl_2^-(aq) + Cl^-(aq) \rightleftarrows CuCl_3^=(aq).$$

A very important point is illustrated by this example. The concentrations in the solubility-product relationship are the actual concentrations in solution *of the species*

---

* Check the approximation: $0.01 + [Cu^+] = 0.01 + 1.85 \times 10^{-5} = 0.0100185 \approx 0.01$.

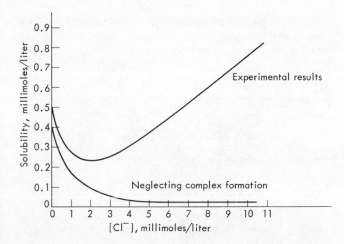

Fig. 3–1. Solubility of CuCl as a function of chloride ion concentration. (After J. N. Butler, *Ionic Equilibrium*, Addison-Wesley, Reading, Mass., 1964, p. 278.)

within the brackets, i.e., Cu^+(aq) and Cl^-(aq) in the present case. However, these concentrations do not include the amount of the species in question which is tied up as complexes in the solution. Therefore, to calculate the solubility of the solid compound, we have to add up the concentrations of *all* the species in the solution which are derived from the elements of the compound. Our calculation for $[Cu^+]$ was correct, but in calculating the solubility of the solid precipitate we must take into account the $CuCl_2^-$ and $CuCl_3^=$ which are also present. Detailed calculations based on equilibrium constants for the complexing equilibria give $[CuCl_2^-]$ = 7.6×10^{-4} M and $[CuCl_3^=]$ = 3.4×10^{-6} M under our conditions. Thus the total solubility of CuCl is

Moles CuCl dissolved/liter

$$= [Cu^+] + [CuCl_2^-] + [CuCl_3^=]$$
$$= (1.85 \times 10^{-5}) + (7.6 \times 10^{-4}) + (3.4 \times 10^{-6})$$
$$= 7.8 \times 10^{-4} \text{ mole/liter.}$$

Figure 3–1 is a plot of the solubility of CuCl as a function of the amount of Cl^- in the solution. Neglecting the complex equilibria leads to very substantial error in calculating the solubility. We have shown that the existence of the complexing equilibria, which increase the solubility of CuCl, makes quantitative precipitation of Cu^+ as CuCl impossible.

Other Factors

Acidity. Factors other than the solubility product and complexing equilibria must also be considered in assessing the solubility of precipitates. One of the most important of these is the acidity of the solution. Just as complexing equilibria have no direct effect on the solu-

bility-product relationship, acidity has no *direct* effect (except to change the environment of the solution slightly, and hence the activity of the ions); it changes the solubility because other equilibria are set up which "use up" the ions that enter into the solubility product and, hence, increase the overall solubility of the solid compound. This effect is strikingly demonstrated by $SrCrO_4$. $CrO_4^=$ is a basic ion, i.e., it reacts with hydrogen ion to give bichromate ion:

$$CrO_4^=(aq) + H^+(aq) \rightleftarrows HCrO_4^-(aq).$$

In this case, the equilibrium lies far to the right, favoring the formation of bichromate ion. Thus addition of acid to a solution of $CrO_4^=$ decreases the concentration of $CrO_4^=$ since it reacts with the acid to form $HCrO_4^-$. If solid $SrCrO_4$ is allowed to come to equilibrium with pure water and then acid is added, $[CrO_4^=]$ will decrease and more $SrCrO_4$ will then dissolve to maintain the solubility-product equilibrium. Many precipitates act in this way; they come out of solution under certain conditions of acidity and redissolve as the acidity (or basicity) is changed. The common characteristic of precipitates that dissolve in acid is that their anions are basic ions like chromate, $CrO_4^=$, oxalate, $C_2O_4^=$, and phosphate, PO_4^{-3}. Further elucidation will be found in Experiments 2 and 17.

Medium. Another factor that can have a large effect on solubility is the medium or solvent in which the reaction is carried out. For example, the addition of ethyl alcohol to an aqueous solution usually reduces the solubility of inorganic ionic compounds in the solution. We usually take advantage of this effect by precipitating compounds like $SrCrO_4$ and $CaSO_4$, which are moderately soluble in purely aqueous solutions from mixed alcohol-water solutions. Sometimes precipitations which are impossible to carry out in aqueous solutions may be carried out in nonaqueous media; for example, potassium perchlorate can be quantitatively precipitated from alcohol, even though the salt is quite soluble in water.

Temperature. As indicated above, the solubility product, like all equilibrium constants, is temperature dependent. In general, solubility products and, hence, solubilities increase with increasing temperature. In certain cases, especially for some precipitates of the alkaline earth ions, Mg^{++}, Ca^{++}, Sr^{++}, and Ba^{++}, and of lead ion, Pb^{++}, which are moderately soluble, filtration should be done at room temperature. For most gravimetric analyses, however, the increase in solubility of the precipitate with an increase in temperature is negligible, and the advantages in the physical form of the precipitate that is prepared and filtered at elevated temperatures (discussed below) far outweigh any slight increase in solubility.

3-2 THE PRECIPITATE

It would be advantageous to have reagents that precipitate whatever substance we wish to analyze specifically, but this is, unfortunately, almost never the case with most common gravimetric reagents. Two reagents that come very close to this ideal are ones that contain the chloride ion, which precipitates silver and mercurous ions (as their chlorides, AgCl and Hg_2Cl_2), and the organic reagent dimethylgyloxime, $C_4H_8O_2N_2$ (reacting as the anion $C_4H_7O_2N_2^-$), which precipitates nickel and palladium [as $Ni(C_4H_7O_2N_2)_2$ and $Pd(C_4H_7O_2N_2)_2$]. In general, however, the precipitating reagents are not very specific, and often preliminary separations of the components of a sample must be made to remove interfering ions. For the purposes of this discussion we shall assume that we have done any initial separations that are necessary and we shall concentrate on understanding the mechanism by which the precipitate of analytical interest is formed.

The Mechanism of Precipitation

Nucleation. The mechanism of precipitation may be described as the initial formation of *nuclei*, aggregates of the ions of the compound which are stable enough to hold together until other ions join them, and their growth into macroscopic particles by the addition of more ions at the surface. (Dust particles and imperfections such as scratches on the walls of the container may also act as nuclei.) Before nucleation or precipitation can occur, the solution must be supersaturated. In other words, the ions will not aggregate and come out of solution until more of them are present than would be present if the solution was in contact and in equilibrium with the solid compound. The number of nuclei formed in nucleation depends on the *relative supersaturation* of the solution. If S is the actual concentration of the ion before precipitation begins and s is the equilibrium solubility, then the relative supersaturation is expressed by $(S - s)/s$. The higher the relative supersaturation, the more nuclei will be formed when precipitation begins and the smaller the particles of precipitate will be. Conversely, the lower the relative supersaturation at the beginning, the larger the particles of precipitate. As explained below, large particles are preferable, so we should try to keep the relative supersaturation of the solution as low as possible before precipitation begins.

Coprecipitation. Even though the ions directly interfering with our analysis have been removed from the solution, other ions will necessarily be present. Since the substance of interest is usually an ion itself, there will be a counter ion of opposite charge in the solution to main-

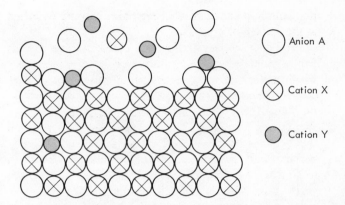

Fig. 3-2. Schematic representation of the formation of a solid precipitate of *XA*.

tain electrical neutrality. The precipitating reagent will probably be ionic also, so again "unreactive" ions will be present. Unfortunately, these other ions are not completely inert, for they may *coprecipitate* with the precipitate of interest.

There are two important mechanisms by which foreign ions are coprecipitated, *surface adsorption* and *occlusion within the crystal lattice*. To understand these processes, we must consider how the surface of the solid interacts with the ions in solution. Let us suppose that we are trying to precipitate the cation X by reaction with the anion A and that cation Y is also present in the solution. The surface of the XA crystal is presumably made up of alternating ions, as indicated very schematically in Fig. 3-2. Since the processes of precipitation and solution are going on simultaneously, some ions are being added to the surface and others are leaving. Both cations X and Y enter the sites available for cations, but X cations usually displace almost all the Y cations, since the XA lattice is more stable than the YA lattice. (If this were not true, then YA rather than XA would presumably be precipitated from the solution.) After a time the supply of X cations will be largely depleted, since they are removed as part of the solid. The concentration of anion A will still be large, since we usually add some excess of the precipitating ion. The anion will then begin to build the next crystal layer as indicated in the figure, but true crystallization will not occur, since there are no longer enough X cations to form a neutral crystal layer. The process of adsorption on a surface forming a charged layer is called *primary adsorption*. The cations in solution are attracted to this negatively charged surface and tend to become concentrated near the surface in a *secondary adsorption layer*. Since the Y cations are now in great excess in the solution, this layer is mostly composed of them. (Adsorption, both primary and secondary, is not limited to ions alone, since molecules, particularly polar molecules, may also become adsorbed at the surface of crystals.)

It is not impossible for one of the foreign cations from the secondary adsorption layer to settle into a site which should be occupied by an *X* cation and not be displaced but become a part of the crystal, as shown in the figure. Such an ion is said to be *occluded* in the crystal structure. If the precipitation occurs quite rapidly, then the chance of foreign ions being occluded becomes very great, because the opportunity for them to be displaced before the next crystal layer is added is small. Even if the precipitation occurs relatively slowly, there will always be some equilibrium number of occluded foreign ions. This process is particularly favorable if the foreign cation *Y* is about the same size as the cation *X* that we are trying to precipitate.

Occlusion, as indicated in Fig. 3–2, usually leads to some disruption of the crystal lattice, which limits the number of foreign ions which can be accommodated by making the whole arrangement unstable. Thus the crystal naturally tends to limit the occlusion of foreign ions. The cases in which this is not true are those of isomorphous (Greek: *isos*, equal; *morphe*, form) substances, such as $PbSO_4$ and $BaSO_4$, which crystallize in exactly the same form. In these cases there is no limit to the amount of one substance which can be occluded into the other. By analogy with liquid solutions we might say that these *solid solutions* are miscible in all proportions.

Flocculation and Peptization.

Ions adsorbed on the surface of very small particles (formed in a system of high relative unsaturation) tend to keep these particles apart and prevent their further aggregation, thus stabilizing a colloidal suspension. As the concentration of foreign ions in the solution increases, particularly those with charge opposite to that of the adsorbed layer, the charge created by the primary adsorption is more and more compensated for by secondary adsorption. When the net adsorbed charge is decreased sufficiently, the particles coagulate and precipitate. This is called *flocculation*. Flocculated precipitates are highly contaminated with adsorbed ions. When such precipitates are washed with pure water, enough of the adsorbed ions may be dissolved to cause the solid particles to regain a high net charge, redissolve as a colloid, and pass through the filter. This process, called *peptization*, can result in a loss of precipitate on washing. For this reason, flocculated precipitates are usually washed with ionic solutions to decrease the tendency for peptization. Also, fortunately, the digestion (Section 3–3) of flocculated precipitates yields more crystalline, purer, and more easily filterable precipitates that are less easily peptized.

Composition

Stoichiometry. A precipitate which satisfies the criteria of quantitativeness, ease of preparation, and freedom from impurities may still be unusable for gravimetric analysis if it cannot be dried to give a compound of constant composition. For example, when hydrous aluminum or iron oxides, $Al_2O_3 \cdot xH_2O$ and $Fe_2O_3 \cdot yH_2O$, are heated at 100 to 200°C, they do not give compounds of definite stoichiometry. The amount of water remaining under these conditions depends greatly on exactly how the precipitation took place. (These compounds can be converted into forms which have a constant stoichiometric composition, Al_2O_3 and Fe_2O_3, by *ignition*, i.e., heating at a high temperature, 1000°C.)

Gravimetric Factor. A final criterion for the choice of a gravimetric technique is that, other things being equal, the precipitate which contains the smallest percentage of the substance being analyzed is the best. The weight percent of the component of interest in a precipitate is called the *gravimetric factor*. For example, the classical technique for the determination of magnesium is to precipitate it as magnesium ammonium phosphate hexahydrate, $MgNH_4PO_4 \cdot 6H_2O$, and then, by ignition, to convert this to magnesium pyrophosphate, $Mg_2P_2O_7$, which is then weighed. The percentage of Mg in this compound is

$$\text{Percent Mg} = \frac{48.62 \times 100}{222.56} = 21.85\%.$$

The newer method for gravimetric determination of magnesium is to precipitate it as magnesium hydroxyquinolate, which can be dried to constant composition, $Mg(C_9H_6ON)_2 \cdot 2H_2O$, at 105°C. The percentage of Mg in this compound is

$$\text{Percent Mg} = \frac{24.31 \times 100}{348.44} = 6.979\%.$$

A given quantity of magnesium will produce a hydroxyquinolate precipitate weighing three times as much as the pyrophosphate from the same amount. The relative amount of error introduced into the determination by weighing errors will be much less with the heavier precipitate, so the overall precision of the determination will be greater, and, on this basis, the newer hydroxyquinolate method is preferable.

3–3 PRACTICAL CONSIDERATIONS

Application of Principles

Crystal Size. Understanding the mechanisms of precipitation and coprecipitation should help us see some ways to obtain purer precipitates. First, adsorption and, in a sense, occlusion are surface phenomena; the higher the surface area of the precipitate, the more chance there is for adsorption and occlusion to occur. To obtain a precipitate which is as pure as possible, we should adjust the conditions of the precipitation so that we obtain the largest possible particles.

Digestion. A precipitate in which impurities are already occluded can, obviously, not be purified by simply being washed. A much more effective method of purifying a precipitate that is contaminated by occlusion is to heat the precipitate in its own solution for a period of time. This is called *digesting* the precipitate. Dissolution and reprecipitation are accelerated by the temperature rise, so that occluded ions may be rapidly exchanged for the ions of interest. (Naturally, an equilibrium number of foreign ions will remain, but this amount will be low, as explained on page 29.)

A very large advantage of digestion is that it encourages the formation of large pure crystals. Because larger particles of precipitate are less soluble than smaller particles, as the solution and the precipitate are heated, the smaller particles dissolve first and recrystallize on the larger crystals. Thus the larger crystals grow at the expense of the smaller. The larger crystals also tend to dissolve and recrystallize, and imperfections are also worked out of these crystals during the process.

Surface Adsorption. It is impossible to prevent surface adsorption completely, but a trick is often used to make its effect very small. The procedure is planned so that the adsorbed species will be removed when the precipitate is prepared for weighing. Precipitates are commonly heated to drive off any excess solvent, so we can try to make sure that any adsorbed material is volatile enough to be removed during this heating. For example, AgCl is usually precipitated in and washed with HNO_3 solution. Thus most of the adsorbed ions are H^+, Cl^-, or NO_3^-, and HCl and HNO_3 are easily volatilized during the heating of the AgCl precipitate.

The Precipitation Procedure

The principles governing precipitation lead naturally to some practical suggestions.

1) The solution of the substance to be determined and the precipitating reagent should be dilute and should be mixed slowly with rapid and efficient stirring. This will decrease the possibility that high local concentrations of the reactants will build up and will increase the possibility that precipitation will be relatively slow, producing large crystals and minimizing the coprecipitation phenomena.

2) Avoid a large excess of the precipitating reagent to decrease the formation of complexes that increase solubility, and to add fewer ions that might be adsorbed on the precipitate or cause peptization of colloidal precipitates.

3) Avoid adding substances that are known to adsorb on or coprecipitate with the precipitate. In case these substances are already present with the ion to be precipitated, the situation can sometimes be improved by filtering off the precipitate, dissolving it in fresh solution, and reprecipitating it in the absence of as many foreign ions as possible.

4) Usually, it is best to carry out the precipitation at an elevated temperature, since the relative supersaturation is lower at higher temperatures and the chance of larger particles being produced is enhanced. High temperature also increases the speed of recrystallization, which promotes the growth of larger, more perfect crystals. (If a precipitate is appreciably soluble at higher temperatures, it will have to be cooled to room temperature or below just before filtration.)

5) Carry out precipitations in beakers (not flasks) to make filtration, washing, and transfer to the filter as easy as possible.

Filtering and Washing the Precipitate

Suction Filtration. Precipitates for gravimetric analysis are best filtered through sintered glass crucibles. (If the precipitate is to be ignited, a different procedure is used, but it will not be discussed in this text.) The bottoms of these crucibles are made of glass particles that have been partially melted together (sintered) to form porous plates. The size of the glass particles and the degree of heating determine the porosity of the filters. Medium-porosity filters are usually most useful for routine analyses, since solvents pass through readily, but most precipitates are quantitatively retained. The walls of these crucibles may be made of glass or porcelain.

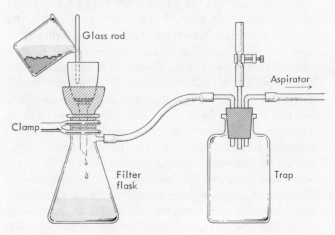

Fig. 3-3. Setup for suction filtration.

Sometimes a number is permanently etched or stained on each crucible for identification. You should record this number in your notebook along with any data pertaining to it. If no such mark appears on your crucibles, you must devise some way to mark them permanently so that you will not get them confused with one another.

To use a sintered glass filter crucible, you need the setup shown in Fig. 3–3. A suction flask containing the filter-funnel assembly is connected by heavy-walled rubber or plastic tubing to the aspirator (or vacuum outlet) through a trap. The trap is imperative (although the vacuum release "valve" on the trap is not), since it will prevent water from backing up from the aspirator into the filter flask; if the filter flask gets too full, it will prevent loss of the filtrate into the aspirator. The trap may be made from an aspirator bottle as indicated or from a flask or a second filter flask. Note the relative positions of the tubing inside the trap.

Never turn off the aspirator while the system is under vacuum. Water would then be sucked back violently into your system. *Also, never try to pull the filter assembly out of the filter flask while the system is under vacuum.* This can cause loss of filtrate and sometimes loss of precipitate if air should rush up through the sintered-glass filter. When you want to release the vacuum, do so *slowly* by *slowly* opening the release valve on the trap or by *slowly* removing the hose from the aspirator.

Washing by Decantation. Precipitates are best washed by decantation. This is especially true of precipitates that consist of very fine particles that would tend to clog the pores of the filter. Retain the bulk of the precipitate in the beaker when you pour the supernatant solution through the filter. You can easily do this by letting the precipitate settle and then decanting off the supernatant liquid, disturbing the solid as little as possible. (If you allow the precipitate to settle while the beaker is firmly supported in an inclined position, the operation will be even easier.) Direct the flow of liquid into the filter crucible with a glass stirring rod, as indicated in Fig. 3–3. Washing should also be carried out by decantation. Add small portions of the wash solution to the beaker, agitate the mixture thoroughly, allow the precipitate to settle, and decant the liquid through the filter. Finally, you can transfer the bulk of the precipitate to the filter crucible with the aid of small amounts of wash solution, as indicated in Fig. 3–4. Some workers prefer to transfer the bulk of the solution by adding a bit of the wash solution to the precipitate, agitating it to form a slurry, and quickly pouring this into the filter crucible. The remaining small amount of precipitate can then be transferred with the wash solution, as in Fig. 3–4. Decantation filtering is a disadvantage only when the

precipitate is relatively soluble, since decantation filtering usually requires a bit more wash solution than would be necessary if the bulk of the precipitate is delivered to the filter straightaway.

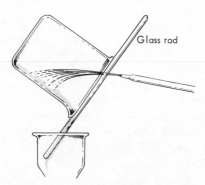

Glass rod

Fig. 3–4. Transferring a precipitate.

General Rules. Remember the rules listed below when filtering and washing precipitates.

1) The solution should, if possible, be hot. A hot solution is much less viscous than a cold one, so it will flow through the filter more rapidly. (This advice is obviously not applicable if the precipitate is appreciably soluble at higher temperatures.)

2) The first few milliliters of solution that pass through the filter should be removed and tested for completeness of the precipitation reaction. (The test used will depend on the particular precipitation reaction.) A test tube may be suspended inside the filter flask so that the liquid from the filter crucible is caught in the test tube. The test can then be carried out in the test tube. (A piece of string or light wire around the test tube is often useful for lowering it into the flask without dropping it and for retrieving it from the flask.) The same technique is used to catch the last few milliliters of wash solution to test for completeness of washing.

3) The solution chosen to wash the precipitate will depend on a number of factors; the solubility of the precipitate, the nature of the contaminants to be removed, the tendency of the precipitate to peptize, and the ease of removing the solution in the final drying operation. Often, some of the wash solutions chosen will contain a common ion to reduce the solubility of the precipitate in the solution. To avoid peptization, some precipitates are washed only with solutions containing ions, preferably ones which will be removed in the later drying steps.

4) A precipitate must be washed immediately after the supernatant solution has been removed. If a precipitate is left unwashed for any length of time, it usually becomes caked and cracked (like mud in the sun after a rainstorm) and is very difficult to wash effectively.

5) *A given volume of wash solution is much more effectively used in a number of small portions than in a few (or one) large portions.*

Illustrative Example: A given precipitate is to be washed with 20 ml of wash solution. When the precipitate is completely drained, 0.5 ml of liquid remains with it. If q is the concentration of substance that is to be removed by washing, a) how much will q be reduced by two washes of 10 ml each? b) how much will q be reduced by four washes of 5 ml each?

a) We assume that initially the contaminant is contained in the 0.5 ml of solution still remaining with the precipitate. Addition of the first 10 ml of wash solution will mean that the contaminant will be contained in $10 + 0.5$ ml of solution, and its concentration there will be

$$[\text{Contaminant}]_1 = \frac{q\,0.5}{10 + 0.5}.$$

After draining off this solution, we will be left with a 0.5-ml solution, containing this reduced concentration of contaminant. The second addition of 10 ml of wash solution will give

$$[\text{Contaminant}]_2 = \frac{[q\,0.5/(10 + 0.5)]\,0.5}{10 + 0.5} = q\left(\frac{0.5}{10 + 0.5}\right)^2$$

$$= \frac{q}{440}.$$

Therefore q is reduced to one part in 440 of its initial concentration by two washes.

b) Show for yourself that with four 5-ml washes, q is reduced to one part in 14,700 of its initial concentration.

Can you develop a general formula to predict this reduction factor, using V as the total volume of wash solution, v as the volume remaining with the precipitate after draining, q as the initial concentration of contaminant, and n as the number of washes made with equal portions of wash solution V/n?

The example deals with an idealized situation in which surface-adsorbed contaminants are ignored, but even in the nonideal case, the conclusion is still valid: many small washes are more effective than a few large ones.

Drying the Precipitate

Before using crucibles, you should dry them to constant weight (within the limits necessary for the experiment) at the same temperature that will be used to dry the precipitate. The washed precipitate in the crucibles will later be dried until constant weight is attained at a temperature which will ensure that the solid has a known stoichiometric composition.

EXPERIMENT 1.   *The Gravimetric Determination of Chloride in a Chromium Compound*

The sample for this experiment will be a chromium compound which has the general formula $CrCl_m \cdot nH_2O$; the chlorine is to be determined gravimetrically. The addition of a moderate excess of silver nitrate solution to a solution of the chromium compound in dilute nitric acid will precipitate the chlorine as silver chloride,

$$Ag^+(aq) + Cl^-(aq) \rightarrow AgCl(s),$$

which will be collected, washed, dried, and weighed.

This gravimetric determination of chloride is one of the most accurate gravimetric analyses known. If you will exercise reasonable care with the experimental procedures discussed above and below, you should obtain quite precise and reproducible results, even if this is your first trial with this type of experiment.

The solubility of AgCl in pure water is 1.8 mg/liter at 25°C and 21.1 mg/liter at 100°C. This solubility is small enough for a good analysis *if* the silver-ion concentration does not exceed 0.01 M. The common-ion effect of a moderate excess of silver ion reduces the solubility greatly, but if the excess is too large, the solubility will be increased. A larger concentration than 0.01 M will also tend to increase coprecipitation phenomena and thus could cause problems in the analysis.

Silver chloride is a good example of a colloidal precipitate. Because of its very low solubility, it is difficult to decrease the relative supersaturation enough to prevent the initial formation of a precipitate made up of very fine particles. Digesting the precipitate promotes the aggregation of these particles, which then settle into a heavy curdy mass remarkably free of adsorbed or occluded foreign ions. The precipitate tends to peptize if washed with pure water, so we use a dilute nitric acid solution to wash it.

One cautionary note must be added: silver chloride, like most silver salts, is light-sensitive. Exposure to light slowly decomposes AgCl into Ag and Cl_2. The silver remains in the undecomposed silver chloride as a solid colloidal dispersion, giving the solid a purplish color. (This, of course, is why a black-and-white photographic negative has dark places, silver particles, where the light struck the film.) If the precipitate starts to decompose photochemically after filtration, it will become lighter in weight because of the loss of the Cl_2, and the calculated value for the chloride will be too low. If the photochemical reaction occurs while the precipitate is still in contact with the supernatant solution containing silver ion, the Cl_2 produced can react with Ag^+,

$$3Cl_2 + 3H_2O + 5Ag^+ \rightarrow 5AgCl + ClO_3^- + 6H^+.$$

Although chlorine is lost from the precipitate through the initial reaction with light, $\frac{5}{6}$ of it recombines with silver ions as AgCl. Since both the metallic Ag and the AgCl formed later are present in the precipitate, the total weight of the precipitate will be increased and the calculated value for the chloride will be too high. If the analysis is carried out in the absence of direct sunlight, the photochemical reaction will not lead to perceptible error in the result.

Silver chloride is very easy to dry to constant weight. A sample dried at 120°C contains 0.03 to 0.04% water, at 260°C it contains 0.01% water, and at the fusion point, 455°C, contains no water at all. Heating to temperatures above 200°C is not required except in extremely precise work, and in this experiment we will be aiming for a precision of only 1 to 2 parts/1000.

Procedure

Obtain a sample of about one gram of the chromium compound. In general, samples to be analyzed should be dried before they are weighed out for the analysis, but in the present case this is impossible because the chromium compound, $CrCl_m \cdot nH_2O$, decomposes to a solid of nonreproducible composition on heating. Therefore you must use it without drying.

Clean two or three 250- or 300-ml beakers and mark them so they can be readily identified and differentiated from each other. The beakers need not be dry, but the final rinse after cleaning should be done with distilled water. Each beaker should also have a watch glass cover and a fire-polished stirring rod.

The chromium compound contains 30 to 50% chlorine. You should calculate (before coming to the laboratory) the weight of sample that is required to produce 0.4 to 0.5 gm of AgCl precipitate. This amount of precipitate will be precisely weighable. The weighing precision, of course, increases with sample size, but larger samples produce an amount of precipitate which takes longer to filter and wash and thus increases analysis time without adding appreciably to the precision obtainable with a smaller amount.

Weigh out accurately, by difference, two or three samples of the proper size, placing one in each beaker that you have prepared. (Note carefully in your notebook which sample is in which beaker.) It is not necessary that your sample weight be exactly that which you have calculated, so long as it is within about 30 mg of the calculated value. Such a procedure is called obtaining a *determinant* sample; the sample need not be exactly the weight you planned to use, but its actual weight must be known accurately.

The remainder of the procedure is given for one sample. You should, of course, carry out two or three parallel analyses rather than doing them one after the other. Plan your work schedule before coming to the laboratory to make the most efficient use of your time.

To one of your beakers add approximately 150 ml of distilled water, stir (but avoid splashing) to dissolve the sample, and acidify the solution with 1 ml of 6 M HNO_3. It is a wise precaution to test the distilled water and the HNO_3 for chloride before they are used by adding one drop of 0.2 M $AgNO_3$ solution to 1 ml of each. If either shows turbidity, consult the instructor before proceeding.

Calculate the amount of 0.2 M $AgNO_3$ solution you will need for your work during one laboratory period and obtain just this much solution in a clean and *labeled* container (preferably a stoppered bottle or a flask) from the stock supply bottle. Use this solution sparingly, since silver compounds are expensive, and carefully, since $AgNO_3$ readily stains hands, clothing, and bench tops. Transfer the amount of 0.2 M $AgNO_3$ solution that you have calculated you will need for one sample from your container to a 50-ml beaker.

Heat one of the sample solutions to 80 or 90°C and keep it hot. (The exact temperature of the solution is not important, so it is not necessary to use a thermometer.) This is probably the most taxing operation of the whole procedure. Unless you are very careful, playing an open burner flame on your beaker of solution will very probably cause "bumping" of the solution, resulting in a partial loss. If a laboratory steam bath is available, it is ideal for this heating; if not, a simple steam bath can be rigged by putting a wire screen over the top of a beaker that is not much bigger than the one you wish to heat. Boil water in this beaker (use boiling chips) and put the beaker with the solution to be heated on top of the screen. Be careful not to knock the whole apparatus over during the next part of the procedure.

(Remember not to carry out the precipitation or the filtration and washing in direct sunlight. It is even advisable to turn off as many room lights as possible. The precipitate will probably discolor even with these precautions, but the effect on the final result will be negligible.)

Add 0.2 M $AgNO_3$ in 1 ml portions from a dropper to the hot solution, stirring as you add them. The tip of the dropper should be held close to the surface of the solution to avoid splashing. Continue vigorous stirring after each addition of $AgNO_3$, but be very careful not to splash solution out of the beaker. Also, be careful not to scratch the beaker, as the precipitate which will form in such scratches will be difficult to remove quantitatively later. When you are not stirring or adding $AgNO_3$, keep the beaker covered with the watch glass.

As precipitation occurs, the colloidal particles should partially aggregate, but the solution will still be rather cloudy. As the chloride concentration is reduced, you will begin to notice that the precipitate is formed more and more slowly. You should correspondingly decrease the amount of $AgNO_3$ solution added in each portion until you are adding the silver ion by drops and observing the effect of each drop before adding the next. At the equivalence point, the point at which the silver ion added is equal to the chloride ion initially present, often most of the precipitate remaining in suspension will suddenly coagulate, and the solution will become relatively (but not perfectly) clear. Add 1 ml more of the 0.2 M $AgNO_3$ by drops after this point has been reached.

The first few times you attempt such a procedure, you will probably worry about whether or not the precipitation is complete. Test for completeness by continuing to stir the hot solution gently until the supernatant liquid is clear enough so that any turbidity would be detectable and then add one more drop of 0.2 M $AgNO_3$. If turbidity is produced, add five more drops of $AgNO_3$ and continue the heating, stirring, and testing until the test for chloride ions is negative.

Once the precipitation has been tested and found to be complete, the precipitate should be digested for about one or two hours by continued heating and occasional stirring until the entire solution is clear. An alternative procedure, perhaps preferable from the standpoint of time, is to allow the covered beakers to stand overnight in the dark or until the next laboratory period (provided this interval is short enough so that the solution will not disappear by evaporation).

While you are carrying out the precipitations, you should also prepare your sintered-glass crucibles to filter, wash, and dry the precipitate. Remove any old bits of precipitate adhering to the crucibles and then wash them carefully by sucking concentrated ammonia solution through them to remove any old AgCl. (*Do this under the hood.*) About three washes with 5- to 10-ml ammonia solution should be sufficient. These washes are best performed by placing the wash solution in the crucible while *not* applying vacuum, allowing the wash solution to sit for about a minute, and then sucking it through. Follow the ammonia washes with a distilled-water wash, a 6 M HNO_3 wash, and finally another distilled-water wash. Place the crucibles in a beaker (not one on top of another) covered with a watch glass and dry them for one hour in an oven at 150 to 170°C. Place the hot dry crucibles from the oven in a desiccator, in the holes in the plate provided for this purpose. *Do not touch the crucibles with your fingers;* use crucible tongs or a piece of folded paper as a handle to move them. When the crucibles are cool, weigh them. They should not be placed directly on the balance pan but on a small watch glass or weighing bottle cover (the reason for this is explained on page 35). The same holder may be used for all the crucibles, but it must be marked in some way so that it can also be used in the later weighings. It is a good precaution to weigh this holder separately so that in case it gets lost or broken you will know the weight of each crucible alone. Record the weight of each crucible along with any identifying marks that will enable you to distinguish it from your others and those of other students. Repeat the drying, cooling, and weighing (*not the washing*) until a constant weight within 0.2 mg is obtained.

You now have clean, dry, and weighed filter crucibles and digested and aged precipitate, so that you are ready to collect and wash the precipitate. Prepare a wash solution by mixing 2 or 3 ml of 6 M HNO_3 with 500 ml of water (enough for three or four samples). Place this solution in a wash bottle or, if you prefer, keep it in a beaker (labeled) and dispense it with a dropper. Place one of the filter crucibles in the suction filtration apparatus shown in Fig. 3–3. Heat the solution and the precipitate, if they are not already hot, and then allow the precipitate to settle for three to five minutes, preferably with the beaker inclined so that the precipitate collects in the "corner" under the pouring lip. Decant the supernatant liquid with the aid of a stirring rod, as shown in Fig. 3–3. The first few milliliters to pass through the filter should be caught in a test tube and tested for completeness of precipitation by adding one drop of 0.2 M $AgNO_3$. Remember to be careful when releasing the vacuum in the suction system. (If precipitation is not complete, as shown by turbidity in this test, return this sample to the flask and go through the final testing and precipitating procedure on the whole sample until precipitation is complete. The digestion will, of course, have to be redone also.) If precipitation is complete, continue the decantation until the supernatant solution has been removed from the precipitate. During this operation and the subsequent washings some of the precipitate will inevitably be transferred to the filter; most of it should remain in the beaker.

You should scrutinize the liquid that passes through the filter for any particles that the filter may not have caught. If you find any, the filtrate will have to be refiltered. Persistence of this effect means that either the precipitate has not been digested long enough or the filter is too coarse for this work. Try further digestion and if this does not work, obtain a new crucible with a finer filter.

When as much of the supernatant solution as possible has been decanted off without all the precipitate also being transferred to the filter, the filtrate in the filter flask should be transferred to another container. This will prevent your having to work up the entire solution once again if by chance the precipitate should start passing through the filter during the washing. The precipitate on the walls of the beaker should be washed down with wash solution, and the precipitate and wash solution should be gently swirled to help equilibrate the wash solution and the contaminants. Allow this mixture to settle and decant it through the filter. Repeat this process three or four times with the wash solution, and finally transfer the precipitate to the filter. The total amount of wash solution used should not exceed 100 to 150 ml. Test the filtrate from the final wash for the presence of silver ions by adding one drop of 6 *M* HCl to 1 ml of filtrate.

Suck air through the precipitate for a few minutes and then dry the precipitate and crucible in the oven for one hour at 150 to 170°C. At this temperature most of the HNO_3 and HCl adsorbed on the precipitate and crucible will be volatilized. After they have cooled in the desiccator, weigh the crucible and precipitate, using the same holder that you used for the empty crucible. The holder is necessary at this point because some acid will adhere tenaciously to the crucible and would corrode the balance pan if the crucible were placed directly on it. Repeat the heating and the weighing until a constant weight has been reached within the limits necessary to attain a precision of 1 part per 1000 for your weight of precipitate.

Discard the AgCl in one of the chemical waste containers, not in the sink. Do not use sharp or pointed objects to dig out the old precipitate, as these will scratch the sintered-glass filter and make it harder to clean next time.

Calculations

1) Calculate the weight percent of chlorine in the sample of $CrCl_m \cdot nH_2O$ for each of your determinations. Compute the mean and the mean deviation of these results. Discuss any value which deviates greatly from the mean (after double or triple checking to make sure that you have not made a computational error).

2) Assuming that *m* and *n* in the empirical formula $CrCl_m \cdot nH_2O$ are integers and relatively small numbers, can you compute them from the calculated chlorine content of your sample? How *accurate* does your analysis have to be to do this?

Further Experimental Problems

Inorganic Coordination Complexes. Early in this century it was discovered that there were often two different "kinds" of chlorine in inorganic complexes like $CrCl_m \cdot nH_2O$. These might be denoted as chlorines bound in the *inner* and the *outer coordination shells* of the central metal ion. The chlorines associated with the outer shell have the same properties as chloride ions in any ionic compound such as NaCl. They are essentially completely lost from the compound in solution and exist as aqueous chloride ions, $Cl^-(aq)$. The chlorines of the inner shell

do not act as ionic chlorides when the compound is in solution, but are more firmly held to the "nucleus" of the compound. When you use the procedure above, you cannot distinguish between these two kinds of chlorine (if there are two kinds in this compound), since the prolonged heating of the sample in the presence of silver ion "forces" any chlorine bound to the inner shell away from the nucleus.

If you would like to test whether two kinds of chlorine do exist in the sample compound, you will have to precipitate and filter any ionic chloride as fast as possible under conditions that inhibit the precipitation of any inner-coordination-shell chlorine. This, in general, requires breaking all the rules we have developed for precipitations. Some pointers for your procedure are listed below.

1) Carry out the precipitation and filtration in ice-cold solutions.

2) Dissolve the sample in ice-cold water immediately before the precipitation.

3) Add the exact quantity of ice-cold $AgNO_3$ solution you need (calculated from the sample weight).

4) Filter the precipitate no longer than five minutes after dissolving the sample.

5) Use a fine-porosity filter for the filtration.

6) Test your procedure on a substance such as NaCl to see how good your chloride recovery is.

Do a series of precipitations with varying amounts of $AgNO_3$ solution corresponding to the number of possible ionic chlorines. For example, if the compound contains two chlorines, in one precipitation add enough $AgNO_3$ to precipitate half the chlorine in the sample, and for another sample add enough to precipitate all the chlorine. If the amount of AgCl produced in both cases is about the same, you can be reasonably certain that only one of the chlorines is ionic (unless the amount produced is very small, in which case probably neither chlorine is ionic).

Before beginning this experiment, write out the procedure you intend to follow and have it checked by your instructor.

Report the number of inner-coordination-shell and outer-coordinate-shell chlorines in your compound and discuss its possible isomers (Greek: *isos*, equal; *meros*, part). Isomers are compounds which have the same empirical formula but different properties because of differences in the way the atoms are joined to form the compound.

Homogeneous Precipitation. A most exciting development in precipitation techniques is the use of the method called *homogeneous precipitation*. In this technique the precipitating agents are produced in the solution itself from some other reagent or combination of reagents that reacts slowly to produce the precipitating agent. Thus the concentration of the precipitating agent is raised very slowly and homogeneously throughout the solution so that the relative supersaturation is very low and the precipitates form large crystals that grow slowly as more of the precipitating agent is produced. Almost ideal conditions for precipitation are maintained throughout this process.

This technique is most commonly used in sulfide precipitations, which in the past involved bubbling H_2S (a vile-smelling and very poisonous gas) through the solution containing the ions to be precipitated as sulfides. Under these conditions a number of metal ions, like Ni^{++}, form sulfides which are highly colloidal and difficult to filter. Now, however, the compound thioacetamide is used very advantageously to produce H_2S

on heating in acidic or basic solution:

$$CH_3CSNH_2 \rightarrow CH_3CONH_2 + H_2S + \text{other products.}$$

Using this technique for sulfide precipitations results in the formation of large crystalline precipitates, even with ions like Ni^{++}. Any H_2S which escapes from the solution can be prevented from entering the laboratory atmosphere by attaching a small balloon to the outlet of the container in which the reaction is carried out. When the solution is cooled, the H_2S collected in the balloon redissolves in the solution, so the noisome vapors are prevented from permeating the laboratory.

Other precipitants besides H_2S may be produced in this manner. Your imagination should provide some ideas for comparing precipitation methods or investigating some of the factors that affect precipitations. Naturally any experiment you intend to carry out should be checked beforehand with an instructor to be sure that it is safe and that the necessary materials are available.

EXPERIMENT 2. Factors Affecting Precipitation

Introduction

In Sections 3–1 through 3–3 many factors were discussed that were alleged to affect precipitation of insoluble salts from solution. What experimental evidence can be brought forward to prove or disprove these statements? In this experiment you will gather enough information to evaluate critically at least some of these statements by studying the precipitation of strontium ion by oxalate; you will examine the effect of oxalate concentration, ionic strength, temperature, and pH on this precipitation.

This experiment utilizes radioisotopic tracer techniques, so you should familiarize yourself with the information in Appendix F before coming to the laboratory. Failure to do so will result in expulsion from the laboratory; an uninformed experimenter can be deadly.

Procedure

Work in groups on this experiment. The instructions given below are written for a liquid-counting apparatus that will hold about 25 ml. No specific activities are given for the radioisotope-tagged solutions, as these would have to be adjusted to meet the requirements of the particular counting apparatus that you have available; however, solutions with an initial activity of 1000 to 2000 counts per minute (cpm) should probably be used. Likewise, volume and dilution factors will have to be adjusted to meet the particular circumstances of your laboratory. Consult your instructor concerning any changes or special procedures that you are to use.

To begin, first measure and record the laboratory background radiation. The background should not be

over 25 to 40 cpm. Then fill the sample tube (or insert the sample tube) and count the sample. (It is a good idea to set the counter to count the background whenever it is not being used to count a sample. In this way a relatively high number of background counts will be recorded and the accuracy of the background-*rate* measurement will be increased.) After a sample has been counted, it should be removed from the apparatus and discarded in the waste container provided for it. The counting tube should be rinsed with dilute HCl until the empty tube counts again at the original background level; rinsings are to be discarded in the waste container so labeled. Remember: a few small rinses are better than one large rinse. (How can you test this statement experimentally?)

This experiment has four parts.

1) Carry out three precipitations,* using for each a 5.0-ml sample of 0.1 M $SrCl_2$, strontium chloride, tagged with Sr^{89}, and 20 ml of $(NH_4)_2C_2O_4$, ammonium oxalate, 0.025 M, 0.05 M, and 0.10 M, respectively. (These oxalate concentrations can be prepared by appropriate dilution of the 0.10 M $(NH_4)_2C_2O_4$ stock solution that will be available in the laboratory.) Allow the precipitate to stand for about five minutes, suction filter through Gooch crucibles with asbestos mats,† and count the filtrate of each with the liquid counter. Also count and record a 5.0-ml sample of tagged 0.1 M $SrCl_2$ diluted

---

* Remember to wear a laboratory apron and disposable plastic gloves to carry out all operations with radioisotopes. All operations are to be carried out in the hood.
† A small Buchner funnel and paper filters may be more convenient.

with 20 ml of distilled water. Counting 5000 to 10,000 counts is best, if the activity is high enough so that an inordinate amount of time is not required (for low counts you may have to sacrifice counting accuracy for time.) Remember to rinse the counter tube after each sample is counted. Make sure that the used Gooch asbestos (or filter paper) is placed in the container for radioactive waste.

2) Prepare four solutions of $SrCl_2$ and NaCl by adding 5.0-ml portions of tagged 0.10 M $SrCl_2$ to 2.5-ml, 5.0-ml, 10.0-ml, and 15.0-ml samples of 2.0 M NaCl; make each solution up to a total of 20 ml with distilled water. Precise pipetting will eliminate error caused by the common ion effect (see Part 1). Add 6.0 ml of 0.10 M $(NH_4)_2C_2O_4$ to each $SrCl_2$-NaCl solution, let stand for about five minutes, filter off the strontium oxalate precipitate, and count the filtrate exactly as in Part 1.

3) Dilute 5.0 ml of tagged 0.10 M $SrCl_2$ to 20 ml with distilled water. Heat the solution to about 90°C and record the actual temperature attained. Add 6.0 ml of 0.10 M $(NH_4)_2C_2O_4$ and keep the solution and precipitate at the constant high temperature for about 5 minutes. (A watch glass placed over the beaker or flask will decrease evaporation losses.) Filter the hot solution rapidly. Make up any evaporation losses by adding water to the filtrate (be exact). Count the filtrate for strontium as before.

Carry out an identical precipitation of SrC_2O_4 at room temperature. Record the temperature of the solution after precipitation, filter, and count the filtrate for strontium as before.

4) Add 6.0 ml of 0.10 M $(NH_4)_2C_2O_4$ to each of four solutions made up as shown in Table 3–1. Measure and record the pH of each solution after precipitation with a pH meter (see Appendix D). Filter the solutions and count the filtrate for strontium as before.

Table 3–1

Solution	$SrCl_2$ (tagged), 0.10 M	HCl, 0.10 M	NaCl, 0.50 M	H_2O
1	5.0	15.0	–	–
2	5.0	5.0	2.0	8.0
3	5.0	5.0	2.9	7.1
4	5.0	–	3.0	12.0

Calculations

For the data of Part 1, plot the fraction of strontium remaining in solution against the reciprocal of the oxalate concentration. Discuss the significance of this plot. Why did we let the solution stand for five minutes before filtering?

Derive a theoretical relationship between the remaining strontium in solution and the ionic strength of the solution (see Sections 9–1 and 9–2) and plot the data obtained in Part 2 accordingly. Comment on the agreement between theory and experiment.

What was the effect of temperature on the solubility of strontium oxalate? Cite experimental proof for your answer.

For the data obtained in Part 4, plot the fraction of strontium remaining as a function of pH. Explain the nature of the observed plot.

Further Experimental Problems

We have left out of consideration in this experiment the role of many other factors in precipitations: the digestion of the precipitate, the solution concentrations, the rapidity of mixing of solutions, etc. Design experiments to test the effect of these other factors and any more you can think of.

REFERENCES

BASOLO, F., and R. C. JOHNSON, *Coordination Chemistry*, W. A. Benjamin, New York, 1964, Chapters 1 and 4.

BUTLER, J. N., *Solubility and pH Calculations*, Addison-Wesley, Reading, Mass., 1964, Chapter 2.

BUTLER, J. N., *Ionic Equilibrium*, Addison-Wesley, Reading, Mass., 1964, Chapters 1, 2, and 8.

CLIFFORD, A. F., *Inorganic Chemistry of Qualitative Analysis*, Prentice-Hall, Englewood Cliffs, N. J., 1961, Chapters 2, 3, 4, and 5.

GORDON, L., and E. D. SALESIN, *J. Chem. Ed.* **38**, 16 (1961) presents a method for the homogeneous precipitation of nickel dimethylglyoxime.

HEIN, R. E., and R. H. McFARLAND, "Radiometric Analysis for Chloride Ion," *J. Chem. Ed.* **33**, 33 (1956) is a simple application of the use of the radioactive silver isotope, Ag^{110}, to a rapid determination of chloride.

HOLDEN, A., and P. SINGER, *Crystals and Crystal Growing*, Doubleday Anchor, Garden City, N. Y., 1960, Chapter 1.

KIEFFER, W., *The Mole Concept in Chemistry*, Reinhold, New York, 1962.

KOLTHOFF, I. M., and E. B. SANDELL, *Textbook of Quantitative Inorganic Analysis*, 3rd ed., Macmillan, New York, 1952, Chapters 2 through 8 and 17.

MATIJEVIC, E., J. P. KRATOHVIL, and M. KERKER, "Simple Demonstration of Some Precipitation and Solubility Effects," *J. Chem. Ed.* **38**, 397 (1961) presents a striking demonstration and good discussion of the various solubility regions in the AgBr system.

MEITES, L., J. S. F. PODE, and H. C. THOMAS, "Are Solubilities and Solubility Products Related?" *J. Chem. Ed.* **43,** 667 (1966) gives a good discussion of a number of points omitted in Section 3–1. In particular you should find a number of ways to criticize our calculations on $SrCrO_4$ solubility and solubility products.

MURMANN, R. K., *Inorganic Complex Compounds*, Reinhold, New York, 1964, Chapter 1.

NASH, L. K., *The Atomic-Molecular Theory*, Harvard University Press, Cambridge, Mass., 1950.

NASH, L. K., *Stoichiometry*, Addison-Wesley, Reading, Mass., 1966.

PIERCE, W. C., E. L. HAENISCH, and D. T. SAWYER, *Quantitative Analysis*, 4th ed., John Wiley & Sons, New York, 1958, Chapters 4, 5, 18, and 19.

RAMETTE, R. "Solubility and Equilibria of Silver Chloride," *J. Chem. Ed.* **37,** 348 (1960) is a discussion of this important system with emphasis on quantitative understanding of the equilibria. The discussion is followed by a number of interesting problems.

SKOOG, D. A., and D. M. WEST, *Fundamentals of Analytical Chemistry*, Holt, Rinehart & Winston, New York, 1963, Chapters 4, 5, and 9.

SWIFT, E. H., and W. P. SCHAEFER, *Qualitative Elemental Analysis*, Freeman, San Francisco, 1962, Chapter 5.

WASER, J., *Quantitative Chemistry*, W. A. Benjamin, New York, 1964, Chapter 4.

WERNER, A., and A. GUBSER, "Concerning the Hydrates of Chromium Chlorides," *Chemische Berichte* **34,** 1579 (1901) is Werner's original work on the hydrates of chromium chloride and his conclusions concerning their structure (in German).

PROBLEMS

1. Barium chloride is normally obtained as the salt $BaCl_2 \cdot mH_2O$, which loses its water of hydration after being heated for a few hours at 120°C. Given that 2.5783 gm of the hydrated salt was heated at 120°C to yield 2.1979 gm of the anhydrous salt, what weight of AgCl would be produced by 0.3567 gm of hydrated barium chloride treated by the procedure of Experiment 1?

2. How precise would your analysis have to be to allow you to distinguish $CrCl_3$ from $CrCl_2 \cdot 2H_2O$ by precipitation of the chloride as AgCl?

3. What is the empirical formula of each of the following compounds? (The numbers given are the weight fractions of the elements.)
   a) Ag, 0.710; C, 0.079; O, 0.210
   b) Fe, 0.725; O, 0.276
   c) Ca, 0.626; C, 0.375
   d) Pb, 0.450; Cl, 0.154; O, 0.381; H, 0.013
   e) C, 0.710; H, 0.040; O, 0.250

4. Given that 0.687 gm of a compound containing C, H, and O was reacted completely with an excess of oxygen to give 1.283 gm of CO_2 and 0.523 gm of H_2O, what is the empirical formula of this compound?

5. Solutions which are known to contain only Na^+ and K^+ cations are sometimes analyzed for these cations by ridding the solution of all anions except Cl^- and NO_3^-, evaporating the solution to dryness to give a mixture of NaCl and KCl (NO_3^- is lost as HNO_3 in the process), weighing the solid, and finally analyzing for the amount of chloride present. A sample containing Na^+ and K^+ yielded 0.5670 gm of solid chlorides, which in turn yielded 1.2953 gm of AgCl. What is the ratio of the weight of Na^+ to the weight of K^+ in the sample?

6. A 2.000 gm sample of a mixture of Al and Al_2O_3 was reacted with oxygen to convert the Al to Al_2O_3. The weight of the sample after oxidation was 2.500 gm. What weight of Al was present in the original sample? If the analysis was made with a precision of 2 parts per 1000, what is the precision of the answer?

7. Assume that a precipitate to be washed retains 0.5 ml of liquid when it is completely drained. Compare the reduction in the initial concentration, q, of a contaminant after one wash with 50 ml of water with that produced by two washes with 15 ml of water in each.

8. If there is a competition between two ionic species in solution to be adsorbed in the secondary adsorption layer of a crystal, the one that forms the least soluble compound with the ions of the primary adsorption layer will be preferentially adsorbed. Which ions, K^+ or Na^+, would you expect to be more strongly adsorbed in the secondary adsorption layer on AgCl in a solution containing excess Cl^-?

9. Obviously, the ions on the surface of a crystal are the ones that can dissolve. The greater the ratio of surface area to volume, the greater will be the tendency for the crystal to dissolve. Show how this explains why small crystals are more soluble than large ones.

10. Ions of opposite charge attract each other to form stable solids. One of the reasons that ions stay in solution is that the solvent around the ions decreases the *effective* charge difference between the ions. A measure of the effectiveness of a solvent for this purpose is its dielectric constant. Is a solvent of high or low dielectric constant the better solvent for ions? Explain. Does this effect explain why an alcohol-water mixture is used as the solvent for some precipitations?

THE SYNTHESIS AND ANALYSIS OF
A COBALT COMPOUND; VOLUMETRIC
4   ANALYSIS AND ION EXCHANGE

4–1 RATIONALE FOR THE SYNTHESIS

Why should we want to synthesize a particular compound in the first place? A century ago, it was important to learn the proportions in which various elements combined with each other, as well as simply to learn about the basic chemistry of the elements, but now that we know atomic weights very accurately, this motive is no longer valid. Chemistry is still an experimental science, however, and we cannot predict the pathway of all reactions, so we often need to study the reactions themselves. By synthesizing compounds you can learn a great deal about the chemistry of the elements, which adds to your store of knowledge and increases your ability to predict the course of other reactions.

Further, however, syntheses can make compounds available which have interesting properties to study. The cobalt compound that you will synthesize by the procedure given in Experiment 3 cannot be bought. This compound, *trans*-dichloro-*bis*-ethylenediamine cobalt(III) chloride, $[Co(C_2H_8N_2)_2Cl_2]Cl$, is a dark green salt which has a number of interesting properties, among which are its reactions in aqueous solution. A few suggestions for a qualitative investigation of these properties are given in Experiment 3. A more detailed quantitative study of one reaction is outlined in Experiment 28; the structure of this compound and the molecular changes that occur in its reactions are also discussed there. (See also the references on inorganic coordination compounds at the end of this chapter.)

Before we can do anything with a newly synthesized compound, we must check to be certain that it actually has the formula of the compound that we have tried to make. This is usually done by quantitatively analyzing the compound for one or more of its elements to ascertain whether the experimentally determined percentage composition matches that calculated from the formula of

the expected compound. If the calculated and experimental results match well, we can have more confidence that the compound we have made is indeed the one that we set out to prepare. Thus you will need to understand the procedures to be used to analyze the cobalt salt and check your work.

4–2 CRITERIA FOR VOLUMETRIC ANALYSES

Definition of Volumetric Analysis

In a gravimetric analysis, we usually add to the solution to be analyzed a slight excess of a precipitating reagent whose concentration is approximately known and then weigh the precipitate. In a volumetric analysis, we usually add to the solution to be analyzed a suitable reagent of accurately known concentration until the *exact* amount of reagent that is stoichiometrically equivalent to the unknown amount of substance being analyzed has been added. The unknown concentration is calculated from the volume, concentration, and stoichiometry of the relevant reaction of the volumetric reagent used.

The reagent solution of exactly known concentration, the *standard solution*, is added to the solution of the substance to be analyzed from a buret. This operation is called a *titration*, and the standard solution in the buret is called the *titrant*. Titration is carried on until the amount of reagent added is equivalent (by the stoichiometry of the chemical reaction that occurs) to the substance whose concentration is sought. This point is called the *equivalence point* and must be detected by some sort of indicator.*

Not all chemical reactions are suitable for volumetric analyses. Before we can discuss specific volumetric

---

* In general there is a difference between the point at which the indicator "indicates the end of the reaction," the *endpoint*, and the true equivalence point. See Section 4–4.

analyses, we should examine some of the factors that help to determine whether a particular reaction is useful in analysis.

Reaction Stoichiometry

The most obvious criterion for any analytical procedure is that the analytical reaction(s) involved should proceed to "completion," so that "all" of the element or compound being determined reacts, and that the reactions be well defined stoichiometrically, so that a particular number of moles of the standard reagent always reacts with a given number of moles of the substance being determined. We have already seen (Section 3–1) that for gravimetric analyses, solubility equilibria prevent us from precipitating "all" of a particular substance, but they do not preclude accurate analyses if the amount of unreacted substance is below the limits of detection anyway. This same consideration holds true for volumetric procedures. The *equivalence point* of a volumetric procedure is that point at which the exact amount of standard reagent has been added to react with all the substance to be determined. If, at the equivalence point, the amount of the substance being analyzed that is left in solution, because of the equilibria involved, is small compared with the limits of the apparatus used, then a good analysis can be performed. The criterion of a "complete" reaction can sometimes be relaxed even further if a suitable correction procedure is available (*vide infra*, Sections 4–4 and 4–5).

Reaction Speed

Volumetric procedures are usually carried out by titrations involving the addition of standard reagent to the solution of unknown concentration over a relatively short period of time, i.e., a few minutes. Therefore it is imperative that with each addition of reagent we must be able to tell within a few seconds what effect the addition has had, i.e., whether we are nearing the equivalence point. This criterion eliminates many reactions which would be suitable from a stoichiometric point of view but which are too slow. If we were to use slow reactions, the great advantage of a volumetric analysis (rapidity) would be lost.

Determination of the Equivalence Point

Unless there is some method for determining when the equivalence point of a reaction has been reached, it is useless for volumetric analyses. Almost all equivalence points are detected in one of two ways: either a chemical indicator is used or some physical or chemical property of the system that changes abruptly at the equivalence point is measured as a function of the amount of standard reagent added. Chemical indicators are usually chosen so that a color change occurs at the equivalence point (or close to it). The use of a few chemical indicators is discussed in Section 4–4. Physical and chemical properties are usually monitored instrumentally, as when a pH meter is used to follow acid-base titrations. Examples of such techniques will be given in succeeding chapters.

Standard Solutions

To perform volumetric analyses, we must have available a stable standard solution (a solution of accurately known concentration) of the reagent to be added. Many otherwise promising reactions are unusable in volumetric analyses because the reagents required are unstable in solution. At a minimum, we desire that a reagent retain its standard concentration for a number of days, so that it does not have to be remade or restandardized too often.

Standard solutions fall into two classes:

1) *Primary standard solutions* can be made up directly by dissolving an accurately weighed quantity of pure solid reagent in a known amount of solvent, usually in a volumetric flask. For example, a standard aqueous solution of Ag^+ made up from dry $AgNO_3$ is a primary standard solution.

2) *Secondary standard solutions* can only be made up approximately and must then be standardized against some primary standard or primary standard solution. The usual reason that these solutions cannot be made up accurately is that no pure stoichiometric compound containing the ion or group of analytical interest is readily available for direct weighing. Two examples are solutions of SCN^- prepared from KSCN, standardized against standard Ag^+ solutions (Experiment 4), and solutions of OH^-, usually standardized against potassium hydrogen phthalate (KHP), $K[OOC(C_6H_4)COOH]$ (Experiment 4).

Primary standard compounds such as $AgNO_3$ and KHP which are used for making up primary standard solutions and for standardizing secondary standard solutions must be obtainable in a form which is very pure, stable indefinitely, and easily weighable without special precautions.

4–3 CLASSES OF TITRIMETRIC REACTIONS USED IN VOLUMETRIC ANALYSES

Ion-Combination Reactions

There are two subgroups in the class of ion-combination reactions used in volumetric analyses:

1) reactions that form precipitates, such as

$$Ag^+(aq) + Cl^-(aq) \rightleftharpoons AgCl(s);$$

(This class of reactions is discussed in detail in the next section.)

2) reactions that form other soluble species, such as

$$H^+(aq) + OH^-(aq) \rightleftharpoons H_2O,$$

$$H^+(aq) + NH_3(aq) \rightleftharpoons NH_4^+(aq),$$

$$OH^-(aq) + CH_3CH_2COOH(aq) \rightleftharpoons$$
$$CH_3CH_2COO^-(aq) + H_2O,$$

and

$$Ag^+(aq) + 2CN^-(aq) \rightleftharpoons Ag(CN)_2^-(aq).$$

The first three of these reactions are acid-base reactions; techniques based on such reactions are called acidimetry or alkalimetry, depending on whether the standard solution is acidic or basic. This very important class of titration reactions is discussed in more detail in Chapter 7. The last reaction is a complexing reaction; information about complexing reactions may be found in standard analytical chemistry textbooks.

Electron-Transfer Reactions

Reactions in which electrons are transferred from one species to another are often called oxidation (loss of electrons)-reduction (gain of electrons) reactions. Examples of such reactions that are common in volumetric analyses are

$$2S_2O_3^=(aq) + I_2(aq) \rightleftharpoons S_4O_6^=(aq) + 2I^-(aq)$$

and

$$3Fe^{++}(aq) + Cr_2O_7^=(aq) + 14H^+(aq) \rightleftharpoons$$
$$3Fe^{+3}(aq) + 2Cr^{+3}(aq) + 7H_2O.$$

Oxidation-reduction reactions are discussed in detail in Chapter 10.

4-4   PRINCIPLES OF SOME PRECIPITATION TITRATIONS

Equilibrium Expressions. The Mass Action Law

In Chapter 3 you encountered the equilibrium expression called the solubility product. In this section we shall discuss the equilibrium expressions for chemical reactions more generally so you can better understand what takes place near the equivalence point in the precipitation reactions we shall consider.

It is an empirical observation that at equilibrium* in the general reaction

$$aA + bB \rightleftharpoons cC + dD, \tag{4-1}$$

---

* An operational definition of equilibrium might be that it is the state when all apparent reaction in the system has ceased. This definition should be used with care, however, since a reaction which shows no perceptible change during the time of observation might be proceeding very slowly and still not be at equilibrium.

the concentrations of the reactants (strictly we should use activities; see Section 2-4) and products are related by the equation

$$K = \frac{[C]^c[D]^d}{[A]^a[B]^b}, \tag{4-2}$$

where K is the equilibrium constant for this particular reaction. (K is a constant only when the temperature is constant; values of equilibrium constants quoted without a reference to the temperature are usually given for the reaction at 25°C.) Let us take as a concrete example the reaction

$$2Fe^{+3}(aq) + 2I^-(aq) \rightleftharpoons 2Fe^{++}(aq) + I_2(aq),$$

which has an equilibrium constant (25°C) of 9.3×10^7. At equilibrium, in other words,

$$K_1 = \frac{[Fe^{++}]^2[I_2]}{[Fe^{+3}]^2[I^-]^2} = 9.3 \times 10^7.$$

Recall, first, that the equilibrium constants have units, although they are usually quoted just as numbers. In this case the units are liters/mole. Why?

If the concentrations of three of the species and the equilibrium constant in an equation like that for K_1 are known, then the fourth is readily determined by solving the equation.

Illustrative Example: Suppose that a solution is 10^{-3} M in Fe^{+3}, I^-, and I_2. If it is at equilibrium, what is the concentration of Fe^{++}?

Substituting the known concentrations and the value of the equilibrium constant in the equilibrium constant expression gives

$$\frac{[Fe^{++}]^2(10^{-3})}{(10^{-3})^2(10^{-3})^2} = [Fe^{++}]^2 10^9 = 9.3 \times 10^7,$$

$$[Fe^{++}]^2 = 9.3 \times 10^{-2},$$

$$[Fe^{++}] = 3.0 \times 10^{-1} M.$$

Conventions Used in Writing Equilibrium Expressions

When one of the reactants or products is water and the reaction occurs in dilute aqueous solution, the water is usually omitted from the equilibrium-constant expression. Let us take as an example the reaction of acetate ion with water in dilute solution,

$$CH_3COO^-(aq) + H_2O \rightleftharpoons CH_3COOH(aq) + OH^-(aq),$$

$$K_2' = \frac{[CH_3COOH][OH^-]}{[CH_3COO^-][H_2O]}.$$

In dilute aqueous solution, however, water has about the same concentration as in the pure state,

$$[H_2O] = \frac{1000 \text{ gm/liter}}{18 \text{ gm/mole}} = 55.5 \text{ moles/liter},$$

so this "constant" might just as well be incorporated into the equilibrium constant, to give

$$K_2'[H_2O] = \frac{[CH_3COOH][OH^-]}{[CH_3COO^-]} = K_2 = 5 \times 10^{-10}.$$

What are the units of K_2 and K_2'?

Another convention we have already encountered is that the "concentration" of a solid reactant or product is usually omitted in the equilibrium-constant expression. An example with which we are familiar is

$$AgCl(s) \rightleftharpoons Ag^+(aq) + Cl^-(aq),$$

$$K_3' = \frac{[Ag^+][Cl^-]}{[AgCl]}.$$

It is conventional to remove the [AgCl] from this expression by incorporating it into the equilibrium constant. This is again possible since the effective concentration of a solid, its activity, (Section 2–4) is a constant as long as some of it is present. Thus

$$K_3'[AgCl] = [Ag^+][Cl^-] = K_{sp} = 3 \times 10^{-10},$$

where K_{sp} is the solubility product discussed in Chapter 3. What are the units of K_{sp} and K_3'?

Illustrative Example: What is the concentration of Ca^{++} in a saturated solution of CaF_2 where $K_{sp} = 2 \times 10^{-10} = [Ca^{++}][F^-]^2$?

We know that a saturated solution of CaF_2 is one which is in equilibrium with solid CaF_2, so use of the equilibrium-constant expression is valid. The dissolution reaction is

$$CaF_2(s) \rightleftharpoons Ca^{++}(aq) + 2F^-(aq).$$

For each Ca^{++} ion that goes into solution, two F^- ions go into solution. Hence for every x moles/liter of Ca^{++} ions in solution, there are $2x$ moles/liter of F^- ions. This information, together with the solubility product, gives us

$$2 \times 10^{-10} = (x)(2x)^2 = 4x^3,$$
$$x^3 = 50 \times 10^{-12},$$
$$x = 3.7 \times 10^{-4}\ M = [Ca^{++}].$$

Equilibrium-constant expressions may be manipulated algebraically to yield a great deal of information. For example, if the general reaction (4–1) is written in reverse,

$$cC + dD \rightleftharpoons aA + bB, \tag{4–3}$$

the equilibrium expression becomes

$$K' = \frac{[A]^a[B]^b}{[C]^c[D]^d}, \tag{4–4}$$

and it is evident by inspection that

$$K' = 1/K, \tag{4–5}$$

where K is defined by Eq. (4–2). Thus the equilibrium constant for a reaction written "in reverse" is just the reciprocal of the equilibrium constant for the reaction written in the "forward" direction.

Equilibrium constants for two or more reactions may be combined. For example, we can consider the two equilibria

$$AgCl(s) \rightleftharpoons Ag^+(aq) + Cl^-(aq),$$
$$Ag^+(aq) + 2NH_3(aq) \rightleftharpoons Ag(NH_3)_2^+(aq)$$

with the equilibrium-constant expressions

$$K_{sp} = [Ag^+][Cl^-],$$
$$K_c = \frac{[Ag(NH_3)_2^+]}{[Ag^+][NH_3]^2}$$

and ask what the equilibrium constant is for the *sum* of these two reactions,

$$AgCl(s) + 2NH_3(aq) \rightleftharpoons Ag(NH_3)_2^+(aq) + Cl^-(aq).$$

We know that the equilibrium-constant expression is

$$K_4 = \frac{[Ag(NH_3)_2^+][Cl^-]}{[NH_3]^2},$$

where [AgCl] is incorporated into K_4. Note that the product of the two individual equilibrium expressions gives

$$K_{sp}K_c = [Ag^+][Cl^-]\frac{[Ag(NH_3)_2^+]}{[Ag^+][NH_3]^2}$$
$$= \frac{[Ag(NH_3)_2^+][Cl^-]}{[NH_3]^2} = K_4,$$

$$K_4 = K_{sp}K_c.$$

We can cancel the $[Ag^+]$ in the numerator against that in the denominator because we are discussing a solution in which both equilibrium expressions must simultaneously be satisfied and, obviously, only one Ag^+ concentration is present in the solution. Thus the equilibrium constant for an equilibrium which is a sum of other equilibria is equal to the product of the equilibrium constants for these constituent equilibria. Similarly, the equilibrium constant for an equilibrium which is the difference of two equilibria is given by the quotient of the two constituent equilibrium constants, the one corresponding to the reaction that is subtracted is in the denominator. Can you prove this, using Eq. (4–5) and the result we have derived for the sum of equilibria?

Further discussion of equilibria and their application to titration curves appears in Sections 7–3, 4, 5, 6, and 10–6.

Complexation Indicator. The Volhard Method for Halides

The Volhard method for the volumetric determination of halides is based on two facts: that silver thiocyanate,

AgSCN, is a very insoluble salt, and that an excess of SCN⁻ in acid solution can be detected very readily with ferric ion, which forms an intensely colored red complex with SCN⁻. Let us take the determination of Br⁻ as an example. An excess of a standard solution of AgNO₃ is added to an acidic solution containing the Br⁻ to be determined. The exact amount of standard solution that is added must be known. (It is obvious that you must have some knowledge of the possible range of concentration of the unknown halide concentration to carry out this step.) AgBr precipitates, leaving behind the excess Ag⁺ in solution. Some ferric ion is added to the solution to serve as an indicator, and then the solution is titrated with standard KSCN solution, which precipitates the Ag⁺ as AgSCN. When all the excess Ag⁺ has reacted, the SCN⁻ concentration will rise abruptly and the iron thiocyanate complex formed will cause the solution to turn red, indicating the endpoint of the titration. The endpoint is not the same as the equivalence point, because at least a small amount of extra SCN⁻ must be added to cause the red color to form.* After correcting the volume of standard KSCN that was added for this excess, you can calculate from the corrected volume the amount of Ag⁺ that reacted with SCN⁻. This is just the amount that did not react with Br⁻, and since you know the total amount of Ag⁺ you added you can easily calculate how much reacted with Br⁻ and, hence, how much Br⁻ is present.

Illustrative Example: Exactly 50.00 ml of 0.100 M AgNO₃ solution is added to 50.00 ml of a solution of Br⁻ of unknown concentration. This is known to give an excess of Ag⁺ which is titrated by the Volhard method with standard KSCN solution; 12.00 ml (corrected for indicator blank) of 0.100 M KSCN is required. What is the concentration of the Br⁻?

We begin by writing the relevant stoichiometric reactions that occur in this analysis:

$$Ag^+(aq) + Br^-(aq) \rightleftharpoons AgBr(s),$$
$$Ag^+(aq) + SCN^-(aq) \rightleftharpoons AgSCN(s).$$

The total number of moles of Ag⁺ added is

$$\text{Total moles Ag}^+ = 0.100 \text{ mole/liter} \times \frac{50.00 \text{ ml}}{1000 \text{ ml/liter}}$$
$$= 5.00 \times 10^{-3} \text{ mole.}$$

---

* The excess titrant that must be added in some titrations is called the *indicator blank*. In certain cases its amount may be determined by doing a run with all conditions the same as in the actual determination except that none of the substance being titrated is present. The titrant is added to this blank solution until the indicator changes color. It is assumed that this same amount of excess is added in the actual titration before the color changes.

The reaction of Ag⁺ with SCN⁻ is such that for every mole of Ag⁺ present in excess, one mole of SCN⁻ must be added to be stoichiometrically equivalent. Thus the number of moles of SCN⁻ added is

$$\text{Moles SCN}^- = 0.100 \text{ mole/liter} \times \frac{12.00 \text{ ml}}{1000 \text{ ml/liter}}$$
$$= 1.20 \times 10^{-3} \text{ mole,}$$
$$\text{Moles SCN}^- = \text{Excess moles Ag}^+ = 1.20 \times 10^{-3} \text{ mole.}$$

Hence the number of moles of Ag⁺ used in the reaction with Br⁻ is

Moles Ag⁺ reacted with Br⁻
$$= \text{Total moles Ag}^+ - \text{excess moles Ag}^+$$
$$= 5.00 \times 10^{-3} - 1.20 \times 10^{-3}$$
$$= 3.80 \times 10^{-3} \text{ mole.}$$

Every Br⁻ reacts with one Ag⁺, so

Moles Br⁻ present in 50.00 ml = 3.80×10^{-3} mole:
$$[Br^-] = \frac{3.80 \times 10^{-3} \text{ mole}}{50.00 \text{ ml}} \times 1000 \text{ ml/liter}$$
$$= 7.60 \times 10^{-2} \text{ mole.}$$

One might anticipate a problem in this titration, because it is possible that any excess SCN⁻ will react with the silver halide already precipitated:

$$SCN^-(aq) + AgX(s) \rightleftharpoons AgSCN(s) + X^-(aq).$$

This is not a problem with Br⁻ or I⁻ since AgBr and AgI are less soluble than AgSCN and little such reaction will occur. In the case of AgCl, however, AgSCN is less soluble than the halide, which may cause trouble. The equilibrium constant for the reaction of SCN⁻ with AgCl can be obtained by combining the solubility products for AgCl and AgSCN:

$$AgCl(s) \rightleftharpoons Ag^+(aq) + Cl^-(aq) \qquad K_{AgCl}$$
$$\underline{-[AgSCN(s) \rightleftharpoons Ag^+(aq) + SCN^-(aq)] \quad K_{AgSCN}}$$
$$SCN^-(aq) + AgCl(s) \rightleftharpoons AgSCN(s) + Cl^-(aq) \quad K_5$$
$$K_5 = \frac{[Cl^-]}{[SCN^-]} = \frac{K_{AgCl}}{K_{AgSCN}} = \frac{1 \times 10^{-10}}{1 \times 10^{-12}} = 10^2.$$

Let us calculate what would happen if, for example, 0.1 ml of 0.1 M KSCN is added to 100 ml of a saturated AgCl solution with solid AgCl present. This adds

$$0.1 \text{ mole/liter} \times \frac{0.1 \text{ ml}}{1000 \text{ ml/liter}} = 10^{-5} \text{ mole SCN}^-$$

to 100 ml, so the concentration of SCN⁻ would be 10^{-4} M if no reaction occurred; but reaction does occur, and for every ion of SCN⁻ that reacts, a Cl⁻ is produced, so if $x = [Cl^-]$ thus produced (at equilibrium), then

$$10^{-4} - x = [SCN^-]$$

remaining in solution, or

$$\frac{[Cl^-]}{[SCN^-]} = \frac{x}{10^{-4} - x} = 10^2,$$

$$x = \tfrac{1}{101} \times 10^{-2} = 0.99 \times 10^{-4} \, M,$$

$$[SCN^-] = 10^{-4} - 0.99 \times 10^{-4} = 10^{-6} \, M.$$

[This calculation neglects any Cl^- in solution due to

$$AgCl(s) \rightleftharpoons Ag^+(aq) + Cl^-(aq).$$

Is this justified?]   Under the usual conditions of the Volhard titration, the amount of SCN^- that can be detected is about $10^{-5} \, M$. Thus it would appear that we would have to add 10 times as much excess KSCN as we did in this example, i.e., 1 ml excess, to detect SCN^-. Such a large difference between the equivalence point and the endpoint would seem to make this a rather useless technique, but we are saved by two factors: first, the reaction of SCN^- with AgCl is very slow, and, second, the addition of a few milliliters of nitrobenzene to the solution to coat the surface of the AgCl particles inhibits the reaction even further. It would also be possible to separate the AgCl by filtration and then titrate the solution containing just the excess Ag^+ ion, but this is time-consuming and yields no better results than the technique outlined in Experiment 4.

Naturally, the Volhard method may be used to analyze directly for the Ag^+ content of a solution, as well as for the determination of halide by the indirect method just discussed.

Adsorption Indicator.   The Fajans Method for Halides

In Section 3–2 we found that precipitates usually adsorb ions from the solution. For example, AgCl adsorbs Cl^- to yield negatively charged particles when Cl^- is in excess, and Ag^+ to yield positively charged particles when Ag^+ is in excess. In the titration of Cl^- with a standard solution of Ag^+, the Cl^- is in excess until it is very close to the equivalence point, so that it is preferentially adsorbed on the AgCl particles. A number of dye molecules (dichlorofluorescein is usually used in this method) are also adsorbed by AgCl but not as strongly as is Cl^-. When these molecules are adsorbed, they change color; for instance, dichlorofluorescein forms a pale yellowish-green fluorescent solution in water but turns red when it is adsorbed on AgCl. As the equivalence point is approached in the titration of Cl^- with Ag^+, less and less Cl^- is present to be adsorbed, so the indicator dye begins to compete favorably for adsorption sites. The endpoint is signaled by the change of the milky white color of AgCl precipitate to a pinkish color as the dichlorofluorescein is adsorbed.*

This titration must be done in neutral or weakly alkaline solution since the color change is due to the adsorption of acid anions from the dye molecules, which are weak acids. If the solution is acidic, then only a small amount of the dye will be ionized and the color change will not occur.

Precipitation Indicator.   The Mohr Method for Halides

When chromate ions, $CrO_4^=$, combine with Ag^+, a precipitate of red silver chromate, Ag_2CrO_4, is formed. In the Mohr method for chloride and bromide a chromate, usually K_2CrO_4, is added to the halide solution, which is then titrated with standard Ag^+ solution. If the conditions are correctly chosen, the halide will react quantitatively before precipitation of the Ag_2CrO_4 begins. The endpoint is signaled by the appearance of the reddish precipitate of the Ag_2CrO_4.

How do we determine the necessary conditions for this reaction? When both AgCl and Ag_2CrO_4 are in equilibrium with the solution, both solubility-product relationships,

$$[Ag^+][Cl^-] = K_{AgCl} = 1 \times 10^{-10},$$

$$[Ag^+]^2[CrO_4^=] = K_{Ag_2CrO_4} = 2 \times 10^{-12},$$

must be satisfied. The $[Ag^+]$ must be the same for both equations, so we can combine the two equations to yield

$$\frac{(K_{AgCl})^2}{[Cl^-]^2}[CrO_4^=] = K_{Ag_2CrO_4},$$

$$\frac{[CrO_4^=]}{[Cl^-]^2} = \frac{2 \times 10^{-12}}{(1 \times 10^{-10})^2} = 2 \times 10^8.$$

At the equivalence point $[Cl^-] = 10^{-5} \, M$. Why? We wish the Ag_2CrO_4 to start precipitating at this point, so we calculate what the $[CrO_4^=]$ must be to cause it to do so:

$$\begin{aligned}[CrO_4^=] &= 2 \times 10^8 [Cl^-]^2 = 2 \times 10^8 (10^{-5})^2 \\ &= 2 \times 10^{-2} \, M.\end{aligned}$$

At this concentration of $CrO_4^=$ we would theoretically expect the Ag_2CrO_4 precipitation to be just beginning. Of course, we realize that a small excess of Ag^+ will have to be added to make the amount of red Ag_2CrO_4 actually perceptible.

Practically, it turns out that a $CrO_4^=$ concentration of $5 \times 10^{-3} \, M$ gives a satisfactory endpoint; the sensi-

---

* An easy experiment to perform is to add a few drops of dichlorofluorescein indicator (0.1% solution in alcohol) to a solution of Ag^+. Add a little Cl^- solution and the solution will turn red. Keep adding Cl^-. What will happen? Why?

tivity is such that about $4 \times 10^{-5} M$ Ag$^+$ is then present. If we titrate 50.00 ml 0.1 M Cl$^-$ with 0.1 M Ag$^+$, the volume of solution at the equivalence point will be 100 ml and we will have to add 0.04 ml more of the titrant to the solution to provide [Ag$^+$] = $4 \times 10^{-5} M$. Prove this to your satisfaction. Has anything been neglected?

The *titration error* is the difference between the endpoint and the equivalence point. For the specific case discussed in the last paragraph we can calculate the relative titration error, e,* as

$$
\begin{aligned}
e &= \frac{\text{Moles Ag}^+ \text{ added} - \text{Moles Cl}^- \text{ originally present}}{\text{Moles Cl}^- \text{ originally present}} \\
&= \frac{0.1 \times 50.04/1000 - 0.1 \times 50.00/1000}{0.1 \times 50.00/1000} \\
&= \frac{5.004 - 5.000}{5.000} \\
&= \frac{0.004}{5.000} = 8 \times 10^{-4},
\end{aligned}
$$

or 0.8 parts/1000, which is negligibly small if an accuracy of 1 or 2 parts/1000 is desired.

The Mohr titration, like the Fajans titration, must be carried out in neutral or weakly basic solution because CrO$_4$$^=$ reacts with hydrogen ion,

$$H^+(aq) + CrO_4^=(aq) \rightleftharpoons HCrO_4^-(aq),$$

lowering [CrO$_4$$^=$] and thus decreasing the sensitivity of the indicator and increasing the titration error in acidic medium.

4-5 TITRATION TECHNIQUE

The most important piece of apparatus in a titration is the buret. Reread the instructions given in Section 1-11 for cleaning and filling your buret before continuing. The usual containers for solutions to be titrated are Erlenmeyer (conical) flasks. Solutions can easily be mixed in these flasks by swirling with little danger of any solution being lost.

To perform a titration use the following procedure.

1) Put the sample to be titrated and any indicators or other reagents in an Erlenmeyer flask. Choose a flask large enough so that the final volume after titration will only fill the flask about half-way.

2) Rinse and fill the buret with the titrant. Make sure the buret is firmly clamped so that it will be easily

operable with one hand. Record the initial volume reading.

3) Begin delivering titrant, holding the flask so that the buret tip is well inside the neck and continuously swirl the flask. You will note that there is usually a local, transient indicator change where a drop enters the solution. As the titration proceeds, this transient change will last longer and spread further through the solution. Why?

4) When the indicator change becomes slow enough that it spreads through a considerable amount of the solution before disappearing, stop the titration and wash down the walls of the flask with a *small* amount of water from a wash bottle.

5) Continue the titration slowly, adding a drop at a time, while constantly swirling the flask. Wait for the indicator change to disappear before adding the next drop. When you get very near the endpoint, you may wish to add partial drops of titrant by letting a drop begin to form at the tip and then stopping the flow and using a clean stirring rod to transfer this bit of solution to the flask.

6) The titration is usually complete when the indicator change is permanent, i.e., when it is stable for five to ten seconds while the solution is vigorously swirled. (If other indications of completion should be used, they will be noted in the instructions.) Record the final volume reading. Record the temperature of the solutions also, in case the volume must be corrected for temperature.

It is sometimes useful when first titrating an unknown solution to use a *titration thief*; this is simply a long dropper into which is drawn about 1 ml of the solution. The thief is left in the flask during the titration. When the endpoint is very near, the solution in the dropper is expelled and the dropper is rinsed by drawing solution in and expelling it a number of times. Then, with the thief rinsed and removed, the titration is continued very slowly to the endpoint. The advantage of this technique is that you can do the initial part of the titration quite rapidly, since if you run a bit past the endpoint there is a little unreacted solution which, mixed with the solution, will restore a pre-endpoint condition and save the titration.

Once you have done one titration on a solution of an unknown concentration, the second and third titrations will be much faster because you can calculate how much titrant you will need and you can add most of it relatively rapidly. Only the last 0.5 ml or so need be added very slowly.

It is a good idea to plan titrations so that a large fraction of the volume of the buret is delivered, since this will make volume reading errors less important.

---

* Another way of defining e is in terms of the volume added at the endpoint, V_{ep}, and the volume that should theoretically have been added at the equivalence point, V_{EP}, $e = (V_{ep} - V_{EP})/V_{EP}$.

Usually you have some idea what the maximum percentage of the substance being titrated will be, so you can use this information to calculate how much of the unknown to take to get maximum use out of the buret. If for some reason it is inconvenient to take a large enough sample, perhaps the concentration of the titrant can be cut down so that more of it will be required. This process cannot, however, be continued indefinitely, since the sharpness of the endpoint indication and the speed of the reactions may be greatly dependent on titrant concentrations. See Section 7–5 for a further discussion of this point.

When possible, you should determine an indicator-blank correction as outlined in the footnote on page 43. In many cases indicator-blank corrections cannot be made in the straightforward way indicated; in such cases samples of accurately known concentration must be titrated under the conditions of the analysis being done, and the difference between the experimentally determined and the calculated concentrations gives the indicator-blank correction. Indicator-blank corrections for the most common analytical techniques may usually be found in standard analytical chemistry textbooks.

4–6 PREPARATION OF STANDARD SOLUTIONS

Primary Standard Solutions

The substances used for preparing primary standard solutions are usually dried prior to being weighed to drive off any adsorbed water. The pure dried reagent is then weighed accurately by difference (Section 1–10) into a volumetric flask. A funnel inserted into the mouth of the narrow flask makes it easy to transfer the solid from the weighing bottle to the flask. Carefully rinse all particles from the funnel into the flask with distilled water. Add distilled water until the water level is almost to the neck of the flask. Remove the funnel and stopper the flask. Swirl the solution (do not invert the flask) until all the solid is dissolved and the solution is thoroughly mixed. Reverse the direction of swirling often. Thorough mixing is imperative; one of the most common causes of erratic results in volumetric analyses is incompletely mixed solutions.

After the initial mixing is complete, add distilled water with a dropper to bring the bottom of the meniscus up to the mark.* Use a buret reader, Fig. 1–15, to help

* If you overfill the flask, all is not lost. Put a gummed label on the neck at the level of the meniscus and then go on with the rest of the procedure. After the solution has been transferred to the storage bottle, refill the flask to the mark with water and then use your buret to add water to bring the water level to where it was for the solution. The sum of the volume added from the buret and the volume of the flask is the volume of solution you made.

read the water level. When the water level is at the mark, blot up any droplets of water clinging to the inside of the neck above the water level with a small piece of filter paper. Stopper the flask and invert it while holding the stopper firmly in place with your thumb. Return the flask to its upright position and swirl to mix the contents. Repeat this procedure at least ten or twelve times. When the solution is thoroughly mixed, measure and record its temperature so that you can make temperature corrections to the volume if necessary. The temperature will probably be close to room temperature, but it is wise to check, since heat is absorbed or released when most salts are dissolved and, if this effect is large enough, the solutions may be appreciably different from room temperature.

Transfer the solution to a clean, dry, stoppered bottle for storage. *Never store solutions in volumetric flasks.* Whenever you pour solution from the storage bottle, be sure to swirl it first to get all the water which may have evaporated and condensed above the solution level back into the solution, so that the concentration will be what you have calculated it to be.

Secondary Standard Solutions

Since secondary standard solutions are standardized after being made up, they may be made up in a much cruder fashion. Weigh out about the correct amount of reagent (usually a rough weighing to 0.1 gm is satisfactory) and place this in the bottle to be used for the solution. Add the correct amount of distilled water, using a graduated cylinder for the measurement. Swirl and invert, if necessary, to dissolve the reagent and thoroughly mix the solution.

Secondary standard solutions may be standardized by comparing them against a primary standard solution or against some other primary standard which is weighed out. Secondary standard solutions should not be used to standardize other solutions since the errors accumulated would render this "standardization" useless for precise (1 to 2 parts/1000) analyses.

Illustrative Example: A solution of NaOH, approximately 0.1 M, is prepared according to the procedure outlined in Experiment 4. It is standardized by using it to neutralize accurately weighed samples of potassium hydrogen phthalate, KHP, dissolved in water. Two samples of KHP weighing 0.7892 and 0.8536 gm require 43.49 and 47.02 ml, respectively, of the NaOH solution to neutralize them. What is the concentration of the standardized NaOH solution?

The "reaction" that occurs is

$$NaOH + K(OOCC_6H_4COOH)$$
$$= H_2O + KNa(OOCC_6H_4COO),$$

so that each mole of NaOH reacts with one mole of KHP.

Thus

Number of moles OH⁻ in 43.49 ml solution

= Number of moles KHP in 0.7892 gm.

Number of moles $OH^- = \dfrac{0.7892 \text{ gm}}{204.2 \text{ gm/mole}}$,

Concentration of $OH^- = \dfrac{\text{Number of moles } OH^-}{\text{Volume in liters}}$

$= \dfrac{0.7892 \times 1000 \text{ ml/liter}}{204.2 \times 43.49 \text{ ml}}$,

$[OH^-] = 0.0887 \ M.$

In the same way, the second run gives

$[OH^-] = 0.0889 \ M.$

The average value is

$[OH^-] = 0.0888 \ M.$

4–7 ION EXCHANGE

Principles of Ion Exchange

Ion exchangers are resins which have active groups incorporated into them that can react with ions in a solution, take them up, and return other ions of the same sign to the solution. The resin itself is basically an organic polymer of high molecular weight that is, for practical purposes, insoluble in water. The polymer "backbone" of the ion-exchange resin is made up of long chains of carbon atoms linked together,

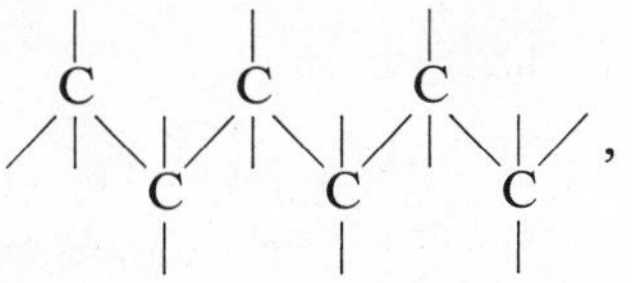

or of polymer chains containing other atoms, usually nitrogen, as well as carbon. The "unused" bonds of the carbon chain, indicated above, bond three types of groups to the "backbone": 1) hydrogen, 2) the active groups, and 3) other polymer chains (thus creating a branched-chain polymer).

The active groups fall into two classes:

1) Active groups present in *cation-exchange resins* exchange positive ions, usually hydrogen, for positive ions in solution. The active groups in such resins are usually —COOH (carboxylic acid group) or —SO₃H (sulfonic acid group), both of which can lose their H⁺ to become negatively charged and thus attract cations.

2) Active groups found in *anion-exchange resins* exchange negative ions, usually hydroxyl ions, for negative ions in solution. The most common active group of this type is —NH₂ (the amine group). The reaction

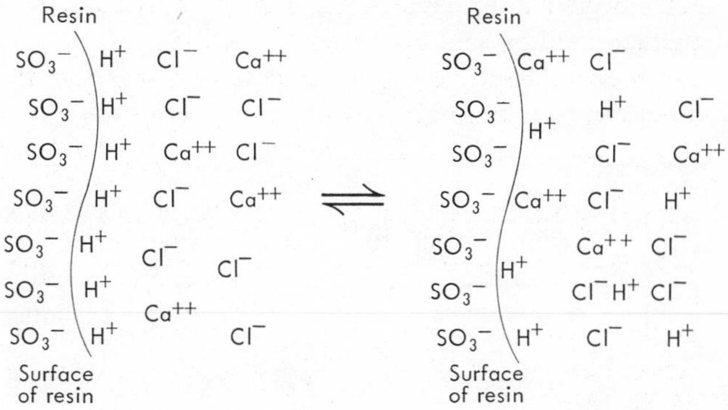

Fig. 4–1. Schematic representation of the action of a cation exchange resin.

in this case is more complex than a simple exchange; the reaction with the anion X can be represented as

$$-NH_2 + H_2O + X^- \rightleftharpoons -NH_3^+X^- + OH^-.$$

An exchange resin is overall electrically neutral and, to maintain the electrical neutrality, the exchanges are of equivalent charge, not simply of equivalent numbers of ions. A very schematic indication of the reaction of a cation-exchange resin with a solution containing Ca⁺⁺ is shown in Fig. 4–1. The most important thing to note about this representation is that the reaction is an equilibrium process, for which we can set up an equilibrium-constant expression. Let us call $[Ca^{++}]_r$ and $[H^+]_r$ the concentrations of Ca⁺⁺ and H⁺ on the resin. We then write the equilibrium as

$$K_{Ca} = \frac{[Ca^{++}]_r[H^+]^2}{[Ca^{++}][H^+]_r^{\,2}}.$$

This expression may be rearranged to

$$\frac{[Ca^{++}]_r}{[H^+]_r^{\,2}} = K_{Ca}\frac{[Ca^{++}]}{[H^+]^2}.$$

A similar expression holds for all cations, for example, Mg⁺⁺:

$$\frac{[Mg^{++}]_r}{[H^+]_r^{\,2}} = K_{Mg}\frac{[Mg^{++}]}{[H^+]^2}.$$

We can divide these last two equations to obtain

$$\frac{[Ca^{++}]_r}{[Mg^{++}]_r} = \frac{K_{Ca}}{K_{Mg}}\frac{[Ca^{++}]}{[Mg^{++}]} = K_{Ca/Mg}\frac{[Ca^{++}]}{[Mg^{++}]}.$$

The equilibrium constant $K_{Ca/Mg}$ indicates the selectivity of the resin for one ion over another. Usually, the heavier the ion in a column of the periodic chart, the tighter it will be held relative to the ions above it in the column. Will $K_{Ca/Mg}$ be larger or smaller than unity?

Also, usually, the greater the charge of the ion, the tighter it will be held by the resin.*

Ion Exchange in Practice

Ion-Exchange Columns. Using an ion-exchange resin is quite simple in concept; one could simply mix the solution containing the ions to be exchanged with the resin, stir until equilibrium is obtained, separate the solution from the resin, and repeat the process until the exchange is complete. In practice, however, such a procedure would be exceedingly tedious. Fortunately, it is possible to obtain exactly the same results by using an ion-exchange column through which the solution is percolated. (*Percolation* is the process of passing a liquid through the interstices of a porous substance. For example, one passes hot water through ground coffee to extract the essence of the coffee flavor.)

The setup for ion exchange is very simple. The solid ion-exchange resin is held in a vertical piece of glass tubing with a stopcock or some other means of controlling the flow of liquid at the bottom of the tubing (an old buret makes an admirable holder for the resin). The solution to be exchanged is poured into the tubing above the column of resin and then is slowly passed through the resin. As the solution percolates down the column, it will continually come in contact with fresh resin and the exchange will occur continuously. If the column is long enough and the flow is slow enough, complete exchange will occur before the solution emerges from the end of the column. (Usually some "washing" of the column with pure solvent is necessary to assure that all the ions that should be displaced from the column have actually been removed. Thus after the solution has been percolated, it should be followed with pure solvent until the solvent comes through unchanged. You can then assume that the exchanger has been returned to its stoichiometrically neutral state.) Hence within a matter of an hour or so the exchange can be completed with very little supervision by you.

Preparation of Ion-Exchange Columns. Anion- and cation-exchange columns are prepared in the same way; only the reagents for regenerating the column are different. We shall discuss here the preparation of a cation-exchange column.

Before packing resin in the column, prepare the resin by treating it with a 10- to 20-fold excess by weight of 1.5 M HCl solution.† Stir this mixture intermittently for fifteen to twenty minutes, let the resin settle, and decant the acid. Wash the resin with water four or five times by decantation.

Put enough water in the tubing to be used for the ion-exchange column to make a column of water about 5 cm high. Insert a plug of glass wool and push it to the bottom of the column to act as a "stop" for the resin. Add a small amount of distilled water to the resin and swirl the mixture to obtain a suspension of the resin, and then pour this into the column. Tap the column as the resin settles to ensure good packing. This operation may be done in stages. At no time should the liquid level fall below the level of the resin, as this will cause uneven packing of the resin and, consequently, poor percolation, destroying the efficiency of the column. Your columns will usually contain about 10 to 25 cm of resin, depending on the efficiency of the exchange, i.e., the size of the equilibrium constant for the exchange.

Wash the resin with distilled water until the effluent from the column tests at the same pH as the water used for the wash (test with pH paper). *Never allow the water level to fall below the level of the top of the resin.* (Do not disturb the resin when adding liquids; inserting a second glass wool plug at the top of the column helps prevent disturbances.) The column is now ready (Experiment 4).

A column should usually be regenerated after 3 or 4 exchanges have been made on it or, if it has been left standing overnight, after an exchange has been made. In the latter case the exchanged ions may have diffused down the column and there is danger that they will be eluted by your sample. A cation-exchange column is regenerated by percolating a solution of 3 M HCl through the column. An amount of acid solution about five times the mass of the resin in the column is usually sufficient. It should be passed through the column at a rate not greater than 2 to 3 ml/min. Follow this treatment by washes with distilled water until the effluent water has the same pH as that used for the washes (test with pH paper). The rate of flow for the wash water can be double that of the acid. An ion-exchange column that has been left unused for a period of time does not need regeneration but should be washed before use to remove the products of the slight decomposition of the resin that will have built up.

Ion-exchange resins do not "wear out" rapidly and can be regenerated a number of times. Put used resin in the containers available for it so that it can then be treated with acid to regenerate it for future use. The resins are relatively expensive and should not be wasted.

---

* Some natural or synthetic aluminosilicate polymers are used for softening water. In their initial state these materials contain Na^+ ions, which are exchanged for the Ca^{++} and Mg^{++} ions in "hard" water. Unlike the latter ions, which react with soap to form an insoluble residue (the bathtub ring), the Na^+ ion in the softened water combines with soap to form a compound that is soluble in water which can easily be rinsed away.

---

† Never treat ion-exchange resins with HNO_3 or other oxidizing acids, as they will attack the polymer itself, releasing much gas which will destroy the resin and the ion-exchange column by forcibly ejecting the resin from the column.

EXPERIMENT 3.   *Preparation of $[Co(C_2H_8N_2)_2Cl_2]Cl$, trans-dichloro-bis-ethylenediamine cobalt (III) chloride*

In this exercise you will prepare a complex of Co(III) with ethylenediamine ($H_2NCH_2CH_2NH_2$ = en) and chloride. Almost all available simple salts of cobalt contain cobalt in its +2 oxidation state, cobalt(II) or Co^{++}. The major reason for this is that the "free" ion, Co^{+3}, unlike Co^{++}, is a powerful enough oxidizing agent to oxidize water and is thus unstable in atmospheric moisture. The oxidation reaction may be represented as

$$4Co^{+3} + 2H_2O \rightleftharpoons 4Co^{++} + 4H^+ + O_2.$$

In complexes in which it is coordinated to species other than water, Co^{+3} is stabilized, i.e., its tendency to oxidize water and, in turn, be reduced to Co^{++} is much less. This is largely a result of the very much enhanced stability of the complexes of Co^{+3} as opposed to Co^{++}. A quantitative measure of the relative stabilities is the equilibrium constant for dissociation of the complexes. As an example, consider the hexamines of Co^{+3} and Co^{++}, whose dissociations may be written as

$$Co(NH_3)_6^{+3}(aq) \rightleftharpoons Co^{+3}(aq) + 6NH_3(aq),$$
$$Co(NH_3)_6^{++}(aq) \rightleftharpoons Co^{++}(aq) + 6NH_3(aq);$$

the respective equilibrium constants are 3×10^{-33} and 7.75×10^{-6}, so the Co^{+3} complex is 10^{27} times more stable. The same considerations apply to the complex ion $(Coen_2Cl_2)^+$, which is stable toward water and may thus be prepared and studied in aqueous solution.

You will start with a solution containing the complexing species plus Co^{++} and will oxidize the cobalt to Co^{+3}. There are complications due to side reactions, so you will not actually carry the reaction to completion. The Co^{+3} complex, however, is less soluble than the Co^{++} species present and may be recovered from the solution by crystallizing it out under conditions where the Co^{++} remains in solution.

The procedure below will make 8 to 10 gm of $(Coen_2Cl_2)Cl$, which is quite adequate for its analysis, Experiment 4, and a study of the kinetics of the reaction it undergoes in aqueous solution, Experiment 28.

Procedure

The detailed procedure for this synthesis is essentially that described in *Inorganic Syntheses*.

Dissolve 20.1 gm of $CoCl_2 \cdot 6H_2O$ (which should actually be written $[Co(H_2O)_6]Cl_2$) in 63 ml H_2O in a 250-ml flask. Slowly add, with stirring, 80 ml of a 10%, by weight, ethylenediamine solution. How many moles of ethylenediamine and cobalt(II) are present in the solution? Does this make sense in light of the compound that you are attempting to prepare?

Draw air through the solution using an arrangement like that shown in Fig. 4–2. This procedure keeps the solution saturated with oxygen, which is the effective oxidizing agent for the Co^{++}. Continue to aerate the solution for 10 to 12 hours. (Check with the instructor to see whether you may start the aeration and have someone turn it off 10 to 12 hours later.)

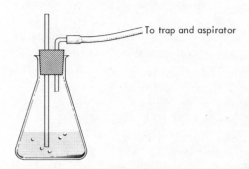

Fig. 4–2.   Aeration of the solution.

When the oxidation is completed, transfer the solution to a 250-ml beaker. Add 44 ml of concentrated 12 M HCl slowly, with stirring, to this solution. (Use the acid to rinse the flask before adding it to the solution.) Place the beaker on a steam bath and evaporate the solution until a thin crust forms on the surface. Remove the beaker from the steam bath, cover it with a watch glass, and set it aside until it is cool, preferably overnight.

Remove the liquid from the lustrous green crystals by suction filtration through a sintered-glass funnel which you can improvise by using a Gooch crucible and its holder. You may save the filtrate and put it back on the steam bath to reduce the volume further and obtain a second crop of crystals, which should be treated in the same way.

Wash the crystals you have collected in the funnel with about 60 ml of methyl alcohol. Use small portions, about 10 ml, of the alcohol and use each aliquot to rinse out the beaker in which the crystallization was performed. When a wash liquid is added to the crystals, the suction should not be on, for it will do no good to suck the wash liquid through instantly; the liquid should be allowed to sit with the crystals for thirty seconds or so before suction is applied. Follow the methyl alcohol wash with a washing of about 60 ml of ethyl ether, also added in small aliquots. (*Warning:* Make certain that there are no open flames within about 10 feet of your work area when you are working with ethyl ether.)

Transfer the washed crystals to an oven-dried (110 to 120°C) and weighed weighing bottle. Dry to constant weight at 110 to 120°C. Calculate the percentage yield of product $[(Coen_2Cl_2)Cl?]$ based on the amount of starting material, $CoCl_2 \cdot 6H_2O$. You should save the bulk of your product in a screw-cap vial which you can obtain from the stockroom. Be sure to label the vial.

(You will note from only a cursory reading of these instructions that much time would be wasted in your laboratory period if all you were to do was this synthesis, since most of the exercise consists of sitting around waiting for something to happen. To use your time efficiently you should start this experiment in your free time during preceding experiments.)

You might find it interesting to use any spare time you have after you have obtained the Co^{+3} complex to obtain its absorption spectrum, i.e., to use a spectrophotometer (see Appendix E) to find out which wavelengths of light are most strongly absorbed and which are least strongly absorbed. A solution of concentration 1 to 2×10^{-2} M is about right for this purpose. (Make the solution slightly acid with HCl.) Make up the solution *immediately* before taking the spectrum and record the spectrum as rapidly as possible. It is adequate to take absorbance (or transmittance) readings every 25 mμ except in regions where the light absorption changes rapidly as a function of wavelength, where the readings should be taken at more closely spaced wavelengths.

It is also interesting to dissolve a small quantity of the complex in water and divide this solution among three test tubes. Leave one as a control; add a few drops

of acid to the second and add a few drops of dilute base solution to the third. Note the results. You might also investigate the effect of temperature on solutions of the complex. Do not use more than 1 or 2 gm of material in these experiments, since you will need the rest later.

Calculations

Your report for this exercise should be very brief. It should include your percentage yield, your observations on the product, and balanced equations for the synthesis steps.

Further Experimental Problems

The mild oxidation with atmospheric oxygen used in this synthesis is time-consuming. Other Co^{+3} complexes are synthesized by more forceful oxidation methods, such as the use of peroxide. Examples are available in the syntheses discussed in *Inorganic Syntheses* in about the same place as the reference for the above experiment. Perhaps you would like to try your hand at developing a faster synthesis based on a faster oxidation method. Remember to check your procedure and method with an instructor before starting.

EXPERIMENT 4.   Analysis of (Coen₂Cl₂)Cl

The procedure for analyzing $(Coen_2Cl_2)Cl$ involves exchanging all the cobalt(III) for an equivalent amount of hydrogen ion on a cation-exchange column, titrating the H^+ with standard base solution, and then analyzing by the Volhard method all the chlorine which passes unchanged through the column as chloride. In doing this, the stability of the Co^{+3} complex is a hindrance, since it will not all dissociate and an amount of H^+ which is not stoichiometrically equivalent (in charge) to the Co^{+3} will be produced. Therefore we first reduce the Co^{+3} to Co^{++}, whose complex is very labile. The reduction is carried out with metallic zinc and may be represented (without the complexing groups on the cobalt) as

$$2Co^{+3} + Zn \rightleftharpoons 2Co^{++} + Zn^{++}.$$

Note that the total positive charge is the same on both sides of this equation. Since in the ion-exchange column *all* cations are exchanged for an equivalent amount of H^+ (equivalent by charge), both the Co^{++} and Zn^{++} will be replaced by H^+. This amount of H^+ will be equivalent to the number of moles of positive charge present in the solution. How is this related to the original number of moles of cobalt(III)?

The chemistry of the chloride analysis has been discussed above, and acid-base titrations are discussed in Chapter 7.

Procedure

Standard solutions of $AgNO_3$, KSCN, and NaOH are necessary for this procedure. To prepare 250 ml of a *standard solution of AgNO₃*, place 4.3 gm of $AgNO_3$ (weighed on a rough balance) in a clean, dry weighing bottle and dry it at 110°C for two hours. After cooling it in the desiccator, weigh the bottle and contents accurately on the analytical balance, transfer the $AgNO_3$ to a 250-ml volumetric flask with the aid of a funnel, and reweigh the weighing bottle and any $AgNO_3$ left in it. Make the solution up to the mark with distilled water as described in Section 4–6 and transfer the solution to a clean dry storage bottle. Compute the accurate concentration of the solution from the exact mass of $AgNO_3$ used and the volume of the solution. Label the stock bottle of the standard $AgNO_3$, indicating the contents and concentration.

A secondary *standard solution of KSCN* is obtained by making up a solution of approximately the correct concentration and then standardizing it by comparing it with a primary standard solution of $AgNO_3$ via the Volhard titration. You will need about 250 ml of KSCN solution for this analysis. Weigh out on a rough balance the amount of KSCN necessary to make up a 0.1 M solution in 250 ml of H_2O and add the solid and water to a clean stoppered bottle. Swirl the bottle to mix and to dissolve the contents. Rinse and fill a buret with this KSCN solution. Pipet into a clean 250-ml flask exactly 25.00 ml of standard $AgNO_3$ solution. Acidify this solution with 5 ml of 6 M nitric acid. (Make sure that the acid is free of nitrogen oxides and chloride. A yellow color in the acid indicates the presence of nitrogen oxides, which can be removed by boiling the acid for a few minutes. After this treatment, add water to make up for the loss by evaporation.) Add 1 to 2 ml of a saturated solution (about 40% by weight) of ferric ammonium sulfate to provide the Fe^{+3} for endpoint detection, and dilute to about 75 ml with water.

Read the buret containing the KSCN solution and record this reading; then titrate the silver solution with the KSCN solution. The first perceptible color change to orange-red occurs about 1% before the equivalence point because some Ag^+ is held out of the solution due to adsorption. Swirl the solution vigorously and continue the titration by drops until the pinkish-brown color remains permanent despite strong swirling for ten seconds. Allow the buret walls to drain and then record the buret reading. No blank correction is necessary in this titration. Repeat the standardization twice more. Calculate the concentration of the KSCN solution. Label the bottle of this solution with its accurate concentration.

A secondary *standard solution of NaOH* is prepared by diluting a very concentrated solution of NaOH and then standardizing the base against potassium hydrogen phthalate, KHP. Solutions of base are very likely to deteriorate rapidly with time if they are often open to the atmosphere, due to the dissolution of CO_2 and the concomitant reactions:

$$CO_2(g) + H_2O \rightleftharpoons CO_2(aq),$$
$$CO_2(aq) + H_2O \rightleftharpoons HCO_3{}^-(aq) + H^+(aq),$$
$$H^+(aq) + OH^-(aq) \rightleftharpoons H_2O,$$
$$HCO_3{}^-(aq) + OH^-(aq) \rightleftharpoons CO_3{}^=(aq) + H_2O.$$

In addition to destroying the standardization of the base solution, these reactions create carbonate in the solution, which will react with acid when titrations are performed to form bicarbonate. As explained in Chapter 7, this effect will tend to blur the endpoint determination and produce inaccurate results. Hence we want to have our solution of NaOH as free of carbonate as possible; Na_2CO_3 is insoluble in concentrated solutions of NaOH, so we usually prepare a solution that is 50% by weight

NaOH, and then either filter off the Na_2CO_3 or allow it to settle and decant the base solution. (This should be done by the instructors because the solution is very corrosive.)

Distilled water usually contains a great deal of $CO_2(aq)$, which is removed by boiling before the water is used to dilute the 50% NaOH solution. Boil a bit more than 500 ml of distilled water for five minutes and allow it to cool. Weigh out on the rough balance an amount of the 50% NaOH solution that will contain enough NaOH to make 500 ml of 0.1 M NaOH solution. (This will be about 3 ml by volume.) Add this, plus 500 ml of boiled and cooled distilled water to your polyethylene bottle. Do not expose either the stock solution or your newly made solution to the atmosphere for any longer than is absolutely necessary. Swirl your capped bottle to mix the contents thoroughly. Standardize the NaOH against KHP as follows:

1) Dry 4 to 5 gm of KHP in a weighing bottle for one hour at 110 to 120°C and cool it in a desiccator.

2) Accurately weigh out by difference two samples of KHP large enough to be stoichiometrically equivalent to 25 to 40 ml of 0.1 M NaOH and place each in a 250-ml flask.

3) To each sample add 25 ml of freshly boiled and cooled distilled water and 4 to 5 drops of phenolphthalein indicator (0.1% solution in alcohol).

4) Rinse and fill your buret with the base to be standardized. Record the initial reading and then titrate one of the acid solutions until the solution turns a light pink which is stable for 10 to 15 seconds without agitation. (The endpoint will fade due to dissolution of CO_2 from the air.) Record the final buret reading. No blank correction is necessary.

5) Refill the buret and titrate the second sample of acid.

6) Calculate the concentration of the standard NaOH solution and label the bottle. The standardization should be performed again after the analysis has been completed to see if the NaOH has changed concentration; if this is the case, you can make an approximate correction at least.

Use all standard solutions sparingly. Remember the time and effort you will have to expend to make them up again if you run out before the end of an experiment.

The Analysis. Assume, for the sake of calculation, that the compound you are analyzing is (Coen₂Cl₂)Cl. Calculate how much of this compound you should take to make up 50 ml of solution with a concentration such that a 10-ml aliquot of this solution will require 25 to 40 ml of standard base to titrate the acid formed on ion exchange. Weigh out accurately by difference about the requisite amount of $(Coen_2Cl_2)Cl$, add it to your 50-ml volumetric flask, and make it up to the mark with distilled water. This will be your stock solution of sample.

Pipet 10 ml of this stock solution into a small beaker. Add about 0.5 gm of granulated zinc and swirl gently. Swirl this solution occasionally for about 30 minutes. At the end of this time the solution will be brick red and should remind you of the solution you began with when you started the synthesis. Meanwhile, prepare or check the ion-exchange column you will use. The columns will be made with Dowex 50 sulfonic acid resin of 50 to 100 mesh or finer. Pass about 10 ml of distilled H_2O through the column at about 2 to 3 ml/min and make certain that the pH of the effluent is the same as that of the water with which you began. Continue washing until this condition is fulfilled; you will be ready to add your sample after draining the water until its level is about 1 cm above the top of the column.

Decant the sample into the column (use a stirring rod to direct the flow), being very careful not to allow any unreacted zinc granules to get into the column. Use 10 ml of H_2O in 1-ml portions to rinse out the beaker and add the washings to the column. Rinse down the sides of the column tubing with about 5 ml more of distilled water. Run this solution through the column at a rate of about 1.0 to 1.5 ml/min and collect the effluent in a 250-ml flask. Follow this with about 15 to 20 ml of distilled water added in aliquots of about 3 to 4 ml when the liquid level falls within 1 cm of the top of the column. If it is still acidic, pass another 8 to 10 ml of distilled water through and check the pH again. The washes may be run through faster, 2 to 3 ml/min. Continue until the effluent pH and that of the distilled water are the same. This should probably take no more than 20 to 30 ml of H_2O.

You now have a flask containing, essentially, a dilute solution of hydrochloric acid. Titrate it with the 0.1 M NaOH which you have previously prepared and standardized, using 4 to 5 drops of phenolphthalein as an indicator. The endpoint, as in the standardization, is not permanent but will fade as CO_2 dissolves from the air.

When you have finished this titration, add to the solution 5 ml of 6 M HNO_3 (free of NO_2 and Cl^-). Add an excess of standard $AgNO_3$ solution, making sure to *record exactly how much is added*. You can calculate the volume of $AgNO_3$ solution that would be equivalent to the chloride present and then add 4 to 6 ml excess. If this total amount of $AgNO_3$ solution can be conveniently added with a pipet, use a pipet; if not, use a buret. Swirl the flask vigorously during the addition. Add 2 ml of a saturated solution of ferric ammonium sulfate as the indicator and 5 ml of chloride-free

nitrobenzene.* Vigorously agitate the mixture and then titrate the excess Ag^+ with the standard KSCN solution until the pinkish brown endpoint is stable for ten seconds while the flask is being vigorously swirled. [*Hint:* instead of rinsing, cleaning, and filling your buret alternately with NaOH and KSCN solution, make a deal with your neighbor and keep NaOH in one of your burets (one with a Teflon® stopcock, if available) and KSCN in the other. Remember *never* to store your buret or any volumetric glassware with base or any other reagent solution still in it.] Repeat the analysis at least once and preferably twice.

Calculations

You have enough information to calculate the percentages of Co and Cl in your complex. Compare your experimental values with the theoretical values for $(Coen_2Cl_2)Cl$.

Ethylenediamine is a base which reacts with hydrogen ion,

$$H_2NCH_2CH_2NH_2(aq) + H^+(aq) \rightleftharpoons$$
$$H_2NCH_2CH_2NH_3^+(aq),$$
$$H_2NCH_2CH_2NH_3^+(aq) + H^+(aq) \rightleftharpoons$$
$$^+H_3NCH_2CH_2NH_3^+(aq),$$

and should therefore interfere with the determination of the H^+ concentration after ion exchange. Why did we not take account of this effect in the experiment? Have we made a bad mistake in technique?

Further Experimental Problems

Even if we obtain good agreement between the theoretical and experimental percentages of Co and Cl in our sample, a nagging doubt should still remain. What if the agreement is fortuitous and the remaining substance is not ethylenediamine? To resolve this doubt, one would have to analyze the compound for ethylenediamine.

A possible approach to this analysis is the gasometric method of D. D. van Slyke, in which the nitrogen liberated by the reaction of nitrous acid with primary amines,

$$HNO_2(aq) + RNH_2(aq) \rightarrow N_2(g) + ROH(aq) + H_2O,$$

is collected and its pressure, volume, and temperature are measured. The perfect gas law, $PV = nRT$, may then be employed to calculate the number of moles of

_____

* The nitrobenzene coats the surface of the AgCl particles and effectively prevents them from reaction with SCN^- (Section 4–4). Use care in handling nitrobenzene as it is poisonous if absorbed through the skin and its vapors are toxic if inhaled for a prolonged length of time.

N_2 released and hence the number of moles of primary amine that reacted. Ethylenediamine contains two primary amine groups and should certainly be susceptible to determination, yielding two moles of N_2 per mole of diamine.

All is not, however, quite as sanguine as one might anticipate at first glance. The Co^{+3} is very strongly bonded to the amine groups of the diamine, so they are not necessarily "free" to participate in this reaction. Perhaps this trouble could be overcome by reducing the Co^{+3} to Co^{++}, which does not bond so strongly with the amine.

Some of the techniques of gasometric analysis may be found in Experiment 29 and other places, and the development of such an analysis for this particular case would be a challenging and stimulating problem. Other methods of analysis for the ethylenediamine could also be explored. Check your procedure and method with

an instructor to be certain that all equipment and reagents are available before you undertake any experimentation.

We have written the chemical formula of *trans*-dichloro-*bis*-ethylenediamine cobalt(III) chloride in a form that indicates that it is a 1 : 1 salt, i.e., an ionic compound made up of singly-charged ions. In this case these are $(Coen_2Cl_2)^+$ and Cl^-. What proof do we have that this is actually the case? Perhaps we could obtain some more information by performing the ion-exchange experiment on a freshly made solution of the cobalt compound that has not been treated with zinc. What might this tell us? We might, further, let a solution of the compound sit overnight and then perform the ion exchange, again without the zinc treatment, and compare this result with that for a freshly prepared solution and a zinc-treated solution. What might you learn from this experiment?

REFERENCES

BASOLO, F., and R. C. JOHNSON, *Coordination Chemistry*, W. A. Benjamin, New York, 1964, Chapters 1, 3, and 4.

BASOLO, F., and R. G. PEARSON, *Mechanisms of Inorganic Reactions*, John Wiley & Sons, New York, 1960, pp. 241–248.

EMELEUS, H. J., and J. S. ANDERSON, *Modern Aspects of Inorganic Chemistry*, Van Nostrand, New York, 1960, pp. 115–119.

FERNELIUS, W. C., ed., *Inorganic Syntheses*, Vol. II, McGraw-Hill, New York, 1946, pp. 222–223, is the source for the preparation of $(Coen_2Cl_2)Cl$.

GOULD, E. S., *Inorganic Reactions and Structure*, revised edition, Holt, Rinehart & Winston, New York, 1962, Chapter 22.

KOLTHOFF, I. M., and E. B. SANDELL, *Textbook of Quantitative Inorganic Analysis*, 3rd ed., Macmillan, New York, 1952, Chapters 28, 30, 33, and 35.

MARTELL, A. E., and M. CALVIN, *Chemistry of the Metal Chelate Compounds*, Prentice-Hall, Englewood Cliffs, N. J., 1952, pp. 1–5.

MORIE, G. P., T. R. SWEET, and G. F. PITSICK, "Anion Exchange Radiochemical Experiment," *J. Chem. Ed.*

41, 389 (1964) presents a separation of Mn, Zn, and Fe by the use of their tartrate complexes and an anion exchange resin. The analysis of the effluent is done by radiocounting of the tagged ions.

MUCCI, J. F., R. L. STEARNS, and H. F. FLEISHMAN, "Cesium-Cobalt-Dowex 50-X2 System in H^+-Form," *J. Chem. Ed.* **41,** 163 (1964) presents an experiment to determine the difference in exchange rates for Co^{++} and Cs^+ on the ion exchange resin.

PIERCE, W. C., E. L. HAENISCH, and D. T. SAWYER, *Quantitative Analysis*, 4th ed., John Wiley & Sons, New York, 1958, Chapters 8, 12, and 17.

SEBERA, D. K., "Preparation and Analysis of a Complex Compound," *J. Chem. Ed.* **40,** 476 (1963). The preparation and analysis of $[Co(NH_3)_5Cl]Cl_2$ are described and an interesting set of questions is posed.

SKOOG, D. A., and D. M. WEST, *Fundamentals of Analytical Chemistry*, Holt, Rinehart & Winston, New York, Chapters 10 and 12.

SWIFT, E. H, *A System of Chemical Analysis*, Prentice-Hall, New York, 1939, pp. 26–47.

WASER, J., *Quantitative Chemistry*, revised ed. W. A. Benjamin, New York, 1964, Chapters 5, 6, 7, and 10.

PROBLEMS

1. Could one make up a stock solution of KSCN, do the analyses, and then standardize the KSCN? Is the same thing feasible for the NaOH solution?

2. How would you regenerate a water softener?

3. Suppose that we have an ion-exchange resin which can exchange 10 millimoles of H^+ for every gram of resin.

The equilibrium constant for the exchange of Na^+ with this resin is $K_{Na} = 2$. What will be the concentration of Na^+ in 25 ml of a solution that is originally $4 \times 10^{-2}\ M$ in Na^+ if it is mixed with 1 gm of this resin and allowed to equilibrate? If the solution is separated from the resin and one gram of fresh resin is added, what will be the final $[Na^+]$ in solution when equilibrium is attained?

5 GASES AND VACUUM TECHNIQUE

Gases are perhaps the best understood physical (and chemical) systems; they are amenable to quite detailed theoretical studies, the results of which agree very well with experimental observations. One of the most useful findings is that at relatively low pressures and relatively high temperatures (compared to the boiling point of the compound tested) the behavior of most gases can be described by the equation

$$PV = nRT, \qquad (5\text{--}1)$$

where P is the pressure of the gas, V is the volume in which the gas is contained, n is the number of moles of gas, R is the gas constant = 0.082 liter-atm/mole-deg, and T is the temperature of the gas in °K. This equation, the ideal gas equation, can be derived from the postulates of the kinetic theory of gases and, hence, lends credence to the theory.

In this chapter we shall describe some of the techniques used in handling gases. We shall explore some of the properties of gases and use these properties to solve other problems.

5–1 PRESSURE MEASUREMENT

The fundamental measurement in most gaseous systems and in vacuum practice is the pressure of the gas with which we are working. Two common pressure-measuring devices are the mercury manometer and the McLeod gauge. Manometers are of many designs; the one suggested for our vacuum system, Fig. 5–3, is an absolute U-tube manometer. This manometer is constructed so that the arms of the U may be completely evacuated. In our system, one arm is then closed off by a stopcock (in other designs more elaborate permanent seals are made), and the gas whose pressure is to be read is admitted to the other arm. Thus the difference in heights of the mercury columns is proportional to the

pressure of the gas in the arm (since no gas is present in the other, evacuated, arm) and is *independent of the pressure outside the system* being measured. The height of the mercury column is read by sighting across the *top* of the meniscus at the scale; avoid parallax.

You will note a capillary constriction at the bottom of the U-tube. It prevents mercury from moving too rapidly from one arm to the other when the pressure is changing rapidly. Thus the mercury does not acquire great momentum since its movement is relatively slow. Fast-moving mercury columns are anathema to glass systems.

Since the density of mercury changes with temperature, you must always record the room temperature when measuring pressures and later correct your reading to 0°C, because pressure is defined in terms of mercury columns at 0°C. To see how such a correction is made, let us define the correct *absolute* pressure (in torr, the torricelli, where 1 torr = 1 mm Hg) at 0°C as P_0; at some other temperature, t (°C), the measured pressure will be P. The relationship between P and P_0 is then

$$P = P_0 + P_0\alpha t,$$

where α is the volume coefficient of expansion for mercury (about $18.2 \times 10^{-5} \text{ deg}^{-1}$). We can rearrange this equation to yield

$$P_0 = \frac{P}{1 + \alpha t}. \qquad (5\text{--}2)$$

As an example, a pressure of 740 torr measured at 20°C corresponds to an absolute pressure of 738 torr at 0°C. (If a wooden scale, such as a meter stick, is used, its change in length with temperature may be neglected, but if a metal scale, usually brass, is used, a correction must also be made for its linear coefficient of expansion with temperature. Such combined corrections are much more easily made by reference to a table of temperature corrections for barometers, found in any handbook.)

One type of McLeod gauge, the tilting McLeod gauge, is shown in Fig. 5–1 and is also shown attached to the vacuum system of Fig. 5–3. McLeod gauges are useful for measuring pressures below about 1 torr; the lower limit of detection varies from about 10^{-3} to 10^{-6} torr (1 to 10^{-3} micron; 1 micron, μ, = 10^{-3} torr), depending on the dimensions of the gauge. The principle of the McLeod gauge is Boyle's Law: at constant temperature the pressure-volume product of a given quantity of gas is a constant, or $P_1V_1 = P_2V_2$. When the McLeod gauge is in the position shown in Fig. 5–1(a), the measuring side of the gauge is empty and open to the system to be measured. Thus the gas in the system at pressure P torr is also in the gauge at the same pressure. Now, as the gauge is tilted (rotated about the connection to the system), mercury flows down and seals off the large volume and measuring capillary from the system, thus trapping a volume of gas, which we will call V mm^3. As we continue to tilt the gauge, the mercury flows into the measuring system, compressing the gas until finally we have the situation shown in Fig. 5–1(b): the mercury level in the reference capillary is exactly level with the closed top of the measuring capillary, and the gas being measured is compressed into the measuring capillary. Let us call the difference in heights of the two mercury columns h mm; this is also the pressure of the gas in the measuring capillary, since we can neglect the very low pressure (otherwise we could not measure it) of gas in the system that is acting on the reference mercury column. Finally, let us call the cross-sectional area of the capillaries (which must be identical to avoid capillarity effects on the mercury levels) a mm^2. The volume of trapped gas has been reduced to ha mm^3. Using Boyle's Law we can write

$$PV = h(ha) = h^2a,$$

$$P = h^2\left(\frac{a}{V}\right), \qquad (5\text{--}3)$$

the McLeod-gauge formula. For a given gauge a and V are constant so the measurement h is proportional to $P^{1/2}$, i.e., the scale is not linear.* Commercial McLeod gauges come with a scale, which implies that they have already been calibrated. Actually this is not the case; the values of a and V are kept to close enough tolerances when constructing each gauge that the same scale may be used for any one of them that meets these tolerances. (How do you think you would go about calibrating a McLeod gauge if the scale were lost or if you had made your own gauge?)

---

* A McLeod-type gauge with a linear scale is described in Problem 5–1.

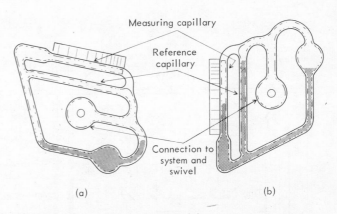

Fig. 5–1. A tilting McLeod gauge: (a) in position to sample gas to be measured, (b) in measuring position.

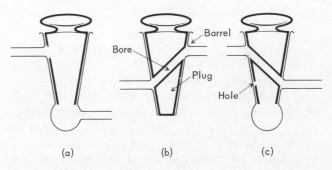

Fig. 5–2. Vacuum stopcock designs (note that all the stopcock plugs are hollow).

5–2 VACUUM SYSTEMS

A vacuum system is an apparatus for obtaining and exploiting low gas pressure. The flow of gas in the vacuum system is controlled by stopcocks. Stopcocks are usually made according to one of the designs in Fig. 5–2. The mating surfaces of vacuum stopcocks are carefully lapped together for a perfect seal. *The parts of similar vacuum stopcocks are not interchangeable.* They are lubricated (and sealed) with a viscous grease of very low vapor pressure ($\sim 10^{-8}$ torr). *A stopcock should never be turned rapidly*, for the grease may not follow quick motions and the seal may be broken. In extreme cases such shock can result in broken glass, personal injury, and a laborious repair job. If a stopcock seems stiff and turns with difficulty, even when turned slowly, call for assistance from an instructor.

Figure 5–3 is a schematic diagram of a glass vacuum system of fairly simple design, which is evacuated with a mechanical pump. The design has been kept simple deliberately so that you can easily understand the manipulations required and do not have to follow a labyrinth of glass tubing to see which stopcock to turn. (Stopcocks are represented by slashed circles.) The ultimate vacuum this system is capable of producing is in the micron range. Higher vacuum, lower pressure, is attainable

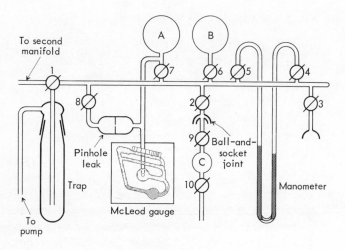

Fig. 5–3. A simple vacuum system.

only by the use of a mercury or oil diffusion pump in conjunction with a mechanical pump.

The vacuum system is supported on a rigid framework ("rack") by means of strategically placed clamps. *Never, under any circumstances, should you disturb one of these clamps in any way.* To do so could result in collapse of the vacuum system or introduction of great strain on the glass. Remember that the force exerted on every square inch of glass surface in a vacuum system is 14.7 pounds. Rupture of the glass could easily send glass shards your way at high velocity. *Always wear safety glasses in the vicinity of a vacuum system.*

Note that the vacuum system design shown in Fig. 5–3 allows two manifolds to be pumped from a single pump-and-trap system. If this is done, stopcock 1

must be of such a design that the two manifolds cannot be opened to each other. This will reduce (but not eliminate) the possibility that a worker on one manifold could inadvertently ruin the experiment being carried out on the other by turning a wrong stopcock. You should also note that other pieces of glassware are connected to the vacuum system via ground-glass ball-and-socket joints. These joints allow a good deal of flexibility in such connections and reduce the possibility of putting strain on the system that may arise when connections are made via the more common tapered joints, like that used for the trap.

When the vacuum system is in use, the trap should be immersed in a Dewar vessel (thermos containers with wide mouths are fine) containing "dry ice" (solid carbon dioxide) and trichloroethylene. The fluid, trichloroethylene, is provided to increase the efficiency of heat transfer from the trap to the dry ice. (Other common fluids used for this purpose are acetone and alcohol, both of which, unfortunately, are flammable. "Trichlor" is not flammable and has the added advantage that dry ice floats in it. Why do you think this could be an advantage?) The temperature of this bath is about $-80°C$, and it traps condensable gases before they get to the pump and befoul the oil. When the vacuum system is to be shut down, the pump is turned off, air is admitted to the system (with the exception of the arms of the manometer) and to the pump (to prevent back-up of pump oil into the system), the cold bath is removed from the trap, and the trap is removed and cleaned out. The cardinal rule to be observed in handling any vacuum system is: *THINK CAREFULLY OF THE CONSEQUENCES BEFORE TURNING ANY STOPCOCK.*

EXPERIMENT 5.   Boyle's and Graham's Laws

Background

We shall use Boyle's Law to calibrate the volumes in our vacuum system and then test Graham's Law of gaseous effusion and use it to determine the molecular weight of an unknown gas.

To use Boyle's Law to determine an unknown volume, we require three things: a vessel of known volume, a measurement of the pressure of a quantity of gas when it is contained in the known volume, and a pressure measurement after the gas has been expanded into the initially evacuated unknown volume. Let us call the known volume V_0 and the unknown, V; the initial pressure of the gas contained in V_0 is P_0, and the final pressure of the gas contained in both V and V_0 is P. We then use Boyle's Law to relate these quantities,

$$P_0 V_0 = P(V_0 + V)$$

and solve for the unknown desired volume,

$$V = \frac{V_0(P_0 - P)}{P}. \tag{5-4}$$

One statement of Graham's Law is that under constant conditions of temperature and pressure, different gases effuse through a tiny orifice into a vacuum at rates inversely proportional to the square roots of their molecular weights. To make clearer what these terms mean, let us consider a very simple derivation of Graham's Law. Figure 5–4 is a diagram of the region near the tiny orifice in the wall of the vessel containing the gas under study. The area of the orifice is A, and the diagram shows an imaginary cylinder of height $\bar{c}$ (the average distance the molecule travels in one second) and base area A constructed perpendicular to the wall of the vessel. Any molecule inside this imaginary cylinder

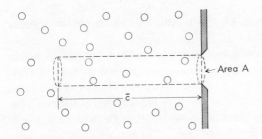

Fig. 5–4. Gaseous effusion.

traveling toward the wall will pass through the orifice within one second. How many molecules are inside the cylinder? If there are N molecules per cm^3 in the vessel, the number inside the cylindrical volume will be $N\bar{c}A$, since the volume of the cylinder is $\bar{c}A$ cm^3. Crudely, we can say that $\frac{1}{6}$ of all the molecules in the cylinder will be moving toward the orifice and thus the number of molecules striking an area A or passing through an orifice of area A in one second is

$$\frac{dN'}{dt} = \frac{1}{6} N\bar{c}A.$$

(A correct derivation indicates that the $\frac{1}{6}$ should be $\frac{1}{4}$ and we shall use the correct figure in the following discussion.) Substituting the expression for $\bar{c}$ derived from the kinetic theory of gases, $\bar{c} = (RT/2\pi M)^{1/2}$, we find that

$$-\frac{dN'}{dt} = \frac{1}{4} NA \left(\frac{RT}{2\pi}\right)^{1/2} \left(\frac{1}{M}\right)^{1/2} \tag{5-5}$$

is the *rate of loss* by effusion, where M is the molecular weight of the gas.

If the rates of effusion of two different gases are compared at the same pressure and temperature, the only variable in Eq. (5–5) is the molecular weight, since N is a function only of the pressure and temperature. In practice, it is difficult to maintain a constant pressure in a gaseous effusion experiment, and it is, in fact, easier to measure the decrease of pressure in the vessel as the gas effuses and relate this to the rate of effusion. The number of molecules per cm^3 in a system is

$$N = nN_0/V,$$

where n is the number of moles and N_0 is Avogadro's number. Substituting P/RT for n/V, we obtain

$$N = PN_0/RT.$$

In our formulation we wrote N' as the total number of molecules effusing per second, and we can relate this to a pressure also:

$$PV = (N'/N_0)RT, \qquad N' = N_0 PV/RT,$$

or

$$dN' = (N_0 V/RT)\, dP \qquad \text{(constant } T\text{)}.$$

Hence, we rewrite Eq. (5–5) as

$$-\frac{N_0 V}{RT}\frac{dP}{dt} = \frac{1}{4}\left(\frac{PN_0}{RT}\right) A \left(\frac{RT}{2\pi}\right)^{1/2} \left(\frac{1}{M}\right)^{1/2},$$

$$-\frac{dP}{dt} = \frac{1}{4} PA \left(\frac{RT}{2\pi V^2}\right)^{1/2} \left(\frac{1}{M}\right)^{1/2},$$

or

$$-\frac{d\ln P}{dt} = \frac{1}{4} A \left(\frac{RT}{2\pi V^2}\right)^{1/2} \left(\frac{1}{M}\right)^{1/2}. \tag{5-6}$$

Therefore in gaseous effusion experiments, we predict that a plot of $\ln P$ versus t will be linear and that the slopes of the lines for different gases at constant T and V will be inversely proportional to the molecular weights of the gases.

So far we have left a major question unanswered: Under what conditions does gaseous effusion occur? Careful consideration of our crude derivation of Graham's Law gives a hint of the answer. Note that we came very close to the result predicted by the correct derivation and, in fact, predicted the correct form exactly by using the very simplest postulates of the kinetic theory of gases. But we know that the approximations of the kinetic theory, in particular that molecules are completely independent of one another, become valid only at very low pressures. In fact, this is the criterion for gaseous effusion, for in the correct derivation, the assumption is made that the distribution of molecular velocities within the vessel is given by the Maxwell-Boltzmann distribution. This will not be true if there is any mass (hydrodynamic) flow through the orifice. To prevent mass flow, the mean free path of the molecules should be more than about ten times the diameter of the orifice. The mean free path of a molecule, λ, is given by the expression $\lambda = (\pi\sigma^2 N)^{-1}$, where σ is the collision diameter of the molecule. At 1-atm pressure (760 torr) $N = 3 \times 10^{19}$ molecules/cm^3, and we will not be far off to choose $\sigma = 3 \times 10^{-8}$ cm as a reasonable choice for many molecules. These choices yield

$$\lambda = \{\pi(3 \times 10^{-8})^2\, 3 \times 10^{19}\}^{-1} \simeq 10^{-5} \text{ cm at 760 torr.}$$

Thus molecular effusion of a gas at atmospheric pressure would occur through an orifice of about 10^{-6}-cm diameter, which is smaller than any we can construct. A reasonable size for an orifice is in the range 0.001 to 0.01 cm (0.01 to 0.1 mm). What pressure will we have to use to obtain a mean free path of say 0.1 cm? Since N is directly proportional to P, λ is inversely proportional to P and we may write

$$\frac{\lambda_2}{\lambda_1} = \frac{P_1}{P_2} = \frac{10^{-1}}{10^{-5}} = \frac{760}{P},$$

$$P = 0.076 \text{ torr} = 76 \text{ microns.}$$

Hence, at pressures below about 100 microns and with an orifice that is 0.01 cm in diameter, molecular effusion should be observed.*

Procedure

Begin by evacuating the vacuum system. (Stopcock numbers, etc., will refer to Fig. 5–3; you should translate their meaning according to the vacuum system you will use.) Be certain that stopcocks 2 and 3 are closed and the others are open; then turn on the pump. When the system is fairly well evacuated, as indicated by the sound of the pump, immerse the trap in a dry ice-trichloroethylene bath (in a Dewar).

Obtain from your instructor a bulb of known volume. This is bulb C in the figure. (The volume is determined by weighing the bulb, drawing in water to fill it, reweighing the bulb filled with water, and calculating the volume from the mass of water required to fill it.) Read the barometric pressure; this is the pressure in the bulb. Attach the bulb to the vacuum system and open stopcock 2 to evacuate the volume down to stopcock 9.

Check the pressure of the system with the McLeod gauge; it should not be greater than 1 or 2 microns. If the pressure is greater than this and does not get lower on continued pumping, ask your instructor to show you how to test your system for leaks. When the leaks have been found and repaired and the pressure is below 2 microns, close stopcock 1, wait a couple of minutes, and measure the pressure again; it should not have risen more than a micron. If it has, there is still a leak that you have not found.

When you are finally satisfied that your system is leak-tight, close all stopcocks except 2 and either 4 or 5. Open stopcock 9, read and record the pressure with the manometer, open 8, read and record the pressure, open 7, read and record the pressure, and finally, open 6 and read and record the pressure. You can now use these data to calculate the various volumes on the vacuum system. Remember that the changing level of the mercury in the manometer causes a volume change that must be accounted for. You might do this by calculating the volume change or by repeating the calibration beginning with a lower (known) pressure in the calibrated bulb C. (How can you get this lower pressure of gas in the bulb?) You can now extrapolate the volumes you have calculated to the values you would have at zero pressure, thus eliminating the manometer volume change. In any case you should repeat the volume calibration for bulb A (including the McLeod gauge and up to, but not beyond,

the pinhole leak) a number of times to obtain a good average value.

The pinhole leak may be made in a number of ways. A metal foil with a small hole pricked in it by a very sharp needle point can be mounted with wax as indicated in Fig. 5–5. A thin bubble of glass blown at the end of a tube can be punctured with the high-frequency spark coil used to test for pinhole leaks and similarly mounted. These leaks should be used in conjunction with a bulb A of such size that a pressure decrease from about 150 to 200 microns to 10 to 20 microns occurs in about 40 to 60 minutes when air is being pumped out of the bulb through the pinhole.

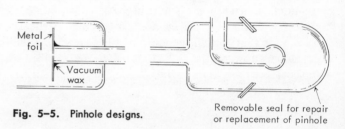

Metal foil

Vacuum wax

Fig. 5–5. Pinhole designs.

Removable seal for repair or replacement of pinhole

Ask your instructor to help you put some nitrogen gas into your system. Close stopcocks 2, 3, 4, and 5, open the other stopcocks, attach the N_2 source (a high-pressure tank, so be careful) to the system through a mercury bubbler (Fig. 5–6), to prevent the pressure from going more than 10 or 20 torr over atmospheric pressure in case the gas is run in too rapidly. (How does the bubbler do this?) With the tank valve closed, attach the bubbler to the valve (Fig. 5–6) and evacuate the bubbler. Close stopcock 1, open the N_2 tank valve slightly to admit a little N_2 (not a full atmosphere), close the N_2 tank valve, and evacuate. Repeat this procedure at least three times to flush the system and finally admit a few torricellis of N_2, close all stopcocks and detach the N_2 tank and bubbler.

Evacuate the manifold and open stopcock 8. Open stopcock 7 very slightly to allow some N_2 to be pumped

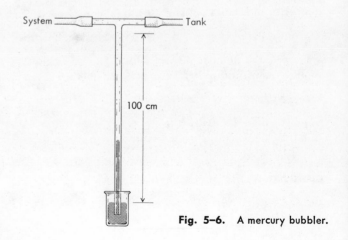

System   Tank

100 cm

Fig. 5–6. A mercury bubbler.

---

* Almost all the experiments usually suggested for testing Graham's Law do no such thing because the gas pressures are usually far outside the range where molecular effusion would actually occur.

from bulb A. Measure the pressure with the McLeod gauge. Continue in this fashion until the pressure in A is in the range 150 to 200 microns. (If you overshoot you can close stopcocks 1 and 8 and admit a bit of N_2 from bulb B to bulb A.) Make certain that stopcocks 1 and 8 are open and all other stopcocks are closed. Follow the pressure in bulb A as a function of time using the McLeod gauge. The time corresponding to a particular pressure reading is the time when the mercury in the McLeod traps the volume of gas in the measuring volume. Take readings every two to five minutes depending on the rate of change in pressure.

Ask your instructor for another gas and repeat the procedure for this sample. Repeat the effusion experiment twice for each gas if time permits.

Calculations

Sketch your vacuum system, label the various volumes, and report the results of your volume calibrations with an estimate of the uncertainty in each volume.

Plot, on a single graph, $\log P$ versus time for your effusion studies. Is Graham's Law obeyed? Over what, if any, pressure range? What is the molecular weight of your second gas? What is the uncertainty in this value? Using the results of your volume calibration and your effusion measurements on nitrogen, calculate the area of the effusion orifice. Assuming that the hole is circular, compute its diameter. Is this value consistent with the range over which you may have found Graham's Law to be obeyed?

EXPERIMENT 6. Molecular-Weight Determination by the Dumas Method

Background

We shall use the classic method of J. B. Dumas to establish the vapor density and from that the molecular weight of an unknown compound. Even sparingly volatile and highly reactive compounds can be characterized by this method.

We begin by introducing into a weighed Dumas bulb an excess of the liquid or solid compound we wish to study. The Dumas bulb we shall use is a vessel of known volume V with a fine glass capillary as its communication with the atmosphere. The system, bulb and sample, is then rapidly heated to some known temperature T above the boiling point of the compound in question. The consequent formation of a large volume of vapor purges the air from the vessel through the narrow capillary vent (the vent is narrow enough that back-diffusion of air is a slow process). When the last bit of sample is volatilized, the bulb will thus be left full of essentially pure vapor at the known pressure of the atmosphere, P, to which the bulb is vented. The bulb is then removed from the bath, quickly chilled to room temperature (so that the vapor recondenses and the bulb refills with air), and reweighed. From the difference of the initial and final weights of the vessel, we establish the mass m of the vaporized compound required to fill the bulb of volume V to a pressure P at a temperature T.

The ideal gas equation, $PV = nRT$, is now used to calculate the molecular weight M of the compound. We can write n, the number of moles of the compound we had as a vapor, as m/M and substitute it into the ideal gas equation to give

$$PV = \frac{m}{M} RT, \tag{5–7}$$

or on rearrangement

$$M = \frac{RT}{PV} m. \tag{5–8}$$

Thus we can calculate M by substitution of our experimental values in this equation. [The value of R is 62.3 torr-liter/mole-deg. Show how this value is derived from that given with Eq. (5–1).]

The value of M obtained by this method is likely to be a few percent high, due to the marked nonideality of the vapor at a temperature only slightly in excess of its boiling point. (What does this deviation imply about m and hence about the forces between molecules under these conditions?) However, given an empirical formula, readily established by an elemental analysis of a compound, even a fairly crude value for its molecular weight suffices to fix a previously unknown molecular weight. (See Nash for a further discussion of this point.)

One further comment that is relevant to many experiments in which gases are "weighed" is necessary. Let us consider the situation in which we twice weigh a vessel containing gas, once with the gas at pressure P_1 and again at a lower pressure P_2. The two weighings will give different results, and the difference will be the mass of gas that is missing in the second determination. We can compute the mass of the missing gas if we know the volume of the vessel, V, and the densities of the gas, ρ_1 and ρ_2, at the pressures P_1 and P_2, respectively. The mass difference will be $\Delta m = V(\rho_1 - \rho_2)$. Show why. The density of a gas is directly proportional to its pressure [see Eq. (5–7)], so we need to know only the density at one of the pressures, say ρ_1 at P_1, and the other may be calculated if the second pressure is known, i.e., $\rho_2 = \rho_1 P_2/P_1$. Thus the mass difference between the two weighings can be written

$$\Delta m = V(\rho_1 - \rho_1 P_2 / P_1) = V\rho_1 \left(\frac{P_1 - P_2}{P_1} \right)$$

$$= V\rho_1 \frac{\Delta P}{P_1}. \qquad (5\text{--}9)$$

The applicability of this discussion to the Dumas experiment is presented in the section on calculations.

Procedure

Obtain a sample from your instructor in a clean, dry, labeled, and stoppered test tube. He will tell you the approximate boiling point and perhaps the results of an elemental analysis on your compound.* The samples for this experiment will be chosen to be relatively non-flammable, but the vapors from some of them may be appreciably toxic and notably hard on the liver. Hence, avoid inhaling the vapor of your sample, keep your sample stoppered until you use it, and set up your equipment so that the bulk of the vapor evolved will be drawn into a hood. (As an expedient, you can mount a funnel attached to an aspirator a few inches above the outlet of your Dumas bulb to suck away most of the vapor which leaves the bulb.)

Obtain also from your instructor a 250-ml flat-bottomed Dumas bulb and a 6-in. hypodermic needle to be used for charging the bulb.† Never evacuate this bulb; its flat bottom makes it very susceptible to collapse when evacuated.

Before using the bulb you must make certain it is clean and dry. Put into the bulb about 10 ml of concentrated detergent solution, using the needle attached to the appropriately labeled stock bottle. After shaking it with the detergent solution, invert the flask and shake out the solution. Add several successive 10-ml rinses of distilled water, using the delivery needle attached to the bottles of distilled water. The rinsing operation will be most effective if you take care to shake out each portion thoroughly before adding the next. Finally, dry the flask by drawing air through it while it is being gently heated. Use a length of heavy-walled rubber tubing to

---

* Latimer and Powell present a list of compounds suitable for this experiment; there are, of course, many others.

† If a Dumas bulb of this type is not available you can make a suitable substitute from a 250-ml flask, a cork, a 6 to 8-cm length of 3-mm heavy-walled capillary tubing, and aluminum foil. Bore the cork so the tubing will fit snugly into the hole, insert the tubing so it is flush with the small base of the cork, wrap the cork with aluminum foil, and punch a small hole in the foil at the point where it meets the capillary opening. Insert the cork tightly in the flask and you are ready to go. The aluminum foil prevents the cork from absorbing sample vapor or water from the water bath used to vaporize the sample.

connect the enlarged end of your hypodermic needle with the aspirator. Clamp the hose close to the needle so that the needle points upward, slide the Dumas bulb down over the needle, and start the aspirator. (Do not blow air into the bulb, since most compressed air lines contain oil and dust.) To speed the drying process, heat the outside of the bulb by brushing it with a "soft" burner flame. *Avoid strong localized heating.* Keep the flame away from the entrance of the bulb to avoid drawing water vapor, formed in the combustion process, into the bulb. When the flask appears dry, leave it to cool in place with the aspirator still running.

When the bulb has cooled, wipe the outside with a clean, very *slightly* damp cloth. (If you use a dry cloth the flask might pick up an appreciable electrostatic charge, which could result in a substantial weighing error.) After wiping the bulb, do not grasp it with your fingers before it is weighed; use a piece of clean towel to carry it. Carry the bulb to the weighing room, place it on a piece of clean paper, marked with your name, and leave it for five to ten minutes to reach temperature equilibrium. Weigh the bulb to the nearest milligram. (Even this accuracy is greater than is necessary to determine the mass of your sample vapor to better than 1-% accuracy, and gas imperfections will probably cause the final result to be more uncertain than that. More accurate weighing is therefore bad technique and a farcical waste of time and effort.)

Set up a heating bath as indicated in Fig. 5–7 (either in a hood or with the funnel and aspirator expedient mentioned above). Fill the 1000-ml beaker about half full of water (add a *few* drops of concentrated HCl to prevent the formation of "boiler scale" on the weighed bulb). Bore a #9 cork stopper with a hole for the capil-

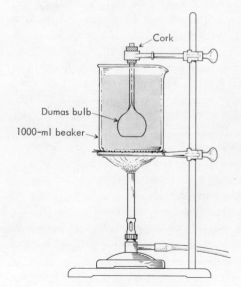

Fig. 5–7. Setup for the Dumas vapor-density determination.

lary tubing, split the cork in half along its axis, fit the two halves around the capillary (taking care not to get cork dust in the bulb), and lock the cork and hence the bulb firmly in the clamp (with the capillary adjusted so that it projects about 1 or 2 mm beyond the upper edge of the cork and clamp). Lower the bulb into the water bath as far as possible without touching the bulb to the bottom of the beaker and/or smashing the rim of the beaker with the clamp. Fill the beaker with water to within 1 cm of the top. Remove the bulb from the bath by sliding the clamp up the ringstand.

Start heating the water bath to a temperature 5 to 10°C above the boiling point of your sample. (There is no reason why you cannot simply boil the water to make a bath at about 100°C, but two sources of inaccuracy might then be introduced: droplets of water might be splashed into the opening of the bulb, ruining your experiment, and, since vapor density is inversely proportional to temperature, fewer molecules will remain in the bulb at higher temperatures, thereby making the mass of vapor we determine smaller and increasing the uncertainty in the final result due to weighing error. However, if this increase in uncertainty is smaller than 1 or 2% it will not affect the overall determination; therefore, if you can avoid the first problem, you might find it easier to use the boiling water bath.) While the bath is heating, introduce about half your sample into the bulb. This is most easily accomplished by sliding your hypodermic needle into the bulb and then running the sample in through the needle. If you use a dropper to handle your sample, be certain it is clean and dry and never allow your sample to come in contact with the rubber dropper bulb (some of which might dissolve).

When the bath has reached the desired temperature, lower the Dumas bulb until it takes its former position in the bath. The sample will now vaporize fairly rapidly. During the vaporization, try to hold the temperature of the water bath steady at the value you have chosen. It is absolutely imperative that *no drop* in temperature, however transient, occur after the vaporization is well under way; such a temperature drop could cause a pressure drop in your bulb with the consequent re-entry of air which you are trying to expel by a steady outflow of vapor. A slow *rise* of temperature during the vaporization will do no harm whatsoever.

After five to twenty minutes of heating, the last trace of liquid will have been expelled. How will you know, since it is difficult to detect a meniscus in the flat-bottomed bulb? It is usually possible to see a stream of vapor issuing from the bulb if you look at the mouth of the capillary against the light from a window. The stream of vapor can also be detected by observing its action on the smoke from a match that has just been blown out and is held, still smoking, above the capillary

exit. Wait until the stream of vapor no longer issues from the bulb, then maintain the temperature at a steady value, with particular care, for two to three minutes, neither more nor less. During this time temperature equilibrium will be established as the vapor in the bulb (slightly cooled by the loss of its heat of vaporization) comes to the temperature of the bath. Record the final bath temperature, loosen the clamp from the ringstand, and slide the clamp and bulb briskly up the ringstand.

At once, quench the vapor by dipping the lower part of the bulb into a beaker of cold water. Note and record the time as the bulb is removed from the quenching bath; call this t_0. Then let the bulb stand in air as it cools to room temperature. As the bulb cools, the influx of air from the atmosphere through the capillary should prevent any appreciable loss of sample vapor. Read and record the barometric pressure (corrected to 0°C). After ten minutes wipe the bulb with a clean *slightly* damp cloth, and without further handling, place it in the balance room to thermally equilibrate for another five to ten minutes. Reweigh the bulb (now containing the condensed sample) to the nearest milligram.

If your sample boils under about 60°C, diffusion of vapor from the bulb may cause the latter to show a continually decreasing mass on the balance pan. There are two simple ways to cope with this difficulty: 1) account for the effect quantitatively or 2) eliminate the cause.

1) Weigh the bulb again, five minutes after making your first measurement, and calculate the *rate* at which vapor is lost. Assuming that this rate is uniform, extrapolate back to time t_0 to determine the weight of the bulb and sample when it was first removed from the quenching dip.

2) To reduce the loss of vapor you must somehow loosely plug the bulb exit. Run a pipe cleaner between your fingers to detach all the loose bits of fluff. Weigh the pipe cleaner to the nearest milligram. Immediately after removing the bulb from the quenching bath (i.e., at t_0), slide the pipe cleaner into the capillary. Finish the experiment as before. (Remember to allow for the weight of the pipe cleaner when making your calculations.)

Run a duplicate determination with the remaining half of your sample. Note that it is neither necessary nor even desirable to clean and dry the bulb between the two runs. Why?

Finally, determine the volume of your Dumas bulb. Shake out the bulk of your unknown sample and fill the bulb with distilled water, using the delivery needle attached to the distilled water bottle. Wipe off the outside of the flask and weigh it to the nearest gram on a triple beam balance (or other high-capacity balance), *not on an analytical balance*. Record the weight and then empty the bulb. (Your instructor can show you how; with the aid of your hypodermic needle, it is easy to drain the bulb.) Dry the bulb before returning it and the hypodermic needle to your instructor.

Calculations

Compute the volume of your bulb, V, from the mass of water required to fill it. The density of water may be taken as unity with sufficient accuracy for this experiment.

The mass of the vapor that filled the bulb is given approximately by the weight gain of the bulb. The degree of approximation can, however, be improved by making one correction. When the bulb was first weighed, it was filled with air at atmospheric pressure; if your sample were completely involatile at room temperature, essentially the same amount of air would be present during the second weighing, and the net weight gain would accurately reflect the weight of the condensed vapor. However, the sample is not completely involatile at room temperature and the pressure of air in the bulb during the second reading is not the barometric pressure, P, but rather $(P - P_s)$, where P_s is the vapor pressure of the sample at room temperature. The change in the air pressure from the first to the second weighing is $\Delta P = P - (P - P_s) = P_s$, and we can substitute this result into Eq. (5–9) to find the difference in mass caused by the missing air:

$$\Delta m = V\rho(P_s/P),$$

where ρ is the density of air at atmospheric pressure and room temperature ($\rho = 0.0012$ gm/ml is sufficiently accurate for our purposes). This mass must be *added* to the net weight gain of the bulb containing the condensed vapor. The vapor pressure of your sample at room temperature could easily be measured (see Experiment 12, for example) but you can estimate it with sufficient accuracy from the following table.

Boiling temperature, °C	45	60	75	90
Vapor pressure at room temperature, torr	310	175	100	60

Using the known values of P, V, T and the (corrected) weight, m, of your sample, calculate its molecular weight. How well do your results agree? If you know the elemental composition of your sample, determine its molecular formula and accurate molecular weight. How does this molecular weight compare with your experimental values?

Further Experimental Problems

How does the apparent molecular weight of a sample vary as a function of the temperature of vapor at which the vapor-density measurement is made? This is a particularly interesting question for samples of polar molecules that might be expected to interact rather strongly. You might, for example, investigate the vapor density of acetic acid or water as a function of temperature. Since both of these substances must be studied above 100°C, a different bath liquid (mineral oil or one of the silicone oils) will be necessary. You must not use an open flame to heat a bath containing an organic liquid. Check with your instructor and outline your plans before embarking on this experiment.

REFERENCES

EDDY, R. D. and S. R. SCHOLES, JR., "A Temperature-Sensitive Stirring Rod: Liquefaction of NO₂," *J. Chem. Ed.* **35,** 527 (1958) gives a short simple procedure for synthesizing and trapping a gaseous inorganic compound, NO₂.

HULME, R., "Kinetic Derivation of the Gas Equation and Colision Frequency," *J. Chem. Ed.* **34,** 459 (1957) presents a derivation for a spherical container rather than the cubical container usually seen in textbook derivations.

KOKES, R. J., M. K. DORFMAN, and T. MATHIA, "A Simple Vacuum System" and "Chemical Equilibrium: The Hydrogenation of Benzene," *J. Chem. Ed.* **39,** 20 and 91 (1962) presents the construction and use of a vacuum system to study a chemical equilibrium system.

LATIMER, W. M., and R. E. POWELL, *A Laboratory Course in General Chemistry*, Macmillan, New York, 1964, pp. 17–20, is a presentation of the Dumas method very much like that we have described.

NASH, L. K., *Stoichiometry*, Addison-Wesley, Reading, Mass., 1966.

PROBLEMS

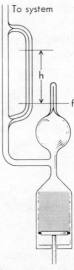

Fig. 5–8

1. a) A linear-scale McLeod gauge is shown in Fig. 5–8. There is a mechanism at the bottom for pushing Hg into the measuring bulb and up the side arms. The cross-sectional areas of the capillaries are identical. Show that, if the Hg is always brought to the level f in the right-hand capillary, the height h to which the mercury rises in the other capillary is a linear function of the pressure.

   b) Given that the volume of the bulb plus its capillary is 202.0 ml and the volume of the right-hand capillary above f is 0.027 ml, what is the pressure in the system when a measurement gives $h = 5.32$ cm?

2. Why is there a hole in the plug of the stopcock shown in Fig. 5–2(c)?

3. Where do the values of the vapor pressure of compounds at room temperature as a function of boiling point (given in Experiment 6) come from?

6 CALORIMETRY

6-1 THERMOCHEMISTRY

Enthalpy

All chemical reactions either produce or require heat as they proceed, and the amount of heat evolved or absorbed is an important quantity in thermodynamics. In the calorimetric experiments outlined below, all the reactions are carried out in open vessels, so that the pressure on the reaction system remains constant (at the prevailing pressure of the atmosphere). The heat evolved or absorbed in a process at constant pressure, q_P, is called the *change in enthalpy* (or heat content), ΔH, for the process:

$$q_P = \Delta H. \tag{6-1}$$

We shall always use the symbol Δ (Greek, capital delta) to denote the difference between the final state of a system and the initial state of the system. Thus $\Delta H = H_f - H_i$. All enthalpies contain an unknown additive factor (*vide infra*), so the enthalpy of a system can never be stated. A change in the system, however, will result in a new enthalpy which contains the same additive factor, so that when we take the difference between two enthalpies, ΔH, the unknown factor cancels out. It is only the differences in enthalpy that are actually measurable.

By convention, *the heat evolved from a process is given a negative sign.* Thus ΔH *for an exothermic process is negative*, e.g.,

$$C(\text{graphite}) + O_2(\text{g, 1 atm}) \rightarrow CO_2(\text{g, 1 atm})$$
$$\Delta H = -94.05 \text{ kcal/mole.} \tag{6-2}$$

Conversely, heat which is taken into a system from the surroundings during some process within the system is given a positive sign, that is, ΔH *for an endothermic process is positive.*

Law of Constant Heat Summation

Leaving aside for the moment the question of measuring the heat changes that occur during a chemical or physical process, let us examine the properties of enthalpy. The most important characteristic is that *enthalpy is a function of the state of the system alone* and not of the previous history of the system. This is a result of the definition of enthalpy of a system,

$$H \equiv E + PV, \tag{6-3}$$

where E is the internal energy of the system, P is the pressure of the system, and V is the volume of the system, and the proof, which you will find in the references, that E is also a function only of the state of the system. It is obvious that the "mechanical properties," P and V, are state functions because the system has a certain pressure and volume regardless of how it attained them; the proof that E is also a state function is based on the First Law of Thermodynamics. If, then, the enthalpy is a function of state, it will not matter how the final state is attained from the initial state; ΔH for the overall process will be the same (Hess' Law of Constant Heat Summation). Thus for this schematic representation of the change of state A to state D,

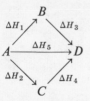

we can write

$$\Delta H_1 + \Delta H_3 = \Delta H_2 + \Delta H_4 = \Delta H_5. \tag{6-4}$$

(This is a particular expression of Hess' Law of Constant Heat Summation.)

Hess' law is exceedingly useful, for it allows us to *calculate* enthalpy changes which are hard to measure by combining the results of easily performed experiments. As an example, the reaction

$$C(\text{graphite}) + \tfrac{1}{2}O_2(\text{g, 1 atm}) \rightarrow CO(\text{g, 1 atm}) \qquad (6\text{-}5)$$

is very difficult actually to carry out stoichiometrically because some of the CO will always react with O_2 by a reaction we can write as

$$CO(\text{g, 1 atm}) + \tfrac{1}{2}O_2(\text{g, 1 atm}) \rightarrow CO_2(\text{g, 1 atm}). \qquad (6\text{-}6)$$

However, since this latter reaction is very easy to carry out in practice and its enthalpy change (q_P) is easy to measure ($\Delta H = -67.63$ kcal/mole) we can carry out the state change represented by Eq. (6-5) by utilizing reactions (6-2) and (6-6), whose ΔH we know:

$$C(\text{graphite}) + O_2(\text{g, 1 atm}) \xrightarrow{\Delta H_2} CO_2(\text{g, 1 atm}).$$
$$\downarrow \Delta H_1 \qquad \nearrow \Delta H_3$$
$$CO(\text{g, 1 atm}) + \tfrac{1}{2}O_2(\text{g, 1 atm})$$

We can obtain the enthalpy change for the process of interest, ΔH_1, by combining ΔH_2 and ΔH_3 in the proper way to represent the change from the initial to the desired final state,

$$\Delta H_1 = \Delta H_2 - \Delta H_3,$$

[ΔH_3 has a negative sign because we are considering the *reverse* of the reaction written here and in Eq. (6-6).]

$$\Delta H_1 = -94.05 - (-67.63) = -26.42 \text{ kcal/mole}.$$

We can obtain the same result by simply combining Eqs. (6-2) and (6-6) algebraically:

$C + O_2 \rightarrow CO_2,$	$\Delta H_2 = -94.05$
$-[CO + \tfrac{1}{2}O_2 \rightarrow CO_2,$	$\Delta H_3 = -67.63]$
$C + O_2 \rightarrow CO + \tfrac{1}{2}O_2,$	$\Delta H_1 = \Delta H_2 - \Delta H_3$
	$= -26.42 \text{ kcal/mole}.$

This algebraic manipulation, identical in result to the process outlined diagrammatically above, is a much more compact way of combining reactions and enthalpy changes to give a new unmeasured (or unmeasurable) enthalpy change.

Conventions

Before we proceed, you should know a few conventions concerning enthalpy changes. First, enthalpy changes are, in general, a function of the temperature at which the reactions are carried out, so a temperature (in °K) is usually given as a subscript to the symbol for the change: ΔH_{298}. Enthalpy changes without such a notation are normally assumed to be given for 25°C (298°K).

Second, the *standard enthalpy change*, ΔH^0, is defined as the enthalpy change between products and reactants at one-atmosphere pressure. Usually, standard enthalpy changes are stated at 298°K and denoted ΔH^0_{298}. The enthalpy changes for reactions (6-2) and (6-6) and, hence, reaction (6-5), by calculation, are the standard enthalpy changes.)

Third, there must be some convenient reference to which all our enthalpy changes may be referred. Since only differences in enthalpies are ever observed, the choice of such a reference cancels out in any calculations and thus can be arbitrary. The most widely used convention is to assign the enthalpies of all the elements in their *standard states* at 298°K as zero, i.e., $H^0_{298} \equiv 0$ for all elements. (The *standard state* of an element is its most stable form at 298°K and one atmosphere pressure.) The enthalpy change associated with the formation of a compound from its elements in their standard states is the *enthalpy of formation* (sometimes referred to loosely as the "heat of formation"). Often enthalpies of formation at 298°K are denoted as ΔH^0_f. Enthalpies of formation are a very compact way to store a great deal of information which may be retrieved by use of the Law of Constant Heat Summation. For example, we might be interested in the enthalpy change in the reaction

$$2CH_4(\text{g, 1 atm}) \rightarrow C_2H_6(\text{g, 1 atm}) + H_2(\text{g, 1 atm}),$$

which is impossible to measure experimentally. We can look up the enthalpies of formation and find

$$\Delta H^0_f(CH_4) = -17.89 \text{ kcal/mole}$$

and

$$\Delta H^0_f(C_2H_6) = -20.24 \text{ kcal/mole}.$$

[What is $\Delta H^0_f(H_2)$? Why?] The enthalpies of formation are the enthalpy changes of the reactions

$$C(\text{graphite}) + 2H_2(\text{g, 1 atm}) \rightarrow CH_4(\text{g, 1 atm}),$$
$$2C(\text{graphite}) + 3H_2(\text{g, 1 atm}) \rightarrow C_2H_6(\text{g, 1 atm}).$$

Now we can combine these two equations (without the state notations) to give the equation of interest by the application of Hess' law.

$2C + 3H_2 \rightarrow C_2H_6$	$\Delta H^0_f(C_2H_6)$
$-2[C + 2H_2 \rightarrow CH_4$	$\Delta H^0_f(CH_4)]$
$2CH_4 \rightarrow C_2H_6 + H_2$	$\Delta H^0 = \Delta H^0_f(C_2H_6)$
	$\quad - 2\,\Delta H^0_f(CH_4),$

$$\Delta H^0 = -20.24 - 2(-17.89) = +15.54 \text{ kcal/mole}.$$

Can you see a general rule exemplified by this specific case from which you can write the enthalpy change for any reaction if the enthalpies of formation of all products and reactants are known? [We must be careful when writing kcal/mole in this case (as in many others) to ask, "Per mole of what?" since we note that 2 moles of CH_4

react, and only 1 mole each of C_2H_6 and of H_2 is formed. In this case 15.54 kcal are *required* for every mole of C_2H_6 (or H_2) formed in the reaction.]

Tables of enthalpies of formation for a few substances are available in a number of textbooks and monographs. Large compendia of thermodynamic data are available in most handbooks, much of which is reprinted from a publication of the National Bureau of Standards.

6–2 PRINCIPLES OF CALORIMETRY

The Calorie

Before we can discuss the principles of heat measurement we have to be familiar with the unit of heat, the calorie, and its operational definition. As originally defined, the (fifteen-degree) calorie was the amount of heat required to change the temperature of 1 gm of water from 14.5°C to 15.5°C.* This measurement is awkward enough to make and subject to enough uncertainty that it has been replaced by a definition in terms of another energy unit, the joule:

$$1 \text{ calorie} \equiv 4.1840 \text{ absolute joules.} \qquad (6\text{–}7)$$

(The joule is defined and measured in terms of electrical work,

$$1 \text{ joule} \equiv 1 \text{ absolute volt-coulomb.}) \qquad (6\text{–}8)$$

The two definitions of the calorie are equivalent within the rather broad limits of uncertainty of the original.

The Calorimetric Measurement

To measure the heat evolved in a particular reaction, it is necessary to somehow "trap" all the heat released and force it to cause some measurable change. This change is then compared with the change in the same "heat trap" brought about by introducing a known amount of heat (or electrical work, *vide infra*). From this information the unknown amount of heat released by the reaction may be calculated.

What sorts of "heat traps" and corresponding changes may be employed in calorimetry? Most direct calorimetric methods may be divided into two classes: adiabatic and isothermal.

Adiabatic Calorimetry. In adiabatic calorimetry we try to keep as much as possible of the heat change that is caused by the reaction of interest confined to the reaction vessel and its contents, i.e., we attempt to keep heat from leaking into or out of the calorimeter, usually by

insulating the reaction vessel as well as possible. When there is no heat leak to the surroundings, then all the heat evolved or absorbed by the reactions of interest must remain in the reaction vessel and its contents, and it raises or lowers their temperature. It is this temperature change which we measure and relate to the heat evolution or absorption that has occurred.

The relationship between the amount of heat that enters or leaves a system, q_s, and the attendant temperature change, $\Delta T = T_{\text{final}} - T_{\text{initial}}$, may be expressed as

$$C = \text{Total heat capacity of the system} = q_s/\Delta T. \qquad (6\text{–}9)$$

If the system is composed of several parts, e.g., of a reaction vessel plus the solution it contains, then the total heat capacity of the system is the sum of the heat capacities of the individual parts,

$$C = \sum_i C_i.$$

Since, in the ideal case, no heat is allowed to enter or escape, the sum of the heat from the reaction, q_r, and the heat that changes the temperature of the system, q_s, must be equal to zero,

$$q_r + q_s = 0,$$

so that

$$q_r + C \, \Delta T = 0,$$
$$q_r = -C \, \Delta T = - \left(\sum_i C_i \right) \Delta T. \qquad (6\text{–}10)$$

Let us stop a moment and make sure that the signs are correct in this equation. The heat capacity is always a positive quantity. [Prove this to your satisfaction using Eq. (6–9).] Therefore, if the temperature of the system rises, i.e., if ΔT is positive, then q_r will be a negative number. (This is just what we would expect for an exothermic reaction, since heat given off by a reaction is given a negative sign.)

In the real world it is impossible to make the perfect calorimeter, one which has no heat leaks, so measuring the temperature change due to the heat from the reaction is complicated by temperature changes from heat leaking into or out of the calorimeter. To correct for these effects, a graphical procedure is usually used to obtain ΔT. Figure 6–1 shows a typical temperature-vs.-time plot for a calorimetric experiment in which the reaction was exothermic. The initial temperature of the reaction vessel and contents was a little below room temperature, so heat was leaking into the system. This explains the slow rise in temperature before the reaction was initiated. After the initial sharp rise in temperature when the reaction was begun, the temperature began to decrease due to heat loss from the calorimeter. At first these readings were a bit erratic, as temperature equilibration was not

---

* This seemingly strange temperature interval was chosen because this was just about the average ambient temperature in the European laboratories at that time.

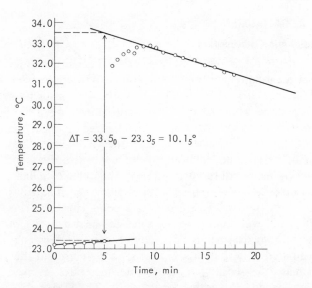

Fig. 6–1. Temperature-vs.-time plot for a calorimetric experiment, described in the illustrative example below. (The reaction was initiated immediately after the five-minute reading was taken.)

On the figure: $\Delta T = 33.5_0 - 23.3_5 = 10.1_5°$

yet attained throughout the system. After a time the equilibration (and the reaction) was complete, the heat loss became steady, and the temperature decreased relatively linearly. Extrapolation of this linear portion of the curve back to the time the reaction began gives a fairly accurate value for *the temperature which would have been attained if the reaction and temperature equilibration had taken place instantaneously* so that no heat loss could have occurred.

An adiabatic calorimeter has to be calibrated to determine the heat capacity of the calorimeter. There are a number of ways to perform the calibration. It is possible to make an absolute calibration using a resistance heating method to relate electrical work and heat experimentally. Let us suppose that an unknown amount of heat released by a reaction is transferred to a mass of water (or other liquid) in the calorimeter and that the temperature rises by an amount ΔT. Into an identical mass of water in the calorimeter we place an electrical resistor with a resistance of R ohms through which we pass a constant current of i amperes. The current passing through the resistor works on the resistor and heats it, and this heat is transferred to the water. We note the exact amount of time, t seconds, required for the temperature of the water to rise by ΔT. From these data we can calculate the exact amount of electrical work that has been done on the resistor and, hence, the amount of heat transferred to the water. The voltage drop across the resistor is $V = iR$, and the number of coulombs (ampere-seconds) that pass through it is it. From the definition of the joule, Eq. (6–8), we find that the

Number of joules $= J = (Vit) = (iR)(it) = i^2Rt.$

From the definition of the calorie, Eq. (6–7), we then find that the

Number of calories $= \dfrac{J}{4.1840} = \dfrac{i^2Rt}{4.1840}.$

Since the measurements of the potential drop across the resistor (or equivalently, the resistance of the resistor), the current, the time, and the temperature can be made quite accurately, this determination of the amount of heat transferred to the water is also very accurate.

Although the resistance heating method is accurate and necessary for absolute calorimetry, it is time-consuming. A faster method is to carry out in the calorimeter some reaction which has an accurately known heat of reaction (How is it known?) and measure its effect. One of the most widely used reactions for this purpose is the heat of neutralization of a strong acid by a strong base, which may be represented as

$$H^+(aq) + OH^-(aq) \rightarrow H_2O,$$
$$\Delta H^0_{298} = -13.36 \text{ kcal/mole}, \tag{6–11}$$

if the concentrations of the acid and base are relatively low, 1 M or less. (For more concentrated solutions the heat evolved on dilution when the solutions are mixed becomes very appreciable and must be taken into account in calculating the overall heat evolution.) The temperature rise accompanying the mixing of a solution of base with a solution of acid at the same initial temperature in a calorimeter is caused by the heat released in the above reaction. Knowing the number of moles of reaction that occur, the specific heat of the aqueous solution (which can usually be taken as 1.0 cal/deg-gm within the accuracy of our experiments), the mass of the solution, and the temperature rise obtained from a plot like Fig. 6–1, we can calculate the heat capacity of the calorimeter.

Another, somewhat less accurate, method of calibration is presented in the following example.

Illustrative Example: The temperature-time plot shown in Fig. 6–1 was obtained by the following experiment. The calorimeter reaction vessel was weighed and then filled about one-half full with distilled water and reweighed. The mass of water contained was 75.3 gm. The temperature of this water was recorded for five minutes and then some water at an initial temperature of $88.2_0°$C was added to the reaction vessel and the temperature was recorded for another ten minutes. The vessel and contents were again weighed and the final mass of water was found to be 94.0 gm. What is the heat capacity of the calorimeter (excluding the contents)?

Although the process that occurs on mixing the hot water with that already in the calorimeter is a complex one, we can *imagine* the process as being broken into two parts: the release of enough heat by the high-temperature water to reduce its temperature from $88.2_0°$C to $33.5_0°$C, and the absorption of this heat by the original water and the calorimeter to raise their temperature from 23.3_5°C to 33.5_0°C. (It is assumed that the initial temperature of the calorimeter and its final temperature are the same as those of the water in contact with it.) Hence

$$q_r = (94.0 - 75.3)\,\text{gm} \times 1.0\,\text{cal/gm-deg}$$
$$\times\,(33.5_0 - 88.2_0)\,\text{deg}$$
$$= 18.7 \times 1.0 \times (-54.7_0)\,\text{cal},$$
$$= -1020\,\text{cal}$$

and

$$q_s = 75.3\,\text{gm} \times 1.0\,\text{cal/gm-deg}$$
$$\times\,(33.5_0 - 23.3_5)\,\text{deg} + C_c \times (33.5_0 - 23.3_5)\,\text{deg}$$

where C_c is the heat capacity of the calorimeter in cal/deg.

$$q_s = 75.3 \times 1.0 \times 10.1_5 + C_c \times 10.1_5$$
$$= 867 + C_c \times 10.1_5\,\text{cal}.$$

We know from our discussion that $q_r + q_s = 0$ so that

$$-1020 + 867 + C_c \times 10.1_5 = 0,$$
$$C_c = \frac{1020 - 867}{10.1_5} = 13.3\,\text{cal/deg}.$$

Isothermal Calorimetry. Just as in the case of adiabatic calorimetry, we attempt to keep all the heat of a reaction in an isothermal calorimeter. The major difference is that we use the "trapped" heat to make a measurable change in a system that remains at a constant temperature. In general, the type of system that must be used is some two-phase equilibrium. The most common system is ice and water at 0°C; if heat enters this equilibrium system, some ice must melt in order to maintain the temperature at 0°C, the equilibrium temperature. Since ice and water have different densities, a volume change will occur when some of the system is melted or frozen. This volume change will be directly proportional to the amount of water that is changed from the solid to the liquid phase (or vice versa) and hence to the amount of heat that has entered (or left) the equilibrium system. Since the densities of solid and liquid water at 0°C (0.917 and 0.9998 gm/ml, respectively) and its *molar enthalpy of fusion*, the number of calories required at 0°C and a constant pressure of 1 atm to melt 1 mole of solid water to 1 mole of liquid water (1436 cal/mole), are known, a measurement of the volume change attendant on the release or absorption of heat in the calorimeter can be directly related to the heat change that has occurred. (An ice calorimeter is an absolute instrument that needs no calibration.) Why is the heat capacity of the calorimeter not taken into account? Further discussion of isothermal calorimetry will be deferred until the construction of an ice calorimeter is outlined in the next section.

6-3 CALORIMETERS

Adiabatic Calorimeters

Adiabatic calorimeters are very easy to construct, since they are usually simply a combination of a reaction vessel, a thermometer, and a method of providing insulation. Three designs for such calorimeters are shown in Fig. 6–2. Each design may, of course, be changed to meet the requirements of a particular experiment. Figure 6–2(a) might be surrounded by a shield to keep drafts from causing temperature fluctuations in the outer container. Figure 6–2(b) may be used without the beaker if aqueous solutions (no organic solvents) are being studied. This alteration will considerably reduce the heat capacity of the calorimeter (the heat capacity of foam drinking cups compared with that of a beaker is very small) and thus increase the sensitivity of the calorimeter for a given heat change. Prove this for yourself. The Dewar flask in Fig. 6–2(c) is a double-walled glass container with a vacuum between the walls. These inner walls are usually silvered. Thus heat loss either by conduction or by radiation through the walls is very low. The major disadvantages of this type of calorimeter are that the heat capacity is high and the usual commercially available Dewar flasks are relatively large and require large amounts of sample. You can probably easily dream up other adiabatic calorimeter designs for yourself.

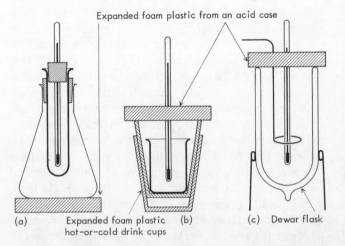

Fig. 6–2. Calorimeters; cross-sectional views of three designs.

Ice Calorimeters

The construction of a simple but very serviceable and precise ice calorimeter is shown in Fig. 6–3(a). The materials necessary for this construction are a "bubble bottle,"* a 15-mm test tube, 50 to 60 cm of 4-mm outer

---

* Any bottle with a square lip will do. Beakers and other containers with beaded lips are not recommended because it is then difficult to make a good seal with a rubber stopper.

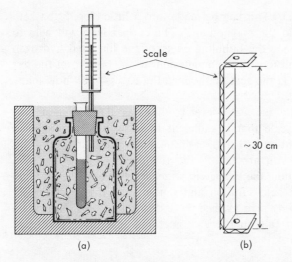

Fig. 6–3. (a) Cross-sectional view of an ice calorimeter; (b) side view of scale (corrugated cardboard cut and bent as indicated with graph-paper scale taped on and holes, through which the glass tubing passes, punched with a pencil point or the reamer on a Swiss army knife).

diameter Pyrex or soft glass tubing, a rubber stopper bored with holes to fit the test tube and tubing tightly, an insulated container (one section of the expanded plastic foam cases used for shipping acids is ideal), and some sort of scale (millimeter graph paper or a metric ruler). [A suggestion for the construction of a very convenient scale which can be made before going to the laboratory is given in Fig. 6–3(b).] The test tube should clear the bottom of the bubble bottle by at least 1.0 cm when the apparatus is assembled. You can make refinements in this design; as an example, if you have a 1.0-ml graduated pipet, graduated in 0.01 ml increments, you can substitute this for the glass tubing and scale and you will avoid the tubing calibration outlined below.

To assemble the calorimeter, begin by placing the bubble bottle in the insulating container and filling the container and bottle with crushed ice. Pour ice water slowly into the bottle (if you pour too rapidly, air bubbles may become trapped in the bottle and ruin your

later measurements) until it overflows and continue adding ice water until the water level in the container is above the mouth of the bottle. Insert the stopper with the tubing and test tube in place. In this operation water will be displaced from the bottle and driven up the tubing. Since water may geyser from the top and might splash into the test tube, it is wise to have the test tube corked during this operation. (If you have been careful there will be no trapped air spaces in the bottle. Almost all very erratic results can be traced to the presence of these air spaces.) Fill the remainder of the container as full as possible with crushed ice and water. Attach the scale to the tubing after wiping it dry.

After assembly, the calorimeter will require fifteen to twenty minutes to reach equilibrium. When thermal equilibrium seems to have been established (when the water level is no longer changing rapidly), start to take height readings every minute for about ten minutes. If the rate of change of the water level is constant between 1 to 2 mm/minute for ten minutes, you are ready to begin a calorimetric run. (Why is there a change in the water level at all under these conditions?)

When a reaction occurs in the test tube, heat will be released or absorbed by the contents of the test tube. This amount of heat will either go to or come from the surroundings, i.e., the ice-water mixture in the bubble bottle. The corresponding melting or freezing of some of this mixture will result in a volume change that will be reflected in a change in the water level in the narrow tubing. How can this change in water level be related to the volume change? One possibility is to weigh the water delivered from the tubing for a known height change and then convert the mass to volume, using the value of the density of water at the proper temperature. Are there any implicit assumptions in this method? It is probably a good idea to obtain a number of such calibrations at a number of different locations in the tubing. Why? An alternative method of calibration as well as further details of operation are presented in the procedure for Experiment 7.

EXPERIMENT 7. *The Enthalpy Change in the Reaction of Magnesium with Acid*

The object of this experiment is to measure the heat evolved when magnesium metal is converted to the aqueous ion in the reaction

$$Mg(s) + 2H^+(aq) \rightarrow Mg^{++}(aq) + H_2(g) \qquad (6\text{–}12)$$

at 0°C and constant (1 atm) pressure. The method outlined utilizes an ice calorimeter, but an adiabatic calorimeter would also be suitable.

Procedure

Since a number of readings and recordings have to be made simultaneously, this experiment should be performed with a partner.

Construct an ice calorimeter and let it equilibrate as indicated in Section 6–3. Just after taking the final reading in the initial set of readings after thermal equilibrium has been established, pipet into the test tube

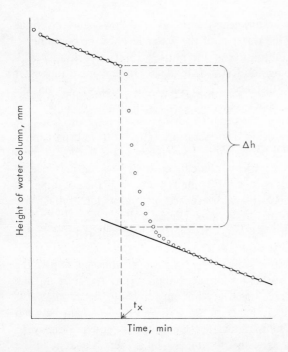

Fig. 6–4. Data from an ice-calorimetric experiment: t_x = time of addition of sample; Δh = change in height caused by heat released by sample.

exactly 10 ml of 2 *M* HCl. Avoid pushing on or otherwise disturbing the rubber stopper assembly, or nonreproducible changes in the liquid height will occur. Record the initial temperature of this solution (in the vessel from which it comes) taken with a calibrated thermometer (Section 1–4). Take readings every thirty seconds until the rate of change of the water level returns to that observed during the initial ten-minute period.* Continue to take readings every minute for five more minutes.

At the end of this time, add about 0.100 gm of magnesium metal weighed to 0.0005 gm and continue to record water-level readings at thirty-second intervals until the rate of change again returns to the initial value and then every minute for about five more minutes. The total elapsed time from the beginning of the readings will probably be less than one hour. To achieve the best results, the magnesium metal should be wrapped with a few turns of clean copper wire (place the wire in dilute HCl for a few minutes, wash it with water, and dry it in

---

* This procedure constitutes a calibration of the apparatus, the glass tubing in particular, since you can easily calculate the heat released as this solution, specific heat 1.0 cal/gm-deg, cools to 0°C and thus relate water-level changes directly to heat released in the test tube. What assumptions are implicit in this procedure? It is instructive to calibrate the glass tubing both this way and by the method suggested in Section 6–3.

the air). This can be made into a little closed "basket" to hold the magnesium. The copper wire will help to overcome the bubbling effect of the liberated hydrogen gas and to sink the magnesium to the bottom of the test tube. Is the acid or the metal in excess? By how many moles?

Plot the water-level readings as a function of time on a scale that is sufficient to show height differences amounting to 1 mm. (You can save time by doing this while you are taking the readings.) From this plot, determine the change in water level due to the addition of the acid solution and that due to the reaction (see Fig. 6–4). Do at least three determinations. Your data should fall on curves something like those shown in Fig. 6–4.

Calculations

Calculate the amount of heat released in each run. Convert these results to values of the enthalpy change, ΔH^0_{273}, in reaction (6–12) per mole of magnesium that reacts. Compute the mean and mean deviation of ΔH^0_{273} for reaction (6–12) per mole of magnesium. What is ΔE^0_{273} for reaction (6–12)?

Further Experimental Problems

Heat of Reaction of MgO and Acid. You may wish to go one step further and apply the calorimetric technique to the reaction

$$MgO(s) + 2H^+(aq) \rightarrow Mg^{++}(aq) + H_2O(l). \quad (6\text{–}13)$$

This reaction is not nearly as rapid as that of Mg with acid at 0°C, so it is difficult to carry out this reaction in an ice calorimeter. You can, however, readily examine it using an adiabatic calorimeter.

From the data on reactions (6–12), (6–13), and $\Delta H^0_f[H_2O(l)]$, you can calculate a value of ΔH^0 for the following reaction:

$$Mg(s) + \tfrac{1}{2}O_2(g) \rightarrow MgO(s). \quad (6\text{–}14)$$

You can compare your value with that found in tables of enthalpies of formation. You should think about and discuss with your instructors the possible causes of any deviations of your experimental value from the tabulated value (also see Problem 3 at the end of the chapter). Reaction (6–14) is a good example of one that is difficult to carry out in simple calorimetric apparatus, but an application of Hess' law allows us to calculate the thermochemistry of the reaction from the results of easily performed experiments.

EXPERIMENT 8. *The Acetone-Chloroform System: Part I*

In the first part of the investigation of the acetone-chloroform system, we shall determine the enthalpy change on mixing acetone, CH_3COCH_3, and chloroform, $CHCl_3$. The first step in this determination is to discover what enthalpy changes occur on mixing acetone and chloroform separately with some "inert" solvent. Thus we shall be able to estimate what part of the enthalpy change occurring on mixing the acetone and chloroform is not due simply to dilution effects. If we find that the heat of dilution of acetone and of chloroform in an "inert" solvent (carbon tetrachloride, CCl_4, in this experiment) is zero or at least very small, then we can assume, as a first approximation at least, that any substantial enthalpy change on mixing the acetone and chloroform is a specific effect, not just a heat of dilution. To what should we attribute such an effect? Before reading Chapter 12, where further aspects of this problem are discussed, try to think it through for yourself.

Procedure

Work in pairs for this experiment.

Calorimeter Calibration. The enthalpy changes of the reactions to be studied are too small to be measured accurately with the ice calorimeter described in Section 6–3, so an adiabatic calorimeter is required. Add an accurately known volume of NaOH solution of accurately known concentration (about 1 M) to the calorimeter reaction vessel, filling it about one-quarter to one-third full. Insert the thermometer and begin taking and recording readings every two minutes. In another container, place an accurately known volume of HCl solution of accurately known concentration (about 1 M). There should be enough HCl to be roughly stoichiometrically equivalent to about 90% of the NaOH. Insert another thermometer which has been calibrated relative to the first (Section 1–4) into this solution. Cool or warm the acid solution slightly until the temperature of the acid is the same as the base (which you have been recording and which is by this time, hopefully, in thermal equilibrium with the calorimeter and its surroundings). Now, quickly add the acid to the base and note the time of addition. Take temperature readings every thirty seconds for a few minutes and then every minute for a few more minutes. (Stirring the solution with the thermometer or a stirrer will reduce the number of erratic readings at the beginning of the series.) Plot the temperature readings as a function of time (you will save time and effort by recording your data directly on such a plot) and treat these data as indicated in Fig. 6–1. Using ΔT from this plot, the heat of the reaction (reaction

6–11), the number of moles of reaction calculated from the limiting number of moles of reactants, and the specific heat of the solution taken as 1.0 cal/gm-deg, you can compute the heat capacity of the calorimeter.

Heats of Dilution and Mixing. Almost the same technique as is used to calibrate the calorimeter is used to obtain the enthalpy changes on making equimolar mixtures of CH_3COCH_3 and CCl_4, $CHCl_3$ and CCl_4, and CH_3COCH_3 and $CHCl_3$. The total volume of liquid in the calorimeter reaction vessel should be about the same at the end of all runs including the calibrations. Why? Before beginning the experiment you must calculate what volume of each of the reagents, acetone, chloroform, and carbon tetrachloride, you will need to satisfy two requirements:

1) The final volumes in each run should be about the same.

2) The number of moles of each reagent used in a particular run should be the same within ±5%. (The densities of CH_3COCH_3, $CHCl_3$, and CCl_4 are 0.79, 1.50, and 1.60 gm/ml, respectively, at 20°C.)

The procedure to be followed for the acetone-carbon tetrachloride reaction will be given here; all the other mixings should be carried out the same way. Place the correct volume of CH_3COCH_3 in a clean, dry, and tightly stoppered container and weigh it to the nearest 10 mg. Transfer the CH_3COCH_3 to the calorimeter and reweigh the container to determine the amount of CH_3COCH_3 in the calorimeter. Begin recording the temperature of the CH_3COCH_3 every two minutes. Place the correct volume of CCl_4 in a clean, dry, and tightly stoppered container and weigh it to the nearest 10 mg. Insert a thermometer into the CCl_4 and bring it to the same temperature as the CH_3COCH_3 in the calorimeter. Add the CCl_4 to the calorimeter, note the time of addition, and take time-temperature readings as described for the calibration procedure. Reweigh the CCl_4 container to determine the mass of CCl_4 added to the calorimeter. Repeat this procedure for $CHCl_3$ and CCl_4 and for CH_3COCH_3 and $CHCl_3$. Perform the calibration and the CH_3COCH_3-$CHCl_3$ mixing at least twice. Do the reactions have to be done in the order presented above?

Calculations

Calculate the heat capacity of the calorimeter. The specific heats of CH_3COCH_3, $CHCl_3$, and CCl_4 are

0.53, 0.24, and 0.20 cal/gm-deg, respectively. (For more accurate values as a function of temperature you might consult the *International Critical Tables*.) The specific heats may be assumed to be additive for mixtures, i.e., a mixture of 10 gm of CH_3COCH_3 and 10 gm of $CHCl_3$ will have an overall heat capacity of $10 \times 0.53 + 10 \times 0.24 = 7.7$ cal/deg. Compute the enthalpy change when 1 mole of each reactant is mixed in the following reactions:

$$CH_3COCH_3(l) + CCl_4(l) \rightarrow \text{Mixture}_1,$$

$$CHCl_3(l) + CCl_4(l) \rightarrow \text{Mixture}_2,$$

$$CH_3COCH_3(l) + CHCl_3(l) \rightarrow \text{Mixture}_3.$$

Assume that the heat of dilution of CH_3COCH_3 by $CHCl_3$ is the same as that by CCl_4 and that the heat of dilution of $CHCl_3$ by CH_3COCH_3 is the same as that by CCl_4. Calculate the enthalpy change which would be expected for the third reaction on this basis. Compare this with the measured enthalpy change. If there is some specific effect, what is the enthalpy change resulting from it when 1 mole of CH_3COCH_3 is mixed with one mole of $CHCl_3$? To what might you attribute any specific interactions in this system? Is the sign of the enthalpy change that which you might expect for such an interaction?

Further Experimental Problems

You ought to check whether the solvent carbon tetrachloride is really inert in this system. Perhaps you can do this by choosing another solvent of a different character, such as cyclohexane, C_6H_{12}, and redoing the dilutions of chloroform and acetone. If the results are different, then you will either have to do another set of experiments with a third solvent or try to rationalize the results on a molecular basis.

EXPERIMENT 9.   The Extent of Solvolysis of the Salt of a Weak Acid and a Weak Base

Background

In the introduction to this chapter it is implicitly assumed that the reactions studied in a calorimeter go to "completion," for no mention is made of the extent of reaction or any attempt to measure it. What happens if the reaction does not go to completion? In certain cases the measurement of the heat evolved in a reaction that does not go to completion can yield information as to the extent of the reaction, if other experimental data are available that allow us to calculate the amount of heat that would be evolved if the reaction did go to completion. As an example of the kind of system we might study in this way we shall consider the weak acid HA, the weak base BOH, and the salt of the acidic anion and the basic cation BA. The acidic and basic equilibrium reactions in aqueous solution and their equilibrium-constant expressions are:

$$HA(aq) \rightleftharpoons H^+(aq) + A^-(aq),$$

$$K_a = \frac{[H^+][A^-]}{[HA]}, \tag{6-15}$$

$$BOH(aq) \rightleftharpoons B^+(aq) + OH^-(aq),$$

$$K_b = \frac{[B^+][OH^-]}{[BOH]}. \tag{6-16}$$

Two reactions that are readily studied calorimetrically are neutralization reactions of the general type:

$$HA(aq) + OH^-(aq) \rightarrow H_2O + A^-(aq), \quad \Delta H_{17}, \tag{6-17}$$

$$BOH(aq) + H^+(aq) \rightarrow H_2O + B^+(aq), \quad \Delta H_{18}, \tag{6-18}$$

which can be forced to "completion" by combining a small excess of one of the reactants, say the acid in each case, with the other, the base in each case. Thus the number of moles of reaction will be limited by the number of moles of base originally present, which is easily calculated. From the calorimetric measurements, therefore, we can obtain ΔH_{17} and ΔH_{18}. We can combine these two neutralization reactions with a third reaction, a strong-acid–strong-base neutralization,

$$H^+(aq) + OH^-(aq) \rightarrow H_2O, \quad \Delta H_{11}, \tag{6-11}$$

to yield the reaction and enthalpy change (if the reaction proceeds to completion) for the neutralization of a weak acid with a weak base

$$HA(aq) + BOH(aq) \rightarrow H_2O + B^+(aq) + A^-(aq),$$

$$\Delta H_{19} = \Delta H_{17} + \Delta H_{18} - \Delta H_{11}. \tag{6-19}$$

(How?) With only a small excess of one of the reactants present this last reaction will not proceed to completion as shown, or, to put it another way, the reactions of the acidic anion, A^-, and the basic cation, B^+, with the solvent, water, will tend to make the reaction proceed in reverse to give the unionized acid and base. In fact, we can ask the question: How far will the solvolysis reaction

$$B^+(aq) + A^-(aq) + H_2O \rightleftharpoons BOH(aq) + HA(aq) \tag{6-20}$$

proceed toward the right when the salt BA is dissolved in water? In other words, what is the value of the equilibrium constant for solvolysis, K_{solv}, which is given by

$$K_{\text{solv}} = \frac{[\text{BOH}][\text{HA}]}{[\text{B}^+][\text{A}^-]} = \frac{K_w}{K_a K_b}. \qquad (6\text{--}21)$$

(Prove that the ratio of equilibrium constants on the right is correct for this expression.)

Experimentally, we can approach this problem by determining the heat evolved when exactly equivalent amounts of BOH and HA are mixed in a calorimeter. If the reaction were to go to completion, the enthalpy change per mole of reaction would be ΔH_{19}. We know, however, that the reaction does not go to completion so the heat evolved and thus the observed enthalpy change per mole of reactant will not be ΔH_{19}, but something less. Let us call this observed enthalpy change ΔH. It should then be apparent that the *fraction* of reaction (6–19), which we shall denote α', that occurs when the reactants are mixed in exactly equivalent amounts will be $\Delta H/\Delta H_{19}$. The fraction of reaction (6–20) that occurs when BA is dissolved in water we shall denote as α. Evidently, since (6–19) and (6–20) are the same reaction written in opposite directions, we can write

$$\alpha = 1 - \alpha'.$$

Why? Hence the fraction of the salt BA that solvolyzes will be

$$\alpha = 1 - \frac{\Delta H}{\Delta H_{19}} = \frac{\Delta H_{19} - \Delta H}{\Delta H_{19}}. \qquad (6\text{--}22)$$

Once α is known it is very simple to calculate K_{solv}. Work out an equation for K_{solv} in terms of α before coming to the laboratory.

The specific system for which instructions are given is the weak acid, boric acid, and the weak base, ammonia. The formula of boric acid (solid) is H_3BO_3, but it is not a "tribasic" acid, in fact, none of the hydrogens are acidic. Solutions of boric acid are acidic because of the following reaction:

$$\text{B(OH)}_3(\text{aq}) + H_2O \rightleftharpoons \text{B(OH)}_4^-(\text{aq}) + H^+(\text{aq}),$$
$$(6\text{--}23)$$

in which the actual "structure" of boric acid is represented. The basic reaction of ammonia is similar. In aqueous solution the reaction is

$$\text{NH}_3(\text{aq}) + H_2O \rightleftharpoons \text{NH}_4^+(\text{aq}) + \text{OH}^-(\text{aq}). \qquad (6\text{--}24)$$

See if you can now work through the earlier background material substituting this actual system for the generalized HA and BOH we used. (For a further discussion of acids and bases, see Section 7–1.)

Procedure

These instructions will be given for an adiabatic calorimeter constructed from foam plastic cups and a foam plastic cover and thermometer holder, Fig. 6–2(b), but other calorimeters would be suitable with appropriate changes in volumes of reagents used. The reagent solutions will be available in stock bottles in the laboratory.

The procedure for calibrating the calorimeter will be given in detail; the procedure for the other runs is the same. Measure out 100 ml of 0.50 M HCl solution* with a graduate and pour this directly into the dry calorimeter. Put the calorimeter cover on with the thermometer in place.

Rinse a clean 50-ml flask with a few milliliters of 1.75 M NaOH solution and pour it out, allowing two seconds for draining. Pipet 25 ml of 1.75 M NaOH into the flask. Rinse a thermometer which has been calibrated relative to the one in the calorimeter, Section 1–4, with a few drops of the basic solution and place it in the flask.

Stir the acid in the calorimeter using the thermometer as a stirrer and read the temperatures of the two solutions. If necessary, adjust the temperature of the basic solution by slight warming or cooling so that it is the same as that of the acidic solution. Continue stirring the acid and record the temperatures every minute for five minutes. Keep the basic solution at the same temperature as the acid. After the last reading, quickly remove the thermometer from the basic solution and pour the solution into the calorimeter, allowing two seconds for drainage. (Pick up the flask with a folded paper "handle" to prevent warming the solution with your fingers.) Continue stirring the solution in the calorimeter and record its temperature every thirty seconds for five minutes and then every minute for about five more minutes. These data will be treated graphically as in Fig. 6–1. (You will save time and effort by recording your data directly on a temperature-vs-time plot.) Using ΔT from the plot, the heat of reaction (6–11), the number of moles of reaction calculated from the limiting number of moles of reactants, and the specific heat of the solution taken as 1.0 cal/gm-deg, you can compute the heat capacity of the calorimeter.

The above procedure should also be used to determine the ΔT attending the mixing of the following pairs of solutions:

1) exactly 25 ml of 1.75 M NaOH solution with 100 ml of 0.50 M H_3BO_3, boric acid, solution,

2) exactly 25 ml of 1.75 M NH_3 solution with 100 ml of 0.50 M HCl solution,

---

* The exact concentrations of all reagents will be given on the stock bottle label.

3) exactly 25 ml of 1.75 M NH_3 solution with a volume of 0.50 M H_3BO_3 solution containing an *exactly equivalent* amount of H_3BO_3.

Which reagent is in excess in the calibration and mixtures (1) and (2)? Repeat each mixing at least once, if time permits.

Calculations

Use your data to calculate ΔH per mole of base for each of the mixtures (1), (2), and (3). If you made more than one run, calculate the mean and the mean deviation of your values.

Make the simplifying assumption that reactions (6–23) and (6–24) proceed to a negligible extent and use your ΔH's for mixtures (1) and (2) and the enthalpy change of reaction (6–11) to calculate the enthalpy changes for reactions (6–23) and (6–24).

From your values of ΔH and that for reaction (6–11) calculate the fraction of the salt ammonium borate that reacts with water when it is dissolved in water (cf. Eq. 6–22). Calculate the equilibrium constant for this solvolysis. Given that $K_w = 1.0 \times 10^{-14}$ and that $K_b = 1.75 \times 10^{-5}$ for ammonia, what is K_a for boric acid?

Questions

1. You have been given K_b for ammonia and have calculated K_a for boric acid. Calculate ΔG^0 for the reactions these equilibrium-constants represent.

2. Calculate ΔG^0 for the solvolysis of ammonium borate.

3. With ΔG^0 and ΔH^0 for reactions (6–23), (6–24), and the solvolysis of ammonium borate in hand (Questions 1 and 2), calculate ΔS^0 for each of these reactions. Do the values of ΔS^0 make sense in terms of a molecular interpretation of entropy?

4. Write all the reactions involved in this experiment.

5. By how many calories would the calculated enthalpy of reaction (6–24) be in error if the temperature rise in the calibration were underestimated by 0.1°C? What would the error be if the underestimation were in the heat evolved from mixture (2)?

6. Use the value of K_b for ammonia and your calculated value of K_a for boric acid to justify the assumption that in mixtures (1) and (2) the base is essentially completely neutralized.

7. What must be the relationship between pK_a, pK_b, and pK_w such that K_{solv} will have a value that is amenable to study by this method? (Appropriate values of K_{solv} are in the range 0.5 to 5. Why?)

Further Experimental Problems

There are a number of other systems of this same type that might be investigated, for example, acetic acid and pyridine (an organic acid and base combination).

An interesting series of compounds that could be studied are substituted phenols. Phenol itself has the structure

The hydrogen attached to the oxygen is weakly acidic. Changes in the acidity occur when other atoms or groups of atoms are substituted for one or more of the hydrogens attached to the ring carbons. Such changes can be quite profound: for example, the pK_a of phenol itself is about 10 whereas that of picric acid, 2,4,6-trinitrophenol,

is about 1. Thus a change in acid strength of 10^9 has been brought about by the substitutions. Such a wide variation in acid strength cannot be studied by this calorimetric method, but smaller changes are amenable to the technique. For instance, one might study phenol,

ortho (*o*)   *meta* (*m*)   *para* (*p*)

ortho-, *meta*-, and *para*-chlorophenol, with the same base, ammonia, and try to relate changes in acidity to the effect of the substituent. Such effects are discussed in most textbooks of organic chemistry.

REFERENCES

CLEVER, H. L., "Heats of Precipitation," *J. Chem. Ed.* **38**, 470 (1961) is particularly useful for the discussion which follows the experimental portion.   Many interesting avenues of thought and perhaps experimentation are opened in this discussion.

DANIELS, F., *et al.*, *Experimental Physical Chemistry*, 5th ed. McGraw-Hill, New York, 1956, pp. 42–46.

GREENE, J. A., "Calorimeter for Determining Heat Capacities of Liquids,"*J. Chem. Ed.* **32**, 577 (1955) shows a very easy-to-construct calorimeter using a constant voltage transformer to give constant power input to the calorimeter so potential drops and current do not have to be measured.

MAHAN, B. H., *Elementary Chemical Thermodynamics*, W. A. Benjamin, New York, 1963, pp. 1–59.

MAHAN, B. H., *University Chemistry*, Addison-Wesley, Reading, Mass., 1965, p. 138.   If you have done Experiment 8, you might find, upon careful reading, a disputable statement on this page.   Do you?

MAHAN, B. H., "A Simple Ice Calorimeter," *J. Chem. Ed.* **37**, 634 (1960).   The ice calorimeter described in this chapter is a modification of the design described in this article. Another modification is found in W. M. Latimer and R. E. Powell, *A Laboratory Course in General Chemistry*, Macmillan, New York, 1964, Assignment 8.

NASH, L. K., *Elements of Chemical Thermodynamics*, Addison-Wesley, Reading, Mass., 1962, pp. 1–28.

NASH, L. K., "Elementary Chemical Thermodynamics," *J. Chem. Ed.* **42**, 64 (1965) is a critical review paper on many aspects of thermodynamics, including thermochemistry.   It includes 221 annotated references.

National Bureau of Standards Circular 500.   A very large compilation of thermodynamic data.

NEIDIG, H. A., H. SCHNEIDER, and T. G. TEATES, "Thermochemical Investigations for a First-Year College Chemistry Course," *J. Chem. Ed.* **42**, 26 (1965) is a review stressing the experiments available in the published literature and is a good source of ideas for further calorimetric experiments.

SHOEMAKER, D. P., and C. W. GARLAND, *Experiments in Physical Chemistry*, McGraw-Hill, New York, 1962, pp. 118–121.

WEISFELD, L. B., "Catalyzed Reaction of Phenyl Isocyanate with Butanol," *J. Chem. Ed.* **38**, 88 (1961) shows how the rate of heat evolution from a reaction can be used to follow the course of the reaction.

ZASLOW, B., "Heat of Mixing of Organic Liquids," *J. Chem. Ed.* **37**, 578 (1960).   Our Experiment 8 is a slight modification of the one outlined in this reference.

PROBLEMS

1. How much error, in calories and in percent, did you make by not cooling the magnesium metal sample and the copper wire before adding them to the acid?   The heat capacity of Mg is 0.2316 cal/gm-deg at 0°C and 0.246 cal/gm-deg at 20°C.   The heat capacity of Cu is 0.0910 cal/gm-deg at 0°C and 0.0921 cal/gm-deg at 20°C.   Assume that the heat capacities vary linearly within this temperature range. Weigh the copper wire.   How could you experimentally determine the magnitude of this error for the magnesium and for the copper?

2. Given that the piece of tubing used has an inside diameter of 2 mm, what would be the limit of detectability (number of calories) of the calorimeter on the assumption that 0.5 mm is the least difference in column height which can be unambiguously detected?

3. a) Exactly 0.005 gm-atom (∼0.3 gm) of metallic zinc is dissolved in dilute aqueous hydrochloric acid in an ice calorimeter.   At 0°C the specific volume of $H_2O(l)$ is 1.001 cm^3/gm, the specific volume of $H_2O(s)$ is 1.091 cm^3/gm, and the heat of fusion of ice is 80 cal/gm. The heat released as the zinc dissolves melts enough ice to produce a volume contraction of 0.169 cm^3 in the ice-and-water mixture surrounding the reaction vessel. Calculate ΔH per gm-atom of zinc dissolved for the reaction

$$Zn(s) + 2H^+(aq) \rightarrow Zn^{++}(aq) + H_2(g).$$

   b) A similar determination is conducted with 0.005 mole of ZnO added to the same volume of aqueous HCl of the same dilution, and we thus find $\Delta H = -15.3$ kcal for the reaction

$$ZnO(s) + 2H^+(aq) \rightarrow Zn^{++}(aq) + H_2O(l).$$

   Given that for $H_2O(l)$, $\Delta H_f = -68.3$ kcal/mole at 0°C, calculate the heat of formation of ZnO, that is, ΔH for the reaction

$$Zn(s) + \tfrac{1}{2}O_2(g) \rightarrow ZnO(s).$$

   c) The calculation in part (b) involves a major implicit assumption that is well justified in the present case by good agreement of the calculated value with that measured directly.   What is that assumption?

   (Problem 3 is taken from L. K. Nash, *Elements of Chemical Thermodynamics*.)

DISTRIBUTION EQUILIBRIA;
7 A POTPOURRI OF EQUILIBRIA

Each of the two experiments outlined at the end of this chapter involve the study of a two-phase system, the immiscible liquids water and carbon tetrachloride. In both cases an equilibrium reaction of a solute in one phase is studied by observing its effect on the equilibrium distribution of that solute between the two phases. Obviously, the minimum number of equilibria that must be considered in such distribution systems is two, and in some cases even more.

In the preceding chapters we have not really treated any equilibrium system in great detail, and if we are to understand the principles involved in these experiments, we must first treat thoroughly some kind of equilibrium system. Since Experiment 10 involves titrations of a weak acid with a strong base and since acid-base reactions are such an interesting and important class of equilibrium reactions, let us discuss acid-base reactions and titrations in detail as a background for understanding other equilibrium calculations. We should begin by defining an "acid" and a "base."

7-1 ACIDS AND BASES DEFINED

Arrhenius Acids and Bases

The oldest definition of an acid is that it is a compound that will ionize in aqueous solution to give $H^+(aq)$, the hydrated proton or hydronium ion. Conversely, a base is defined as a compound that will ionize to give $OH^-(aq)$; an acid-base reaction will then be represented as

$$H^+(aq) + OH^-(aq) \rightleftharpoons H_2O. \qquad (7-1)$$

This definition of acids and bases, formulated by Arrhenius, is often not very helpful, since, for example, although ethylenediamine ($H_2NCH_2CH_2NH_2$) solutions in water are "basic," i.e., they give indicator color tests (litmus paper, etc.) characteristic of solutions containing $OH^-(aq)$, it is difficult to see how this compound can ionize to give $OH^-(aq)$.

Brønsted Acids and Bases

To overcome the shortcomings of Arrhenius' definitions, Brønsted proposed that an acid be defined as any compound that contains an ionizable hydrogen and a base as any compound that will act as an acceptor for the proton donated by an acid. The most important concept in this formulation is to think of acids and bases as conjugate pairs in acid-base reactions, which is best explained by example. Representing $H^+(aq)$ as H_3O^+ for convenience, we write the reaction of the acid H_3O^+ with the base NH_3 (both in aqueous solution) as

$$H_3O^+ + NH_3 \rightleftharpoons H_2O + NH_4^+. \qquad (7-2)$$
Acid I　　Base II　　Base I　　Acid II

In this case, H_2O is the *conjugate base* of the acid H_3O^+ and NH_3 is the conjugate base of the acid NH_4^+.

Let us define the strength of a conjugate base as proportional to its tendency to accept protons; then the stronger the conjugate base, the weaker the conjugate acid will be, since the tendency of an acid to donate protons obviously decreases as the tendency of its conjugate base to accept protons increases. In any solution containing more than one conjugate base, there will be a competition among the bases for the available protons. The stronger the base, the more protons it will gain and the more of its conjugate acid will be formed. In reaction (7-2), since the conjugate base NH_3 is much stronger than the base H_2O, there will be a tendency for the reaction to proceed to the right as written.

It is very important to note that a given compound may be classified by the Brønsted definitions either as a base or as an acid, depending on the particular reaction being discussed. As an example, let us consider

$$H_2O + NH_3 \rightleftharpoons OH^- + NH_4^+. \qquad (7-3)$$
Acid I　　Base II　　Base I　　Acid II

In this case NH_3 is a much weaker base than OH^- (the strongest base that can exist in aqueous solution) so it will lose in the competition for protons, and the reaction will tend to proceed to the left as written. [Since both reactions (7–2) and (7–3) are in equilibrium, there will always be some of all four species in each system, but they will tend to proceed in the directions stated.] Thus H_2O acts as a base in reaction (7–2) and as an acid in reaction (7–3).

Lewis Acids and Bases

The Brønsted classification is quite satisfactory for discussing aqueous acid-base chemistry, but it is not adequate to describe "acid-base" reactions in which no hydrogen ions (protons) are involved. As an example of such a reaction, when BF_3, which acts as an acid in many reactions, and NH_3, which we have already seen is a base, are combined in the gas phase, they form a new compound, BF_3NH_3:

$$BF_3 + NH_3 \rightleftharpoons BF_3NH_3. \qquad (7\text{--}4)$$

This is an example of a "Lewis acid-base reaction." G. N. Lewis defined a base as a compound containing an unshared pair of electrons in its "valence shell." Such a compound can react with another compound or atom that is deficient in electrons, a Lewis acid, to form a chemical bond between them. Obviously, H^+, with no electrons, is electron-deficient and is classed as an acid; BF_3, with the electronic structure

$$
\begin{array}{c}
\ddots \\
: F : \\
\ddots \quad \ddots \\
: F : B \\
\ddots \quad \ddots \\
: F : \\
\ddots
\end{array}
$$

where dots represent "valence-shell" electrons, is also electron-deficient in the Lewis sense because it has only six electrons surrounding it.* In the same way, NH_3 may be represented as having the electronic structure

$$
\begin{array}{c}
H \\
\ddots \\
H : N : \\
\ddots \\
H
\end{array}
$$

and it is evident from this representation that NH_3 contains an unshared pair of electrons and will act as a Lewis base. Hence the product of reaction (7–4), a Lewis

---

* A rule of thumb, which is not necessarily valid in all cases is that elements in the second row of the periodic table, Be through Ne, tend to form compounds in which the atom is surrounded by eight "valence-shell" electrons. This is the so-called "octet rule," which must be carefully interpreted and even more carefully used, since it is only a useful approximation and not a hard-and-fast rule.

acid-base reaction, is

$$
\begin{array}{c}
\ddots \\
: F : H \\
\ddots \quad \ddots \quad \ddots \\
: F : B : N : H \\
\ddots \quad \ddots \quad \ddots \\
: F : H \\
\ddots
\end{array}
$$

which is "neutral" in that all second-row atoms have attained the "stable octet."

Note that the three acid-base definitions are of increasing generality. The earlier definitions, still valid in the systems to which they were originally applied, are simply special cases of the later ones.

7-2 GENERAL CONSIDERATIONS CONCERNING EQUILIBRIA

The problems in equilibria we have met so far in Chapters 3 and 4 have usually been glossed over lightly or adulterated with noticeable approximations to make them easy to solve. At this point, however, we must begin to attack these problems rigorously for two specific reasons. First, we are going to discuss some acid-base titrations that do not go to "completion" and in which very substantial errors would be made if the equilibria were not accounted for quantitatively. Second, we shall be using an instrumental method (the pH meter) to follow a titration reaction, and we want to be able to correlate our instrumental readings quantitatively with the conditions in the solution to obtain information concerning the equilibria and concentrations of the solution.

The rigorous approach we shall use is that presented in the texts by J. N. Butler. Basically, the method is:

1) Write as many equations representing the system as there are unknowns that appear in the equations. (Such equations usually fall into three classes: equilibrium-constant expressions (Section 4–4), mass-conservation equations, and charge-conservation equations.) Now, the equilibrium problem is, in theory, solvable, although the algebra involved in a straightforward solution may be quite formidable.

2) Utilize your chemical intuition and stored fund of knowledge to make approximations that will simplify the equations you must solve. (This should be done *after* exact equations have been written down or derived.)

3) Solve the simplified approximate equations for the desired quantities.

4) Check the approximations for validity by substituting the calculated results back into the exact equations to make sure that, for instance, "negligible" terms are indeed negligible. If the approximations prove to be incorrect, you must solve the more exact equations.

7-3 STRONG ACID-STRONG BASE TITRATION

Strong acids and bases are those which ionize "completely" in solution. For our purposes we can assume complete ionization if the equilibrium constants* for the general reactions

$$HA(aq) \rightleftharpoons H^+(aq) + A^-(aq) \tag{7-5}$$

and

$$BOH(aq) \rightleftharpoons B^+(aq) + OH^-(aq) \tag{7-6}$$

are greater than unity. (Is this definition of strong acids consistent with the definition of acid and base strength given for Brønsted acids and bases?) Among these compounds are the common laboratory acids, HCl, HNO_3, H_2SO_4 (first ionization constant), and $HClO_4$, and bases, NaOH, KOH, and $Ba(OH)_2$.

Our usual interest in strong acid-strong base systems is for titrations of one against the other, as in the analysis in Experiment 4. Doing calculations based on these titrations will give us an opportunity to construct a simple *titration curve* (more complex examples will be treated in succeeding sections). A titration curve is a plot of some function of concentration vs. the volume of added titrant, or a direct function thereof, such as the fraction of the sample titrated. In acid-base reactions the most common concentration function is the pH ($-\log[H^+]$) or pOH ($-\log[OH^-]$).†

To make the discussion easier to follow, let us concentrate on the case of the titration of the strong base BOH with the strong acid HA. The initial molar concentration of the base solution will be M_b and that of the acid solution will be M_a. We begin with a volume of the base solution V_b, and the volume of acid we add as titrant will be V_a.

What reactions and equilibria must we take into account? We assume that reactions (7-5) and (7-6) proceed essentially to completion, so that the initial concentrations in the two solutions, the base and the acid, will be

$$[OH^-]_{BOH} = [B^+] = M_b, \tag{7-7}$$

$$[H^+]_{HA} = [A^-] = M_a. \tag{7-8}$$

An equilibrium that is always set up in aqueous solutions is

$$H_2O \rightleftharpoons H^+(aq) + OH^-(aq), \tag{7-9}$$

for which the equilibrium constant is usually written

$$K_w = [H^+][OH^-] = 10^{-14} \quad \text{(at 25°C).} \tag{7-10}$$

Note that the concentration (essentially constant) of H_2O has been included as part of the equilibrium constant K_w, as is conventional (Section 4-4).‡ Finally, because the solution must be electrically neutral, we can sum up the number of moles of positive charge and set this sum equal to the sum of the number of moles of negative charge:

$$[H^+] + [B^+] = [OH^-] \quad \text{(base solution),} \tag{7-11}$$

$$[H^+] = [A^-] + [OH^-] \quad \text{(acid solution).} \tag{7-12}$$

Initially the concentration of hydroxyl ion in the base solution is

$$[OH^-] \simeq M_b. \tag{7-14}$$

How good is this approximation? Let us substitute (7-14) into (7-10) to find out that:

$$K_w = [H^+]M_b = 10^{-14}$$

$$[H^+] = \frac{10^{-14}}{M_b} \le 10^{-8}$$

$$\text{(if } M_b = [OH^-]_{BOH} \ge 10^{-6} M).$$

From the stoichiometry of reaction (7-9) it is evident that $[OH^-]_{H_2O} = [H^+]$, so that $[OH^-]_{H_2O} \le 10^{-8}$ if $M_b = [OH^-]_{BOH} \ge 10^{-6} M$. Less than 1% error is made by assuming $[OH^-] \simeq M_b$ under these conditions. Similarly, in the acid solution we can show that $[H^+] \simeq M_a$ if $M_a \ge 10^{-6} M$.

What is the situation when V_a ml of acid have been added to the V_b ml of base? The H^+ and OH^- react and the reverse of reaction (7-9), i.e., reaction (7-1), occurs. The equilibrium constant for the reaction written this way is 10^{14} (why?); it may be assumed to proceed essentially to completion. Thus, for every mole of acid added, 1 mole of OH^- is neutralized. The number of moles of H^+ added is V_aM_a and the number of moles of OH^- initially present from the base is V_bM_b, so the number of moles of OH^- remaining after V_a ml have been added is $V_bM_b - V_aM_a$;

$$[OH^-]_{BOH} = \frac{V_bM_b - V_aM_a}{V_a + V_b}. \tag{7-15}$$

---

* These equilibrium constants are often called ionization constants, for obvious reasons.

† Correctly, the pH is defined as $-\log a_{H^+}$, the negative logarithm of the activity of the hydrogen ion in solution. As usual, we assume that activity and molar concentration are close enough that they may be equated.

‡ The existence of this equilibrium in aqueous solution gives rise to a simple relationship between pH and pOH. Taking logarithms of both sides of (7-10) and changing all the signs, we get $-\log[H^+] - \log[OH^-] = 14$, and using the definitions of pH and pOH we find that pH + pOH = 14. This relationship is always valid in aqueous solutions at 25°C. Why is the pH of a "neutral" solution or pure water 7?

Equation (7–15) may be simplified somewhat by introducing a quantity f, the fraction of the equivalent volume of titrant added (or the fraction of the solution titrated). For the reaction under discussion, f may be written

$$f = \frac{V_a M_a}{V_b M_b}. \qquad (7\text{–}16)$$

(Show that this is the case to your own satisfaction.) Substitution of Eq. (7–16) into (7–15) and rearrangement gives

$$[OH^-]_{BOH} = (1 - f)M_b \left(\frac{V_b}{V_a + V_b} \right). \qquad (7\text{–}17)$$

It should be obvious from the discussion in the preceding paragraph that $[OH^-] \simeq [OH^-]_{BOH}$ as long as $[OH^-]_{BOH} \geq 10^{-6} M$. Thus (7–17) can be used to calculate $[OH^-]$ at any point in the titration if we know V_a, V_b, M_a, and M_b, and the value calculated is greater than $10^{-6} M$.

Let us take a particular example in which we start with 50.00 ml of 0.100 M NaOH solution and titrate it with 0.100 M HCl solution. Before the titration begins $V_a = 0.00$ ml, so that $f = 0$ and we write (7–17) as

$$[OH^-]_{NaOH} = 0.100 \times \frac{50.00}{50.00}$$
$$= 1.00 \times 10^{-1} M.$$

What will be the result when the solution has been 90% titrated, i.e., when $f = 0.90$? The amount of titrant acid added at this point may be calculated from Eq. (7–16),

$$V_a = \frac{f V_b M_b}{M_a} = \frac{0.90 \times 50.00 \times 0.100}{0.100}$$
$$= 45.00,$$

and therefore

$$[OH^-]_{NaOH} = 0.10 \times 0.100 \times \frac{50.00}{95.00}$$
$$= 5.26 \times 10^{-3} M.$$

In precisely the same way other values of $[OH^-]_{NaOH}$ for $f < 1.00$ can be calculated; a few of these are given in Table 7–1. It is evident that even up to the point where the titration is 99.99% complete, the approximation $[OH^-] \simeq [OH^-]_{NaOH}$ is valid in this case.

What happens at the equivalence point, $f = 1.00$ (see Section 4–2 for the definition)? Equation (7–17) gives $[OH^-]_{BOH} = 0.00$ at this point, and obviously the OH^- from the water dissociation, (7–9), is no longer negligible. In fact, it is the only source of OH^- in the solution, since we have assumed that the acid-base reaction goes to completion. Since there is also no other source of H^+, we can easily see from the stoichiometry

Table 7–1

THE TITRATION OF 50.00 ml OF 0.100 M NaOH WITH 0.100 M HCl

f	V_a	$[OH^-]_{NaOH} \simeq [OH^-]$	$[H^+]_{HCl} \simeq [H^+]$	pOH	pH
0.0000	0.00	1.00×10^{-1}		1.00	13.00
0.5000	25.00	3.33×10^{-2}		1.48	12.52
0.9000	45.00	5.26×10^{-3}		2.28	11.72
0.9900	49.50	5.02×10^{-4}		3.30	10.70
0.9990	49.95	5.00×10^{-5}		4.30	9.70
0.9999	49.99$_5$	5.00×10^{-6}		5.30	8.70
1.0000	50.00	(0.00)	(0.00)	7.00	7.00
1.0001	50.00$_5$		5.00×10^{-6}	8.70	5.30
1.0010	50.05		5.00×10^{-5}	9.70	4.30
1.0100	50.50		4.98×10^{-4}	10.70	3.30
1.1000	55.00		4.76×10^{-3}	11.68	2.32

of (7–9) that $[H^+] = [OH^-]$ at this point.* Substitution in (7–10) gives

$$[H^+]^2 = [OH^-]^2 = 10^{-14},$$
$$[H^+] = 10^{-7}, \qquad [OH^-] = 10^{-7},$$

as could be expected on the basis of the footnote on p. 78.

If more than the equivalent amount of acid is added, what will happen to the concentrations in the solution? It is evident that (7–17) can no longer be used, since, if $f > 1$, the calculated concentration will be negative, an absurd result. Intuitively it is also evident that (7–17) will no longer be useful, because all the base has reacted so there will be no $[OH^-]_{BOH}$. Indeed, when $f > 1$ we are in effect adding acid to a neutral solution of BA. The total number of moles of acid added in excess is $V_a M_a - V_b M_b$, so the concentration of H^+ from the excess acid is

$$[H^+]_{HA} = \frac{V_a M_a - V_b M_b}{V_a + V_b}. \qquad (7\text{–}18)$$

Substitution from Eq. (7–16) gives

$$[H^+]_{HA} = \left(\frac{f - 1}{f} \right) M_a \left(\frac{V_a}{V_a + V_b} \right). \qquad (7\text{–}19)$$

Equation (7–19) allows us to calculate $[H^+]_{HA}$ beyond the equivalence point. We know from above that $[H^+]_{HA} \simeq [H^+]$ if $[H^+]_{HA} \geq 10^{-6} M$, so the values presented in Table 7–1 for $f > 1$ represent $[H^+]$ very well. (Note that (7–19) gives $[H^+]_{HA} = 0$ for $f = 1$, as it must on the basis of our assumptions. Explain.)

---

* Essentially the solution at this point is a solution of BA (NaCl in our example) in water; B^+ and A^- are, respectively, the cation of a strong base and the anion of a strong acid, so they have no tendency to react with the water to form H^+ or OH^-. Write the equations for these reactions that do not proceed and try to interpret them in terms of the Brønsted acid-base theory.

With the values in Table 7–1 in mind, we can now plot the titration curve for the titration of 0.100 M NaOH with 0.100 M HCl, which is shown in curve (a) in Fig. 7–1.

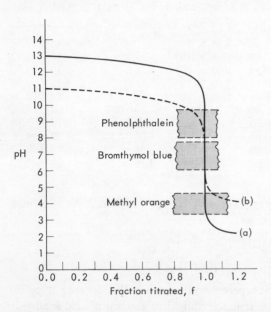

Fig. 7–1. (a) Titration curve for 0.100 M NaOH with 0.100 M HCl; (b) titration curve for 0.00100 M NaOH with 0.00100 M HCl (see Problem 1 at the end of the chapter). The pH range for the color change of three indicators is also shown.

After following all the reasoning through this far, you might logically inquire, "What good are all these calculations?" After all, we usually do not know the concentration of the solution being titrated; why else do we perform the titration? Therefore the fraction titrated is not a calculable quantity, and we cannot construct a titration curve a priori unless all concentrations are known. The curve and the calculations that go into its construction show that there is a large jump in the pH of the solution, 5.40 pH units, between the points 0.1% (1 part per 1000) before and after the equivalence point for this particular example. In practice, this means that in any such titration of a strong base with a strong acid or vice versa at the equivalence point there will be a large jump in the pH within a very small range of titrant volume added.* Thus any *indicator* that will give its signal in the pH range 5.0 to 9.0 will be suitable for a titration such as this and will result in a negligible titration error.

---

* This statement is true only for moderately concentrated solutions (10^{-3} M or greater), since the contribution of the water dissociation to the H^+ and OH^- concentrations will be appreciable further from the equivalence point as the initial concentrations of the solutions are decreased. See Fig. 7–1(b) and Problem 1 at the end of the chapter.

7–4 ACID-BASE INDICATORS

The usual acid-base indicators are weak acids whose equilibrium in aqueous solution may be represented as

$$HIn(aq) \rightleftharpoons H^+(aq) + In^-(aq) \qquad (7\text{–}20)$$

with an equilibrium constant

$$K_{In} = \frac{[H^+][In^-]}{[HIn]}. \qquad (7\text{–}21)$$

Either the acidic or the basic form of the indicator (or both) is colored, and the solution changes color when the indicator is converted from one form to the other.† The indicator we choose for a particular titration will depend on the pH at which we desire the indication to occur (we shall see below that this is not pH = 7 for all acid-base titrations).

As a good rule of thumb it may be assumed that the ratio of basic to acidic form of the indicator must be ten to one for the basic form's color to predominate in the solution and vice versa. We can use (7–21) to obtain an indication of the pH where the color of a particular indicator changes. Rearrange (7–21) and take logarithms of both sides of the equation:

$$\log K_{In} - \log [H^+] = \log ([In^-]/[HIn]).$$

Now if we define pX as $-\log X$ for any sort of function X, we can write this equation as

$$-pK_{In} + pH = \log ([In^-]/[HIn]). \qquad (7\text{–}22)$$

If the ratio $[In^-]/[HIn] = 1$, i.e., if the concentrations of the acidic and basic forms are equal, then we find

$$pH = pK_{In}.$$

For $[In^-]/[HIn] = 10$,

$$pH = pK_{In} + 1;$$

and for $[In^-]/[HIn] = 0.1$,

$$pH = pK_{In} - 1.$$

Thus in the range of pH = $pK_{In} \pm 1$ the indicator will change from predominantly one form to predominantly the other. We usually choose an indicator whose pK_{In} is about that of the pH we should like to detect at the equivalence point of our titration.

Implicit in this argument is the assumption that the indicator gives a faithful representation of the interesting reaction and does not itself change the acid-base characteristics of the solution. Obviously, some amount of the H^+ or OH^- in the solution will have to react with the

---

† The structural change that occurs when one indicator, bromcresol green, is converted from the basic to the acidic form is shown in Experiment 15.

Table 7–2

PROPERTIES OF SOME COMMON ACID-BASE
INDICATORS

Indicator	pK_{In}	Transition range, pH	Color change, acid to base
Methyl orange	3.5	3.1 to 4.5	red to yellow
Bromcresol green	4.7	3.9 to 5.5	yellow to blue
Methyl red	5.0	4.4 to 6.2	red to yellow
Bromthymol blue	7.1	6.0 to 7.6	yellow to blue
Phenol red	7.8	6.4 to 8.0	yellow to red
Cresol purple*		7.4 to 9.0	yellow to purple
Phenolphthalein	9.3	8.0 to 9.6	colorless to red
Thymolphthalein	9.7	9.4 to 10.5	colorless to blue

* This indicator also undergoes a color change from red to yellow in the pH range 1.2 to 2.8. Can you devise a way to obtain pK_{In} for this indicator (or any other)? See Experiment 15.

indicator in its basic or acidic form to change it. If this amount of H^+ or OH^- is insignificant compared with the total added to react with the unknown solution, then our assumption will be valid. For this to be the case, the indicator must be present only in very low concentration. Thus for a weak acid to be useful as an indicator, its acidic or basic form (or both) must be intensely colored so that a very small amount will be easily detectable visually. A list of a few common acid-base indicators and their properties is given in Table 7–2. The pH range of the indicator color change is shown for three indicators in Fig. 7–1: see Problem 2 at the end of the chapter.

7–5 WEAK ACID-STRONG BASE TITRATION

In this section the titration of a weak acid with a strong base will be treated in detail; the opposite case, the titration of a weak base with a strong acid, is completely analogous. We shall begin with V_a ml of a solution whose initial concentration of the weak acid HA is M_a and titrate this with a solution of a strong base of concentration M_b. The amount of base added at any time will be V_b.

Before the titration is begun, $V_b = 0$ and there will be two equilibria to consider:

$$HA(aq) \rightleftharpoons H^+(aq) + A^-(aq),$$

$$K_a = \frac{[H^+][A^-]}{[HA]}; \tag{7–23}$$

and

$$H_2O \rightleftharpoons H^+(aq) + OH^-(aq),$$

$$K_w = [H^+][OH^-] = 10^{-14}. \tag{7–10}$$

Charge balancing yields

$$[H^+] = [OH^-] + [A^-]. \tag{7–24}$$

So far we have three equations, (7–23), (7–10), and (7–24), and four unknowns, $[H^+]$, $[OH^-]$, $[HA]$, and $[A^-]$. We can obtain a fourth equation by realizing that the number of moles of A^- will be conserved whether they are present as HA or as A^- and, since the overall molarity is M_a,

$$M_a = [HA] + [A^-]. \tag{7–25}$$

Now combining (7–10) and (7–24) with some rearrangement, we find that

$$[A^-] = [H^+] - \frac{K_w}{[H^+]},$$

and substituting (7–25) and this expression into (7–23), we obtain

$$K_a = \frac{[H^+]([H^+] - K_w/[H^+])}{M_a - ([H^+] - K_w/[H^+])}$$
$$= \frac{[H^+]^3 - K_w[H^+]}{M_a[H^+] - [H^+]^2 + K_w}. \tag{7–26}$$

Equation (7–26) may be considerably simplified when $[H^+] \geq 10^{-6}\ M$ and/or $M_a \gg [H^+]$. Examine these cases for yourself. These conditions are usually assumed in deriving the expression for $[H^+]$ in a solution of a weak acid, which is usually written

$$[H^+] = (K_a M_a)^{1/2}. \tag{7–26a}$$

Likewise, for the solution of a weak base we have

$$[OH^-] = (K_b M_b)^{1/2},$$
$$[H^+] = \frac{K_w}{(K_b M_b)^{1/2}},$$

where K_b is the base equilibrium constant analogous to (7–23) for a weak acid.

When we begin to add the titrant base, the reaction

$$HA(aq) + OH^-(aq) \rightleftharpoons H_2O + A^-(aq) \tag{7–27}$$

occurs, and in general, for useful titrations, the equilibrium constant for this reaction is large, so the reaction goes essentially to completion. This reaction may be considered to be the sum of two reactions,

$HA \rightleftharpoons H^+ + A^-$,	K_a,
$H^+ + OH^- \rightleftharpoons H_2O$,	$1/K_w$,
$HA + OH^- \rightleftharpoons H_2O + A^-$,	$K = K_a/K_w$,

and the equilibrium constant is as indicated (see Section 4–4). Since $K_w = 10^{-14}$, K_a may be fairly small, i.e., the acid may be quite weak, and the equilibrium constant for this reaction will still be quite large: for example, if $K_a = 10^{-8}$, then $K = 10^6$. If we write the charge-balance equation in this solution we obtain

$$[H^+] + \frac{M_b V_b}{V_a + V_b} = [OH^-] + [A^-]. \qquad (7\text{--}28)$$

The second term on the left-hand side is the concentration of the positive counter-ion (multiplied by the absolute value of the charge on the ion, which is taken to be unity in this case) added with the OH^- titrant solution. We can also write the mole-conservation equation for A^-, taking into account the dilution of the solution, as

$$\frac{M_a V_a}{V_a + V_b} = [HA] + [A^-]. \qquad (7\text{--}29)$$

After some of the titrant base has been added to the acid solution, the concentration of A^- formed in reaction (7–27) will be large relative to the concentration of hydroxyl ion in the acidic solution, i.e., $[A^-] \gg [OH^-]$, and we can write (7–28) as

$$[H^+] + \frac{M_b V_b}{V_a + V_b} \simeq [A^-]. \qquad (7\text{--}28a)$$

Let us now introduce the fraction titrated, f, given in this case by

$$f = \frac{M_b V_b}{M_a V_a}. \qquad (7\text{--}30)$$

Equation (7–28a) may then be written

$$[A^-] \simeq f M_a \left(\frac{V_a}{V_a + V_b} \right) + [H^+]. \qquad (7\text{--}28b)$$

Substitution of (7–28b) into (7–29) and collection of terms yields

$$[HA] \simeq (1 - f) M_a \left(\frac{V_a}{V_a + V_b} \right) - [H^+]. \qquad (7\text{--}31)$$

Now, substituting (7–31) and (7–28b) into (7–23) we get

$$K_a \simeq [H^+] \left\{ \frac{f M_a [V_a/(V_a + V_b)] + [H^+]}{(1 - f) M_a [V_a/(V_a + V_b)] - [H^+]} \right\}. \qquad (7\text{--}32)$$

[The approximation $[A^-] \gg [OH^-]$ is very good, as you can prove for yourself, so Eq. (7–32) may be used to calculate a precise value of K_a from a measured $[H^+]$ (pH meter) at a given M_a, V_a, and V_b.] If f is between but not very near to either 0 or 1 (i.e., not the very beginning or the equivalence point) and $M_a \geq 10^2 K_a$, the first terms in the numerator and denominator of (7–32) will be large compared with $[H^+]$ (show this for yourself), so under these conditions

$$K_a \simeq [H^+] \frac{f}{1 - f}$$

or $\qquad\qquad\qquad\qquad\qquad\qquad\qquad (7\text{--}32a)$

$$[H^+] \simeq \frac{1 - f}{f} K_a.$$

Equation (7–32a) may be used to calculate the portion of the titration curve before the equivalence point for an acid of known K_a.

The calculations for this portion of the titration curve are often pointed out as examples of buffer-solution calculations. Buffer solutions contain a weak acid (or base) and a salt of the acid (or base); the usual expression for $[H^+]$ in an acidic buffer is

$$[H^+] = K_a \frac{C_a}{C_s},$$

where C_s is the molar concentration of the salt. Similarly, for a basic buffer,

$$[OH^-] = K_b \frac{C_b}{C_s}.$$

Using assumptions that are essentially the same as those made in deriving the preceding formulas, we can show that (7–32a) is indeed identical to the acidic buffer equation. We write $(1 - f)/f$ in terms of volumes and initial concentrations as

$$\frac{(M_a V_a - M_b V_b)/M_a V_a}{M_b V_b/M_a V_a} = \frac{M_a V_a - M_b V_b}{M_b V_b}$$
$$= \frac{(M_a V_a - M_b V_b)/(V_a + V_b)}{M_b V_b/(V_a + V_b)}.$$

Assuming that the titration reaction (7–27) goes to completion, we see that $(M_a V_a - M_b V_b)/(V_a + V_b)$ is the concentration of acid left untitrated after V_b ml of base has been added. Since all the base added goes to form BA (which, of course, is dissociated to B^+ and A^-), $M_b V_b/(V_a + V_b)$ is the concentration of this salt formed in the reaction. Hence

$$\frac{1 - f}{f} = \frac{C_a}{C_s},$$

and substitution of this into (7–32a) at once gives the acidic buffer expression.

At the equivalence point we have a solution of BA in water, just as for the strong acid-strong base titration, but in this case the anion is the anion of a weak acid, and the reaction

$$A^-(aq) + H_2O \rightleftharpoons HA(aq) + OH^-(aq) \qquad (7\text{--}33)$$

occurs to some extent. Obviously the solution will be basic (pH > 7) due to the formation of OH^- and thus the equivalence point will not be at pH = 7. Where will it be? Let us begin our calculation with the equilibrium expression for (7–33):

$$\frac{[HA][OH^-]}{[A^-]} = K_s = \frac{K_w}{K_a}, \qquad (7\text{--}34)$$

where K_s represents the equilibrium constant for reaction with the solvent, sometimes called *solvolysis*. Show where the value of K_s comes from. K_s may also, of course, be interpreted as a basic equilibrium constant for the Brønsted base A^-. Naturally, we still have the water-dissociation equilibrium (7–10) and the charge-balance and mole-conservation equations (7–28) and (7–29). If we assume the solution is basic, then $[OH^-] \gg [H^+]$, and we can write (7–28) as

$$\frac{M_b V_b}{V_a + V_b} \simeq [OH^-] + [A^-]. \tag{7–28c}$$

Substitution of (7–28c) into (7–29) yields

$$\frac{M_a V_a}{V_a + V_b} \simeq [HA] + \frac{M_b V_b}{V_a + V_b} - [OH^-],$$

which is reduced to

$$[HA] \simeq [OH^-] \tag{7–35}$$

at the equivalence point. Why? Now we substitute (7–35) into (7–34) and (7–29) to obtain

$$\frac{[OH^-]^2}{M_a V_a/(V_a + V_b) - [OH^-]} \simeq K_s. \tag{7–34a}$$

If K_s is small, reaction (7–33) will not proceed far and most of the A^- will remain unreacted, i.e.,

$$M_a V_a/(V_a + V_b) \gg [OH^-],$$

so we can write (7–34a) as

$$\frac{[OH^-]^2}{M_a V_a/(V_a + V_b)} \simeq K_s, \tag{7–34b}$$

or

$$[OH^-] = \left(K_s \frac{M_a V_a}{V_a + V_b}\right)^{1/2}.$$

This formulation (and its derivation) is that usually seen for the salt of a weak acid and strong base and is often written

$$[OH^-] = \left(\frac{K_w C_s}{K_a}\right)^{1/2}$$

where C_s is the molar concentration of the salt. This may be rewritten as

$$[H^+] = \left(\frac{K_a K_w}{C_s}\right)^{1/2}$$

to give $[H^+]$ or pH directly. (Show how this equation is derived from the other.) Likewise, for the salt of a strong acid and a weak base we find that

$$[H^+] = \left(\frac{K_w C_s}{K_b}\right)^{1/2},$$

where K_b is the base equilibrium constant. When using these equations, be careful to remember that they are only approximations and must be justified in any particular case.

Beyond the equivalence point we are adding base to a solution of the salt BA. If K_s is small, then we are essentially adding the base to pure water and can calculate the $[OH^-]$ or $[H^+]$ simply from the concentration of the base added, i.e.,

$$[OH^-] \simeq \frac{M_b V_b - M_a V_a}{V_a + V_b},$$
$$[H^+] \simeq \frac{K_w(V_a + V_b)}{M_b V_b - M_a V_a}. \tag{7–36}$$

Of course, before using (7–36) we must prove in each particular case that the assumption that reaction (7–33) is negligible is valid.

Illustrative Example: Construct the titration curve for the titration of 50.00 ml of a 0.100 M solution of the weak acid HA, $pK_a = 5.00$, with 0.100 M NaOH solution.

Before the titration begins, we have a solution of HA, for which we may calculate the pH, using (7–26a);

$$pH = \frac{pK_a + pM_a}{2} = \frac{5.00 + 1.00}{2} = 3.00.$$

(Note that $[H^+] = 10^{-3} \gg 10^{-6}$ and $M_a = 10^{-1} \gg [H^+] = 10^{-3}$, so the approximations made in the above calculations are justified.)

After the titration has begun, but before the equivalence point has been reached, we can use (7–32a) to calculate the pH,

$$pH = pK_a + p(1 - f) - pf.$$

The results based on this calculation are given in Table 7–3. Show that the use of this equation is valid at least up to $f = 0.999$.

At the equivalence point we have 100.00 ml of a solution that is 5.00×10^{-2} M NaA. We can calculate the pH as

$$pH = \frac{pK_a + pK_w - pM_s}{2} = \frac{5.00 + 14.00 - 1.30}{2} = 8.85.$$

To show that the approximations that led to this formulation are valid, we need to show that the extent of reaction (7–33)

Table 7–3

THE TITRATION OF 50.00 ml OF 0.100 M HAc ($pK_a = 5.00$) WITH 0.100 M NaOH

f	V_b	pH
0.000	0.00	3.00
0.100	5.00	3.95
0.250	12.50	4.52
0.500	25.00	5.00
0.750	37.50	5.48
0.900	45.00	5.95
0.990	49.50	7.00
0.999	49.95	8.00
1.000	50.00	8.85
1.001	50.05	9.70
1.010	50.50	10.70
1.100	55.00	11.68
1.250	62.50	12.05

is small. Our calculation gives [OH$^-$] = 7.1 $\times$ 10^{-6} M, so we can write, using (7–34),

$$\frac{[HA]}{[A]} = \frac{K_w}{K_a \times [OH^-]} = \frac{10^{-14}}{10^{-5} \times 7.1 \times 10^{-6}} = 1.4 \times 10^{-4}.$$

Since the ratio [HA]/[A$^-$] is so small, it is therefore obvious that very little of the A$^-$ has reacted and the approximations are valid.

Beyond the equivalence point we use (7–36) to calculate the [H$^+$] and, hence, the pH. These results are given in Table 7–3.

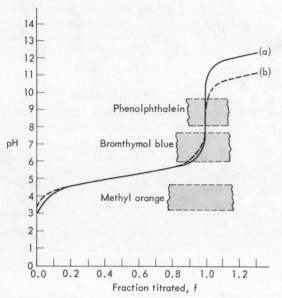

Fig. 7–2. (a) Titration curve for 0.100 M HA (pK_a = 5.00) with 0.100 M NaOH; (b) titration curve for 0.0100 M HA (pK_a = 5.00) with 0.0100 M NaOH (see Problem 3 at the end of the chapter). The pH range for the color change of three indicators is also shown.

Figure 7–2(a) is a plot of the data given in Table 7–3, i.e., the titration curve for the titration of 50.00 ml of 0.100 M HA, pK_a = 5.00, with 0.100 M NaOH. Note that the most significant difference in Fig. 7–2(a) compared with Fig. 7–1(a) is the much shorter "jump" in pH at the equivalence point. It is evident from the indicator ranges shown in the figure that only phenolphthalein is a suitable indicator; methyl orange is completely unsuitable and the color change in bromcresol green occurs over a range of a few milliliters of added titrant before the equivalence point.

Figure 7–2(b) is a titration curve for 50.00 ml of 0.0100 M HA with 0.0100 M NaOH. You might calculate the data required to construct this curve yourself; see Problem 3 at the end of the chapter. We see that before the equivalence point the curves for the 0.100 and the 0.0100 M solutions are almost identical. This is due to the formation of buffer solutions in both cases. The pH of such solutions should depend only on the *ratio*

of the concentrations of the salt and acid (or salt and base) and not on the actual concentrations themselves, as was pointed out earlier. The curves diverge as expected beyond the equivalence point. Just as for the more dilute case shown in Fig. 7–1(b), the most significant change in going to the more dilute solution here is that the range of the pH "jump" at the equivalence point is smaller; hence the choice of suitable indicators is more limited and the precision of the titration is usually lower.

7–6 MATHEMATICAL TREATMENT OF TITRATION DATA

Up to this point we have used titration curves principally to help us choose the correct indicator for acid-base titrations. If we could continuously monitor the pH of a solution of acid with an instrument as a titrant base is added (or vice versa), then we could simply plot the pH readings as a function of volume of titrant added and could determine the equivalence point from the titration curve by inspection. Although it is instructive to plot this sort of curve for an instrumentally-followed titration (acid-base, reduction-oxidation, or other kind) once, after the initial exercise, the pedagogical value decreases rapidly. Since errors in judgment also enter into this graphical procedure, its chemical value is somewhat suspect as well. Therefore we shall explain a method that you should use to determine analytically (i.e., mathematically) the equivalence points that are usually obtained from titrimetric exercises.

The Basis of the Method

The treatment is based on the fact that a titration curve has an inflection point at the equivalence point. In other words, the slope of the titration curve (its first derivative) is a maximum at this point. We shall try to justify (though not prove) this statement for the particular case of a weak acid-strong base titration.

Equation (7–32a) is an equation for the titration curve before the equivalence point is reached. Let us take logarithms of both sides of (7–32a) to obtain

$$pH = pK_a + \log \frac{f}{1-f}, \tag{7–37}$$

$$pH = pK_a + \frac{1}{2.303} \ln \frac{f}{1-f}, \tag{7–38}$$

and, by differentiation,

$$\frac{d(pH)}{df} = \frac{1}{2.303} \frac{1}{f(1-f)} = \frac{0.4343}{f(1-f)}. \tag{7–39}$$

We readily recognize that this derivative approaches a maximum as f goes to 0 and 1, and the latter point is the equivalence point.

Thus the slope of the titration curve does tend to a maximum at the equivalence point. This is a necessary condition for the curve to have an inflection, but it is not a sufficient condition. The sufficient condition is that the second derivative of the curve must be zero at an inflection point. Unfortunately, it is a rather involved argument to show that this condition is indeed fulfilled by titration curves. The root of the problem lies in the complexity of the correct expressions for the titration curve, for in the vicinity of the equivalence point exact equations must be used. (Approximate expressions usually give mathematical discontinuities at the equivalence point which obviously do not exist physically.) We shall therefore have to be content with stating that the sufficiency condition can be proved and thus that the equivalence point is an inflection point of the titration curve.

Explanation and Application of the Method

Although all our preceding discussion has been about acid-base reactions, the method to be presented below is usually applicable to any titration system. We shall underscore this point by applying the method to a precipitation problem followed potentiometrically.

If we have a solution of Ag^+ and insert into it a silver electrode and some reference electrode, in general there will be a potential difference between the two electrodes that will depend on the $[Ag^+]$, calculated from the Nernst equation (see Chapter 10). If we add KI solution to this Ag^+ solution, the potential will change, because $[Ag^+]$ is reduced due to the reaction

$$Ag^+(aq) + I^-(aq) \rightleftharpoons AgI(s).$$

Beyond the equivalence point for the titration of the Ag^+ with KI the solution will be essentially one of I^-, and the common ion effect (see Section 3–1) will determine

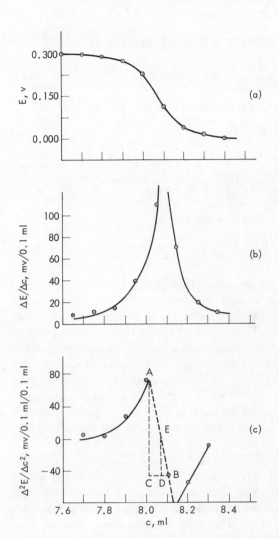

Fig. 7–3. Graphical presentation of the data of Table 7–4.

$[Ag^+]$ and hence the potential difference. In Table 7–4 some data are given for such a titration.

You note that column 3 is a rough measure of the slope of the titration curve and column 4 is roughly the slope of the slope, or the second derivative of the titration curve. In Fig. 7–3 are plotted E, $\Delta E/\Delta c$, and $\Delta^2E/\Delta c^2$ versus c. Such plots are actually unnecessary for the data analysis we shall carry out, but they will help to indicate what we are doing. The method is based on the fact, as noted previously, that the second derivative of a curve goes to zero at an inflection point. The equivalence point is, therefore, the point E in Fig. 7–3(c). All we need to do is calculate the volume of titrant added to get to point E and we shall have calculated the equivalent volume. It is evident from the figure that the distance from point C to point D, $\overline{CD}$, added to the volume reading corresponding to point A (or C) will be the required equivalent volume. The problem is thus reduced to a plane-geometric exercise in obtaining $\overline{CD}$ in terms of known values. The triangles $\triangle ACB$ and

Table 7–4

TITRATION OF 50 ml 0.000161 M AgNO$_3$
WITH 0.00100 M KI*

KI added, ml	E, v	$\Delta E/\Delta c$, mv/0.1 ml	$\Delta^2E/\Delta c^2$, mv/0.1 ml/0.1 ml
0	+0.387		
5.0	0.356		
7.6	0.305		
7.7	0.299	6	6
7.8	0.287	12	2
7.9	0.273	14	27
8.0	0.232	41	79
8.1	0.112	120	−46
8.2	0.038	74	−55
8.3	0.019	19	−7
8.4	+0.007	12	
8.6	−0.003		
9.0	−0.021		

* Data from I. M. Kolthoff and E. B. Sandell, *Textbook of Quantitative Inorganic Analysis*, 3rd ed. Macmillan, New York, 1952, p. 488.

$\triangle EDB$ in Fig. 7–3(c) are congruent, hence

$$\frac{\overline{AC}}{\overline{ED}} = \frac{\overline{CB}}{\overline{DB}}. \tag{7-40}$$

The distance we desire is $\overline{CD}$, which is given by

$$\overline{CD} = \overline{CB} - \overline{DB}. \tag{7-41}$$

Substitution of (7–40) into (7–41) yields

$$\overline{CD} = \overline{CB} - \frac{(\overline{ED}) \cdot (\overline{CB})}{\overline{AC}},$$

which on rearrangement gives

$$\overline{CD} = \frac{\overline{AC} - \overline{ED}}{\overline{AC}}\,\overline{CB}. \tag{7-42}$$

Let us now switch from plane geometry to analytical geometry to evaluate these distances in terms of the graphical coordinates we know, namely those of points A and B. The quantity $\overline{AC} - \overline{ED}$ is readily seen to be just the vertical distance from the zero of the ordinate to the point A and is given by the value of $\Delta^2 E/\Delta c^2$ for this point, $(\Delta^2 E/\Delta c^2)_A$. The quantity $\overline{AC}$ is the vertical distance from point A to the ordinate corresponding to point B; since the value of $\Delta^2 E/\Delta c^2$ for point B is negative, we have to change signs, so we get in effect

$$\overline{AC} = (\Delta^2 E/\Delta c^2)_A - (\Delta^2 E/\Delta c^2)_B.$$

Finally, $\overline{CB}$ is simply the increment in volume of titrant added in going from A to B, V_{AB}; and, of course, $\overline{CD}$ is the volume increment which when added to the total volume at A, V_A, gives the equivalent volume, V_E. Therefore we rewrite (7–42) in terms of the coordinates and add the result to V_A to get V_E:

$$V_E = V_A + \frac{(\Delta^2 E/\Delta c^2)_A}{(\Delta^2 E/\Delta c^2)_A - (\Delta^2 E/\Delta c^2)_B}\,V_{AB}. \tag{7-43}$$

This result is completely general and does not have to be expressed in terms of potentials. If X is a function of the concentration of interest then we can write (7–43) as

$$V_E = V_A + \frac{(\Delta^2 X/\Delta c^2)_A}{(\Delta^2 X/\Delta c^2)_A - (\Delta^2 X/\Delta c^2)_B}\,V_{AB}, \tag{7-44}$$

remembering that point A is the last positive value and point B the first negative value of $\Delta^2 X/\Delta c^2$.

When we apply this result to the numerical values involved in our example, we can calculate the equivalent volume; $V_A = 8.0$ ml, $(\Delta^2 E/\Delta c^2)_A = 79$, $(\Delta^2 E/\Delta c^2)_B = -46$, and $V_{AB} = 0.1$ ml, so

$$V_E = 8.0 + [79/(79 + 46)]\,0.1 = 8.0 + 0.06,$$

$$V_E = 8.06 \text{ ml}.$$

You should note that the actual values of the quantity X are not important in this analysis. We can use the treatment so long as the relative values of X are known. In other words, in the example above, if a different reference electrode had been chosen, the values in column 2 of Table 7–4 would be different, but those in columns 3 and 4 would remain unchanged since the *differences* on which this treatment is based are due only to the change in the interesting concentration.

Also, take cognizance of the fact that we would not have had to add equal increments of the titrant solution, for we can calculate $\Delta X/\Delta c$ and $\Delta^2 X/\Delta c^2$ regardless of the actual magnitudes of the increments. On the other hand, adding equal increments is not difficult and makes the computations much easier. The actual size of the increments that should be added is a function of the particular system under study. If we add increments which are too large, the approximation that we are looking at something that approaches the mathematical limit of differentiation breaks down, and there will be a large error in our calculated V_E. Conversely, if the increments are too small, the reading error from the buret becomes disproportionately large. The proper increment to add in any real case can be judged only by experience, but a rule of thumb would be to add increments as large as the smallest scale divisions on the buret. If this gives poor results, finer increments can be taken or a different buret with smaller scale-division differences should be used. Of course it is not necessary to add these small increments throughout the titration; it is simply a matter of practice to realize from the instrumental readings whether or not you are fast approaching the equivalence point and whether you need to begin adding small increments of titrant. In the titrations you carry out you will probably be well advised to begin adding small increments when you approach within about 3% of the equivalence point.

EXPERIMENT 10.   Equilibria in the System Water-Carbon Tetrachloride-Propionic Acid

Background

The object of this experiment is to study three equilibria and their interactions. Basically, we desire to determine the equilibrium constants for the particular systems under study. This is complicated in the system we shall treat here because the equilibria are not independent. On the other hand, the analysis of the problem and the treatment of the data should give you an appreciation of the way in which a fairly complex situation may be studied.

The system chosen for this study is the partitioning of propionic acid, CH_3CH_2COOH, between H_2O and

CCl_4. (All carboxylic acids contain the functional group

the carboxyl group, attached to an organic radical, R—, and so they may be written RCOOH. This general notation will be used throughout this experiment.) Water and carbon tetrachloride are almost completely immiscible and when mixed they separate into two layers; the density of H_2O at 20°C is 0.998 gm/ml, and that of CCl_4 is 1.595 gm/ml. Propionic acid is soluble to a fairly large extent in both H_2O and CCl_4. If a mixture of RCOOH, H_2O, and CCl_4 is shaken together and then allowed to stand, two layers will separate: an RCOOH + H_2O layer and an RCOOH + CCl_4 layer. If enough time is allowed, this system will be at equilibrium; when this occurs, the free energy of the RCOOH will be the same in both phases, and we can write

$$K_1 = e^{-\Delta G_1^0/RT} = \frac{a_{RCOOH(CCl_4)}}{a_{RCOOH(H_2O)}},$$

$$\Delta G_1^0 = G_{RCOOH(CCl_4)}^0 - G_{RCOOH(H_2O)}^0.$$

This distribution equilibrium is not the only one of concern, however, for the acid in the H_2O layer may undergo dissociation,

$$RCOOH(aq) \rightleftharpoons RCOO^-(aq) + H^+(aq),$$

with an equilibrium constant K_a. If this reaction occurs to an appreciable extent, the activity of RCOOH will be reduced below what we would predict from its molar concentration. If we imagine that the distribution equilibrium is set up and that we allow the acid dissociation to occur, we see that the RCOOH activity will be reduced and hence some RCOOH will have to pass from the CCl_4 phase to the H_2O phase to maintain the distribution equilibrium. A knowledge of K_a will allow us to calculate the concentration of RCOOH(aq), if we know the number of moles per liter of RCOOH present. In the absence of other information we shall be *forced to use the approximation that activity equals concentration* and, thus, that the activity of RCOOH(aq) equals our calculated concentration.*

In the CCl_4 phase another equilibrium is set up,†

$$n\,RCOOH_{(CCl_4)} \rightleftharpoons (RCOOH)_{n(CCl_4)},$$

* Since RCOOH is not changed it is a very good approximation to set the activity equal to the molarity. (see Section 9–1)
† How could you prove that this statement is true? Perhaps this would be a worthwhile experimental problem, since all the succeeding arguments assume this equilibrium occurs and the calculations would be completely invalid if this assertion were false.

with an equilibrium constant we shall call K_2. When K_a is known, it is possible to obtain the values of n, K_2, and K_1 by determining how the molar concentrations of RCOOH in the H_2O and CCl_4 phases vary as the total molar concentration of RCOOH is varied. (Again we are making the approximation that activity equals concentration.)

The experimentally observable quantities are K_a, c_1 = total molar concentration of RCOOH in the H_2O phase, and c_2 = total molar concentration of RCOOH in the CCl_4 phase:

$$c_1 = [RCOOH]_{H_2O} + [RCOO^-]_{H_2O}, \tag{7-45}$$

$$c_2 = [RCOOH]_{CCl_4} + n[(RCOOH)_n]_{CCl_4}. \tag{7-46}$$

Let us begin our analysis by assuming that K_a is small enough to neglect, so that

$$c_1 \simeq [RCOOH]_{H_2O}. \tag{7-47}$$

(If it turns out in practice that K_a is not negligible, then you will have to calculate $[RCOOH]_{H_2O}$ and use it in place of c_1 in the following expressions.) Let us write the equilibrium constants K_1 and K_2 in terms of concentrations:

$$K_1 = \frac{[RCOOH]_{CCl_4}}{[RCOOH]_{H_2O}}, \tag{7-48}$$

$$K_2 = \frac{[(RCOOH)_n]_{CCl_4}}{[RCOOH]_{CCl_4}^n}. \tag{7-49}$$

Now, we substitute (7–47) into (7–48) and rearrange to get

$$[RCOOH]_{CCl_4} \simeq K_1 c_1 \tag{7-50}$$

and similarly for (7–46) and (7–49),

$$K_2 = \frac{c_2 - [RCOOH]_{CCl_4}}{n[RCOOH]_{CCl_4}^n}. \tag{7-51}$$

We could proceed from (7–50) and (7–51) in a straightforward manner, but let us first make another approximation which only our data can justify or prove false, and then return to the more rigorous formulation later. We shall assume at this point that the equilibrium constant K_2 is large and that, therefore,

$$c_2 \simeq n[(RCOOH)_n]_{CCl_4} \gg [RCOOH]_{CCl_4}$$

and thus

$$K_2 \simeq \frac{c_2}{n[RCOOH]_{CCl_4}^n}. \tag{7-52}$$

Now substitute (7–50) into (7–52):

$$K_2 \simeq \frac{c_2}{n(K_1 c_1)^n}. \tag{7-53}$$

Rearrange (7–53) and take logarithms of both sides:

$$\log(nK_2 K_1^n) + n\log(c_1) \simeq \log(c_2). \tag{7-54}$$

If our approximation is reasonably valid, Eq. (7–54) indicates that a plot of $\log(c_2)$ vs. $\log(c_1)$ will be a straight line with a slope n and an intercept of $\log(nK_2K_1^n)$, when $\log(c_1) = 0$, where $c_1 = 1$. Thus such a procedure should readily indicate the value of n (which is presumably an integer) even if the plot is not perfectly linear.

Armed now with our knowledge of the probable value of n, let us return to the "exact" equations (7–50) and (7–51) and combine them:

$$K_2 \simeq \frac{c_2 - K_1 c_1}{n(K_1 c_1)^n}. \qquad (7\text{–}55)$$

This equation may be rearranged to the form

$$c_2 \simeq ac_1 + bc_1^n, \qquad (7\text{–}56)$$

where

$$a = K_1, \qquad b = nK_2 K_1^n.$$

Since we have some idea of what n is, (7–56) is an equation in two unknowns, a and b, once we have substituted a pair of experimental values of c_1 and c_2. We can write as many equations like (7–56) as we have pairs of experimental values and any two will suffice to yield a solution for the constants a and b; hence we can obtain the values of the constants K_1 and K_2 and from them a measure of the difference in free energies of the species that enter into the equilibria.*

Experimental Procedure

A solution of propionic acid approximately 0.5 M will be available. Obtain about 150 to 200 ml of this solution in a clean stoppered bottle. Use this sample for all further work. For your determination of pK_a and the accurate value of the concentration of your sample, use aliquots of the RCOOH sample that will require about 25 ml of 0.1 M NaOH to titrate to equivalence. You will need enough standardized 0.1 M NaOH (Experiment 4) to perform about 15 such titrations.

The first step in this experiment is to determine pK_a for propionic acid. You will do this by titrating a sample of the acid with standardized 0.1 M NaOH, following the titration with a pH meter (see Appendix D) and then, using Eq. (7–32), you will calculate pK_a.

The procedure for performing pH titrations followed with a pH meter is as follows (directions that are pertinent only to the determination of a pK_a, or pK_b, are given in parentheses):

1) Standardize the pH meter as explained by the instructor and thoroughly rinse with distilled water and then dry the electrodes: glass and calomel.

2) Immerse the electrodes and a thermometer in the solution to be titrated, contained in a 150- to 250-ml beaker. Some means of stirring the solution must be provided (a magnetic stirrer and stirring bar are ideal) and there should be enough solution in the beaker, 50 to 100 ml, so that the electrode tips are covered but in no danger of being struck by the stirring bar. (The solution volume must be known for the pK determination. Why? To add a little further interest to the experiment, add 4 or 5 drops of phenolphthalein indicator to the acid solution and later record the pH at which the indicator color change occurs.)

3) After waiting a minute or two for thermal equilibrium to be attained, measure and record the solution temperature and adjust the pH meter to compensate for this temperature. Read and record the pH of the solution.

4) Adjust a buret filled with titrant so that the tip of the buret is close to the surface of the solution in the beaker. Read and record the buret level.

5) Turn on the stirrer and add titrant until either the pH has changed by 0.2 pH units or the amount of titrant added is 4 to 5 ml.

6) Continue stirring for thirty seconds. Stop the stirrer. Read and record the pH and buret level.

7) Resume stirring and repeat the addition of titrant and the reading and recording. (Try to work as quickly as possible without being sloppy, since CO_2 dissolving in the solution can cause appreciable error in the result. You might devise some protective cover for the titration vessel, if you are so inclined.)

8) [When you have reached a point within about 3 to 5% of the equivalence point (how can you tell?), begin adding small equal-size increments suitable to the use of the mathematical titration curve presented in Section 7–6.]

9) Continue the titration until about 1.1 equivalents of titrant have been added.

10) Rinse the electrodes with distilled water and leave them immersed in distilled water to protect them. Do not allow a glass or calomel electrode to stand out of water for any appreciable length of time.

After computing the pK_a of propionic acid, find the indicator in Table 7–2 that will provide the most accurate equivalence point determination for the titration of the acid with NaOH. Use this indicator in two further titrations of the acid (not using the pH meter) so as to obtain an accurate value of the concentration of your stock solution of acid.

To determine the distribution of RCOOH between H_2O and CCl_4, make up samples as follows: pipet 25 ml

---

* Is there a more economical procedure you can use for calculating a and b?

of CCl_4 into a *clean and dry* stoppered container. Follow this with an aliquot of your standardized RCOOH solution of such a volume that when enough H_2O is added to make the total volume of the aqueous solution 25 ml, you will have the concentration of RCOOH with which you want to begin. (To save a good deal of pipetting in this procedure you might work with your neighbor. Fill one of your burets with a standardized RCOOH solution and the other with H_2O. Deliver the proper amount of RCOOH solution and then enough H_2O to make a total of 25 ml of aqueous phase.) Stopper the containers and shake intermittently for an hour or so to help attain equilibrium. Keep the containers out of drafts and direct sunlight so they are neither cooled nor heated, since all equilibria are temperature dependent. When you feel that equilibrium has been attained, pipet aliquots of the aqueous phase into flasks for analysis of the RCOOH remaining therein by titration with standard 0.1 M NaOH. Use the indicator best suited to this titration as indicated by the pK_a of the RCOOH. Run duplicate analyses on each sample. Remove a large enough aliquot of the aqueous phase that 12 to 25 ml of 0.1 M NaOH will be used for the titration. (You can estimate the size of the aliquot needed by assuming that all of the original RCOOH still remains in the H_2O, since this is the maximum concentration possible. To make the removal of aliquots easier you might pour your solution (or the aqueous phase, if this is possible) into a large test tube that is clean and dry and pipet from there. This is easier since the depths of the layers are greater and thus control of the depth of insertion of the pipet is less critical. Be careful not to get any of the CCl_4 solution as a contaminant in the aqueous aliquot. If a drop of the CCl_4 solution were taken with the H_2O solution, how much error would result for the most concentrated solution? Good results can be obtained with RCOOH with initial concentrations in the aqueous

phase of 0.5 M, 0.4 M, 0.3 M, 0.2 M, and 0.1 M. (For the last concentration use 50-ml volumes of CCl_4 and aqueous solution so that you can obtain two aliquots large enough to perform accurate analyses.)

Calculations

Plot the titration curve for propionic acid. Use the mathematical analysis outlined in Section 7–6 to ascertain the equivalence point and hence the concentration of propionic acid in your stock solution. Compare this value with the mean from your noninstrumental titrations. You can compute a number of values of pK_a from your data. Compute the mean and the mean deviation. At what point in the titration should you obtain the most precise value of pK_a? What is the standard free energy change for the dissociation of propionic acid?

Assuming that any RCOOH absent from the aqueous layer is in the CCl_4 layer, you have enough information (including the temperature of the room) to calculate K_1, K_2, n, and thermodynamic functions derived therefrom. Do so. The derivation in the introduction neglects the dissociation of RCOOH in H_2O. Correct your results for this neglect and compare your corrected and uncorrected values.

Discuss the possible structures for the molecule $(RCOOH)_n$ consistent with your value of n. What is the nature of the forces holding this molecule together?

Further Experimental Problems

As an extension of the basic experiment above, one could study a different acid, say chloropropionic, or the effect of adding "inert" ions to the aqueous phase. As pointed out in Chapter 9, this latter change can profoundly affect equilibria. A further possibility is to study the effect of temperature on these equilibria.

EXPERIMENT 11.   *The Complex Iodide Ion*

Introduction

Iodine is not very soluble in water: a saturated solution has a concentration only slightly greater than 0.001 moles/liter. Adding some iodide ion to the water, however, increases the solubility of the iodine quite markedly. The iodine thus dissolved shows all of the characteristic reactions of iodine itself, including the rapid reaction with the thiosulfate ion. (Why is this latter observation important in assessing the utility of iodine titrations with thiosulfate?) A reasonable hypothesis to explain these observations is that the iodine and

the iodide react to form a complex ion and that the reaction is readily reversible.

It is the purpose of this experiment to investigate this reaction in more detail to determine whether or not the hypothesis of the complex ion can quantitatively explain the observations. If the hypothesis is correct, the experiment will also provide enough information to determine the formula of the complex ion and its dissociation constant. In fact, this is how the experiment is developed: we assume the hypothesis is correct, develop a procedure to obtain the postulated equilibrium constant for the complex dissociation constant, and, if internally consistent results are obtained for the dissociation constant, we rejoice and say we have "proved" our hypothesis.

The method we use is to shake a solution of iodine in carbon tetrachloride, CCl_4, with an aqueous iodide solution of known concentration until equilibrium is established. Then the concentration of the iodine in the carbon tetrachloride and the total amount of iodine dissolved in the water are determined by titrating with standard thiosulfate solution. (See Experiment 17 for a further discussion of this titration.)

The analysis of these data depends on some easily verifiable chemical facts. (Can you suggest any ways to "easily verify" these "facts"?) One is that water and carbon tetrachloride are immiscible; almost none of one will dissolve in the other. (In the present experiment the minute amount of intermixing which does occur may be neglected.) Another fact is that inorganic ions do not dissolve in CCl_4. Therefore neither the iodide ion nor whatever complex ion might be formed will dissolve in the CCl_4. Finally, we know that the equilibrium ratio of the concentration of *iodine molecules*, I_2, in the carbon tetrachloride to the concentration of *iodine molecules* in the aqueous phase has a constant value. This is just another way of stating the fact that the equilibrium constant for the process

$$I_2(aq) \rightleftharpoons I_2(CCl_4),$$

which is

$$K = \frac{[I_2]_{CCl_4}}{[I_2]_{H_2O}},$$

is indeed a constant at a given temperature. (When equilibrium has been established, the free energy of the I_2 molecules in each phase is the same, so there is no net transfer of I_2 from one phase to the other.) This equilibrium constant is called the distribution constant, and its determination is a necessary part of the experiment.

The analysis of the data is then carried out. Since the iodine is present in the carbon tetrachloride phase only as molecules (how do we know this?), the concentration of these molecules is easily determined by a thiosulfate titration. When the aqueous phase contains no iodide, the iodine is again present only as molecules (how do we know?), and again their concentration can be determined by titration, and the value of the distribution constant can be calculated. When iodide ion is present in the aqueous phase, then the concentration of iodine molecules in this phase can be determined from the known distribution constant and the concentration of iodine molecules in the carbon tetrachloride phase (determined by titration) that is in equilibrium with this particular aqueous phase. Titration of the aqueous phase gives the concentration of iodine molecules plus the concentration of iodine in the complex. If the formula

of the complex is known, then its concentration can be found by a subtraction. The concentration of the iodide ion can be found by subtracting the amount of iodide which is bound up in the complex from the amount initially present.

There is, of course, a spanner in the works; this method of analysis depends on knowing the formula of the complex ion, which, naturally, we do not know. Therefore it is necessary to assume a formula for the complex and see if this formula will explain the data. If not, we try another formula. If no satisfactory formula can be found, then it must be assumed that the experimental results cannot be explained on the basis of our postulated complex ion. In your calculations you might begin by trying the formulas I_3^- and I_5^-. (You should try both and perhaps even others, even if the first formula you try explains your data quite well.) These formulas correspond to the equilibrium reactions in aqueous solution

$$I_2 + I^- \rightleftharpoons I_3^-,$$
$$2I_2 + I^- \rightleftharpoons I_5^-,$$

with equilibrium constants we might denote as K_3 and K_5, respectively. Write the equilibrium-constant expressions for these two reactions.*

An advantage of this particular system for quantitative study is that we can neglect, to a very good degree of approximation, nonideality of the ionic solutions. Why is this? When we write the equilibrium-constant expressions for either of the complexing reactions, we should use activities rather than concentrations to be absolutely correct; for example, we should write

$$K_3 = \frac{a_{I_3^-}}{a_{I_2}a_{I^-}}.$$

The activity of uncharged species like I_2, however, is very well approximated by its molarity. The activity of the ions can be written as the product of the molarity of the ion and its activity coefficient in that particular solution, γ (see Section 9-1 and Experiment 15 for a discussion of ionic solution theory). Thus K_3 becomes

$$K_3 = \frac{\gamma_{I_3^-}[I_3^-]}{[I_2]\gamma_{I^-}[I^-]}.$$

However, the theory goes on to predict that, at least in dilute solution, $\gamma_{I_3^-} = \gamma_{I^-}$. Thus we find that

$$K_3 = \frac{[I_3^-]}{[I_2][I^-]},$$

---

* We have not considered reactions such as $I_2 + 2I^- \rightleftharpoons I_4^{--}$ because it seems improbable that two negative ions would form a particularly stable complex. However, this does not prove that they do not; you might like to try this sort of formula for the complex ion as well.

which is just what we would have written down as an approximation neglecting activity effects. We therefore neglect nonideal effects, not because they are not present, but because they cancel out. Show that these same arguments hold for K_5.

Procedure

The experimental mixtures which it is recommended that you study are:

1) 300 ml of distilled water and 25 ml of CCl_4 containing I_2 (This solution should be saturated with I_2.),

2) 125 ml of 0.1 M KI and 40 ml CCl_4 containing I_2,

3) 25 ml of 0.1 M KI, 100 ml of distilled water, and 40 ml of CCl_4 containing I_2,

4) 100 ml of 0.1 M KI, 20 ml of CCl_4 containing I_2, and 50 ml of pure CCl_4, and

5) 40 ml of 0.1 M KI and 40 ml of CCl_4 containing I_2. The only one of these solutions which it is necessary to make up carefully is solution 3, in which the ratio of the amounts of KI solution and water must be known within 1%. In this case it is necessary to use pipets, but in all other cases the amounts of solution which are taken need not be accurately known (why?), so a graduated cylinder is quite sufficient for the measurements.

The solutions should be made up in labeled ground-glass stoppered bottles or flasks and shaken well. They should then be immersed up to the neck in a constant-temperature water bath at about 25°C. Either a bath improvised out of an expanded foam acid case or a thermostated and regulated bath is adequate. During the first twenty minutes or so that the equilibration vessels are in the water bath, they should be taken out and shaken at *frequent intervals*. Then the vessels should remain undisturbed for twenty minutes or so to allow the aqueous and CCl_4 phases to become well separated. If you have a mixture prepared but do not have time to run an analysis on it, it will keep in your desk so long as it is stoppered. The shaking and settling just described must be redone before the analysis is carried out.

Analyze the solutions by pipetting out small samples of known volume of each phase and then titrate these samples with a standardized 0.02-M thiosulfate solution. To avoid temperature changes, which would disrupt the equilibrium, the samples should be removed for titration while the vessels are still in the water bath or immediately after they have been removed. Since both iodine and carbon tetrachloride are somewhat poisonous, it is more imperative than ever that a pipet bulb be used to fill the pipets. In pipetting the CCl_4 samples, avoid wetting the inside of the pipet with the aqueous phase by closing the upper end with the finger of one hand and grasping the bulb of the pipet with the other hand just before the pipet is plunged into the mixture. As the pipet tip is passed through the aqueous phase, the heat from your hand serves to expand the enclosed air and prevent entry of the aqueous solution. For reasonable volumes of thiosulfate to be obtained for the titrations, the following sample sizes are recommended (note that duplicate or triplicate analyses may be run, if necessary).

Mixture	Aqueous sample, ml	CCl_4 sample, ml
1	100*	5
2	10	10
3	25	10
4	25	25
5	10	10

The procedure to be followed in making up and standardizing a solution of sodium thiosulfate, $Na_2S_2O_3$, is given in Experiment 17. The procedure for each of the titrations for this experiment is as follows:

For the CCl_4-phase samples, pipet the sample into a 250-ml flask, add 15 ml of distilled water and 5 ml of freshly made KI solution, 15% by weight, and titrate the mixture with the standard $S_2O_3^=$ solution. It is very easy to overshoot the endpoint in this titration. Before the iodine in the CCl_4 phase can react with the thiosulfate, which remains in the aqueous phase (why?), the iodine must diffuse into the aqueous layer. To help speed up this process the high concentration of KI is added and the flask should be agitated vigorously throughout the titration. If the thiosulfate is added too rapidly, it is possible to have an excess of it in the aqueous phase while there is still iodine in the CCl_4. Therefore it is important that the thiosulfate be added slowly near the endpoint. If desired, 5 ml of starch indicator solution can be added near the endpoint to make the color change in the aqueous phase more visible. The color of the CCl_4 is also a good endpoint indicator, but remember that it "reacts" slowly to changes in the aqueous phase.

For the aqueous-phase samples, pipet the sample into a 250-ml flask, add 5 ml of freshly made 15% KI, and carry out the titration as usual. Again, 5 ml of starch indicator may be added near the end to make the endpoint easier to detect. The large amount of KI is added here to increase the solubility of the I_2 and thus decrease the possibility that it will be lost into the vapor phase during the titration (I_2 is rather volatile).

Calculations

Calculate the distribution constant at the temperature of your experiments. For each solution, calculate the concentrations of the ions and molecules that would be present on the assumption that a complex of the formula

---

* Use a 10-ml buret when titrating the aqueous phase of mixture 1.

I_3^- is formed; do the same for I_5^- and for any other complex formula you wish to test. It is much easier to keep track of these calculations if a table is made up to record the numbers obtained in the various stages of the calculations, as well as the values of the equilibrium "constants."

Does postulating the existence of either I_3^- or I_5^- complex provide an explanation of your data? Is the lack of agreement between any explanation you propose and your experimental results within the experimental error, or is the lack of agreement enough that your experiments prove the explanation is not exactly correct? To answer this last question you will have to do a good error analysis.

Further Experimental Problems

Perhaps you could gain even more information about this system if you do temperature studies to determine, if possible, the thermodynamics of the reactions we have postulated.

An interesting question you might try to answer experimentally is: If a complex such as I_5^- does exist in these solutions, are all the iodine atoms equivalent in the complex? If you were to add some iodide ion to a solution of iodine, would some of the iodine atoms originally present as ions eventually end up as part of a dissolved molecule or would the two species retain their identities?

REFERENCES

BOLIE, V. W., "An Exact Titration Equation," *J. Chem. Ed.* **35**, 449 (1958) works out the exact equation for a precipitation titration.

BUTLER, J. N., *Solubility and pH Calculations*, Addison-Wesley, Reading, Mass., 1964.

BUTLER, J. N., *Ionic Equilibrium*, Addison-Wesley, Reading, Mass., 1964.

DAVIES, M., and H. E. HALLAM, "The Determination of Molecular Association Equilibria from Distribution and Related Measurements," *J. Chem. Ed.* **33**, 322 (1956) discusses methods of data evaluation.

FORSBERG, H. G., B. WIDELL, and L.-G. ERWALL, "Distribution Coefficients and Ionization Constant of HAuCl₄," *J. Chem. Ed.* **37**, 44 (1960) uses a radiotracer technique which gives the distribution as well as dissociation constant for chlorauric acid, $HAuCl_4$. There are many species present in the system which adds to the fun.

LUDER, W. F., and S. ZUFFANTI, *The Electronic Theory of Acids and Bases*, 2nd ed. Dover, New York, 1961.

PROBLEMS

1. Calculate the titration curve for the titration of $0.00100\ M$ NaOH with $0.00100\ M$ HCl. (See Fig. 7–1.)

2. Which indicator from the list in Table 7–2 would you choose to detect the equivalence point in the titration described in Problem 1?

3. Calculate the titration curve for the titration of $0.00100\ M$ HA ($pK_a = 5.00$) with $0.00100\ M$ NaOH. (See Fig. 7–2.)

4. Which indicator from the list in Table 7–2 would you choose to detect the equivalence point in the titration described in Problem 3?

8 INDIRECT MEASUREMENT OF THERMODYNAMIC QUANTITIES

In Chapter 6 we discussed how to measure directly a thermodynamic quantity, the amount of heat released in a chemical (or physical) change. Sometimes it is impossible or impractical to carry out direct calorimetric measurements on chemical systems of great interest. Often we can use indirect methods, based on the inter-relationships of the thermodynamic variables, to obtain, for example, heats of reaction. Indeed, indirect methods are chosen in preference to direct methods in some cases because the experiments are easier to carry out. Let us then first discuss how thermodynamic quantities can be obtained indirectly and then go on to an important rule that will help us to interpret our measurements.

8-1 FREE ENERGY, EQUILIBRIUM, AND TEMPERATURE

The fundamental equation relating the standard free energy change and the equilibrium constant for a process at a given temperature is

$$\Delta G^0 = -RT \ln K. \tag{8-1}$$

The standard free energy change is also related to the standard enthalpy change, ΔH^0, and the standard entropy change, ΔS^0, for the process; at constant temperature and pressure the relationship is

$$\Delta G^0 = \Delta H^0 - T \Delta S^0. \tag{8-2}$$

(You will find both of the preceding equations derived in any one of the thermodynamics books listed in the references.) Obviously, then, the equilibrium constant is related to the enthalpy and entropy changes:

$$-\ln K = \frac{\Delta H^0}{RT} - \frac{\Delta S^0}{R}. \tag{8-3}$$

Although ΔH^0 and ΔS^0 are temperature dependent, their dependence on temperature is weak. The equations

for the temperature dependence of ΔH^0 and ΔS^0 are

$$\frac{d \Delta H^0}{dT} = \Delta C_p$$

and

$$\frac{d \Delta S^0}{dT} = \frac{\Delta C_p}{T}.$$

It is easy to see that if ΔC_p, the difference in constant-pressure heat capacity between the products and the reactants in the process of interest, is small, the variation of ΔH^0 and ΔS^0 with temperature will be very small also. Thus we can make the approximation that, over a short temperature range, ΔH^0 and ΔS^0 are independent of temperature and make very little error. Using this assumption, let us investigate the temperature dependence of K, the equilibrium constant. We shall call the equilibrium constants at the temperatures T_1 and T_2, respectively, K_1 and K_2,

$$-\ln K_1 = \frac{\Delta H^0}{RT_1} - \frac{\Delta S^0}{R}$$

$$-\left[-\ln K_2 = \frac{\Delta H^0}{RT_2} - \frac{\Delta S^0}{R} \right]$$

$$\overline{-\ln K_1 + \ln K_2 = \frac{\Delta H^0}{R}\left(\frac{1}{T_1} - \frac{1}{T_2}\right)}$$

$$\ln \frac{K_2}{K_1} = -\frac{\Delta H^0}{R}\left(\frac{1}{T_2} - \frac{1}{T_1}\right). \tag{8-4}$$

Equation (8-4) may be used to predict an equilibrium constant at a temperature T_2 if ΔH^0 and K_1, are known; we can also use it to determine ΔH^0 for a process from measurements of the equilibrium constants as a function of temperature. If more than two such measurements are made, it is convenient to use a graphical method to determine ΔH^0. Equation (8-3) has the form of a straight-line plot on a graph of $\ln K$ versus $1/T$. The slope of the line is $-\Delta H^0/R$. (If the plot shows curvature, then we know that our approximation that ΔH^0 is constant has failed, but ΔH^0 at any temperature can still be obtained from the slope of the tangent to the curve at the point corresponding to the temperature in question.)

Note that this determination automatically yields values for ΔG^0 and ΔS^0 for the process of interest: ΔG^0 at any of the temperatures examined may be calculated from K and Eq. (8-1). You can then obtain ΔS^0 by substituting ΔG^0, ΔH^0, and the value of T into Eq. (8-2) and solving it. A reverse procedure is also possible: The intercept of the $\ln K$ versus $1/T$ plot at $1/T = 0$ is $\Delta S^0/R$, so ΔH^0 and ΔS^0 from the plot may be used to obtain ΔG^0 at any temperature from Eq. (8-2). Keep in mind when using these manipulations that ΔH^0 and ΔS^0 are approximately independent of temperature but ΔG^0 and K are definitely not.

Any equilibrium process which has a measurable equilibrium constant that can be studied over a range of temperature can be analyzed by the foregoing procedure. In the three experiments presented in this chapter, the equilibria you might analyze are a liquid-gas phase equilibrium, a solubility equilibrium, and a gas-liquid-solid reaction equilibrium.

8-2 THE PHASE RULE

To examine any chemical system quantitatively we must know how many variables of the system must be specified to describe the equilibrium system completely. To determine this, we must figure out how many possible variables the system has and then subtract from this number the number of constraints imposed on the system by thermodynamics. Let us examine a system (containing a specified amount of material) that is made up of C components, i.e., chemically independent species, and P phases, i.e., portions of the system sharply separated from the others by discontinuous boundaries, such as a gas and a liquid or two different solids.

How many variables does this system have? In general, each component could appear in each phase of the system so the maximum number of variables would appear to be the product PC. All these variables, however, are not independent of one another. Since matter is conserved (at least to a very high degree of approximation in chemical systems), once we have specified the amounts of all but one of the components, $C - 1$, we will not be able to vary the final one without altering the overall composition of the system. Thus, there are only $P(C - 1)$ possible variables arising from the number of phases and components present. There are two other variables we must take into account, the temperature and

the pressure. These must be accounted for because we use the free energy, which is temperature and pressure dependent, as a criterion for equilibrium.* Thus, finally, we find that the total number of variables of the system is

$$P(C - 1) + 2.$$

How many constraints are imposed on this system at equilibrium? At equilibrium there is no net transfer of components across phase boundaries. This implies that across each phase boundary the free energy difference between a particular component in one phase and the same component in the other phase is zero. There are P phase boundaries, but only $P - 1$ of these are independent, since after establishment of the correct conditions across $P - 1$ independent boundaries the conditions in all the phases will be fixed. Since there are C components, each of which may be distributed in this way, the total number of constraints on the system is

$$C(P - 1).$$

The total number of independently variable parameters, degrees of freedom, F, will be the difference between the total number of variables and the number of constraints:

$$F = P(C - 1) + 2 - C(P - 1),$$
$$F = PC - P + 2 - CP + C,$$
$$F = C - P + 2. \tag{8-5}$$

Equation (8-5) is called the phase rule.

Let us see how the phase rule works in a very familiar case, the equilibrium between ice and water in an open vessel. Here we have two components, H_2O and air,† and three phases: solid (ice with dissolved air), liquid (water with dissolved air), and gas (water vapor and air). From the phase rule, then, we expect that we will have $F = 2 - 3 + 2 = 1$ degree of freedom. Thus, when one of the variables we can control is fixed, all the others will also be fixed. In the present case there is such a variable fixed, the pressure. Since the vessel is open, the pressure is the barometric pressure prevailing at the location of the system. Hence, there are no degrees of freedom left to the system. But we could have guessed this already, for we know that an ice-water mixture at atmospheric pressure is always at 0°C when equilibrium has been established. Any effort to change the temperature only results in melting some of the ice or freezing some of the water with no change in temperature so long as both ice and water are present. If one or the other phase disappears (say, all the ice melts) then we have

---

* Note that we are neglecting effects due to gravitational fields, magnetic fields, etc.

† For the purpose of this problem "air" is a single chemical species.

$F = 2 - 2 + 2 = 2$ degrees of freedom, and we can vary the temperature at will (within the limits 0°C to 100°C) while the pressure is fixed at one atmosphere. The phase diagrams that you find in your textbooks and references are graphical illustrations of the phase rule that you should ponder.*

EXPERIMENT 12.   *The Isoteniscopic Determination of Vapor Pressure and Enthalpy of Vaporization*

Introduction

Imagine a pure liquid situated in an initially evacuated chamber. Molecules will leave the liquid and pass into the gas phase until the pressure has reached a particular equilibrium value determined by the identity of the liquid and the temperature of the system. So long as liquid is present, this equilibrium vapor pressure is independent of the relative volumes of the liquid and vapor phases.† We write the equilibrium constant for the process in terms of activities, as

$$K = \frac{a_{\text{vapor}}}{a_{\text{liquid}}}.$$

The activity of a pure liquid is by definition unity, and if the vapor behaves as an ideal gas, the activity of the vapor is its pressure P, the equilibrium vapor pressure of the liquid at this temperature. Thus the equilibrium-constant expression becomes

$$K = P. \qquad (8\text{-}6)$$

Now if we measure P as a function of temperature, we have measured K as a function of temperature, and we can substitute P, the equilibrium vapor pressure, into Eq. (8–3) to obtain

$$\ln P = \frac{\Delta H^0_{\text{vap}}}{RT} + \frac{\Delta S^0_{\text{vap}}}{R}, \qquad (8\text{-}7)$$

where the subscripts on ΔH^0 and ΔS^0 remind us that the process we are considering is vaporization of a liquid. We predict that the plot of $\log P$ versus $1/T$ for a pure liquid should be a straight line whose slope is $-\Delta H^0_{\text{vap}}/2.303\ R$ and intercept at $1/T = 0$ is $\Delta S^0_{\text{vap}}/2.303R$. (Where does the 2.303 factor come from?)

The Isoteniscope

Now we must consider how we can test this prediction experimentally. An ideal method for measuring vapor pressures is to use an *isoteniscope* (a "constant tension" device, where "tension" in this case is the pressure in the system). One form of the operative part of an iso-

teniscope is shown in Fig. 8–1 (the complete apparatus for the vapor-pressure determinations is sketched in Fig. 8–2). Suppose that we begin with tube B completely filled with the same pure liquid used to charge the test tube and that we place the whole setup in a water bath at some constant temperature as indicated in the figure. By evacuating the test tube through tube A we can reduce the pressure until the liquid begins to boil. Bubbles of vapor will then form throughout the liquid and, most important for our purposes, at the mouth of tube B, which will now be full of vapor. If this boiling at reduced pressure is continued for a few minutes, the vapor thus generated will sweep any traces of air from tube B. (If the tube is not originally filled with liquid but with air, several minutes of boiling will still suffice to purge it completely of air.) At the end of this boil-out operation, we are thus assured that tube B contains nothing but the vapor in question.

Holding the temperature constant, we then very carefully admit air into the system (Fig. 8–2) connected through tube A. As the pressure exerted on the surface X is thus increased, the rate of bubbling diminishes and at last ceases and, with further rise of pressure, the liquid begins to back up into tube B. We continue to admit air slowly until the liquid level within tube B is even with

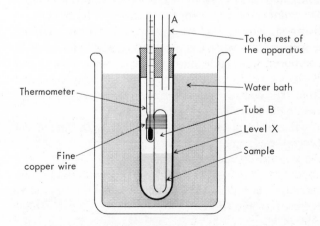

Fig. 8–1. A simple isoteniscope.

---

† This situation is easily characterized by the phase rule. We have one component and two phases so $F = 1 - 2 + 2 = 1$ degree of freedom. When the temperature is fixed, then the pressure of the system (and all other variables) is also fixed.

* Be careful to note that the phase diagram for water that appears ubiquitously is not the diagram for the water-air system we have discussed, but for the pure water system where the pressure of the system is the pressure of the water vapor. What changes will this make?

level X.* The equality of the levels signifies that the pressure of the pure vapor in the inner tube is equal to the pressure on the external surface X. This latter pressure can be easily read as an air pressure, if a manometer is part of the system connected to tube A. This manometric measurement thus establishes the vapor pressure of the liquid at the temperature of the bath (read on the thermometer in direct thermal contact with the liquid of interest). To ensure that this vapor-pressure value is not corrupted by the presence of some residual air in tube B, we only need to lower the external pressure to the point at which boiling again begins. We continue this second boil-out for a few minutes, once again admit air very gradually to the system, and establish the value of the equilibrium pressure at which the inner and outer liquid levels are equal. If the temperature has been held constant and if all air was in fact originally purged from tube B, this second measurement will agree with the first. If it does not, the boil-out and pressure-balancing are again repeated until agreement between successive runs is attained.

After agreement has been reached, we proceed to a determination of the vapor pressure at a higher temperature. We raise the temperature of the bath 5 to 10°C above the first value. As the temperature rises, the increased vapor pressure within tube B will drive the liquid back down the tube. However, we can counter this incipient displacement by progressive admission of small amounts of air to the system. Ultimately the temperature becomes steady at its new value and we again bring the liquid levels even with each other by careful admission of air and/or withdrawal of any excess air admitted to the system. The value of the pressure prevailing in the system at this equilibrium point (read from the manometer connected to the system through tube A) is the vapor pressure exerted by the liquid in tube B. This datum can be checked by reducing the system pressure until tube B bubbles gently for a minute or so and then readjusting the pressure so the liquid levels are again equal. If the manometer readings agree, we again increase the temperature by 5 to 10°C and repeat the procedure. Once you have mastered the

operation of the isoteniscope and the accompanying manometric system, you will be able to obtain vapor-pressure values for different temperatures at a rate of about three or four per hour.

Procedure

You should work as partners on this experiment. The experiment can easily be carried out by a single person but it is less tedious when one person can devote his attention to controlling the temperature of the bath while another concerns himself with controlling the pressure in the system and reading the manometer. Both experimenters should keep a complete record of the data obtained and should exchange jobs at least once so each will learn both of them.

Obtain from your instructor a mercury manometer, Fig. 8–2. Take great care not to spill the mercury, as mercury vapor is rather poisonous. There should be a few millimeters of dilute (about 1 M) aqueous sulfuric acid on both mercury surfaces to prevent fouling of the containing surfaces and/or sticking of the mercury in the narrow vertical tube.

When you read the manometer against the meter stick, keep your line of sight horizontal to avoid parallax. Read the *top* of the mercury meniscus, not the less well-defined position of the mercury surface in contact with the glass. (Ignore the presence of the sulfuric acid layer when reading the manometer: it would take a 13-mm column of dilute sulfuric acid to exert a pressure equivalent to 1 mm of mercury. Why?) Don't forget to record *both* the height of the mercury in the vertical tube *and* the height of the mercury in the test tube: it is only the *difference* of these two heights that is significant.

Assemble the apparatus as shown in Fig. 8–2.† (Remember the technique for inserting glass tubing through rubber stoppers discussed in Section 1–6.) Starting at the left end of the system as shown in the figure, set up a ring stand, placing the iron ring and wire gauze at the proper height for heating the water bath over a bunsen burner.‡ Obtain a two-hole rubber stopper that will enter a 25 × 150-mm test tube for the greater part of the length of the stopper. (This fit will be snugger when the two holes in the stopper are occupied by the glass to be inserted through them.) Carefully introduce a thermometer through one hole to the position shown

---

* Successive introductions of small amounts of air may be required to hold the levels even. The liquid will be cooled by evaporation during the boil-out operation. Thus when boiling is first terminated the vapor pressure exerted will correspond to a temperature a degree or so below that of the heating bath. Once the boiling is halted, however, the temperature will rise rapidly to equal the temperature of the bath. The increase in vapor pressure corresponding to this rise in temperature will drive the liquid back down the inner tube. This movement can easily be checked by admitting a little more air to the system, thus slightly increasing the pressure acting on surface X. Ultimately, you will be able to bring the inner and outer liquid levels to approximate equality at a steady external pressure (and temperature).

---

† If a vacuum system with a manometer is available, it can be used to advantage for this experiment by attaching the isoteniscope to the system via a long length of 7-mm tubing bent at the top as indicated in Fig. 8–2. In this case, it is a wise idea to protect the pump from any condensable vapors by having a cold trap between it and the isoteniscopic system.

‡ You can, instead, use the immersion heaters that are often used in college and university dormitories for heating water for hot drinks in the cup. These are available in almost any variety store for less than one dollar.

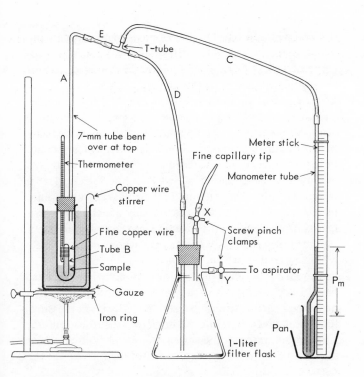

Fig. 8–2. The isoteniscope and attached system.

in Fig. 8–1. Through the other hole insert a length of glass tubing about 45 cm long with an outside diameter of 7 mm. The upper end of this tubing should be bent over as shown so that no liquid that gets beyond the end of the tubing can drain back into the isoteniscope. Clean any water or glycerol used to lubricate the glass off the stopper, thermometer, and tubing (inadequate cleaning will result in contaminated samples). Then carefully dry the stopper and the outside of the thermometer and tubing with a clean, dry towel and dry the inside of the long tube by drawing air through it with the aspirator. Make tube *B* from a short length (about 5 to 7 cm) of glass tubing with an outside diameter of 5 mm, firepolishing the open end until it is slightly constricted. Attach this isoteniscope tube to the thermometer with a few turns of fine copper wire. Slide the test tube onto the stopper, pressing it into place firmly but not violently. Attach a short length of rubber pressure tubing (i.e., heavy-walled rubber tubing) to the down-turned end of the 7 mm tubing. Obtain a T-tube from your instructor, and insert one of the arms into the short length of pressure tubing. Attach longer lengths of pressure tubing, as shown, to the other two arms of the T-tube. (To ensure that these connections will all be tight, the glass should extend at least 2 cm into the rubber tubing.) Attach one of these to the top of your manometer and the other to your filter flask, fitted with the attachments shown in the figure. The pressure controls are all attached to this flask, which should be placed in a readily accessible position on the laboratory table. (This large flask is used as a ballast, minimizing the

change of pressure produced by a small amount of air admitted to the system. A heavy-walled filter flask is used because flat-bottomed flasks of normal wall thickness tend to collapse, producing glass shrapnel, when evacuated.)

When the entire apparatus has been assembled, pump it down with the aspirator or laboratory vacuum. (A vacuum pump may be used, but should be protected from any condensable vapors by a cold trap between it and the isoteniscope system.) When a steady low pressure has been achieved (pinchclamp *X* is, of course, tightly closed), isolate the system from the vacuum source by shutting pinchclamp *Y*. Read the manometer immediately and again after sixty seconds. If the apparatus is sufficiently leak-free, the manometer reading should change by less than 1 mm in this interval. If the apparatus is not leak-free, proceed systematically to locate (and repair) any leak(s). For example, if the manometer reading continues to drift even after a pinchclamp has been applied and tightened at *C* in the figure, you know that there is a leak somewhere between *C* and the manometer, presumably at the connection to the manometer. To correct such a leak, secure the rubber tubing to the glass with a turn of heavy (18 gauge) copper wire twisted to tighten it and seal the rubber tubing against the glass tubing. If the manometer reading drifts for the system as a whole but not when a pinchclamp is applied at *D*, the leak lies between *D* and *Y*. Similarly, if a leak is halted by applying a pinchclamp at *E*, the leak must be in the isoteniscope, most probably around the stopper of the test tube, which should perhaps be thrust into place more firmly. Consult with your instructor if you have trouble finding and/or repairing the leaks in your system.

When you have a leak-free system, admit air through *X* and remove the test tube. Make sure the test tube, stopper, thermometer, and tubing are clean and dry. Obtain (in your test tube) from your instructor the liquid sample you will use to test the predictions we have made about the temperature dependence of vapor pressure. Detach tube *B* and use a *clean* dropper to fill it completely with your sample. Invert the tube and reattach it to the thermometer so it will be in the position shown in Fig. 8–1 when it is inserted in the test tube. (Take care not to jar tube *B* when the stopper is being inserted into the test tube, since air bubbles may then get into it. If some air does get in at this stage, you can easily get rid of it by somewhat prolonging the initial boil-out period. This will certainly be necessary if the sample is too volatile to remain in tube *B* when its open end is down.) Lubricate the stopper by "wetting" it with a little of your sample; then press the test tube firmly onto the stopper. Place a water bath, with water at room temperature, around the test tube, and you are ready to go.

Close pinchclamp X and cautiously open pinchclamp Y so that the pressure in the system drops gradually. Let the pressure drop until a continuous stream of bubbles issues from tube B, and then hold the pressure at this value for several minutes. (With some samples, boiling may be unattainable even at the lowest pressure you can reach with an aspirator, about 25 torr. This means that the vapor pressure of the sample is too low to be measured readily at this temperature. In this case, raise the temperature of the water bath by about 10°C and try again.) When tube B has been well swept out, close pinchclamp Y and cautiously open pinchclamp X to admit air into the system very slowly. (You may find it easiest to control the flow of air by applying a finger to the fine-tipped tube attached to X as well as by manipulating X.) Continue to admit air until the liquid levels inside and outside tube B remain approximately even for about one minute. ("Exact" equality of level is superfluous: A 13-mm inequality in level will represent a pressure difference of the order of 1 torr of mercury. Why?) At once read (to the nearest 0.5 mm) and record the mercury levels in the two arms of your manometer and, by subtraction, compute the difference in pressure between the atmosphere and the inside of your system. Cautiously open Y and repeat the boil-out for a minute or so. Repeat the leveling procedure and pressure measurement. Continue in this fashion with the bath temperature held constant until two successive balancing pressure measurements are concordant to about 1 torr.

Now raise the bath temperature some 5 to 10°C, cautiously admitting air through X if the bubbling (because of the rise in vapor pressure with temperature) becomes too violent. When the bath temperature is constant at the desired value, again read and record the balancing pressure, allow a few bubbles of vapor to escape from tube B, and repeat the measurement of balancing pressure. After concordant values are obtained, raise the temperature again and read the balancing pressure again. Continue in this fashion until the vapor pressure has risen close to 1 atmosphere or the temperature has risen close to 100°C, whichever comes first.

You will now have a series of measurements showing the manometer readings corresponding to a series of temperature readings. This manometer indicates only the *difference* between atmospheric pressure and the pressure prevailing in your system. To find the absolute value of the latter pressure(s) you must know the atmospheric pressure in the laboratory. About midway through your determination on each day you work on the experiment, read the barometer in the laboratory. (Ask your instructor to show you how to read the barometer.) In principle, the barometric reading should be corrected for temperature (which affects both the density of mercury and the length of the brass scale on the barometer), but we will ignore this correction since it is comparable with the intrinsic uncertainty of our measurements. (Any handbook will tell you how to make this correction, if you are interested.) If P_b is the measured barometric pressure and P_m is a pressure difference read from the manometer, the pressure, P, actually prevailing in the system is

$$P = P_b - P_m.$$

This is also the vapor pressure of the sample at the temperature of the measurement.

Calculations

Tabulate your vapor-pressure values (in torr) corresponding to each temperature at which a measurement was made. Enter the corresponding values of $\log P$ and $1/T$ in your tabulation. Plot $\log P$ versus $1/T$. What conclusions do you draw about the validity of Eq. (8–7)? What is ΔH^0_{vap}, in calories, for your sample? (Is it valid to use $\log P$, where P is expressed in torr, for this determination?) What is ΔG^0_{vap}? If more than one value of ΔH^0_{vap} can be obtained (see the discussion in Section 8–1) compare a ΔH^0_{vap} value at a lower temperature with that at a higher temperature. How do you rationalize the relative sizes of these two enthalpies? Using your data, determine the boiling point of your sample. What is the calculated value of ΔG^0_{vap} at the boiling point? How does this compare with the theoretical value?

EXPERIMENT 13.   *The Temperature Dependence of a Solubility Equilibrium*

Introduction

The reaction we shall study is the solubility of naphthalene, $C_{10}H_8$, in diphenylamine, $C_{12}H_{11}N$, which can be written (for a saturated solution)

Naphthalene (pure solid) $\rightleftharpoons$

Naphthalene (solution, mole fraction X).

The equilibrium constant for this reaction is

$$K = \frac{a_{\text{naphthalene (solution)}}}{a_{\text{naphthalene (solid)}}}.$$

The activity of a pure solid is unity, so

$a_{\text{naphthalene (solid)}} = 1,$

and, if we assume the solution is ideal, the activity of

naphthalene in the solution is equal to its mole fraction: $a_{\text{naphthalene (solution)}} = X$. Therefore the equilibrium constant is $K = X$. By the arguments of Section 8–1, we would predict that the temperature dependence of this solubility equilibrium would be

$$\ln \frac{K_2}{K_1} = \ln \frac{X_2}{X_1} = \frac{-\Delta H^0}{R}\left(\frac{1}{T_2} - \frac{1}{T_1}\right);$$

this is the prediction we will test.

The temperature dependence of this equilibrium is found by determining the temperature at which naphthalene first precipitates from liquid mixtures of naphthalene and diphenylamine. This is, of course, the temperature, T, at which this solution, mole fraction X in naphthalene, is saturated with naphthalene. We are predicting that a plot of log X will be a straight line of slope $-\Delta H^0/2.303\ R$.

What interpretation do we give to the ΔH^0 that we may obtain in this way? Let us break our overall equilibrium reaction into two steps

Naphthalene (solid) $\rightleftharpoons$ Naphthalene (liquid)

$\rightleftharpoons$ Naphthalene (solution, X).

The enthalpy change for the first step is obviously the enthalpy of fusion of naphthalene. Since we are assuming that the solutions are ideal, the enthalpy change for the second step is zero (this is the definition of an ideal solution). Thus the enthalpy change for the overall reaction, ΔH^0, is equal to the enthalpy of fusion of naphthalene, ΔH^0_{fus}. We then have a second prediction to check: if we can obtain ΔH^0 from the temperature-dependence data, it should be equal to the directly measured value of ΔH^0_{fus} for naphthalene.

It is also interesting to see what the phase rule indicates about the system we shall study. We have two components and (in the system of interest) two phases. (We are neglecting here the air which exerts pressure on the system, thus assuming that neither component is appreciably volatile and that air is not appreciably soluble in the components of interest.) Thus the number of degrees of freedom is $F = 2 - 2 + 2 = 2$, of which one is used up because we shall work at a constant pressure of one atmosphere. Thus, for any particular composition of the liquid solution, there is only one temperature at which the solid phase and the liquid phase can be in equilibrium, since the choice of liquid composition has used up the remaining degree of freedom. (This is exactly what is implied by writing $K = X$, since, at a given temperature, K is a constant and only one composition is then allowed to the liquid phase.)

When a solution of liquids cools, the temperature drops almost linearly with time until the point is reached when the solution is saturated with respect to one or the other component. This component then begins to precipitate, and the rate of cooling of the sample changes. If the temperature of such a solution is plotted as a function of time, a plot called a cooling curve is obtained, Fig. 8–3. The intersection of the straight line extrapolations of the two portions of the cooling curve is a very good estimation of the temperature at which solid should ideally first begin to appear. You should use this temperature in your calculations. (Because solutions such as these tend to supersaturate very easily, solid does not usually first appear at this temperature.)

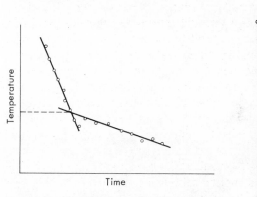

Fig. 8–3. A typical cooling curve (note that the solution was supersaturated before precipitation began).

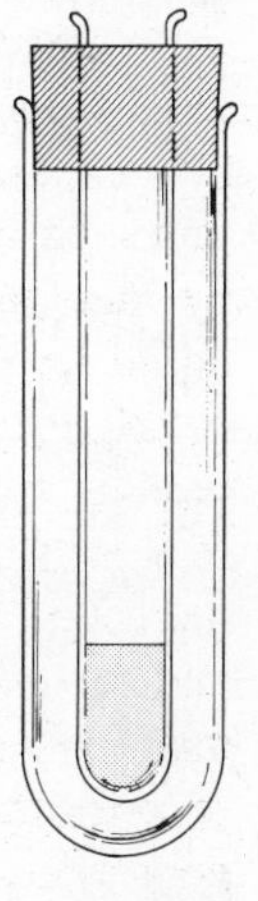

Fig. 8–4

Procedure

Work with a partner for this experiment. Construct the simple apparatus shown in Fig. 8–4 from a six-inch test tube, an eight-inch test tube, and a cork. Place in the smaller test tube about 20 gm of naphthalene (accurately weighed). Heat this test tube in a boiling water bath until the naphthalene is all melted. Remove the test tube, wipe it dry, place it inside the larger test tube, insert a thermometer into the molten naphthalene, and stir with the thermometer while taking temperature readings every thirty seconds until solid begins to appear. Continue stirring and recording temperatures for about five minutes after solid appears.

Weigh out (accurately) enough diphenylamine to give a mixture that is about 0.8 mole fraction in naphthalene when the amine is added to the naphthalene already in the test tube. Add the amine to the test tube and again heat in the hot water bath until the mixture is completely molten. Stir with the thermometer to assure good mixing. Remove the test tube from the bath and proceed as before. Record the temperature at which solid first appears as well as the other temperature-time data.

Repeat this procedure for a second and third addition of diphenylamine such that the mole fractions of naphthalene will be about 0.6 and 0.4.

Calculations

From your four temperature versus time plots find the temperature at which solid should ideally first appear in each determination. Plot $\log X$ versus $1/T$ for your four determinations. If possible, determine ΔH_{fus}^0 for naphthalene and compare with the value you find in your textbook or a handbook. Also, if possible, find ΔS_{fus}^0 for naphthalene in two ways from your data (see Section 8–1). Do these values agree?

Consider what is meant by ΔG^0 and ΔG for the reaction being studied: ΔG^0 is the difference in free energy between pure solid and pure liquid naphthalene, while ΔG is the free-energy difference between the naphthalene in solution at concentration X and the pure solid. Also, ΔG^0 is a function of temperature and is equal to zero only at the melting point of pure naphthalene. (This is the only temperature where pure solid and pure liquid are in equilibrium at 1-atm pressure.) On the other hand, the condition for equilibrium at all temperatures is that $\Delta G = 0$. At equilibrium, $T \Delta S = \Delta H$, and if ΔH^0 is independent of temperature, $T \Delta S = \Delta H^0$. Thus, for an equilibrium to occur at a lower temperature than the melting point of the solute (naphthalene), ΔS must be greater than ΔS_{fus}^0. Give a molecular interpretation of this increase in the entropy change of the reaction in terms of increase in "disorder."

Further Experimental Problems

The equilibrium studied in this experiment may also be regarded as a problem in the freezing-point depression of a solvent (naphthalene) by a solute (diphenylamine). This is a good system for this study because a wide range of concentrations may be employed. Use your experimental data to determine in two ways the molal freezing-point depression constant for naphthalene.

Other solvents for freezing-point depression studies that are relatively convenient are benzene, water, and camphor. Benzene and water solutions freeze in the neighborhood of 0°C, so they may be studied using ice-water or ice-water-salt mixtures to lower the temperature around the larger test tube in the cooling curve apparatus we used. Camphor freezes around 170°C so it must be heated in an oil bath to get it to melt. For studies of solutes in these solvents (or these compounds as solutes in experiments like that outlined above) you should not use mixtures containing more than about 5 to 10 weight percent of the solute.

The data from freezing-point depression studies often yield a great deal of information regarding the state of aggregation of the solute in the solution. Systems you might find interesting to study are NaCl, CdCl$_2$, and HgCl$_2$ in water or propionic acid in benzene (see Experiment 10).

EXPERIMENT 14.   The Aniline-Sulfur Dioxide System, An Experiment Using Vacuum Technique

Introduction

The reaction we shall study is a typical Lewis acid-base reaction between sulfur dioxide, SO$_2$ (acid), and aniline, C$_6$H$_5$NH$_2$ (base), to yield a "neutral salt":

$$C_6H_5NH_2(l) + SO_2(g) \rightleftharpoons C_6H_5NH_2 \cdot SO_2(s). \qquad (8\text{–}8)$$

The electronic structure of aniline and sulfur dioxide (showing only the valence electrons about the atoms of interest) and of the "neutralized" product are

See Section 7–1 for a further discussion of acid and base definitions and the book by Luder and Zuffanti for a fairly extensive introduction to the Lewis acid-base concept. The "neutralized" adduct is not very stable and will decompose even at room temperature if left in an open vessel.

We can write the equilibrium constant for the decomposition of the adduct as

$$K = \frac{a_{SO_2} \cdot a_{C_6H_5NH_2}}{a_{C_6H_5NH_2 \cdot SO_2}}.$$

The activities of pure liquids and solids are always taken as unity for convenience in defining standard states. If we assume that the solid adduct and gaseous SO$_2$ are not appreciably soluble in liquid aniline, then the solid and liquid are essentially pure, and we can write the equilibrium constant as

$$K = a_{SO_2}.$$

The activity of gases which are assumed to behave ideally is just their pressure, so we finally reduce the equilibrium constant to $K = P_{SO_2}$. A measurement of P_{SO_2} is, therefore, a measurement of the equilibrium constant for this system. We therefore predict that a plot of $\log P_{SO_2}$

versus $1/T$ will be a straight line from which we can obtain the standard enthalpy change and other thermodynamic quantities for reaction (8-8), the reverse of the decomposition reaction.

You might object that our assumption that the solid adduct and the gaseous SO_2 are not soluble in liquid aniline is unwarranted. If we assume that the solubilities are not negligible, won't this drastically alter the simple conclusion we have reached? It is easiest to answer this question by appealing to the information we can derive from the phase rule. The system we shall study consists of three phases and two components (two components, not three, because we cannot independently vary the amount of the solid adduct, an example of the care we must use in applying the phase rule), so the number of degrees of freedom is $F = 2 - 3 + 2 = 1$. If we fix the temperature of the system, then the composition of each phase of the system is also fixed. For the gas phase, SO_2, this means that P_{SO_2} is fixed (so long as both liquid aniline and solid adduct are present) at a given temperature. Thus the system can be characterized in terms of P_{SO_2} and, since the equilibrium constant for the reaction is a function only of temperature, we can identify P_{SO_2}, also a function only of the temperature, as a measure of the equilibrium constant for the reaction.

Procedure

Work in groups of three or four on this experiment. Before doing the experiment, study the material on vacuum systems and technique in Chapter 5. Remember the cardinal rule: *Think carefully of the consequences before turning any stopcock.*

The sample for this experiment is contained in a bulb with a stopcock and ball joint for attaching it to the vacuum system. The contents of the bulb are aniline, sulfur dioxide, the adduct and a Teflon-coated stirring bar. This mixture was made up by allowing SO_2 to react with aniline in the bulb at 0°C on a vacuum system so no other gases would be present. The stopcock on the bulb should never be opened to a system containing air (air oxidizes aniline).

Attach the bulb to the vacuum system and surround it (below the stopcock) with a beaker of water at room temperature or somewhat above.* Be sure to stir the contents of the bulb vigorously throughout the experiment with the Teflon-coated stirring bar in the bulb and a magnetic stirrer. While waiting for temperature equilibrium, evacuate the vacuum system up to the

---

* The water bath should be well stirred throughout the experiment to ensure a uniform temperature at all points on the reaction bulb. You can heat the water in the beaker with a burner or an immersion heater (coffee cup heaters are fine). One section from an expanded foam acid carton can be used as a bath if an immersion heater is used, and this makes temperature control easier.

stopcock on the bulb. Be sure all stopcocks except that on the bulb and others leading to the atmosphere are open. Immerse the vacuum system cold trap in a solid CO_2-trichloroethylene bath; see your instructor about the technique required at this point. When the system is evacuated, isolate the system from the cold trap and pump and monitor the system pressure for three to five minutes. If the pressure is constant, the system is leak-free. If it is not leak-free, consult your instructor for the procedures to be used to detect and repair leaks. When the system is leak-free and evacuated, make sure the system is isolated from the cold trap and pump and that the manometer is prepared to function; then open the reaction bulb to the vacuum system. Make several measurements of pressure until P_{SO_2} has reached a constant value. Record this value and the temperature of the bath.

Raise the bath temperature to about 30°C and again obtain the equilibrium pressure of SO_2 and record the temperature of the bath. (Do not rush the measurement. It takes time to reach an equilibrium SO_2 pressure.) Raise the bath temperature and make successive readings of the equilibrium SO_2 pressures at 40° and 50°C. (Do not go over 50°C.) Then allow the bath to cool, and make measurements at 45° and 35°C. Remember that the bath temperature must be held steady over a relatively long period of time for the pressure to reach a steady value.

Finally, cool the bulb to 0°C, measure the equilibrium system pressure again, and close off the stopcock on the bulb. Do these three things whenever you shut down no matter at what stage of the experiment you are. Follow up by very slowly admitting air to the system (but not the reaction bulb) at 1-atm pressure. Re-evacuate the system. Turn off the pump, readmit air slowly, and go through the rest of the procedure (cleaning the trap) for shutting down the vacuum system.

Calculations

Determine ΔH^0 for the decomposition reaction by graphical treatment of your data. Remember to correct your manometer readings to 0°C. (The correction factor is in all standard handbooks.) A correction should also be made for the pressure of aniline in the system (the vapor pressure of aniline is 1.0 torr at 34.8°C and 10.0 torr at 69.4°C). From your data, calculate ΔG^0 and ΔS^0 at 25°C for the decomposition reaction. Calculate the standard free energy of formation of the addition compound, given that ΔG_f^0 for liquid aniline and gaseous SO_2 are $+35,400$ cal/mole and $-71,735$ cal/mole, respectively.

Is the decomposition reaction spontaneous at room temperature? If the decomposition is (is not) spontaneous, at what temperature does it become nonspontaneous (spontaneous)?

REFERENCES

EDDY, R. D., "The Solubility Curve of Borax: A Student Laboratory Experiment," *J. Chem. Ed.* **35,** 364 (1958) is an experiment much like Experiment 13 in this text except that it uses a different chemical system.

HILL, A. E., "Reaction of Amines with SO_2. I. Aniline and Sulfur Dioxide," *J. Am. Chem. Soc.* **53,** 2598 (1931) is the original (and, it appears, final) work on this system.

KOKES, R. J., M. K. DORFMAN and T. MATHIA, "Chemical Equilibrium: The Hydrogenation of Benzene," *J. Chem. Ed.* **39,** 91 (1962) describes an experiment using vacuum techniques to study a chemical equilibrium.

LINDAUER, M. W., "Simple Isteniscope and an Improved Method of Vapor Pressure Measurement," *J. Chem. Ed.* **37,** 532 (1960) is the source of our Experiment 12.

LUDER, W. F. and S. ZUFFANTI, *The Electronic Theory of Acids and Bases*, 2nd ed. Dover, New York, 1961.

MAHAN, B. H., "Temperature Dependence of Equilibrium," *J. Chem. Ed.* **40,** 293 (1963) is the source of Experiment 13.

MAHAN, B. H., *Elementary Chemical Thermodynamics*, W. A. Benjamin, New York, 1963.

MIKULAK, R., and O. RUNQUIST, "Molecular Weights by Cryoscopy," *J. Chem. Ed.* **38,** 557 (1961) uses the technique of Experiment 13 to determine the properties of a solute in solution. The solvent suggested for this experiment is cyclohexanol which has a convenient freezing point: 24°C.

NASH, L. K., *Elements of Chemical Thermodynamics*, Addison-Wesley, Reading, Mass., 1962.

STERNBERG, J. C., "Simplified Isteniscope for Vapor Pressure Measurements," *J. Chem. Ed.* **34,** 442 (1957) and S. W. Tobey, "Vapor Pressure Apparatus," *J. Chem. Ed.* **35,** 352 (1958) give two other designs for vapor pressure measuring apparatus.

WASER, J., *Basic Chemical Thermodynamics*, W. A Benjamin, New York, 1965.

WOLTHIUS, E., M. VISSER, and I. OPPENHUIZEN, "Molecular Weight Determination by Boiling Point Elevation," *J. Chem. Ed.* **35,** 412 (1958) suggests a simple experimental technique for this determination. Just as freezing point lowering (solubility) measurements can be used to obtain molecular weights, so can boiling point elevation measurements. The principle is the same in both cases.

In previous chapters (3, 4, and 7) we discussed ionic equilibria from increasingly comprehensive points of view. With little exception, however, these discussions have been a bit out of focus because we were not discussing systems for which you had gathered experimental data. To remedy this, a number of experiments are presented in this chapter in which you will actually study ionic equilibria in solutions, both aqueous and non-aqueous. Thus you will be able to apply your theoretical background knowledge to the interpretation of the experimental data gathered in these experiments and, in the process, increase your knowledge of the methods used to study ionic equilibria. Before launching into the experiments, however, it is necessary to deal with one further topic that we have thus far avoided: the relationship of the activity of a species in solution to its molar concentration.

9–1 ACTIVITIES OF IONS IN SOLUTION

Ionic Interaction

Most introductory chemistry textbooks point out at some point that ions in solution influence one another even if they do not react directly, but none gives a quantitative feeling for the theoretical methods used to deal with these interactions. Qualitatively, the interactions are relatively easy to rationalize; in a solution containing ions it is reasonable to suppose that ions will tend to attract other ions of opposite charge as nearest ionic neighbors, whether or not the two ionic species actually interact in a "chemical" manner. If a "cloud" of oppositely charged ions tends to congregate about an ion, then the influence of this ion's charge on others farther away in the solution will be reduced. We might say, therefore, that the "effectiveness" of the ion for reaction is reduced, i.e., that its activity is reduced. The problem then is to calculate how the activity depends on the environment in which an ion is found.

The Debye-Hückel Limiting Law

It requires more mathematical background and more knowledge of electrostatic theory than is presumed by this discussion actually to derive the expression for the potential energy, U, of an ion in a medium in which it is surrounded by other charges (ions). For now we shall content ourselves with simply stating the result obtained *for very dilute solutions:*

$$U = \frac{ze}{\epsilon r} - \frac{\sqrt{\beta}\, ze}{\epsilon}, \tag{9–1}$$

$$\beta = \frac{8\pi Ne^2\mu}{1000\epsilon kT}, \tag{9–2}$$

where z is the amount of charge on the ion of interest (a dimensionless quantity), e is the magnitude of the electronic charge = 4.80×10^{-10} esu (esu is charge in the cgs system), ϵ is the dielectric constant of the medium = 78.54 for H_2O at 25°C, N is Avogadro's number = 6.023×10^{23} molecules/mole, μ is the ionic strength = $\frac{1}{2}\sum_i c_i z_i^2$, c_i is the molar concentration of the ith ion of charge z_i, k is Boltzmann's constant = 1.38×10^{-16} erg/°K, T is the temperature, °K, and 1000 = cm^3/liter.

The first term on the right-hand side of (9–1) is simply the work required to bring a unit charge from infinity to within a distance r from the ion of interest in the absence of any other charges in the medium. Evidently, then, the final term in (9–1) is a correction term due to the presence of other ions; it is this term which is important for our discussion.

Our approach will be that usually taken when trying to relate "potential to do work" with physically observable quantities.* We simply eliminate all possible

---

* This same approach is taken in relating the potential difference (voltage) between two electrodes of an electrochemical cell with the free energy change of the cell reaction (see Chapter 10).

sources of work in the system, at constant pressure and temperature, except that due to the potential function of interest and then say that any free energy changes have to be due to this cause. We shall do this here by breaking down contributions to the free energy into two terms, one of which is related to the above correction term for the ionic "atmosphere" in an ionic solution. We have seen that by analogy with gas phase derivations we can define a free energy in solution as

$$G = G^0 + RT \ln a,$$

where a is the activity of the species in question and the standard state is defined such that $a^0 = 1$. Since activities are, in general, concentration dependent, we write $a = \gamma c$, where γ is the activity coefficient and c is the concentration of the species, usually the molarity, molality, or mole fraction in solutions. Hence we can write

$$G - G^0 = RT \ln \gamma c,$$
$$G - G^0 = RT \ln c + RT \ln \gamma. \tag{9-3}$$

If the solutions were ideal, γ would be unity and

$$G_{\text{ideal}} - G^0 = RT \ln c,$$

but γ is usually not unity, and indeed its variation is what we seek. Thus the term $RT \ln \gamma$ may be considered a correction term, $\Delta G_{\text{nonideal}}$, which when added to the ideal free energy will give the actual free energy,

$$G = G_{\text{ideal}} + \Delta G_{\text{nonideal}}. \tag{9-4}$$

It is just this term, $\Delta G_{\text{nonideal}}$, that measures the nonideal effects due to ionic interactions in ionic solutions. If, then, we can relate the free energy effect to the potential energy due to the ionic interactions, we can identify this quantity as $RT \ln \gamma$.

First we must obtain an expression for the energy of a charge, Q, and then relate this to our problem. The work done in adding to a charge a small additional amount of charge, dQ, when the potential energy of the system is U, is given as

$$w = U \, dQ. \tag{9-5}$$

For this situation the potential, U, in (9-5) is related to the charge, Q, and we can write

$$U = \text{const } Q. \tag{9-6}$$

If we substitute (9-6) into (9-5) and integrate from the condition where no charge is present to that when Q is present we get

$$w_{\text{total}} = \text{const} \int_0^Q Q \, dQ = \frac{\text{const}}{2} Q^2,$$
$$w_{\text{total}} = UQ/2. \tag{9-7}$$

Now, if U is given by the final term in (9-1), the ionic interaction term, and Q is replaced by ze, the charge of interest to us in the ionic solution, then w_{total} calculated from (9-7) may be set equal to $\Delta G_{\text{nonideal}}$. This is observed to be correct because the work so calculated will be just that due to the nonideal ionic interactions, and this is what the correction term, $\Delta G_{\text{nonideal}}$, is designed to take into account. Hence for an Avogadro's number of ions, one mole, we obtain

$$\Delta G_{\text{nonideal}} = \left(\frac{ze}{2}\right)\left(\frac{-\sqrt{\beta}\,ze}{\epsilon}\right) N = \frac{-z^2 e^2 \sqrt{\beta}\,N}{2\epsilon}. \tag{9-8}$$

Since

$$\Delta G_{\text{nonideal}} = RT \ln \gamma,$$

we get

$$\ln \gamma = \frac{-z^2 e^2 \sqrt{\beta}\,N}{2RT\epsilon}, \tag{9-9}$$

and substitution of (9-2) into (9-9) yields

$$\ln \gamma = -\left(\frac{e^2}{\epsilon kT}\right)^{3/2}\left(\frac{2\pi N}{1000}\right)^{1/2} z^2 \mu^{1/2}. \tag{9-10}$$

This is the Debye-Hückel limiting law (applicable only within the limit of dilute solutions), which shows how one may calculate the activity coefficient of an ion. The whole derivation was made under the assumption that the ion was positively charged, but we observe that in the final expression the charge is squared and therefore that (9-10) is equally valid for positive and negative ions.

Let us now substitute into (9-10) the values of the constants for an aqueous solution at 25°C and convert to logarithms to the base 10. You can do this to show for yourself that

$$\log \gamma = -0.509 z^2 \mu^{1/2}. \tag{9-11}$$

This relationship was the first one derived by Debye and Hückel; later they modified this result to take into account the fact that ions have size. In the initial theory, the assumption was made that the ions were point charges. When this assumption is discarded the more accurate expression that results is

$$\log \gamma = \frac{-0.509 z^2 \mu^{1/2}}{1 + Bd\mu^{1/2}}, \tag{9-12}$$

where

$$B = \left(\frac{8\pi e^2 N}{1000\epsilon kT}\right)^{1/2} = 0.329 \times 10^8 \, \text{cm}^{-1},$$

and d = average effective diameter of the ion in centimeters. This improved expression fits the experimental data much more closely, though there are still discrepancies. Because of these, another equation which is often used contains an empirical correction term

$$\log \gamma = \frac{-0.509z^2\mu^{1/2}}{1 + Bd\mu^{1/2}} + z^2b\mu. \qquad (9\text{--}13)$$

There is little agreement on the interpretation of the empirical constant b in this expression. It must be determined experimentally for each system; in Experiment 15 you should gather enough information to estimate it for the bromcresol green dianion.

Part of the purpose of this short discussion and Experiment 15 is to acquaint you with the rather pronounced nonideality of ionic solutions, which you should keep in mind whenever you carry out ionic reactions. It is a good exercise to try to think of ways to use each new technique you learn to ascertain something about the activities of species in solution. Another good exercise that you may do right now is to return to the discussion above and be certain that derived numerical quantities are correct. Do the units check? What are the units of the constant 0.509 in Eq. (9–11), (9–12), and (9–13)? This is another habit you should form: always check through very complex expressions like these (and simple ones as well) to make certain that the dimensions are correct. This can lead to a good deal of enlightenment about the origin of some terms and can readily uncover misprints in such complex formulas.

EXPERIMENT 15. The Effect of Ionic Strength on an Equilibrium Quotient (A Class Study)

Background

As a prelude to this discussion, first study Appendix E, since the analysis of this system is done spectrophotometrically. The reaction chosen for this experiment is the acid-base dissociation equilibrium of the indicator bromcresol green in aqueous solution. Basically this system is chosen to help reinforce your understanding of the principles of acid-base equilibria through their practical application and to introduce and illustrate the importance of "inert" ionic species in the behavior of ionic-equilibrium systems.

The structural formula for the acidic form of bromcresol green (3',3'',5',5''-tetrabromo-m-cresol-sulfonaphthalein) is as follows:

The hydrogen of the phenol group is weakly acidic, and it is its pK with which we shall be concerned. The solid indicator is usually purchased as the sodium salt of the sulfonic acid (a strong acid). The basic form of the indicator cannot be represented by a single structure but is a "resonance hybrid" of a number of forms such as

Although this molecule is rather complex, under the conditions of our experiment, aqueous solutions of varying pH, it acts as a monoprotic acid. We shall abbreviate the acidic form HB^- and the basic form $B^=$. The species HB^- absorbs light in the short wavelength part of the visible spectrum, and its solutions appear yellow. When the proton is removed, at higher pH values, the resulting solutions of $B^=$ are an intense blue because the absorption maximum of this form is in the red region of the visible spectrum.*

Let us write the reaction of interest in terms of this abbreviated nomenclature:

$$HB^-(aq) \rightleftharpoons H^+(aq) + B^=(aq),$$

$$K = \frac{a_{H^+(aq)}a_{B^=(aq)}}{a_{HB^-(aq)}}. \quad (9\text{-}14)$$

From Section 9–1 we recall that $a_x = \gamma_x[X]$, so we may rewrite (9–14) in terms of concentrations:

$$K = \frac{\gamma_{H^+}\gamma_{B^=}}{\gamma_{HB^-}} \frac{[H^+][B^=]}{[HB^-]}. \quad (9\text{-}15)$$

We shall *define the equilibrium quotient,*† Q, as

$$Q = \frac{[H^+][B^=]}{[HB^-]}, \quad (9\text{-}16)$$

and we observe that as the solution becomes more dilute and approaches ideality, all the activity coefficients tend toward unity, so that Q approaches K in this limit.

Now let us consider what the Debye-Hückel limiting law tells us about (9–15). If we assume that the effective ionic diameters of $H^+(aq)$ and $HB^-(aq)$ are about the same (This is surely not a good approximation, but the dependence of the activity coefficients on the ionic diameter is weak. Thus the rest of this argument will probably have greater validity than the initial assumption.), then the theory, Section 9–1, shows that

$$\gamma_{H^+} \approx \gamma_{HB^-} \quad (9\text{-}17)$$

because H^+ and HB^- are both singly charged ions. Now we combine (9–15), (9–16), and (9–17) to obtain

$$K \approx Q\gamma_{B^=}$$

and take logarithms of both sides:

$$\log K \approx \log Q + \log \gamma_{B^=},$$

or

$$pQ \approx pK + \log \gamma_{B^=}. \quad (9\text{-}18)$$

From the Debye-Hückel theory, on the assumption that the ionic diameter of $B^=(aq)$ is 7Å,‡ we can calculate

(for dilute solutions at 25°C)

$$\log \gamma_{B^=} = \frac{-0.509(2)^2\mu^{1/2}}{1 + (0.329 \times 10^8)(7 \times 10^{-8})\mu^{1/2}}$$

$$= \frac{-2.04\mu^{1/2}}{1 + 2.3\mu^{1/2}} \quad (9\text{-}19)$$

$$= -2.04\mu'.$$

On substitution of (9–19) into (9–18) we obtain

$$pQ \approx pK - 2.04\mu', \quad (9\text{-}20)$$

where μ' may be obtained from (9–19). Equation (9–20) predicts that a plot of pQ versus μ' (calculated and controlled in this experiment) should be linear with a slope of -2.04 and an extrapolated intercept equal to the thermodynamic value, pK.

As the ionic strength of the solutions we use becomes higher, the Debye-Hückel limiting law begins to break down, and we should expect deviations from linearity of our plots. These might be amenable to description by the addition of the empirical "extension term," $z^2b\mu$, where b is a constant to be determined.

How are we to obtain Q? Review the calculation given in Appendix E, Section E-3, to obtain pK_{In} for the indicator methyl red. The approach used here will be identical except that more than one pH in the region of the color change will be investigated. You will use buffer solutions to control and calculate pH (using the buffer formula given on page 82 for the calculation).§ The only colored species in the solutions will be HB^- and $B^=$, so we can write the necessary equations from Appendix E as

$$A_b = a_{B^=}b[B^=], \quad (9\text{-}21)$$

$$A_a = a_{HB^-}b[HB^-], \quad (9\text{-}22)$$

$$\frac{[B^=]}{[HB^-]} = \frac{A - A_a}{A_b - A}, \quad (9\text{-}23)$$

where A is the absorbance of the solution at a particular pH in the color change region.‖ The value for the ratio $[B^=]/[HB^-]$ is combined with the $[H^+]$ for this solution to compute Q.

---

* This change is related to an increase in the effective volume occupied by the electrons whose induced changes in energy are responsible for the absorption of certain wavelengths. This "delocalization" of the electrons is a result of the "resonance" in the basic form of the molecule. For a further discussion of these phenomena, look up "resonance" in any textbook of organic chemistry or in books such as those listed in the references at the end of Chapter 11.

† The equilibrium quotient is what we have been previously setting equal to the equilibrium constant where the assumption is made that molar concentration and activity are equal.

‡ How might this be arrived at?

§ You might ask why we simply do not use a pH meter to measure the pH of the solutions. This would actually be less accurate than the calculational procedure, since the acetic acid-acetate (HOAc-OAc⁻) buffer system used has been extensively studied and the equilibrium quotient $Q_a = [H^+][OAc^-]/[HOAc]$ as a function of ionic strength is well known (Fig. 9–1) so $[H^+]$ is easy to calculate for these solutions.

‖ Naturally, all absorbance readings used are taken at the same wavelength.

Experimental Procedure

This experiment is to be a cooperative effort of the whole class. You will be assigned an ionic strength which you will use for your solutions. When you have finished the experiment, you will post the results in the place provided. When all results are in, you will select a representative sampling of the overall data to use in interpreting ionic strength effects on the dissociation equilibrium of bromcresol green.

Stock solutions of sodium acetate, acetic acid, bromcresol green, and potassium chloride will be available in the laboratory. Pipet 5 ml of the stock solution of 0.200 M sodium acetate (NaOAc) into a 100-ml volumetric flask.* Add (pipet) 10 ml of the stock solution of 3×10^{-4} M bromcresol green. Use the buret provided in the laboratory to add enough 1.00 M KCl solution to give you your assigned ionic strength when the volume is made up to 100 ml with distilled H_2O.† Dilute to the mark and mix. Pour this solution "quantitatively" into a 250-ml beaker (or bottle).

Clean the volumetric flask, pipet into it 10 ml of the stock solution of 5.00 M acetic acid (HOAc), and then add enough 1.00 M KCl solution to make the ionic strength the same in this solution as in the one above. Remember that in the solution above you have 1 millimole of NaOAc which contributes to the ionic strength, whereas in this solution the only ionic species of any importance are K^+ and Cl^-. Dilute to the mark and mix well.

Determine the absorption spectrum of the NaOAc solution of bromcresol green between 400 and 640 mμ. Take readings every 20 mμ except in the region of maximum absorption, where you should take readings at more closely spaced intervals. Be sure to take a very precise reading at the wavelength of maximum absorbance. Pour the sample back into the beaker. (Be careful not to lose any, since you will need to know the volumes for later calculations.) Use your buret or a 1-ml pipet to add to the beaker precisely 1.00 ml of the HOAc solution you prepared, mix well with a stirring rod, and measure the absorption at the wavelength you previously found for the absorption maximum of the dye. (Use the same sample cell (cuvette) for all measurements. The reference sample (blank) for all measurements may be distilled water.)

Repeat this procedure for additional 1.00-ml aliquots of the HOAc solution, and, for the 2-ml case, again measure the entire absorption spectrum. After a total of five such additions, add 1.0 ml of 6 M HCl to convert the dye to the yellow form "completely," and again measure the entire spectrum.

Calculations

Use Fig. 9–1 to obtain Q_a for acetic acid at the ionic strength you used‡ and then calculate the pH of all seven of the bromcresol green solutions whose absorbance you measured. Why is it not necessary to take into account the acid-base equilibrium constant for bromcresol green when calculating these pH's?

Assume that pQ of bromcresol green is near 5 and show whether the compound is quantitatively ($>99.9\%$) in its basic form, $B^=$, in the first solution which contains only NaOAc, KCl, and the indicator. If this is the case, then we can use the absorbance of this solution, at the wavelength of maximum absorbance, as A_b in Eqs. (9–21) and (9–23). Again assuming that the pQ of the indicator is 5, show whether the pH in the final solution, after the addition of HCl, is sufficient to cause quantitative conversion of the indicator to the acidic form. If it is, then we can use the absorbance of this solution, at the same wavelength as before, as A_a in Eqs. (9–22) and (9–23). (See the next paragraph for a correction to this value that must be made.)

If the foregoing calculations prove to yield values for A_b and A_a, the other five values of the absorbance at this wavelength can be used to calculate $[B^=]/[HB^-]$ for the five intermediate solutions. You should note at this point, if you have not already done so when studying the Appendix, that for this approach, the so-called Bjerrum method for obtaining pQ, you do not have to know the actual value of the total concentration of bromcresol green, i.e., $[B^=] + [HB^-]$, but merely the absorbances for a series of solutions having the *same* total concentration. Naturally, you observe immediately that the total concentration is not constant, since each addition of acid dilutes the solution. This effect is small, but its neglect would cause an appreciable error in the results.§ Therefore you need to correct each absorbance reading by multiplying by the factor $(100 + v)/100$, where v is the volume of acid solution added (both HOAc and HCl) when that reading was taken. Show that this procedure will give the absorbance that would

---

* Of course, you will not pipet directly from the stock bottle.
† Please check with the instructor to be certain that the amount of KCl you intend to add is correct. Remember, you are not alone in this experiment; others are depending on your results.

‡ It is interesting to show that the Q_a values of Fig. 9–1 follow the Debye-Hückel theory quite well at low ionic strengths but are subject to large deviations from it as the ionic strength increases. How would you proceed to show this?

§ Basically this is because the results are obtained in part from a calculation in which we take the difference of two rather large numbers, both dependent on the total concentration, to get a fairly small number. Any error in the total concentration will be greatly magnified in this process.

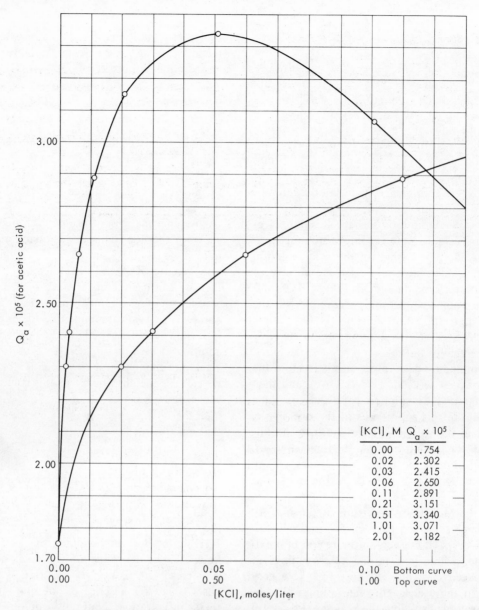

[KCl], M	$Q_a \times 10^5$
0.00	1.754
0.02	2.302
0.03	2.415
0.06	2.650
0.11	2.891
0.21	3.151
0.51	3.340
1.01	3.071
2.01	2.182

Fig. 9–1. The dissociation quotient of HOAc in KCl solutions. The data used are from Harned and Hicke, *J. Am. Chem. Soc.* **59**, 1284, 2303 (1937).

have been obtained if no dilution had occurred. Use your corrected absorbance values to calculate $[B^=]/[HB^-]$.

Now, using the foregoing results, calculate the five values of Q for bromcresol green and the average value of pQ at your ionic strength. Enter your average value of pQ and your value of μ' on the class report.

When the class results have been entered on the report sheet, choose 8 to 12 which seem fairly representative of the whole range of μ' and use these for your analysis of the effect of ionic strength on Q. Compute pK. Discuss the agreement (or lack thereof) between the class results and the Debye-Hückel limiting law predictions. Consider a few of the points that deviate at high ionic strength and see if you can obtain a consistent value for the "extension constant" b in the extended form of the law.

Plot the corrected absorbance vs. wavelength, the absorption spectrum, for the three cases in which you took the necessary data. Put all three absorption spectra on the same graph. You will note the appearance of an isosbestic point. Show that as long as the total concentration of two species which are in equilibrium is constant, their ratio may take any value and the absorbance at the isosbestic point will remain constant.

Further Experimental Problems

It would be interesting to observe whether there is any specific ionic effect in this system by doing the experiment over the same ionic strength range but with a different "inert" salt, perhaps of the 1:2 ($MgCl_2$) or 2:1 (Na_2SO_4) variety instead of the 1:1 (KCl) type.

EXPERIMENT 16.   *The Synthesis of Calcium Iodate**

We have considered previously (in Experiments 3 and 4) the synthesis and analysis of an inorganic compound. In this experiment you will prepare calcium iodate, $Ca(IO_3)_2$. The reason for this choice is threefold: 1) the techniques required are relatively simple but will expand your knowledge of chemical technique; 2) the preparation illustrates some interesting oxidation-reduction chemistry which will be further discussed in Chapter 10; and 3) the product, $Ca(IO_3)_2$, will be used in Experiment 17 for the determination of the solubility product of $Ca(IO_3)_2$ and the dissociation constant of iodic acid, HIO_3.

In aqueous solution, chlorate reacts *very slowly* with iodine, according to the following equation:

$$ClO_3^- + I_2 \rightarrow IO_3^- + ICl.$$

The iodine monochloride (ICl) thus formed, however, reacts *rapidly* with chlorate:

$$ClO_3^- + ICl \rightarrow IO_3^- + Cl_2.$$

To get the reaction to proceed at a reasonable rate, it is then necessary only to ensure that a small amount of Cl_2 is formed at the outset, because this free chlorine will promptly produce some ICl by the following rapid reaction:

$$I_2 + Cl_2 \rightarrow 2ICl.$$

Observe how the last two reactions complement each other.

The free chlorine necessary to get the reaction started can easily be produced by adding a small amount of strong acid to the reaction mixture. As a result of that addition, one forms a little chloric acid, which rapidly decomposes to form oxygen and free chlorine. The (molecular) equations for these initiating reactions are:

$$NaClO_3 + HNO_3 \rightarrow NaNO_3 + HClO_3,$$
$$4HClO_3 \rightarrow 2H_2O + 5O_2 + 2Cl_2.$$

Procedure

This reaction must be carried out in the hood. Obtain from the stockroom a 100-ml round-bottom, long-neck flask. The flask is yours for two laboratory periods (one should be ample for this preparation) and *must* be returned at the end of that time. Weigh out, on a rough balance, 5 gm of sodium chlorate and 5 gm of crystalline iodine. (Note: iodine is both expensive and corrosive.

Take care not to spill it.) Place these reagents in your flask, add 20 ml of distilled water, and swirl the mixture until the chlorate dissolves. Add 0.5 ml of concentrated $16\ M$ HNO_3 to the flask. Cover the mouth of the flask with an inverted 50-ml beaker and clamp the flask vertically *inside the hood*.

Heat the flask *very* gently, with a small flame, until all the iodine has reacted. *Very gentle* heating is prescribed because it is desirable that all the iodine react: if the mixture is heated too strongly, much of the iodine will sublime into the neck of the flask where it is out of contact with the other reactants. If a small amount of iodine sublimes into the neck of the flask, it will be washed back into the body of the flask by liquid refluxing from the neck. If an excessive amount of iodine sublimes, you will have to wash it down with a small amount of distilled water from a wash bottle.

When all the iodine has disappeared (i.e., has been oxidized to iodate), remove the beaker from the mouth of the flask, and gently boil off the remaining chlorine. You can test for the presence of chlorine by using its power to bleach damp litmus paper. When all the chlorine has been expelled, pour the solution from the flask into a 250-ml beaker. Dilute the solution with 30 ml of distilled water, portions of which can be used to wash out the flask. Heat the contents of the beaker to boiling; then reduce the flame and hold the reaction mixture just at its boiling point. (These operations can be performed outside the hood.) Prepare a solution of 2.5 gm of calcium chloride in 50 ml of hot water. Pour this solution, in a thin stream, into the 250-ml beaker while continuously stirring the contents of the beaker. Calcium iodate will precipitate. Allow the mixture to cool to room temperature, and separate the precipitate by filtration in a sintered glass crucible. Wash the precipitate several times with 20-ml portions of cold distilled water. Using a spatula to break up the mass of product (but *not* to scratch the sintered glass plate), transfer the product to a 250-ml Erlenmeyer flask. Add about 100 ml of distilled water, cap the flask with aluminum foil, and let this system stand for several weeks. This "digestion" should result in the formation of sizable, well-formed, clear crystals of product. Also, impurities included in the original product should, at this stage, pass out of the solid phase into the solution.

Collect the final product by filtration, wash once with cold distilled water, dry by drawing air through the precipitate, and transfer to a large watch glass. Place a V-shaped glass rod on this watch glass and invert another watch glass over the first to prevent contamination of the product with dust. Allow this assembly to stand on your desk for some hours, until the crystals are "air-dry." Weigh a 1-oz bottle on a rough balance,

---

* Adapted by R. Little from pp. 470 ff. of W. G. Palmer, *Experimental Inorganic Chemistry*, London: Cambridge University Press, 1954.

transfer your product to the bottle, and reweigh to determine the amount of product you have obtained. Stopper the bottle, label it with your name, the name of the product, the weight of the product obtained, and the date that the product was obtained.

Calculations

Compute the percentage yield of product based on the amount of $CaCl_2$ used. Repeat the computation for the amount of I_2 used.

EXPERIMENT 17.   Equilibrium Constants for Calcium Iodate Solubility and Iodic Acid Dissociation

Background

This experiment is reminiscent of Experiments 10 and 11 in that we shall study a system in which two competing equilibrium reactions are involved. One of these is the dissolution reaction of calcium iodate, $Ca(IO_3)_2$, in water,

$$Ca(IO_3)_2(s) \rightleftharpoons Ca^{++}(aq) + 2IO_3^-(aq), \qquad (9\text{-}24)$$

with an equilibrium constant

$$K_s = [Ca^{++}][IO_3^-]^2. \qquad (9\text{-}25)$$

[Note that we have replaced activities by molarities and incorporated the (constant) activity of the solid calcium iodate into the equilibrium constant.] The iodate anion, IO_3^-, is the anion of a moderately weak acid, iodic acid, HIO_3. Thus if $Ca(IO_3)_2$ is dissolved in acidic solutions, the IO_3^- will react as follows:

$$H^+(aq) + IO_3^-(aq) \rightleftharpoons HIO_3(aq). \qquad (9\text{-}26)$$

This reaction will use up the IO_3^- in the solution so more $Ca(IO_3)_2$ will have to dissolve to maintain the equilibrium represented by Eqs. (9-24) and (9-25). Thus the solubility of $Ca(IO_3)_2$ will be higher in acidic solutions than in solutions without added acid. Reaction (9-26) is also, of course, described by an equilibrium constant. Usually we speak of acid dissociation constants, K_a, so we write the equilibrium constant for the reverse of reaction (9-26),

$$K_a = \frac{[H^+][IO_3^-]}{[HIO_3]}. \qquad (9\text{-}27)$$

Thus we have a competitive equilibrium: The IO_3^- is the focus of a competition between the Ca^{++}, which reacts to hold the IO_3^- as insoluble $Ca(IO_3)_2$ and H^+, which reacts to hold IO_3^- as HIO_3. The actual composition of the final equilibrium mixture must, in all cases, reflect the relative strengths of the two competitors. These strengths are quantitatively expressible in terms of the two equilibrium expressions, (9-25) and (9-27), both of which must be satisfied in the final equilibrium mixture. In addition to these two restrictions, a third stoichiometric relation must be satisfied. The only source of Ca^{++} and IO_3^- in the solution is the $Ca(IO_3)_2$. For each mole of $Ca(IO_3)_2$ that dissolves, 1 mole of

Ca^{++} and 2 moles of IO_3^- are introduced into the solution, so for every mole of Ca^{++} present in the solution 2 moles of IO_3^- will be present *in some form*. To be sure, the IO_3^- need not remain as such; some will be present in the form of HIO_3. However, the sum of the concentrations of the IO_3^- moiety contained in *all* species in solution will be twice the Ca^{++} concentration:

$$2[Ca^{++}] = [IO_3^-] + [HIO_3]. \qquad (9\text{-}28)$$

The composition of the final equilibrium mixture, then, must satisfy all three of the restrictions expressed in the relationships (9-25), (9-27), and (9-28).

In our experiment we shall determine the molar solubility, S (number of moles per liter), of solid calcium iodate in solutions of known (and constant) acidity. What we shall observe is the variation of S with $[H^+]$ of the solutions. Let us see how we can relate this to the equilibrium constants that we wish to determine, i.e., K_s and K_a.

We can rewrite (9-25) and (9-27) in the forms

$$[IO_3^-] = \left(\frac{K_s}{[Ca^{++}]} \right)^{1/2},$$

and

$$[HIO_3] = \frac{[H^+][IO_3^-]}{K_a} = \frac{[H^+]}{K_a} \left(\frac{K_s}{[Ca^{++}]} \right)^{1/2},$$

and then substitute these expressions into (9-28):

$$2[Ca^{++}] = \left(\frac{K_s}{[Ca^{++}]} \right)^{1/2} + \frac{[H^+]}{K_a} \left(\frac{K_s}{[Ca^{++}]} \right)^{1/2},$$

which may be rewritten

$$2[Ca^{++}]^{3/2} = K_s^{1/2} + \frac{K_s^{1/2}}{K_a}[H^+]. \qquad (9\text{-}29)$$

Since reaction (9-24) tells us that 1 mole/liter of Ca^{++} will be produced for every mole/liter of solid $Ca(IO_3)_2$ that dissolves, it is clear that $[Ca^{++}] = S = $ molar solubility of $Ca(IO_3)_2$. Substitution of this equivalence into (9-29) yields

$$2S^{3/2} = K_s^{1/2} + \frac{K_s^{1/2}}{K_a}[H^+]. \qquad (9\text{-}30)$$

Our experiments will yield a set of coordinated values of S and $[H^+]$. For each value of S we can easily calculate the value of $2S^{3/2}$. If the derivation we have made is sound, a plot of our values on a graph of $2S^{3/2}$ versus $[H^+]$ should define a straight line. (Why?) The value of the intercept of this line is $K_s^{1/2}$ and its slope is $K_s^{1/2}/K_a$.* Thus K_s can be obtained easily by squaring the value of the intercept, and dividing the intercept by the slope yields K_a. In principle, then, we have the possibility of finding both K_a and K_s from a single set of measurements.

As for the actual experiment, we will determine the solubility of $Ca(IO_3)_2$ in a series of aqueous solutions of perchloric acid, $HClO_4$, a strong acid, which ranges from 0.0 to 1.0 M in $HClO_4$. Such a wide span of concentrations should give a considerable range of solubilities and should permit us to make accurate measurements of the *variation* of solubility with $[H^+]$, i.e., accurate measurements of the *slope* on our graph. However, such a wide span of concentrations can produce a serious problem. We know from Section 9–1 and Experiment 15 that the activities of ions in aqueous solution are a function of the ionic strength of the solution, and in these solutions of $HClO_4$ the ionic strength will vary greatly from one solution to the next. Hence the approximation that molarity is equal to activity can surely be expected to break down, so that K_s and K_a calculated from (9–25) and (9–27) might vary from one solution to another. Fortunately, there is an easily accessible way around this difficulty. Instead of simply using $HClO_4$ solutions, we will use solutions containing mixtures of $HClO_4$ and $NaClO_4$. The *total* combined concentrations of the acid and the salt will be held constant at 1.0 M. Unlike $HClO_4$, $NaClO_4$ has no specific interaction with $Ca(IO_3)_2$, but like $HClO_4$, $NaClO_4$ is a strong electrolyte, i.e., it is completely dissociated into Na^+ and ClO_4^- in aqueous solution. Thus in all solutions we will have a 1.0 M concentration of a uniunivalent strong electrolyte and, consequently, an ionic strength that is at least approximately constant throughout a series of solutions containing radically different concentrations of $HClO_4$. (What is the ionic strength?) Under these conditions, K_s and K_a should be constant enough to support the derivation we performed above.†

How is the solubility determination to be made? We shake an excess of solid calcium iodate with each of the perchloric acid-perchlorate solutions and, after equilibrium is reached, determine the amount of dissolved calcium iodate per unit volume of the solution. We do this by removing a known amount of the equilibrium solution and, after establishing the amount of calcium iodate therein, at once calculating the number of moles of calcium iodate per liter of solution, the molar solubility. Either Ca^{++} or $IO_3^- + HIO_3$ could be determined volumetrically, but the method for $IO_3^- + HIO_3$ is probably easier and more accurate.‡ In the presence of excess H^+ and I^-, IO_3^- and HIO_3 react as follows:

$$IO_3^- + 5I^- + 6H^+ \rightarrow 3I_2 + 3H_2O, \qquad (9\text{--}31)$$

$$HIO_3 + 5I^- + 5H^+ \rightarrow 3I_2 + 3H_2O. \qquad (9\text{--}32)$$

In either case, we get three I_2 molecules per IO_3^- ion or HIO_3 molecule present.§ The iodine thus formed can be analyzed with great accuracy by titration with standard sodium thiosulfate, $Na_2S_2O_3$, solution, which reacts with the I_2 as follows:

$$2S_2O_3^= + I_2 \rightarrow S_4O_6^= + 2I^-. \qquad (9\text{--}33)$$

Thus each mole of I_2 formed by reactions (9–31) and (9–32) requires two moles of $S_2O_3^=$ in the titration. Assuming that a v-ml aliquot of the equilibrium solution of calcium iodate, treated with excess H^+ and I^-, requires V ml of a standard M molar thiosulfate solution for the titration represented by Eq. (9–33), work out for yourself an equation that will give you S, the molar solubility, in terms of v, V, and M. Remember that $[Ca^{++}] = S$ and that $2[Ca^{++}] = [IO_3^-] + [HIO_3]$. Do this *before* coming to the laboratory.

Procedure

Standard Thiosulfate Solution. Solutions of $Na_2S_2O_3$ are not stable for long periods of time (they are decomposed by sulfur-metabolizing bacteria) and so they must be made and standardized a short time (a few days at most) before use. To standardize the thiosulfate we use an accurately prepared, i.e., standard, solution of KIO_3 (which is perfectly stable). We treat an aliquot of this solution with excess H^+ and I^- and titrate the resulting solution, containing I_2 formed by reactions (9–31) and (9–32), with the thiosulfate solution being analyzed. This standardization procedure has the advantage of being done exactly the same way as the actual determinations in this experiment; any systematic errors in the titration procedure should cancel out. (Why?)

---

* If the line seems to show some curvature (if the slope changes), use the slope of the line in the immediate vicinity of the intercept.

† It must be noted that the values of K_s and K_a will *not* refer to solutions of $Ca(IO_3)_2$ and HIO_3 in otherwise pure water but, rather, to solutions in which the ionic strength is that of 1.0 M $NaClO_4$. One can *estimate* the magnitude of the difference in K_s in these two cases by determining the difference in the solubility of $Ca(IO_3)_2$ in pure water and in 1.0 M $NaClO_4$ solution. Why is this only an estimate?

‡ Suggestions for a volumetric calcium determination are given in the section on further experimental problems.

§ In solutions containing excess I^-, the I_2 reacts to form complexes such as I_3^-, but these react just as I_2 does in the titration with $S_2O_3^=$, so we have in these equations eliminated the complexation reaction for simplicity.

For this experiment the thiosulfate solution should be about 0.05 M, and we would like to use about 25 to 35 ml in the standardization titration to make it a relatively precise determination. If we use a 5.00-ml aliquot of the standard KIO_3 solution, how concentrated must we make this solution to use the proper amount of $S_2O_3^=$ solution for the titration? We know that 35 ml of 0.05 M $S_2O_3^=$ solution contains

$$(35 \times 10^{-3})(5 \times 10^{-2}) \text{ moles of } S_2O_3^=.$$

We see from Eq. (9–33) that 1 mole $S_2O_3^=$ reacts per $\frac{1}{2}$ mole I_2 and from Eqs. (9–31) and (9–32) we observe that 3 moles of I_2 are formed per mole of IO_3^- (or HIO_3). Thus one mole of IO_3^- produces enough I_2 to react with 6 moles of $S_2O_3^=$, or

$$(\text{Number of moles } IO_3^-) = \tfrac{1}{6} (\text{number of moles } S_2O_3^=)$$

and hence the number of moles of KIO_3 that must be contained in 5.00 ml of the KIO_3 solution is

$$(\text{Number of moles } KIO_3) = \tfrac{1}{6} (35 \times 10^{-3})(5 \times 10^{-2})$$
$$\simeq 3 \times 10^{-4}.$$

Thus the molarity of the solution should be

$$[IO_3^-] = \frac{3 \times 10^{-4} \text{ moles}}{5 \times 10^{-3} \text{ liter}} = 6 \times 10^{-2} \ M.$$

The molecular weight of KIO_3 is 214.0. To make 100 ml of KIO_3 solution that is 6×10^{-2} M will require $(6 \times 10^{-2})(100 \times 10^{-3})(214) = 1.3$ gm KIO_3.

Roughly weigh about 1.5 gm of reagent-grade KIO_3 into a clean dry weighing bottle. Put the bottle on its side in a beaker and dry the sample for one hour at 150°C. Let the bottle cool in your desiccator. Accurately (to the nearest 0.0002 gm) weigh out by difference the proper amount of KIO_3 to make a 6×10^{-2} M solution in your 100-ml volumetric flask. Add distilled water, mix, make up to the mark, and mix thoroughly. (See Section 4–6 for detailed instructions on making up standard solutions.) Calculate and record the exact concentration of this standard KIO_3 solution. Transfer the standard KIO_3 solution to a clean, dry, stoppered, and labeled bottle for storage.

Standardize thiosulfate solutions within a few days of the time they will be used. Obtain from your instructor 500 to 600 ml of a solution that is about 0.05 M in $S_2O_3^=$. In a clean container, prepare a solution of 10 gm of potassium iodide, KI, in 25 ml of distilled water. (This solution must be made fresh each day since oxygen from the air slowly oxidizes I^- to I_2 in aqueous solution. This would ruin your determinations. Why?) Obtain from the reagent shelf about 60 ml of 1 M HCl or prepare it by dilution of the concentrated (12 M) acid. Fill your buret with the $S_2O_3^=$ solution to be standardized. Pour

some of the standard KIO_3 into a clean, dry beaker, rinse your 5-ml pipet with this solution, and then pipet 5.00 ml of the KIO_3 solution into a clean 250-ml flask. Add 20 ml of distilled water, 5 ml of the KI solution (Is this an excess of I^- over IO_3^-? How much?), and 10 ml of 1 M HCl. The solution will immediately turn dark red as I_2 is formed, and you must carry out the titration *at once*. Run the thiosulfate into the flask with steady (but not violent) swirling until the iodine color has faded to pale yellow. Then, *but not before*, add 5 ml of the starch suspension used as an iodine indicator. The intensely blue-black starch-iodine complex will be formed. Continue adding thiosulfate cautiously with constant swirling of the reaction mixture until the color is bleached to a barely perceptible tint. Observe that you must *not*, in this case, overshoot the endpoint. Even if one were to put the KIO_3 solution in a buret, one could not repair an overtitration by backtitrating with KIO_3. The reason is that in acid solution thiosulfate decomposes according to the equation:

$$S_2O_3^= + 2H^+ = H_2SO_3 + S.$$

This reaction is slow enough that it does not occur significantly as long as I_2 is available in the solution to react (very swiftly) with the $S_2O_3^=$ added. (It is to avoid any local depletion of I_2 that steady swirling is recommended in this titration.) However, any *excess* thiosulfate will undergo the above reaction, rendering back titration a wholly ineffectual measure.

After the standardization is complete, read and record the volume of thiosulfate used. Repeat the standardization at least twice more and calculate the molarity of the thiosulfate solution. Label your bottle containing thiosulfate with its molarity.

The Solubility of $Ca(IO_3)_2$ in $HClO_4$-$NaClO_4$ Solutions.

Prepare seven clean dry test tubes; label them from 1 to 7; and fit them with clean cork stoppers. Put about 0.2 gm of solid calcium iodate, prepared in Experiment 16,* in each test tube. Place the test tubes in your test-tube rack, and fill test tubes 1 through 6 to about the half-way point with the $HClO_4$-$NaClO_4$ solution of the corresponding number from the following tabulation:

Solution	Composition, M	
	$HClO_4$	$NaClO_4$
1	1.0	0.0
2	0.8	0.2
3	0.6	0.4
4	0.4	0.6
5	0.2	0 8
6	0.0	1.0

* Commercial calcium iodate will work just as well after digestion for a few weeks in distilled water, just as our preparation is digested.

If these solutions have not already been made up by the instructors, they may easily be prepared by mixing in a clean dry test tube or beaker the appropriate quantities of the 1.0 M $HClO_4$ and 1.0 M $NaClO_4$ solutions that will be available in the laboratory. (The solutions may be dispensed from burets; work with your neighbor and fill one buret with $HClO_4$ and the other with $NaClO_4$ solution.) Do not be wasteful of these stock solutions. To test tube 7, add a corresponding volume of pure distilled water. Stopper the test tubes tightly and set them aside for a minimum of a week or ten days. To hasten the attainment of equilibrium, stir each sample with a *clean dry* stirring rod each time you come to the laboratory. Take great care not to splash the solutions on the cork stoppers, as perchlorates are strong oxidants and will attack the cork.

At the end of the time allotted, analyze the solutions by exactly the same procedure as you used to standardize the $S_2O_3^=$ solution. Rinse your 5.00-ml pipet with a milliliter or so of one of the solutions, *being very careful not to draw any solid* $Ca(IO_3)_2$ *into the pipet.* Pipet a 5.00-ml aliquot of the solution into a 250-ml flask, again being very careful not to get any solid $Ca(IO_3)_2$ into the pipet. (Why?) Add 20 ml of distilled water, 5 ml of KI solution, and 10 ml of 1 M HCl. Titrate immediately with your standard $S_2O_3^=$ solution, again using the starch indicator when you are very close to the endpoint. Remember that you must *not* overshoot the endpoint. Repeat the determination with a second 5.00-ml aliquot of the solution. Treat all seven solutions in this manner.

Calculations

Calculate the molar solubility of calcium iodate, S, in the seven solutions. Compare and discuss the differences between solutions 6 and 7. Tabulate the values of $[H^+]$, S, and $2S^{3/2}$ for solutions 1 through 6. Plot these data on a graph of $2S^{3/2}$ (ordinate) versus $[H^+]$ (abscissa) and from the graph determine K_s and K_a.

All these calculations assume that $[H^+]$ is that which we add as $HClO_4$, but obviously some of the added H^+ is used up by reaction with IO_3^-. Given your result

for K_a, show that it is a good approximation to neglect this reaction in computing $[H^+]$.

Further Experimental Problems

Although it is stated above that $NaClO_4$ has no specific interaction with $Ca(IO_3)_2$, this has not been proved. One approach to such a "proof" is to redo the experiment with some other "inert" salt, such as KNO_3 or $Mg(ClO_4)_2$, added to keep the ionic strength constant to see if different salts cause differences to be observed in K_s and/or K_a.

The volumetric determination of calcium is almost always carried out complexometrically. The complexing agent used for this determination is ethylenediaminetetraacetic acid, EDTA, which has the structure

$$HOOCCH_2 \qquad\qquad CH_2COOH$$
$$\diagdown\qquad\qquad\qquad\diagup$$
$$N-H_2C-CH_2-N$$
$$\diagup\qquad\qquad\qquad\diagdown$$
$$HOOCCH_2 \qquad\qquad CH_2COOH$$

This compound is often abbreviated as H_4Y, where the four acidic hydrogens are those on the carboxyl (COOH) groups. When all four H^+'s are lost, we get Y^{-4}, which is a very powerful complexing agent in part because this one molecule can "wrap itself around" many six-coordinate metal ions so that it takes up all six coordination positions (the nitrogens are at two of the positions and the oxygens at the other four). This complexing ability may be compared with that of ethylenediamine, $H_2NCH_2CH_2NH_2$, the parent compound, which can coordinate only two positions (see Experiments 3 and 26). Because this complexing reaction goes to "completion," it can be used as the basis for a volumetric quantitative analysis for certain metal ions with standard solutions of Y^{-4}. You might find it interesting to check your titrations of IO_3^- by analyzing a sample of $Ca(IO_3)_2$ solution for Ca^{++} as well as IO_3^-. The procedure for EDTA titrations and more of the theory of these titrations and the indicators used will be found in most textbooks of quantitative analysis, a few of which are listed in the references.

EXPERIMENT 18. *The Solubility of Silver Acetate*

Introduction

Solid silver acetate might dissolve to give a variety of species in solution. In addition to the free hydrated Ag^+ and OAc^- (acetate ion, CH_3COO^-), undissociated molecules such as AgOAc may be found at high concentrations of OAc^-. It will be our task in this experiment

to determine as much as we can about the relative importance of these species and the equilibrium constants that govern their behavior.

In our treatment we assume that: the activity coefficients of all univalent ions are equal (we shall denote this activity coefficient as γ), the activity coefficients of neutral molecules (e.g., AgOAc) in solution are unity, and higher acetate complexes (e.g., $Ag(OAc)_3^=$) may be neglected. The species Ag_2OAc^+ may be important in the presence of added Ag^+; however, we will work only with extra OAc^- from added sodium acetate.

The following three reactions define the equilibrium constants needed to describe our system, under the limitations imposed above:

$$AgOAc(aq) \rightleftharpoons Ag^+ + OAc^-,$$
$$K_i = \frac{\gamma^2[Ag^+][OAc^-]}{[AgOAc(aq)]};$$

$$AgOAc(s) \rightleftharpoons Ag^+ + OAc^-,$$
$$K_s = \gamma^2[Ag^+][OAc^-];$$

$$Ag(OAc)_2^- \rightleftharpoons Ag^+ + 2OAc^-,$$
$$K_c = \frac{\gamma^3[Ag^+][OAc^-]^2}{\gamma[Ag(OAc)_2^-]}$$
$$= \frac{\gamma^2[Ag^+][OAc^-]^2}{[Ag(OAc)_2^-]}.$$

These three equations may be solved for the concentrations of silver-containing species in terms of γ and $[OAc^-]$:

$$[Ag^+] = K_s/\gamma^2[OAc^-],$$
$$[AgOAc(aq)] = K_s/K_i,$$
$$[Ag(OAc)_2^-] = K_s[OAc^-]/K_c.$$

(Show how these are derived from the preceding three equations.) The solubility of silver acetate, S, found by titrating the total silver in solution by the Volhard method will be

$$S = [Ag^+] + [AgOAc(aq)] + [Ag(OAc)_2^-] \qquad (9\text{--}34)$$
$$= (K_s/\gamma^2)\left(\frac{1}{[OAc^-]}\right) + K_s/K_i + (K_s/K_c)[OAc^-].$$

Thus, sufficiently accurate measurements of solubility with varying (and known) amounts of added acetate under conditions such that γ is essentially the same in all solutions will enable us to determine the relative significance of K_s, K_i, and K_c and values for some or all of these numbers. Constant γ is achieved in practice by maintaining a constant ionic strength. For univalent ions, this is equivalent to maintaining a constant concentration of salt. [Can you show how this is true from the definition of ionic strength following Eq. (9–2)?] Since sodium nitrate does not precipitate in reactions with silver ion, our solutions will be prepared so that $[NaOAc] + [NaNO_3] = $ const (2.0 M for this experiment).

Procedure

Work with a partner on this experiment. Teamwork and division of labor are helpful throughout.

Prepare eight solutions of varying sodium acetate concentrations and constant $[NaOAc] + [NaNO_3]$ and saturate them with silver acetate as follows. Pipet the specified volume of 2.0 M NaOAc into a 100-ml volumetric flask and fill to the mark with 2.0 M NaNO$_3$. (The NaOAc and NaNO$_3$ solutions will be available in the laboratory.) The volume of 2.0 M NaOAc to be used in each of the eight solutions is: 0.00 ml, 2.00 ml, 4.00 ml, 5.00 ml, 10.0 ml, 25.0 ml, 50.0 ml, and 100 ml. (By starting with the solution most dilute in sodium acetate and working up the concentration range, you will need only one 100-ml volumetric flask, which need not be dried before preparing the next solution.) Pour each mixture into a 250-ml flask, add 2 to 3 gm of solid silver acetate (from the reagent shelf), and warm the mixture, with swirling, in a beaker of hot water at about 60°C. (Heating will bring enough AgOAc into the solution to supersaturate it at 25°C and will speed the attainment of solubility equilibrium at the lower temperature.) Stopper the flask with a clean rubber stopper and suspend it in a 25°C constant-temperature bath to equilibrate.* Use a length of copper wire around the neck of the flask to hang it in the bath, which should be covered in some manner to protect the solutions from light, since silver salts photodecompose. Be certain that each flask is clearly labeled with the sample number and your initials.

After equilibration of your mixtures (you should probably wait until the next laboratory period or longer) remove two 25.0-ml aliquots of the solution from each flask for titration with standard 0.0500 M KSCN solution by the Volhard method.† Each partner should titrate four of the eight solutions and, as a check on individual work, the samples for each partner should be alternated, that is, one person should *not* titrate the four samples of lowest acetate concentration. Care is required in removing the aliquots from the mixture to avoid getting any solid silver acetate, which would also be titrated by the thiocyanate solution, into the pipet. One approach is to use a pipet fitted at the tip with a filter consisting of a short (2 or 3 cm) piece of clean rubber tubing packed with glass wool. Remove the filter before adjusting the level of the liquid in the pipet to the mark. Use a different glass wool filter for each of the solutions and rinse out the pipet with a few milliliters of the filtered solution before taking the sample.

---

* If constant temperature baths are not available, it is probably satisfactory to use one-half of an expanded foam acid carton with the center dividers cut out to act as a bath. When this is filled with water at room-temperature and covered with the other half of the carton, any temperature fluctuations inside it will be very small. Measure the temperature of the bath at intervals to convince yourself of this.

† If the standard thiocyanate solution is not available in the laboratory, directions for preparing and standardizing KSCN solutions are given in Section 4–9.

The procedure for performing the Volhard titration is given in Experiment 4; we will give here only those instructions that pertain to the present situation. Add to each sample to be titrated 1 to 2 ml of a saturated (about 40%) ferric ammonium sulfate indicator solution and then just enough 3 M HNO$_3$ to discharge the red color which would mask the endpoint. (The red color is probably due to a complex formed between ferric ion and acetate ion. How does the addition of acid prevent this complexation reaction?) The volume of acid required will vary with the acetate concentration. Titrate with the standard KSCN to the usual endpoint. Each partner will presumably do eight titrations unless for some reason you take a third aliquot of some of the mixtures.

Calculations

Calculate the solubility, S (total silver titrated), of AgOAc in moles/liter in each solution.

Plot S vs. the concentration (after dilution) of added sodium acetate, [NaOAc], to get a qualitative indication of the nature of this equilibrium system. *If*, at low concentrations of added OAc$^-$, the [Ag(OAc)$_2^-$] is small compared to the first two terms of Eq. (9–34), then the following material balances are valid (show these for yourself):

$$[OAc^-] = [NaOAc]_0 + [Ag^+],$$

$$S = [Ag^+] + [AgOAc(aq)],$$

$$[OAc^-] = [NaOAc]_0 + S - [AgOAc(aq)],$$

$$S = \frac{K_s}{\gamma^2} \left(\frac{1}{[NaOAc]_0 + S - [AgOAc(aq)]} \right) + [AgOAc(aq)].$$

From your initial plot, make an estimate (Will this be a maximum or a minimum value?) for K_s/K_i and use this to make a plot of S versus $1/([NaOAc]_0 + S - [AgOAc(aq)])$. Extrapolate the plot to find the intercept so you can check your value of [AgOAc(aq)].

Find out as much as possible about K_c from other plots and manipulations of your data. Consult with your instructor if you are unable to proceed *after* meditating on this problem.

For 2.0 M NaNO$_3$, $\gamma \simeq 0.48$. Evaluate the equilibrium constants and comment on the accuracy of these numbers.

Further Experimental Problems

Two interesting sidelights of this experiment that you might like to follow up are the investigation of possible cationic complexes (e.g., Ag$_2$OAc$^+$) that might be formed when excess Ag$^+$ is added to the solution and the investigation of the nature of the red complex formed in solutions containing acetate and ferric ions. The former problem might be studied just as the anionic complexes were studied in this experiment. A possible first approach to the latter problem would be a continuous variation treatment as outlined in Experiment 20.

EXPERIMENT 19.   Solvent Systems Other Than Water: The Acidity Function

Introduction

The greatest problem in defining an acidity scale in solvents other than water is that pH is not defined in such solvents. There are bases which are too weak to accept protons, H$^+$, from water but which can accept protons from a more acidic solvent, and it would be valuable to study their properties and to derive the pK_a's of the acidic forms. This problem can be attacked by using a new concept, the "acidity function" (introduced by Hammett), which defined an empirical acidity scale in a solvent more acidic than water.

The Acidity Function

The acidity function, H_0, is a measure of the ability of a solvent medium to donate protons; in dilute aqueous solutions it becomes equivalent to pH. Measurements of H_0 are based on the *assumption* that any given solvent medium will show the same tendency to donate protons to any uncharged base, regardless of the nature of that base. Therefore, uncharged indicator bases may be used to measure H_0 directly for any solvent medium.

Consider the reaction

$$A + H^+ \rightleftharpoons HA^+$$

which has an equilibrium constant for the reverse (acidic) reaction,

$$K_a^A = \frac{a_{H^+} a_A}{a_{HA^+}}.$$

We shall take logarithms of both sides of this equation and introduce molar concentrations and activity coefficients for A and HA$^+$ to get

$$\log K_a^A = \log \frac{a_{H^+} a_A}{a_{HA^+}} = \log \frac{a_{H^+} \gamma_A}{\gamma_{HA^+}} + \log \frac{[A]}{[HA^+]},$$

or

$$pK_a^A = -\log \frac{[A]}{[HA^+]} - \log \frac{a_{H^+} \gamma_A}{\gamma_{HA^+}}. \tag{9–35}$$

(Do you see how Eq. (9–35) follows from the preceding equation?) Since a_{H^+} and γ_A/γ_{HA^+} have definite values in any solvent (even though these values are unknown to us) and since these values will be independent of the nature of base A (the result of our assumption above), the term

$$-\log \frac{a_{H^+}\gamma_A}{\gamma_{HA^+}}$$

must have a definite value for a given solvent system. For a given pK_a, you can see that the magnitude of this term determines [by Eq. (9–35)] how much of base A is present in the form of its conjugate acid, HA^+. This term is, therefore, a measure of the solvent's ability to donate protons, and it is defined as the acidity function,

$$H_0 = -\log \frac{a_{H^+}\gamma_A}{\gamma_{HA^+}}. \qquad (9\text{–}36)$$

From Eq. (9–35) we see then that

$$H_0 = pK_a^A + \log \frac{[A]}{[HA^+]}, \qquad (9\text{–}37)$$

which is our starting point for determining H_0 or pK_a^A experimentally.

If the indicator base, A, is colored and its conjugate acid, HA^+, is not colored (or vice versa), it is a simple matter to determine the ratio $[A]/[HA^+]$ in any solvent system. If the pK_a^A of the indicator is known, H_0 can be readily determined and conversely.

In the present experiment we will determine H_0 for a series of sulfuric acid-water mixtures. We shall begin with the base p-nitroaniline,

$$O_2N-\underset{\bigcirc}{}-NH_2$$

whose pK_a is known, and measure H_0 directly with this indicator. For low concentrations of sulfuric acid this will be fine, but after the concentration of sulfuric acid reaches about 12%, no further change in the $[A]/[HA^+]$ ratio will occur with increasing sulfuric acid concentration; indeed, a calculation would indicate that essentially all the indicator is in the acidic form, HA^+, in these solutions. This means that it is not possible to measure H_0 with this indicator for solutions having concentrations of sulfuric acid greater than 12%. We will then select another indicator that is a weaker base than p-nitroaniline, o-nitroaniline,

$$\underset{\bigcirc}{}\overset{NH_2}{\underset{NO_2}{}}$$

(Note that the designations p, para, and o, ortho, refer to the position of the nitro, NO_2, group relative to the amino, NH_2, group. The "parent compound" is assumed to be aniline,

$$\underset{\bigcirc}{}-NH_2$$

for the purpose of naming.*) This will allow us to extend the range of acid concentration for which we can measure H_0. To make this measurement, we must know pK_a for this second indicator. Let us say that the second indicator is B and that the reaction $B + H^+ \rightleftharpoons HB^+$ is the one of interest, so that

$$K_a^B = \frac{a_{H^+}a_B}{a_{HB^+}}.$$

Now, if there is some particular solvent mixture in which both $[A]/[HA^+]$ and $[B]/[HB^+]$ are measurable, but not of the same value (Why?), then from Eq. (9–37)

$$pK_a^A + \log \frac{[A]}{[HA^+]} = pk_a^B + \log \frac{[B]}{[HB^+]},$$

and

$$pK_a^A - pK_a^B = \log \frac{[B]}{[HB^+]} - \log \frac{[A]}{[HA^+]}. \qquad (9\text{–}38)$$

Equation (9–38) enables us to calculate pK_a^B for the indicator B and, using this value in Eq. (9–37), we can calculate H_0 for any acid-water mixture in which we can measure $[B]/[HB^+]$.

Measuring the Fraction of an Indicator in a Given Form

How do we measure the indicator ratios we need? We can use spectrophotometric measurements if one or the other of the forms of the indicator absorbs light in a convenient spectral region. The basic assumption we shall make is that in distilled water the equilibrium $A + H^+ \rightleftharpoons HA^+$ lies far enough to the left that essentially all the indicator is present in the basic form A. Then we can apply the Beer-Lambert Law, $A_0 = ab[A]_0$, where $[A]_0$ is the concentration of the indicator in the distilled water (when it is all in the form A). Now, if we measure the absorbance (at the same wavelength) of a solution in which part of the indicator has been converted to the acid form, HA^+ (which is colorless or at least does not absorb at the wavelength we have chosen), we will observe a smaller absorbance, $A_1 = ab[A]$, where [A] is the concentration of A in this solution.

---

* A better way of naming these two compounds, p- and o-nitroaniline, is to use positional numbers, i.e., 4-nitroaniline and 2-nitroaniline, respectively, where the 1-position is that to which the NH_2 group is attached.

Thus

$$\frac{A_0}{A_1} = \frac{ab[A]_0}{ab[A]} = \frac{[A]_0}{[A]}.$$

Now if both solutions contain the same molarity of indicator, i.e., if $[A] + [HA^+] = [A]_0$ in both cases, then $[A] = [A]_0(A_1/A_0)$. Since the total number of moles of indicator must be conserved,

$$[HA] = [A]_0 - [A] = [A]_0\{1-(A_1/A_0)\},$$

and therefore

$$\frac{[A]}{[HA]} = \frac{[A]_0(A_1/A_0)}{[A]_0\{1 - (A_1/A_0)\}}$$

$$= \frac{(A_1/A_0)}{1 - (A_1/A_0)} = \frac{A_1}{A_0 - A_1}.$$

We can substitute this relationship into Eq. (9–37) to obtain

$$H_0 = pK_a + \log \frac{A_1}{A_0 - A_1}, \qquad (9\text{–}39)$$

from which H_0 may be calculated if pK_a for the indicator and A_0 and A_1 (absorbance of the indicator in the solvent of interest) are known. If H_0 is known and the absorbance measurements are made, then pK_a of the indicator is readily obtained.

Note that in this treatment it is not necessary to know the concentration of the indicator if the total concentration is the same in all solutions and if it is valid to assume that it is all present in the basic form in distilled water. For the indicators to be used in this experiment this is a valid assumption. (How might we check it?)

Procedure

Work with a partner on this experiment. The data are not difficult to obtain, but working as partners will reduce the amount of volumetric glassware the class will need.

Prepare 100 ml of each of the following sulfuric acid-water mixtures as accurately as possible, using pipets and graduated cylinders (it is even more imperative than usual that you do NOT pipet solutions by mouth): 2, 5, 8, 16, 25, 30, and 40 weight percent H_2SO_4. (Concentrated sulfuric acid has a specific gravity of 1.84.) Keep these solutions in labeled *stoppered* vessels. Sulfuric acid solutions are very hygroscopic and will readily absorb water from the atmosphere.

Obtain about 10 ml of each of the indicator stock solutions: *p*-nitroaniline (PNA), $4 \times 10^{-5}\,M$, *o*-nitroaniline (ONA), $10^{-4}\,M$, and *p*-chloro-*o*-nitroaniline

(CNA), $10^{-4}\,M$. Pipet 1.00 ml of each indicator into separate 25-ml volumetric flasks and make up to the mark with distilled water.

Using a spectrophotometer or spectrocolorimeter, measure the absorbance of each solution at the indicated wavelength: PNA, 380 mμ; ONA, 405 mμ; CNA, 420 mμ. Use distilled water as the blank for each measurement.

Prepare the following solutions of indicators by pipetting 1.00 ml of the indicator into a 25-ml volumetric flask and making up to volume with the indicated sulfuric acid solution. (Once a solution has been made and mixed it may be transferred to another clean, dry, labeled, stoppered or capped vessel.)

Solution number	Indicator	Percent H_2SO_4
1	PNA	2.00
2	PNA	5.00
3	PNA	8.00
4	ONA	5.00
5	ONA	8.00
6	ONA	16.00
7	ONA	25.00
8	CNA	16.00
9	CNA	25.00
10	CNA	30.00
11	CNA	40.00

Measure the absorbance of each of these solutions at the appropriate wavelength as indicated above for the water solutions. Remember, the solvent blank must contain the same percentage of sulfuric acid as the solution being measured.

Calculations

Tabulate the fraction of indicator that is in the acidic form in each of the sulfuric acid-water mixtures.

Given only that pK_a for *p*-nitroaniline is 1.11, calculate H_0 for each of the sulfuric acid-water mixtures studied in this experiment. Put these results in your tabulation. Be certain to explain fully how you interpolate between indicators.

Plot H_0 as a function of percent sulfuric acid (do not forget the dilution by the indicator solution). Calculate pK_a for *o*-nitroaniline and *p*-chloro-*o*-nitroaniline. (How would you name the latter compound using positional numbering?)

If you had forgotten to take the absorbance readings for ONA and CNA in distilled water, could you determine H_0 in all the solutions? If you could, you might check the above calculations by ignoring the measured absorbances of these indicators in distilled water, calculating H_0, and comparing these results with your previous tabulation.

Further Experimental Problems

An assumption made in this experiment is that the acidic form of each indicator does not absorb light at the monitoring wavelength we use. Prove or disprove this assumption.

You might find it interesting to extend this treatment to relatively concentrated solutions of other acids, e.g., HCl in the range 0.1 to 4 M. (See Hammett's book and the review article by Paul and Long cited in the references at the end of the chapter for further discussions of the acidity function.)

An experiment that points out the usefulness of the acidity function concept is outlined in the article by Dawber, Brown, and Reed. The proposed experiment is a study of the acid-catalyzed rate of inversion of sucrose and a test of the mechanism of the reaction to determine whether it is dependent on the concentration of acid in the solution, $[H^+]$, or on the proton-donating ability of the solvent, H_0. This reaction may be quite conveniently followed colorimetrically rather than polarimetrically as described in the article. See Experiment 31 for details of the colorimetric method.

Other references in the book and articles cited in the previous paragraphs will give you even more ideas for further tests of the concept and utility of the acidity function.

EXPERIMENT 20.   The Iron(III)-Sulfosalicylic Acid Complex; The Method of Continuous Variations

Iron(III) and sulfosalicylic acid (SSA)

form a strongly colored complex in acid solution. The formula of the complex in terms of the SSA/Fe ratio can be determined from spectrophotometric measurements by the technique of continuous variations.

The Method of Continuous Variations

The continuous-variation method, sometimes called Job's method, is often useful for studying the stoichiometry of equilibrium reactions, especially those with relatively large equilibrium constants. Any measurable manifestation of an equilibrium reaction can be used to study the reaction by this method, which involves determining the extent of the reaction in a series of mixtures of the reactants in which the *sum* of the number of moles of each reactant is held constant but their *ratio* is varied "continuously."

To explain the use of Job's method, let us begin with the general reaction

$$mA + nB \rightleftharpoons A_mB_n.$$

We shall assume that this reaction occurs in solution and, further, that we are able to obtain a measure of the amount of A_mB_n present at equilibrium.* The equilib-

rium constant for this reaction is

$$K = \frac{[A_mB_n]}{[A]^m[B]^n}.$$

The constraint we impose on any system we study by this method is that the number of moles of A plus the number of moles of B must be a constant. If we work always with the same volume of solution, then this requirement may be written

$$c_A + c_B = c$$

where c_A and c_B are the concentrations of A and B that would be present if no reaction occurred. To make the mathematics easier to follow, we shall let $c_A = x$ and $[A_mB_n] = y$ so that $[A] = x - my$ and $[B] = c - x - ny$. The equilibrium constant is then

$$K = \frac{y}{(x - my)^m(c - x - ny)^n}.$$

We know that if K were infinitely large, the reaction would go to completion and hence be limited by the amount of A or B initially present, whichever would disappear first. In this case if A is the limiting reagent, then $my = x$; if B is the limiting reagent, then $ny = c - x$. Why? A plot of y as a function of x would, in this case, be a pair of straight lines that would intersect where

$$\frac{1}{m}x = \frac{1}{n}(c - x) \qquad \text{or}$$

$$\frac{n}{m} = \frac{c - x}{x}. \qquad (9\text{-}40)$$

Figure 9-2 shows such a plot.

Although K may be large, it is not infinitely so, and such straight-line theoretical plots are only more or less closely approximated by actual experimental data. This does not, however, spell the doom of this method for obtaining the n/m ratio. Let us differentiate the equilib-

---

* In most applications spectrophotometric measurements are used, but this is not mandatory. For example, if A_mB_n is a solid that is precipitated when A and B are mixed, then we might separate the solid and weigh it as a measure of the amount formed.

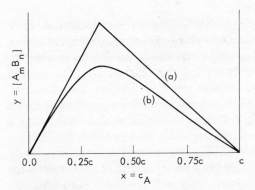

Fig. 9–2. A continuous variation plot for the cases where (a) K is infinitely large, and (b) K is finite.

rium-constant expression implicitly with respect to x to obtain

$$Km(x - my)^{m-1}(c - x - ny)^n[1 - m(dy/dx)]$$
$$+ Kn(x - my)^m(c - x - ny)^{n-1}[-1 - n(dy/dx)]$$
$$= dy/dx.$$

The condition for a maximum in the y-versus-x plot is that $dy/dx = 0$, so that the foregoing equation can be reduced to

$$m(c - x - ny) - n(x - my) = 0$$

and hence

$$\frac{n}{m} = \frac{c - x}{x}.$$

(Show how this series of transformations comes about.) Thus at the maximum in the plot of y versus x the same relationship holds as if the equilibrium constant were infinitely large, and the empirical formula of the complex can be obtained regardless of the value of K, Fig. 9–2. Obviously the maximum in the curve will be more pronounced if K is large, so the method is more accurate for reactions with larger equilibrium constants.

Since the absorbance of a solution due to a colored species present in it is directly proportional to the concentration of that species, this method is particularly applicable to compounds that form spectrophotometrically detectable complexes or compounds. Thus, in the present example, if A_mB_n is the only absorbing species in the solution at a particular wavelength, we can write the absorbance, A, as

$$A = aby$$

and can plot A as a function of x and obtain a Job's method plot from which n/m can be found. (Do you see why this is so?) Naturally, if other absorbing species are present in the solution, corrections to the measured absorbance will have to be made. Often the unreacted species A and/or B also absorb light at the wavelength of interest. A true correction for this situation would involve knowing m, n, and K. Since they are not known,

the correction usually applied is to assume that no reaction has occurred and subtract the appropriate amount from the measured absorbance. This is an overcorrection, but it usually makes little difference, since we try to choose wavelengths for the analysis where such interference is very small. (A tacit assumption made throughout this paragraph is that the absorbance of the complexes or compounds of interest follows Beer's Law. Can you think of any ways to check this assumption?)

A complication that must be borne in mind when the method of continuous variations is used is that more than one reaction may occur; more than one complex may be formed. If the relative amounts of various complexes change as the variations are made, it will be very difficult to study any one of them. This is particularly true if they interfere with one another in the analysis. Moreover, many of the reactions one might study in this way are pH dependent and will change as variations are made unless the pH is held constant. If spectrophotometry is used as the analytical tool, these complications can be lumped together under the heading of deviations from Beer's Law. To be more certain of the systems you are studying, take complete absorption spectra of all solutions. If everything is as it should be, the spectra will all be the same (after the fact that the concentration of the species of interest is not the same in all the solutions is considered).

An Application

In our application of the method of continuous variations we will make light-absorbance measurements on equal volumes of solutions in which the sum of the moles of iron(III) and of sulfosalicylic acid present is held fixed and their ratio is varied "continuously." The absorbance of the iron(III)-SSA complex at its wavelength maximum follows Beer's Law, i.e., it is linear with concentration. (This is an unproved assertion. How can you check it experimentally?) When, within the condition of fixed total moles (and fixed volume), the ratio of SSA to iron(III) is that of the formula of the complex, there will be a maximum concentration of complex and hence maximum absorption. From a plot of absorbance vs. the ratio (moles Fe)/(moles Fe + moles SSA), with the moles Fe + moles SSA as the fixed quantity, the point of maximum absorbance can be found and the formula deduced.

A 1:1 iron(III)-SSA complex might have the structure

where the iron has replaced two acidic hydrogens. (The hydrogen on the $-SO_3H$ group is strongly acidic and is completely dissociated in aqueous solution.) Thus such a complex formation would almost certainly be pH dependent, since iron and hydrogen ion are both competing for the SSA positions; the pH must, therefore, be controlled. We shall do this by making up the solutions in a bisulfate-sulfate, $HSO_4^-:SO_4^=$, buffer solution. This might add complications because Fe(III) forms sulfate complexes, but the concentration of sulfate is constant in all these solutions so the amount of such complexing will be proportional to the amount of iron present. Thus the same percentage of Fe(III) is used in each case, and our method of analyzing this problem is not invalidated. (See Waser's text for a short discussion of this point.)

To perform the experiment, solutions of Fe(III) and SSA of accurately known concentrations must be available. Neither solution can be made up by dissolving accurately weighed samples in water, since SSA is usually not completely dry and will decompose on prolonged heating and Fe(III) compounds are not sufficiently stoichiometrically pure. The concentration of SSA in a solution can, however, be determined by titration with standard base. Two equivalents of base are required for the titration, since both the $-SO_3H$ and $-COOH$ groups are titrated at a phenolphthalein endpoint; pK_a for the $-COOH$ group is 2.67.

The concentration of Fe(III) in a solution is most easily obtained by reduction of the Fe(III) to Fe(II) and then titration with a standard solution of an oxidizing agent such as dichromate, $Cr_2O_7^=$. The reduction of Fe(III) is usually done with stannous ions, Sn(II), added to the solution as stannous chloride. The reaction

$$Sn^{++} + 2Fe^{+3} \rightarrow Sn^{+4} + 2Fe^{++}$$

is very fast at elevated temperatures. Obviously any excess Sn(II) that is added must be destroyed before the titration is carried out. This is accomplished by adding Hg(II) to the solution in the form of mercuric chloride, which is reduced to Hg(I) and precipitates as mercurous chloride, Hg_2Cl_2. Mercurous chloride is not readily reactive with the oxidizing agents used to titrate ferrous ion. The only precaution which must be observed in this reduction is that no more than a slight excess of Sn(II) may be added to the Fe(III) solution or there will be a danger of the Hg(II) being partially reduced to Hg metal,

$$Sn^{++} + HgCl_2 \rightarrow Sn^{+4} + Hg + 2Cl^-.$$

The formation of Hg metal, indicated by a gray or black precipitate, may ruin a determination because the metal in this finely divided form reacts with the oxidizing

agents used for Fe(II) titrations. The reaction of Sn(II) with Hg(II) is always carried out in a cool solution and the $HgCl_2$ is added as rapidly as possible to prevent the occurrence of this undesirable side reaction. The solution is then titrated with a standard solution of an oxidizing agent, potassium dichromate in this case. The endpoint of this oxidation-reduction titration is detected with a *redox indicator*, diphenylamine sulfonate, which changes color when the oxidizing power of the solution suddenly increases at the equivalence point. (The theory of such oxidation-reduction titrations is discussed in Chapter 10.) If only chloride or sulfate ions are present in this titration, the endpoint is not sharp and occurs too early because the indicator is partially oxidized before the equivalence point is reached. If phosphoric acid is added, however, a sharp color change does occur at the equivalence point. The phosphoric acid forms a complex with the ferric ions that effectively lowers the concentration of these ions and makes the change in oxidizing power of the solution at the equivalence point larger and sharper. (See Kolthoff and Sandell, Chapter 14 in Waser, and Section 10-6 for further discussions of this titration.)

Procedure

A standardized solution, about 0.0100 M, of SSA will be available in the laboratory. Use this solution sparingly; you will need only about 25 ml of it.

Make up a stock solution of Fe(III) and standardize it by titration with standard dichromate solution.* Make up 200 ml of a solution that is about 0.01 M in Fe(III) by weighing out the requisite amount of $Fe_2(SO_4)_3 \cdot (NH_4)_2SO_4 \cdot 24H_2O$ and dissolving it in distilled water. One milliliter of 1 M H_2SO_4 should be added to this solution to prevent formation of a hydrous ferric oxide precipitate. This solution does not have to be made up in volumetric flasks; graduated cylinders are fine.

The Fe(III) standardization procedure must be carried out rapidly, and once you begin you cannot stop. The reagents you should have available for this procedure (to be found on the laboratory reagent shelf) are:

1) concentrated hydrochloric acid, HCl, 12 M,

2) stannous chloride solution, $SnCl_2$, 0.5 M, (A liter of this solution can be made by dissolving 113 gm of iron-free $SnCl_2$ in 500 ml of 6 M HCl and diluting it to

---

* If standard dichromate is not available in the laboratory it may be made by drying about 0.25 gm of $K_2Cr_2O_7$ for an hour at 110°C, weighing this amount accurately by difference into a 500-ml volumetric flask, and making up to volume with distilled water. This solution will be about 0.002 M; calculate the exact concentration from the volume and weight data. Dichromate solutions are stable indefinitely.

1 liter. If about 15 gm of "mossy" tin is added to the container the solution will keep longer, but it should not be made more than a few days in advance of its use since it is subject to air oxidation.)

3) saturated mercuric chloride solution, about 75 gm of $HgCl_2$ per liter of water,

4) concentrated sulfuric acid, H_2SO_4, 18 M,

5) 85% phosphoric acid, H_3PO_4, 14.6 M,

6) standard potassium dichromate, $K_2Cr_2O_7$, about 0.002 M,

7) sodium diphenylamine sulfonate indicator, a 0.2% solution of the salt in water.

Pipet 25.0 ml of the Fe(III) stock solution into a 250-ml flask. Add 3 ml of concentrated HCl. Heat to boiling and add 0.5 M $SnCl_2$ solution drop by drop with stirring until the yellow ferric color (due to the presence of the ion $FeCl_4^-$) disappears. Then add 1 or 2 drops more. Cool the solution below 25°C by running cold tap water over the outside of the flask; then, while vigorously swirling the flask, add 7 ml of saturated $HgCl_2$ solution all at once. The precipitate, if any, should be white, silky, and small in amount. (If it is grayish or if a precipitate does not form, continue the procedure. If the precipitate is black, too much elemental Hg has been formed and the run is ruined.) Wait about 2 minutes; then add 130 ml of a solution made up beforehand consisting of 11 parts water, 1 part concentrated H_2SO_4, and 1 part 85% H_3PO_4 by volume. Add 5 to 7 drops of sodium diphenylamine sulfonate indicator and titrate with standard dichromate until the pure green color (the color of chromic ions, Cr^{+3}, produced in the titration reaction) changes to gray-green. Continue the titration by fractional drops with swirling until the solution turns purple. Repeat this standardization at least once more or until you are satisfied that you have an accurate value for the Fe(III) concentration. To calculate this concentration you will have to write a balanced equation for the reaction of $Cr_2O_7^=$ with Fe^{++}. You know the reactants and products, so this should be simple. Calculate the concentration of your Fe(III) stock solution.

Make up in a 100-ml volumetric flask a solution that is 0.050 M in $(NH_4)_2SO_4$, 0.025 M in H_2SO_4, and *exactly* 2.00 × 10^{-3} M in Fe(III). Stock solutions of $(NH_4)_2SO_4$, 0.20 M, and H_2SO_4, 0.10 M, will be available in the laboratory. Use your buret to add *exactly* the amount of your stock Fe(III) solution that is necessary. Make the solution up to the mark with distilled water.

Make up in a 100-ml volumetric flask another solution that is 0.050 M in $(NH_4)_2SO_4$, 0.025 M in H_2SO_4, and *exactly* 2.00 × 10^{-3} M in SSA. Again use a buret to dispense *exactly* the correct amount of SSA stock solution. Make the solution up to the mark with distilled water.

Since it is desirable to cover the range from 0 to 1 in the ratio (moles Fe)/(moles Fe + moles SSA), about nine mixtures (each 10 ml total volume) of your 2.00 × 10^{-3} M Fe(III) and SSA solutions should be made up. The following ratios are easy to work with: 1:9, 2:8, 3:7, 4:6, 5:5, 6:4, 7:3, 8:2, and 9:1. Join with your neighbor and use two burets, one to dispense the Fe(III) solution and the other to dispense the SSA solution. Probably the easiest thing to do is to have enough clean, dry, labeled test tubes to make all your solutions at once. Then as a spectrophotometer becomes available you can run your whole series of mixtures plus the pure 2.00 × 10^{-3} M Fe(III) and SSA solutions. You need to take readings of the absorbance only at the wavelength of maximum absorbance of the complex. Thus you will first have to use either a manual or recording spectrophotometer to determine the absorption spectrum of one of your samples so as to find the wavelength of maximum absorbance to be used for your measurements.

Calculations

Make a plot of the absorbance A vs. the mole ratio of iron in the samples. The absorbance of each solution should be corrected for any absorbance due to Fe(III) or SSA so that the plot will truly be that of the absorbance of the complex. Assuming that each complex contains only one iron, use the plot to determine the formula of the complex, Fe(SSA). Include in your report your analytical calculations for the Fe(III) determination.

Discuss the shape of the plot you have made and any further information you can derive from it about the equilibrium constant of the reaction. (Remember that straight lines drawn tangent to the extreme points on either side of the plot do not in general meet at the same mole ratio as that at which the maximum in the plot occurs. If they do, what can you learn about the equilibria in the system?

Questions

1. What is n/m for the complex A_mB_n whose continuous variation plot is given in Fig. 9-2(b)?

2. What is the pH of the solutions you made up containing Fe(III) and SSA in varying amounts? Take the second pK_a for sulfuric acid as 2.0.

3. From your data, estimate the equilibrium constant for the reaction

$$Fe^{+3} + nSSA^{-3} \rightleftharpoons Fe(SSA)_n^{+3-3n}.$$

Using this value, estimate the absorptivity (a in the equation $A = abc$) for the complex at the wavelength you used in your study.

Further Experimental Problems

Among the many systems that can be studied by the method of continuous variations are other Fe(III) complexes with species such as thiocyanate, SCN^-. Waser's text and the articles by Ramette and Carmody discuss this and other complexes, and Chaberek and Martell cover some further extensions of the method that you might find useful.

A Nonaqueous Titration. It was indicated above that the titration of SSA in aqueous solution does not "resolve" the first two acidic hydrogens, i.e., that a titration using a pH meter will not show a break in the titration curve until two equivalents of base are added. Try this for yourself. An experiment with a solvent, ROH, which is similar to water but with different acid-base properties, dielectric constant, and autoionization constant (K for the reaction: $2ROH \rightleftharpoons ROH_2^+ + RO^-$) may produce a titration curve of completely different character. A possible solvent for this test is isopropanol, $CH_3CHOHCH_3$.

Since strong bases like KOH and NaOH are not very soluble in isopropanol, some other strong base will have to be used. Tetraethyl ammonium hydroxide, $(CH_3CH_2)_4N^+OH^-$, a strong base, is soluble in isopropanol. Tetraethyl ammonium hydroxide is not very stable so it must be prepared shortly before use. The appropriate amount of tetraethyl ammonium bromide is dissolved in about one-tenth to one-fifth the final desired volume of isopropanol and a small excess of freshly prepared hydrous silver oxide (made by adding sodium hydroxide solution to a silver nitrate solution, filtering, and washing the gray-black precipitate) is added to the solution. Protect this solution from the air and stir until the precipitate is yellow, AgBr, rather than black. Filter rapidly through sintered glass and then dilute the filtrate to the desired final volume. This solution rapidly dissolves CO_2, which destroys the base, so it should be opened to the atmosphere as little as possible.

SSA made up in isopropanol is titrated by the same technique as in water. A combination of a glass electrode and a calomel reference electrode is used for the measurement. A plot of the apparent "pH" in isopropanol on the same scale as the aqueous titration curve may show interestingly different effects.*

If the results of aqueous and nonaqueous titrations are different, discuss the possible reasons for this.

REFERENCES

BUTLER, J. N., *Ionic Equilibrium*, Addison-Wesley, Reading, Mass., 1964, Chapter 12, gives an account of the utility and necessity for nonideality corrections in a number of systems.

CARMODY, W. R., "Variation of the Solubility Product Constant with Ionic Strength," *J. Chem. Ed.* **36,** 125 (1959) suggests a demonstration and discusses the striking effect of ionic strength variation on the solubility of $Cd(IO_3)_2$.

CARMODY, W. R., "Demonstrating Job's Method with Colorimeter or Spectrophotometer," *J. Chem. Ed.* **41,** 615 (1964).

CHABEREK, S., and A. E. MARTELL, *Organic Sequestering Agents*, John Wiley & Sons, New York, 1959, pp. 78–87, gives a further discussion of the details and some extensions of the method of continuous variations.

CORSARO, G., "Ion Strength, Ion Association, and Solubility," *J. Chem. Ed.* **39,** 622 (1962) suggests a solubility study of $CaSO_4$ as a function of ionic strength and concentration of chloride ion (forms complexes with Ca^{++}). See, however, *J. Chem. Ed.* **40,** 327, 328 (1963) for some further discussion of this system.

DAWBER, J. G., D. R. BROWN, and R. A. REED, "Acid-Catalyzed Hydrolysis of Sucrose," *J. Chem. Ed.* **43,** 34 (1966) shows how the concepts of total acidity and the

acidity function can be used to learn about the mechanism of a reaction.

DIRKSE, T. P., "Ionization Constant of Water," *J. Chem. Ed.* **38,** 260 (1961) points out that the activity of water is unity only in dilute solutions (or pure H_2O) and thus K_w is only *constant* under these conditions.

HAMMETT, L. P., *Physical Organic Chemistry*, McGraw-Hill, New York, 1940. Chapter 9 is an exposition of the theory and usefulness of the acidity function by its originator.

HART, C. S., "Use of Activities in Student Calculations," *J. Chem. Ed.* **32,** 314 (1955) explains, with a number of examples, the use of activities in ionic solution problems.

INDELLI, A., and G. SAGLIETTO, *Trans. Faraday Soc.* **58,** 1033 (1962). These authors investigated the ionic strength effect on pQ for a number of dyes including bromcresol green and also investigated to discover whether there were specific ion effects. You might compare your results with theirs.

KOKES, R. J., M. K. DORFMAN, and T. MATHIA, "Equilibria in Ionic Solutions," *J. Chem. Ed.* **39,** 93 (1962) is very

---

* Remember that pH is not really defined in nonaqueous solvents so standardization of the pH meter is unnecessary.

much like our Experiment 17 but uses the solubility of silver chloroacetate to investigate the ionization of chloroacetic acid.

MEITES, L., J. S. F. PODE, and H. C. THOMAS, "Are Solubilities and Solubility Products Related?," *J. Chem. Ed.* **43,** 667 (1966) is a discussion, with illustrative examples, of the errors you can make if ionic strength and competing equilibria are not accounted for in solubility studies.

PAUL, M. A., and F. A. LONG, "*H₀* and Related Indicator Acidity Functions," *Chem. Rev.* **57,** 1 (1957) is a review article with many references.

PIERCE, W. C., E. L. HAENISCH, and D. T. SAWYER, *Quantitative Analysis,* 4th ed. John Wiley & Sons, New York, 1958.

RAMETTE, R. W., "Meaningful Solubility Studies in Elementary Quantitative Analysis," *J. Chem. Ed.* **33,** 610 (1956) suggests studying the solubility of $AgBrO_3$, $CaSO_4$, and $PbSO_4$ in ionic solutions in ways similar to those suggested for AgOAc in Experiment 18.

RAMETTE, R. W., "The Dissociation Constant of Iodic Acid," *J. Chem. Ed.* **36,** 191 (1959) presents a solubility experiment with $Cu(IO_3)_2$ that is much like our Experiment 17.

RAMETTE, R. W., "Formation of Monothiocyanatoiron(III)," *J. Chem. Ed.* **40,** 71 (1963) discusses a continuous variation experiment very much like our Experiment 20. Thiocyanate complexes rather than sulfosalicylate complexes are studied in this experiment.

RAMETTE, R. W., "The Bromcresol Green Dissociation Quotient," *J. Chem. Ed.* **40,** 252 (1963) is a presentation of Experiment 15 as it is performed at Carleton College. In the main, our experiment is lifted directly from this article.

SKOOG, D. A., and D. M. WEST, *Fundamentals of Analytical Chemistry,* Holt, Rinehart & Winston, New York, 1963.

WASER, J., *Quantitative Chemistry,* revised edition, W. A. Benjamin, New York, 1964.

WOLFENDEN, J. H., "Two Student Experiments on Chemical Equilibrium," *J. Chem. Ed.* **36,** 490 (1959) suggests two experiments that the author uses as sort of a "laboratory practical" examination. Certain procedures are suggested in detail, and then others, not totally prescribed, are suggested, and alternatives based on the initial results can be followed up.

10 ELECTROCHEMICAL CELLS AND REDOX REACTIONS

There is substantial confusion among many students (and their instructors) concerning the nomenclature of electrochemistry, in particular the conventions used in handling the signs of electrochemical potentials. We shall try here to define our terms carefully and thus eliminate this confusion.

10–1 CELL POTENTIALS AND THERMODYNAMICS

The immensely important aspect of measurements made on electrochemical cells is the connection between the cell potential or voltage and the free energy of the cell reaction. It is easy to show (see Mahan, Nash, or Waser) that for a cell that works reversibly the free-energy change for the cell reaction is

$$\Delta G = -n\mathfrak{F}\,\Delta\mathcal{E}, \tag{10–1}$$

where $\Delta\mathcal{E}$ is the cell potential, the difference in electromotive force (usually given in volts) between the two electrodes of the cell. The sign of the cell potential depends on the direction in which we write the cell reaction, as will be discussed below. In Eq. (10–1) n is the number of moles of electrons transferred from one electrode to the other when one mole of the stoichiometric cell reaction occurs. The Faraday, $\mathfrak{F}$, is the charge on one mole of electrons, which has the value 96,461 coulomb/mole = 23,062 cal/volt-mole.* If the reactants and products are in their standard states, then

$$\Delta G^0 = -n\mathfrak{F}\,\Delta\mathcal{E}^0. \tag{10–2}$$

Considering the generalized cell reaction

$$a\mathrm{A} + b\mathrm{B} \rightleftharpoons c\mathrm{C} + d\mathrm{D}$$

---

* We see that the quantity $n\mathfrak{F}\,\Delta\mathcal{E}$ has the units of work (a volt-coulomb is a joule), as it must have, since it is the electrochemical work that the cell can perform.

we can write

$$\Delta G = \Delta G^0 + RT\ln\frac{a_\mathrm{C}^c a_\mathrm{D}^d}{a_\mathrm{A}^a a_\mathrm{B}^b} = \Delta G^0 + RT\ln Q$$

as for any reaction. We can substitute for ΔG and ΔG^0 in terms of cell potentials to obtain

$$\Delta\mathcal{E} = \Delta\mathcal{E}^0 - \frac{RT}{n\mathfrak{F}}\ln\frac{a_\mathrm{C}^c a_\mathrm{D}^d}{a_\mathrm{A}^a a_\mathrm{B}^b} = \Delta\mathcal{E}^0 - \frac{RT}{n\mathfrak{F}}\ln Q, \tag{10–3}$$

called the *Nernst equation*. Substituting $\log_{10}$ for $\ln_e$ at 25°C we get the factor $2.303RT/\mathfrak{F} = 0.059$, so we may then write the Nernst equation as

$$\Delta\mathcal{E} = \Delta\mathcal{E}^0 - \frac{0.059}{n}\log Q. \tag{10–3a}$$

Note that the ratio of activities is not necessarily the equilibrium ratio but rather the ratio that actually exists in the cell system. If the ratio is the equilibrium ratio, i.e., if

$$\frac{a_\mathrm{C}^c a_\mathrm{D}^d}{a_\mathrm{A}^a a_\mathrm{B}^b} = \left(\frac{a_\mathrm{C}^c a_\mathrm{D}^d}{a_\mathrm{A}^a a_\mathrm{B}^b}\right)_{\mathrm{eq}} = K,$$

then $\Delta G = 0$, the definition of equilibrium, and hence $\Delta\mathcal{E} = 0$ as well, and in this case Eq. (10–3) becomes

$$\Delta\mathcal{E}^0 = \frac{RT}{n\mathfrak{F}}\ln K. \tag{10–4}$$

[This result could also have been derived by combining the equation $\Delta G^0 = RT\ln K$ with Eq. (10–2).] Thus cell-potential measurements can be used to determine equilibrium constants.

The temperature dependence of the cell potential allows one to obtain other thermodynamic variables. We know that (at constant pressure)

$$\frac{d(\ln K)}{dT} = \frac{\Delta H^0}{RT^2},$$

124

and we can substitute for ln K in terms of the cell potential

$$\frac{d(n\mathfrak{F}\,\Delta\mathcal{E}^0/RT)}{dT} = \frac{\Delta H^0}{RT^2},$$

$$\frac{d(\Delta\mathcal{E}^0/T)}{dT} = \frac{\Delta H^0}{n\mathfrak{F}T^2},$$

$$\frac{1}{T}\left(\frac{d\,\Delta\mathcal{E}^0}{dT}\right) + \mathcal{E}^0\left(\frac{d(1/T)}{dT}\right) = \frac{1}{T}\left(\frac{d\,\Delta\mathcal{E}^0}{dT}\right) - \mathcal{E}^0\left(\frac{1}{T}\right)^2$$
$$= \frac{\Delta H^0}{n\mathfrak{F}T^2},$$

and solve for ΔH^0:

$$\Delta H^0 = n\mathfrak{F}\left[T\left(\frac{d\,\Delta\mathcal{E}^0}{dT}\right) - \mathcal{E}^0\right]. \qquad (10\text{--}5)$$

With this expression for ΔH^0 in hand we can substitute into the equation relating ΔG^0, ΔH^0, and ΔS^0 to obtain

$$\Delta S^0 = -\frac{\Delta G^0 - \Delta H^0}{T} = \frac{n\mathfrak{F}\,\Delta\mathcal{E}^0}{T} + \frac{n\mathfrak{F}}{T}\left[T\left(\frac{d\,\Delta\mathcal{E}^0}{dT}\right) - \mathcal{E}^0\right]$$
$$= n\mathfrak{F}\left(\frac{d\Delta\mathcal{E}^0}{dT}\right). \qquad (10\text{--}6)$$

Thus if the rate of change of cell potential with temperature, $(d\,\Delta\mathcal{E}^0/dT)$, is known, ΔH^0 and ΔS^0 for the cell reaction can be calculated.

10–2 ELECTROCHEMICAL CELLS

Now that we have seen how powerful a tool the knowledge of cell potentials can be, we must examine the more practical aspects of nomenclature and measurement on electrochemical cells. We need to know how to construct an electrochemical cell and how to measure the cell potential and its sign. Let us take a completely empirical approach to these problems, remembering that the final results must be consistent with our knowledge of thermodynamics.

One of the simplest electrochemical cell setups is that shown schematically in Fig. 10–1. The cell consists of two beakers of metal ion solutions with a strip of the corresponding pure metal dipped into each. When the two beakers are connected by a U-tube *salt bridge*, as shown in the figure, the potential difference between the two metallic electrodes can be measured with a voltmeter. Before we proceed to a discussion of the results of such a measurement let us introduce a shorthand notation for electrochemical cells. The cell of Fig. 10–1 is represented as

$$\text{Ag} \mid \text{Ag}^+(0.1\ M) \parallel \text{Cu}^{++}(0.1\ M) \mid \text{Cu}. \qquad (10\text{--}7)$$

The vertical bars are "punctuation marks" that indicate phase boundaries. Certainly it is obvious that there are phase boundaries between the metal electrodes and the

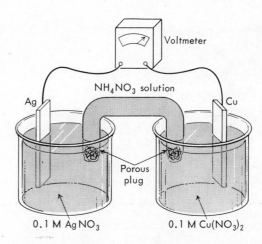

Fig. 10–1. An electrochemical cell (the silver-copper cell).

solutions. At the porous barriers in each end of the salt bridge there are also phase boundaries, and the double bar is used to denote these two boundaries. (It is conventional to use the double bar without denoting what the salt bridge solution is unless it is of special significance.)

The voltmeter used to measure the cell potential also tells us which of the two metallic electrodes is more positive, i.e., it indicates the direction of current flow. This is true because of the design of such meters. If the positive lead from the cell is not correctly attached to the voltmeter, the meter needle will tend to go toward negative readings and, hence, not be on scale. Thus we can learn two things from our measurement: the magnitude of the cell potential and the signs of the electrodes. You might object that our measurement is bad since reactions occur that change the ion concentrations when current is drawn from the cell; therefore, we don't know what the cell conditions are that correspond to the measured potential. This is true; we would like to make our measurements with a device that draws no current. Often this condition is approximated by using a vacuum-tube voltmeter (such as a pH meter) as the potential measuring device: For accurate work (with low-impedance electrodes) we use a more nearly ideal device, the potentiometer. A schematic illustration of a potentiometer is shown in Fig. 10–2. When the standard cell is connected to the circuit with the double-pole double-throw (dpdt) switch, the slide wire is set (with a dial on the instrument) to read the known voltage of this cell, and the resistance R is varied until the current flowing through the galvanometer is zero. At this point the potential drop (from A to C), iR, just balances the potential of the standard cell, $\Delta\mathcal{E}_{\text{standard}}$, so no current flows. Now the dpdt switch is set to connect the unknown cell to the circuit and the slide wire is adjusted until no current flows through the galvanometer. From the new setting we read the potential of the unknown cell directly from

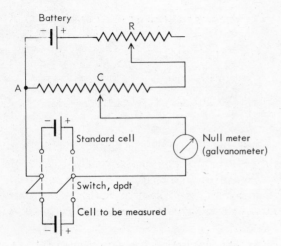

Fig. 10–2. A schematic diagram of a potentiometer.

the scale of the slide wire. Also, we automatically obtain the signs of the electrode leads, since we will not be able to null the meter if the unknown cell is attached with the polarity opposite to that shown in the figure.

The results of a series of measurements on three cells are given in Table 10–1. Note that we can construct these three cells using three beakers of metal ion solutions with corresponding metal electrodes and a salt bridge. Connecting any two of the beakers with the salt bridge will create one of the cells represented in the table. One would, therefore, expect to find interrelationships among the data. It is heartening to see that there is an obvious relationship among the cell potentials, $\Delta \mathcal{E}$: any two of them can be combined to yield the third. We are still, however, faced with the question, "What are the reactions that are occurring in the cells?" To answer this question and to generate some very useful and widely applicable concepts, let us examine the cell, not as a whole, but as made up of two components.

Table 10–1

THE RESULTS OF SOME CELL MEASUREMENTS

Cell	$|\Delta \mathcal{E}|$, volts	Positive electrode
1 Ag $\mid$ Ag$^+(a=1) \parallel$ Cu$^{++}(a=1) \mid$ Cu	0.46	Ag
2 Ag $\mid$ Ag$^+(a=1) \parallel$ Zn$^{++}(a=1) \mid$ Zn	1.56	Ag
3 Cu $\mid$ Cu$^{++}(a=1) \parallel$ Zn$^{++}(a=1) \mid$ Zn	1.10	Cu

10-3 HALF-CELLS, HALF-REACTIONS, AND HALF-CELL POTENTIALS

Both our cell notation and the physical setup of a cell seem to point to a clear division of the cell into two parts, corresponding to the parts of the system separated by the salt bridge. (In some cells, without a salt bridge,

the division is not so obvious, but is still present.) If this is the case, then perhaps we can treat each of these *half-cells* individually and for each write a *half-reaction* corresponding to an oxidation or reduction of the species in that half-cell. For example, when the silver-silver ion half-cell is connected by means of a salt bridge to any other half-cell and current is drawn from the cell thus produced, the only changes in the silver half-cell are that the silver ion concentration either increases or decreases and, correspondingly, the silver electrode either loses or gains metallic silver. Evidently the silver ion and silver metal are the only reactants (and products) in this half-reaction. We could write this reaction as

$$Ag^+ = Ag$$

except that this equation is not balanced because the charges are not balanced. We need to write

$$Ag^+ + e^- = Ag. \qquad (10–8)$$

Where does the electron come from? It comes from the other half-reaction required to complete the cell. Conversely, reaction (10–8) could run in reverse and furnish electrons to the other half-reaction. The other half-reactions we are concerned with at the moment are

$$Cu^{++} + 2e^- = Cu, \qquad (10–9)$$

$$Zn^{++} + 2e^- = Zn. \qquad (10–10)$$

Note that *we have written our half-reactions as reductions*; this is the *convention* we shall continue to use for reasons that will become evident below.

If we continue our analogy between half-cells and cells, we should assign a *half-cell potential* to each of our half-cells or to the half-reactions that occur therein. Thus we will have $\mathcal{E}^0_{Ag^+|Ag}$ for reaction (10–8) when all species are in their standard states. If the species are not in their standard states, then the Nernst equation must be used to determine the half-cell potential:

$$\mathcal{E}_{Ag^+|Ag} = \mathcal{E}^0_{Ag^+|Ag} - \frac{RT}{n\mathcal{F}} \ln \frac{1}{a_{Ag^+}}.$$

(By convention, the electrons are not shown in the Nernst equation.) We have used a script $\mathcal{E}$ without a Δ to denote half-cell potentials and thus to differentiate them from cell potentials, $\Delta \mathcal{E}$.

Although half-cells seem to have a physical existence apart from each other, *a half-cell potential is not a measurable* quantity. There is no conceivable way of measuring the potential of a half-cell without connecting it to another and hence creating a complete cell whose potential is a combination of the effects of two half-cells. However, if we were to choose (arbitrarily) a value for one half-cell potential, then all others could be measured relative to this "standard."

To see how this works, let us return to the data of Table 10–1. For cell 1 we must have some combination of half-reactions (10–8) and (10–9) and their half-cell potentials.

$$
\begin{array}{ll}
-2(Ag^+ + e^- = Ag) & \varepsilon_{Ag^+|Ag} \\
\underline{Cu^{++} + 2e^- = Cu} & \underline{\varepsilon_{Cu^{++}|Cu}} \\
Cu^{++} + 2Ag = Cu'' + 2Ag^+ & \Delta\varepsilon_1 = \varepsilon_{Cu^{++}|Cu} - \varepsilon_{Ag^+|Ag}
\end{array}
$$

What is the reason for this combination? The choice of the direction of the overall reaction was arbitrary; we could just as well have subtracted (10–9) from twice (10–8) to give the reverse reaction and all the opposite signs on the potentials. ($\Delta\varepsilon_1$ refers to the reaction as written; $-\Delta\varepsilon_1$ to the reverse reaction.) The factor of 2 is necessary for the electrons to cancel out. The algebraic combination of the half-cell potentials is the same as that of the half-reactions, but the multiplicative factor 2 is *not* used, because the ε's are potentials, intensive quantities, that are not dependent on the number of moles of reaction that occur. To see this, note that $\varepsilon = \Delta G/n\mathcal{F}$ for a half-reaction; ΔG and n are both directly proportional in the same way to the amount of reaction that occurs. Thus ε is independent of the amount of reaction occurring.

Let us now *arbitrarily* choose $\varepsilon_{Ag^+|Ag} = 0$ for the half-cell we are considering; then

$$\Delta\varepsilon_1 = \varepsilon_{Cu^{++}|Cu} - 0 = \varepsilon_{Cu^{++}|Cu}.$$

In the same way we can show from (10–9) and (10–10) that

$$\Delta\varepsilon_2 = \varepsilon_{Zn^{++}|Zn} - 0 = \varepsilon_{Zn^{++}|Zn},$$

where $\Delta\varepsilon_2$ refers to the reaction

$$Zn^{++} + 2Ag = Zn + 2Ag^+.$$

What signs are appropriate for the half-cell potentials (and, hence, the cell potentials)? Consider the signs of the cell electrodes; in both cells 1 and 2 the silver is the positive electrode. This must mean that *electrons are being consumed at the silver electrode;* reaction (10–8) must be proceeding as written in both cells. Thus the reactions that tend to occur *spontaneously* in these cells are

$$Cu + 2Ag^+ = Cu^{++} + 2Ag, \qquad -\Delta\varepsilon_1 = +0.46\ v$$

and

$$Zn + 2Ag^+ = Zn^{++} + 2Ag, \qquad -\Delta\varepsilon_2 = +1.56\ v.$$

The signs of the cell potentials, 0.46 and 1.56 v, must be positive to be consistent with Eq. (10–1) and the spontaneous tendency of these reactions. In other words, a positive cell potential is required for a spontaneous reaction to give the negative free energy change that is consistent with thermodynamics. The free energy changes are

$$
\begin{aligned}
\Delta G_1 &= -n\mathcal{F}\,\Delta\varepsilon_1 = -2 \times 23{,}060 \times 0.46 \\
&= -21.2\ kcal/mole,
\end{aligned}
$$
$$
\begin{aligned}
\Delta G_2 &= -n\mathcal{F}\,\Delta\varepsilon_2 = -2 \times 23{,}060 \times 1.56 \\
&= -72.0\ kcal/mole.
\end{aligned}
$$

Now that we have cell potentials consistent with thermodynamics, we can return to the half-cell potentials and find

$$
\begin{aligned}
\Delta\varepsilon_1 &= -0.46\ v = \varepsilon_{Cu^{++}|Cu}, \\
\Delta\varepsilon_2 &= -1.56\ v = \varepsilon_{Zn^{++}|Zn}.
\end{aligned}
$$

Half-cell potentials give us a relative measure of the tendency of the respective half-reactions to proceed as written; the more positive the half-cell potential, the greater the tendency to proceed. (This is a consequence of our insistence that cell and half-cell potentials be consistent with thermodynamics.) What reaction would occur spontaneously in a copper-zinc cell made from the half-cells we have been discussing?

$$
\begin{array}{ll}
Cu^{++} + 2e^- = Cu & \varepsilon_{Cu^{++}|Cu} = -0.46\ v \\
\underline{-(Zn^{++} + 2e^- = Zn)} & \underline{\varepsilon_{Zn^{++}|Zn} = -1.56\ v} \\
Cu^{++} + Zn = Cu + Zn^{++} & \Delta\varepsilon_3 = \varepsilon_{Cu^{++}|Cu} - \varepsilon_{Zn^{++}|Zn} = +1.10\ v
\end{array}
$$

This reaction has a positive potential and, hence, a tendency to proceed spontaneously as written. (This, of course, can be attested to by anyone who has ever dipped a piece of zinc into a copper ion solution and found copper metal depositing on the zinc.) We thus predict that Cu^{++} will be reduced to Cu, and Zn oxidized to Zn^{++} when the circuit is closed. This means that the Cu electrode will be positive since electrons are being consumed by the reaction in that half-cell. Note from Table 10–1 that the magnitude of the cell potential and the positive electrode are just as we have predicted from the half-cell potentials.

We can now combine our observations into rules relating half-cell potentials, half-reactions, cell potentials, and cell reactions:

1) When two half-cells are combined to form a cell, the electrode in the half-cell with the more positive half-cell potential, when the half-reaction is written as a reduction, will be the positive electrode.

2) The cell reaction and cell potential will be the algebraic difference between the half-reactions (with appropriate factors to eliminate electrons) and the half-cell potentials.

3) If the cell potential so derived is positive, the cell reaction you have written is spontaneous and is the one that tends to proceed in the cell when the circuit is closed.*

10–4 STANDARD HALF-CELL POTENTIALS

We have now seen how useful it is to know half-cell potentials (at least relative ones) and we have seen the necessity of choosing some standard half-cell. The *standard hydrogen electrode*, SHE (now usually referred to as the NHE, normal hydrogen electrode), has been chosen as the reference standard. The SHE is the half-cell

$$Pt \mid H_2(1 \text{ atm}) \mid H^+ \ (a = 1)$$

with the corresponding half-reaction

$$2H^+ + 2e^- = H_2, \qquad \mathcal{E}^0_{H^+|H_2} \equiv 0 \qquad (\text{at } 25°C).$$

$$(10\text{--}11)$$

When the SHE is coupled with any other half-cell (at 25°C) the half-cell potential of the second half-cell is the cell potential with the sign corresponding to the sign of its electrode. The results of such measurements give

$$\mathcal{E}^0_{Ag^+|Ag} = +0.7994 \text{ v},$$
$$\mathcal{E}^0_{Cu^{++}|Cu} = +0.337 \text{ v},$$
$$\mathcal{E}^0_{Zn^{++}|Zn} = -0.7628 \text{ v}.$$

Can these values be shown to be consistent with the results for cell 3 in Table 10–1?

$$Cu^{++} + 2e^- = Cu$$

$$-(Zn^{++} + 2e^- = Zn)$$

$$Cu^{++} + Zn = Cu + Zn^{++}$$

$$\mathcal{E}_{Cu^{++}|Cu} = \mathcal{E}^0_{Cu^{++}|Cu} - \frac{0.06}{2} \log \frac{1}{[Cu^{++}]},$$

$$\mathcal{E}_{Zn^{++}|Zn} = \mathcal{E}^0_{Zn^{++}|Zn} - \frac{0.06}{2} \log \frac{1}{[Zn^{++}]},$$

$$\Delta\mathcal{E}_3 = \mathcal{E}_{Cu^{++}|Cu} - \mathcal{E}_{Zn^{++}|Zn},$$

$$\Delta\mathcal{E}_3 = \mathcal{E}^0_{Cu^{++}|Cu} - \mathcal{E}^0_{Zn^{++}|Zn} - \frac{0.06}{2} \log \frac{[Zn^{++}]}{[Cu^{++}]}$$

$$= 0.34 - (-0.76) - \frac{0.06}{2} \log \frac{0.1}{0.1},$$

$$\Delta\mathcal{E}_3 = +1.10 \text{ v}.$$

Thus we find, as we must, that the reference choice for half-cell potentials makes absolutely no difference in the final result for an overall cell. If we had wished to predict only which electrode would be positive, we would have calculated

$$\mathcal{E}_{Cu^{++}|Cu} = +0.37 \quad \text{and} \quad \mathcal{E}_{Zn^{++}|Zn} = -0.73.$$

Since $\mathcal{E}_{Cu^{++}|Cu} > \mathcal{E}_{Zn^{++}|Zn}$, the copper electrode is positive by our first rule, and, of course, this is borne out experimentally.

---

* Go back now and assure yourself that these rules are valid when applied to cells 1 and 2.

Illustrative Example: Write the balanced stoichiometric equation and the standard free-energy change for the (incomplete) reaction

$$Cu^{++} + I^- = CuI(s) + I_3^-.$$

What are the half-reactions we must consider? Evidently copper is being reduced in this system, since it goes from the cupric to the cuprous state. Thus iodide must be oxidized; we see that this is true since we have oxidized I^- to I_2 (I_3^- may be looked on as $I_2 + I^-$). The half-reactions are

$$Cu^{++} + I^- + e^- = CuI(s),$$
$$I_3^- + 2e^- = 3I^-.$$

It is easy then to combine the half-reactions and standard half-cell potentials (see Appendix G) to yield the desired results:

$$2[Cu^{++} + I^- + e^- = CuI(s)] \qquad \mathcal{E}^0_{Cu^{++}|CuI} = +0.85 \text{ v} \qquad \Delta\mathcal{E}^0 = 0.85 - 0.54 = +0.31 \text{ v,}$$
$$\frac{-(I_3^- + 2e^- = 3I^-)}{2Cu^{++} + 5I^- = 2CuI(s) + I_3^-} \quad \frac{\mathcal{E}_{I_3^-|I^-} = +0.535 \text{ v}}{\Delta\mathcal{E}^0 = \mathcal{E}^0_{Cu^{++}|CuI} - \mathcal{E}^0_{I_3^-|I^-}}; \quad \frac{\Delta G^0 = n\mathcal{F}\,\Delta\mathcal{E}^0 = -2 \times 23,060 \times (+0.31),}{\Delta G^0 = -14,300 \text{ cal.}}$$

Thus the reaction tends to proceed as written. (Test this prediction by mixing solutions of cupric ion and iodide ion to see if any reaction occurs.)

A further discussion of electrochemical cells, half-cell potentials and electrode potentials is given in the article by Anson.

10–5   THE POTENTIOMETRIC DETERMINATION OF CONCENTRATION

So far we have been mostly concerned with calculating $\Delta\mathcal{E}$, $\mathcal{E}$, and thermodynamic quantities derivable therefrom for cells and half-cells when the concentrations (strictly, activities) of the species in the cells are known. However, we can reverse this procedure and use potential measurements to determine concentrations; indeed, this is one of the important uses of electrochemical measurements. For example, let us examine the problem of determining the concentration of hydrogen ion in a solution.

The Hydrogen Electrode

The most direct method of approach to this problem is to set up a hydrogen electrode as indicated in Fig. 10–3. Reaction (10–11) is the half-reaction that takes place at this electrode, so the half-cell potential is given by the Nernst equation (at 25°C) as

$$\mathcal{E}_{H^+|H_2} = \mathcal{E}^0_{H^+|H_2} - \frac{0.059}{2} \log \frac{a_{H_2}}{(a_{H^+})^2}.$$

The activity of the H_2 is unity, since its pressure is 1 atm.

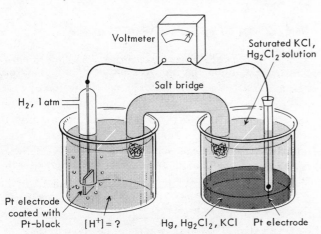

Fig. 10–3. A hydrogen electrode connected via a salt bridge to a saturated calomel electrode.

Therefore we obtain

$$\mathcal{E}_{H^+|H_2} = 0 - \frac{0.059}{2} \log \frac{1}{(a_{H^+})^2} = -0.059 \log \frac{1}{a_{H^+}}$$
$$= -0.059 \text{ pH}.$$

Thus we only have to determine the half-cell potential to obtain the pH of the solution.

To make this determination we must link our hydrogen half-cell through a salt bridge with some reference half-cell. The saturated calomel half-cell (a sketch of a commercial version is shown in Appendix D) is one of the most convenient and reproducible reference half-cells (Fig. 10–3). (Calomel is a common name for mercurous chloride, Hg_2Cl_2.) The half-reaction for the calomel half-cell is

$$Hg_2Cl_2(s) + 2e^- = 2Hg(l) + 2Cl^-, \qquad \mathcal{E}^0_{cal} = 0.268 \text{ v,}$$

and the Nernst equation is

$$\mathcal{E}_{cal} = \mathcal{E}^0_{cal} - \frac{0.059}{2} \log \frac{(a_{Cl^-})^2 (a_{Hg})^2}{a_{Hg_2Cl_2}}.$$

The potential obviously depends on the chloride concentration, and in the *saturated calomel electrode*, $\mathcal{E}_{SCE} = +0.246$ v at 25°C, relative to the SHE. The measured potential of the completed cell will be the difference between the potentials of the two half-cells (one of which we know and one we would like to determine)

$$\mathcal{E}_{cal} = \mathcal{E}_{SCE}$$
$$\frac{-(\mathcal{E}_{H^+|H_2} = -0.059 \text{ pH})}{\Delta\mathcal{E} = \mathcal{E}_{cal} - \mathcal{E}_{H^+|H_2} = \mathcal{E}_{SCE} + 0.059 \text{ pH}}.$$

(Note that you must know which electrode lead is positive to give $\Delta\mathcal{E}$ its correct sign.)

Illustrative Example: The setup of Fig. 10–3 was used to measure the pH of a solution. The potential of the cell was 0.453 v at 25°C and the lead from the saturated calomel electrode was positive. What is the unknown pH?

The potential is $\Delta\mathcal{E}$, which equals $\mathcal{E}_{SCE} - \mathcal{E}_{H^+|H_2}$. Since the lead from the SCE is positive, $\mathcal{E}_{SCE}$ is positive with respect to $\mathcal{E}_H$, and $\Delta\mathcal{E}$ must be positive. Thus we can write

$$+0.453 - (0.246) = 0.059 \text{ pH,}$$
$$\text{pH} = \frac{0.207}{0.059} = 3.51.$$

Although the hydrogen electrode method is conceptually the simplest way to approach the problem of measuring the concentration of hydrogen ion in a solution (and is always used for very precise work), it is awkward to handle and somewhat dangerous since large quantities of gaseous hydrogen are used. Let us try to think of some alternative, less direct approaches.* Any oxidation-reduction reaction that involves H^+ is potentially useful for this purpose; consider, for example

$$2IO_3^- + 12H^+ + 10e^- = I_2(s) + 6H_2O,$$
$$\varepsilon^0_{IO_3^-|I_2} = +1.19 \text{ v.}$$

The potential of this couple is obviously a very sensitive function of $[H^+]$ (strictly, a_{H^+}),

$$\varepsilon_{IO_3^-|I_2} = \varepsilon^0_{IO_3^-|I_2} - \frac{0.059}{10} \log \frac{[I_2]}{[IO_3^-]^2[H^+]^{12}}.$$

We could add to the solution to be measured a known quantity of I_2 and IO_3^-, dip a platinum electrode into this solution, connect this half-cell with a reference half-cell through a salt bridge, measure the cell potential, and calculate (from the cell potential) the concentration of H^+. Although feasible, this method is very imprecise because IO_3^- and I_2 react readily with a very wide variety of substances that might well be present along with H^+ in an unknown solution. As a result, we would no longer know the concentrations of I_2 and IO_3^- and hence would not be able unequivocally to relate the cell potential to $[H^+]$.

The Quinhydrone Electrode

A more suitable half-reaction involving H^+ is the quinone-hydroquinone couple:†

C₆H₄O₂ Quinone, Q   C₆H₄(OH)₂ Hydroquinone, H₂Q

(The hexagons are benzene rings and are understood to have a carbon at each corner with a hydrogen attached if no other group is shown.) This is a reversible reaction, so a platinum electrode dipped into a solution of hydro-

quinone, quinone, and hydrogen ion accurately reflects the potential of this couple,

$$\varepsilon_{QH} = \varepsilon^0_{QH} - \frac{0.059}{2} \log \frac{[H_2Q]}{[Q][H^+]^2}.$$

To use this couple, we take advantage of the fact that quinone and hydroquinone react with each other to form a loose compound in which one molecule of quinone is united with one molecule of hydroquinone; this compound is called *quinhydrone*. Quinhydrone is moderately soluble in water and is largely dissociated into quinone and hydroquinone in solution. Thus if we add quinhydrone to a solution whose pH we desire to measure potentiometrically we are assured that the concentration of quinone and hydroquinone will be the same, since one mole of each is formed for each mole of quinhydrone that dissociates. Now, when we look at the equation for the potential of the H_2Q-Q couple, we see that it is the *ratio* $[H_2Q]$:$[Q]$ that we need to know, not the actual concentrations of these species. However, the ratio in a solution to which quinhydrone has been added is unity, so we can write

$$\varepsilon_{QH} = \varepsilon^0_{QH} - \frac{0.059}{2} \log \frac{1}{[H^+]^2} = \varepsilon^0_{QH} + 0.059 \log [H^+].$$

When quinhydrone is added to a solution in which $[H^+] = 1$ (pH = 0) and this quinhydrone electrode is coupled to an SHE, the cell potential is 0.699 v and the lead from the quinhydrone half-cell is positive; hence $\varepsilon^0_{HQ} = +0.699$ v. (Why?) We can then write

$$\varepsilon_{QH} = 0.699 + 0.059 \log [H^+] = 0.699 - 0.059 \text{ pH},$$

and we again have an equation relating a half-cell potential directly to pH. (These derivations are valid for pH below about 8. In more basic solution the hydroquinone, H_2Q, begins to act as an acid and the simple 1:1 ratio of $[H_2Q]$:$[Q]$ is no longer valid.)

10–6 OXIDATION-REDUCTION TITRATIONS

So far we have considered only systems in which we have spatially separated the half-reactions that might occur. In such systems we can vary the concentrations of the various species independently to observe the effect on the cell potential. Indeed, such experiments play a vital role in determining equilibrium constants from cell potentials. The systems thus studied are not usually in equilibrium (they are only if $\Delta\varepsilon = 0$). What will happen if we constrain an oxidation-reduction system to be in equilibrium, e.g., by mixing all the species together in one vessel and waiting long enough for equilibrium to be attained? (The same result can be accomplished by short-circuiting an electrochemical cell and waiting until the potential goes to zero. In this case the species of the

---

* In Appendix D the commercial solution to this problem, the glass electrode, is discussed.

† If you have had any experience with photographic developing you are probably familiar with hydroquinone, a reducing agent often used in developers. Oxidation of hydroquinone yields quinone.

two half-reactions will still be physically separated but their concentrations will be the same as though they had been mixed in the same vessel. This is the type of system we must consider when we discuss oxidation-reduction (redox) titrations.

The conditions needed for redox titrations are the same as for any other titrations: quantitative and stoichiometric reactions, rapid reactions, availability of stable standard solutions, and some means of detecting the equivalence point. Some of the most common titrants used for redox titrations are MnO_4^-, $Cr_2O_7^=$, I_3^-, and $S_2O_3^=$. Many times a titrant or the substance titrated acts as its own indicator: For example, the permanganate ion, MnO_4^-, is a very deep reddish-purple color, whereas the reduced product of its reaction with reducing agents is the colorless manganous ion, Mn^{++},

$$MnO_4^- + 8H^+ + 5e^- = Mn^{++} + 4H_2O,$$
$$\mathcal{E}^0_{MnO_4^-|Mn^{++}} = 1.51 \text{ v}.$$

The solutions titrated with standard MnO_4^- solutions are usually colorless to begin with and turn pink at the endpoint when no reducing species are left to react with the added MnO_4^-. Conversely, in the titration of iodine solutions with standard thiosulfate, $S_2O_3^=$, the solutions are colored until the endpoint is reached when all the iodine has disappeared. (Sometimes starch, which forms an intensely purple complex with I_3^-, is added to make this endpoint sharper and easier to detect.)

The Potential Curve for a Redox Titration

As an example of a redox titration, let us examine the dichromate, $Cr_2O_7^=$, titration of ferrous ion, Fe^{++} (see Experiment 20). The half-reactions and potentials of interest are

$$Cr_2O_7^= + 14H^+ + 6e^- = 2Cr^{+3} + 7H_2O,$$
$$\mathcal{E}^0_{Cr} = 1.33 \text{ v},$$

$$Fe^{+3} + e^- = Fe^{++}, \qquad \mathcal{E}^0_{Fe} = 0.70 \text{ v,}^*$$

and the overall titration reaction is

$$6Fe^{++} + Cr_2O_7^= + 14H^+$$
$$= 6Fe^{+3} + 2Cr^{+3} + 7H_2O,$$
$$\Delta\mathcal{E}^0 = 0.63 \text{ v}.$$

This potential yields $\Delta G^0 = -6 \times 23{,}062 \times (+0.63) = -87{,}200$ cal, so the reaction (with all reactants and

---

* This is the potential of this half-reaction in 1 M HCl solution. It is termed a *formal potential* because although the solution is made up to be 1 M in both iron species there are complexes formed with the Cl^- which make the actual concentrations different from 1 M. The standard half-cell potential for $Fe^{+3} | Fe^{++}$ is 0.771 v. Does Fe^{+3} or Fe^{++} form the more stable complexes with chloride?

products in their standard states) tends to go spontaneously and the equilibrium lies very far toward the right as written. (What is the equilibrium constant for this reaction?)

If some $Cr_2O_7^=$ solution is added to a solution initially containing only Fe^{++} (and H^+), a reaction will occur to form Cr^{+3} and Fe^{+3}. When equilibrium is reached (very rapidly in this system) the half-cell potential of each of the redox couples $Fe^{+3} | Fe^{++}$ and $Cr_2O_7^= | Cr^{+3}$ must be equal, i.e.,

$$\mathcal{E}_{Fe} = \mathcal{E}_{Cr} = \mathcal{E},$$

$$\mathcal{E}_{Fe} = \mathcal{E}^0_{Fe} - 0.059 \log \frac{[Fe^{++}]}{[Fe^{+3}]},$$

$$\mathcal{E}_{Cr} = \mathcal{E}^0_{Cr} - \frac{0.059}{6} \log \frac{[Cr^{+3}]^2}{[Cr_2O_7^=][H^+]^{14}},$$

where concentrations have been substituted for activities. How can $\mathcal{E}$ be measured? We place an inert sensing electrode, such as platinum, in the solution, connect the solution by means of a salt bridge to another half-cell, and then measure the potential difference between the two cells. For simplicity, let us assume that the other half-cell is the SHE, so that the potential we measure for the complete cell will be the potential of the half-cell of interest, $\mathcal{E}$, which we shall now set out to calculate.

Let us begin with 50.0 ml of 0.1000 M Fe^{++}, which we shall titrate with 0.01667 M $Cr_2O_7^=$ solution. Initially, no chromium species are present, but since there will be a very small and indeterminate amount of Fe^{+3} present, no meaningful potential for the solution can be calculated. The addition of 1.0 ml of the $Cr_2O_7^=$ solution will introduce $1.667 \times 10^{-2} \times 10^{-3}$ moles of $Cr_2O_7^=$ to the solution, which, by the stoichiometry of the reaction, will react with $6 \times 1.667 \times 10^{-5} = 1.000 \times 10^{-4}$ moles of Fe^{++}, the amount present in 1.0 ml of the Fe^{++} solution ($1.000 \times 10^{-1} \times 10^{-3}$). Thus 50.0 ml of the $Cr_2O_7^=$ will be required to titrate the Fe^{++} to the equivalence point.

We may first calculate $\mathcal{E}$ at the equivalence point. At this point the stoichiometry of the equation dictates the conditions that

$$[Fe^{+3}] = 3[Cr^{+3}],$$
$$[Fe^{++}] = 6[Cr_2O_7^=].$$

(Why?) We combine the two half-reactions as follows

$$\mathcal{E} = \mathcal{E}^0_{Fe} - 0.059 \log \frac{[Fe^{++}]}{[Fe^{+3}]}$$

$$6\mathcal{E} = 6\mathcal{E}^0_{Cr} - 0.059 \log \frac{[Cr^{+3}]^2}{[Cr_2O_7^=][H^+]^{14}}$$

$$\overline{7\mathcal{E} = \mathcal{E}^0_{Fe} + 6\mathcal{E}^0_{Cr} - 0.059 \log \frac{[Fe^{++}][Cr^{+3}]^2}{[Fe^{+3}][Cr_2O_7^=][H^+]^{14}}}$$

and substitute the relationships between concentrations to get

$$7\varepsilon = \varepsilon_{Fe}^0 + 6\varepsilon_{Cr}^0 - 0.059 \log \frac{[Fe^{++}](\frac{1}{3})^2[Fe^{+3}]^2}{[Fe^{+3}]\frac{1}{6}[Fe^{++}][H^+]^{14}},$$

$$\varepsilon = \frac{\varepsilon_{Fe}^0 + 6\varepsilon_{Cr}^0}{7} - \frac{0.059}{7} \log \frac{2[Fe^{+3}]}{3[H^+]^{14}}.$$

Since the reaction goes essentially to completion we can at least begin with the approximation that all the iron is present as $[Fe^{+3}]$ (0.0500 M). The potential we are using for the iron couple is that in 1 M HCl, so we shall assume that $[H^+]$ is equal to 1 throughout the titration. The equation for ε then becomes

$$\varepsilon = \frac{0.70 + 6 \times 1.33}{7} - \frac{0.059}{7} \log (\tfrac{2}{3} \times 0.0500)$$

and

$$\varepsilon = 1.24 + 0.01 = 1.25 \text{ v}.$$

We can check our approximation concerning the extent of the reaction by substituting into the Nernst equation for the iron couple and solving for $[Fe^{++}]$:

$$1.25 = 0.70 - 0.059 \log \frac{[Fe^{++}]}{0.0500},$$

$$10^{-0.55/0.059} = \frac{[Fe^{++}]}{5 \times 10^{-2}} = 10^{-9.3} = 5 \times 10^{-10},$$

$$[Fe^{++}] = 2.5 \times 10^{-11}.$$

The quantity 2.5×10^{-11} is certainly negligible with respect to 5×10^{-2}, so the approximation that the reaction is "complete" is satisfied.

To calculate the potential before the equivalence point, it is easiest to use the Nernst equation for the iron couple. For example, when the titration is 99.9% complete we can begin assuming that $[Fe^{+3}] = 999[Fe^{++}]$ (Why?) so that

$$\varepsilon = 0.70 - 0.059 \log \frac{[Fe^{++}]}{[Fe^{+3}]} = 0.70 - 0.059 \log \tfrac{1}{999}$$

$$= 0.70 + 0.18 = 0.88 \text{ v}.$$

To obtain this result we have tacitly assumed that all the $Cr_2O_7^=$ added has reacted to oxidize Fe^{++} to Fe^{+3}. We check this by substituting into the Nernst equation for the chromium couple:

$$0.88 = 1.33 - \frac{0.059}{6} \log \frac{[Cr^{+3}]^2}{[Cr_2O_7^=][H^+]^{14}},$$

$$10^{6 \times 0.45/0.059} = \frac{[Cr^{+3}]^2}{[Cr_2O_7^=]} = 10^{45}.$$

(The pH is still assumed to be zero.) Thus about one part in 10^{22} of the chromium is present as $Cr_2O_7^=$. The oxidation reaction has gone essentially to completion.

Beyond the equivalence point it is easiest to use the Nernst equation for the chromium couple to calculate the potential. When the titration is 100.1% complete we can write that $[Cr^{+3}] = 2000[Cr_2O_7^=]$ (the factor of 2000 arises because we get two moles of Cr^{+3} for every mole of $Cr_2O_7^=$ that reacts and we have added 1000 times as much $Cr_2O_7^=$ before the equivalence point as after) so that

$$\varepsilon = 1.33 - \frac{0.059}{6} \log \frac{[Cr^{+3}]^2}{[Cr_2O_7^=][H^+]^{14}}$$

$$= 1.33 - \frac{0.059}{6} \log \frac{[Cr^{+3}]}{2000}.$$

At this point $[Cr^{+3}] = 0.00833$ (from the stoichiometry);

$$\varepsilon = 1.33 - \frac{0.059}{6} \log \frac{8.3 \times 10^{-3}}{2 \times 10^3} = 1.38 \text{ v}.$$

There is no need to check this result since essentially all the Fe^{++} was reacted at the equivalence point and it will surely still be all reacted.

By continuing this sort of calculation you can obtain enough data to calculate a titration curve like that shown in Fig. 10-4. Note that the titration curve is not symmetric about the equivalence point. Also note that the slope of the curve before the equivalence point is much steeper than that after the equivalence point. Both these phenomena result because the chromium half-reaction involves six electrons, while the iron half-reaction involves only one electron. As you can see from the Nernst equation, the smaller n is, the greater will be the change brought about in ε by a change in the argument of the logarithm. This explains the difference in slopes.

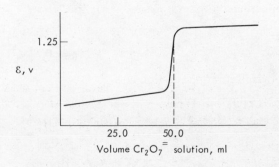

Fig. 10-4. The titration curve for the titration of 50.0 ml of 0.100 M Fe^{++} in 1 M HCl with 0.01667 M Cr_2O_7.

Potential Indicators

Although following a redox titration by measuring the change in potential as a function of amount of titrant added is an accurate and sometimes necessary technique, it is not so convenient and rapid as using an indicator that would give a visual indication of the equivalence point. Such an indicator will exist in reduced, I_r, and oxidized, I_o, forms with a half-reaction and potential

$$I_o + ne^- = I_r, \qquad \mathcal{E}_I^0.$$

The Nernst equation for this indicator is*

$$\mathcal{E} = \mathcal{E}_I^0 - \frac{0.059}{n} \log \frac{[I_r]}{[I_o]}.$$

Let us assume, as usual, that when the ratio $[I_r]:[I_o]$ changes from 10 to 0.1, a detectable color change will

occur in the solution. How large a change in the potential of the solution is required for this ratio change?

$$\mathcal{E}_{10} = \mathcal{E}_I^0 - \frac{0.059}{n} \log 10 = \mathcal{E}_I^0 - \frac{0.059}{n}$$

$$\mathcal{E}_{0.1} = \mathcal{E}_I^0 - \frac{0.059}{n} \log 0.1 = \mathcal{E}_I^0 + \frac{0.059}{n}$$

$$\overline{\mathcal{E}_{10} - \mathcal{E}_{0.1} = - \frac{2 \times 0.059}{n} = - \frac{0.12}{n}}$$

Thus when the potential of the solution changes by $0.12/n$ v in the neighborhood of $\mathcal{E}_I^0$, there will be a color change in the solution. This potential, $\mathcal{E}_I^0$, is sometimes called the transition potential.

A commonly used potential indicator for the Fe^{++} titration with $Cr_2O_7^=$ is the diphenylamine sulfonate ion,

This indicator is oxidized in a two-step process:

Diphenylbenzidine sulfonate ion

Diphenylbenzyl violet

The first step is not reversible and forms the colorless diphenylbenzidine sulfonate ion; the second step is reversible and is responsible for the indicator action.†

---

* We are neglecting other species that may be present in the indicator redox couple. Assuming that these other concentrations are constant in the solution, they simply add a constant factor to the right-hand side of the Nernst equation.

† Obviously a bit of the titrant must be used up to oxidize the indicator, and it would be preferable to have this be as small as possible. In fact, you might think we could begin with diphenylbenzidine sulfonate ion and get just as good an endpoint indication using even less titrant. This is indeed the case, but since sodium diphenylamine sulfonate is more readily available and more soluble in water, it is usually used to make stock indicator solutions.

At this point you might think back a bit and ask how we can use this indicator for the ferrous ion titration with dichromate. After all, our calculations indicate that the range of indicator action is about $0.83 \pm \frac{1}{2}(0.12/2) = 0.80$ to 0.86 v, and the titration is only 99.9% complete at 0.88 v, so the endpoint indication will come too soon. This criticism is merited and, in fact, when this indicator is used in ferrous ion solutions acidified only with HCl, the endpoint is not sharp and tends to come too early. The problem can be eliminated, however, by adding H_2SO_4 and H_3PO_4 to the ferrous ion solution. The complexes of ferric ion with phosphate and sulfate are stronger than the corresponding ferrous complexes, so the activity of the ferric ion is reduced in these solutions, as evidenced by the potential

$$Fe^{+3} + e^- = Fe^{++}, \qquad \varepsilon^0 = 0.61 \text{ v}$$

in a solution that is $1\ M\ H_2SO_4$ and $0.5\ M\ H_3PO_4$. If you use this potential to calculate the solution potential

at 99.9% titration, the result is 0.79 v, so the indicator color change will occur between 99.9 and 100% titration. You will find the error in this endpoint is less than one part per thousand. Work this out for yourself.

A few other common redox indicators and their properties are listed in Table 10–2.

Table 10–2

OXIDATION-REDUCTION INDICATORS IN DILUTE ACID SOLUTION

	Color		
Indicator	Reduced	Oxidized	Transition potential, v
5-nitro-1,10-phenanthroline iron(II) complex (nitroferroin)	Red	Pale blue	1.25
1,10-phenanthroline iron(II) complex (ferroin)	Red	Pale blue	1.12
Diphenylamine sulfonic acid	Colorless	Red-violet	0.83
Diphenylamine	Colorless	Violet	0.76

EXPERIMENT 21. *Potentiometric Determination of Equilibrium Constants*

We shall use measurements of cell potentials to calculate the equilibrium constant for the dissociation of acetic acid and the solubility product for silver chloride. There are other methods of determining acid dissociation constants (see Experiments 10, 15, and 17) which may be compared with the potentiometric determination. However, it is very difficult to measure the solubility product of a very insoluble compound by any method other than potentiometry. Potentiometric methods are very well suited for measuring very large or very small equilibrium constants.

In these experiments we shall use the quinhydrone electrode extensively (see Section 10–5). We have stated that the quinhydrone electrode functions reversibly and is a faithful indicator of hydrogen ion concentration in a solution (up to pH of about 8). Since our experiments depend on the validity of these statements, they are worth testing. To test them, we shall measure the cell potential for a cell made up of two quinhydrone half-cells containing different concentrations of hydrogen ion. Let us call these half-cells 1 and 2, where $[H^+]_1 >$ $[H^+]_2$. We know from our discussion of the quinhydrone electrode that the potentials of these two electrodes will be

$$\varepsilon_1 = 0.699 + 0.059 \log [H^+]_1,$$

$$\varepsilon_2 = 0.699 + 0.059 \log [H^+]_2.$$

Which electrode will be positive? Since $[H^+]_1 > [H^+]_2$,

$\log [H^+]_1 > \log [H^+]_2$ and therefore ε_1 will be more positive than ε_2; in other words, we predict that the lead from the quinhydrone electrode containing the higher $[H^+]$ will be positive. What will be the value of the cell potential, $\Delta\varepsilon$?

$$\begin{aligned} \Delta\varepsilon &= \varepsilon_1 - \varepsilon_2 \\ &= 0.059 \log [H^+]_1 - 0.059 [H^+]_2 \\ &= 0.059 \log \frac{[H^+]_1}{[H^+]_2}; \end{aligned}$$

$\Delta\varepsilon$ as defined here is positive, since ε_1 is more positive than ε_2. Therefore if $[H^+]_1$ and $[H^+]_2$ are known, we can calculate $\Delta\varepsilon$ and compare this value with that actually measured. If the theoretical and calculated values agree reasonably well, we can have greater confidence in the quinhydrone electrode.

We determine an acid dissociation constant by combining the buffer equation (see Section 7–5)

$$[H^+] = \frac{K_a C_a}{C_s},$$

where C_a and C_s are the known molar concentrations of the acid and a salt of the acid (with the cation of a strong base) in a solution, with a potentiometric determination of $[H^+]$ using the quinhydrone electrode. Since C_a, C_s, and $[H^+]$ are known, K_a is easily calculable.

The solubility product of AgCl is determined by measuring $[Ag^+]$ potentiometrically in a solution of known $[Cl^-]$. For this purpose a silver wire is dipped into the solution, thus creating the couple

$$Ag^+ + e^- = Ag, \qquad \mathcal{E}^0_{Ag} = 0.7994 \text{ v.}$$

This silver half-cell is coupled to a reference half-cell, the cell potential and electrode signs are determined, and the $[Ag^+]$ is calculated as outlined for other cases in Section 10–5.

Procedure

Using three small, clean, dry, labeled beakers as containers, obtain 35-ml samples of each of three buffer solutions with pH's of 1, 4, and 7 (the exact pH of each buffer will appear on the stock container label). Prepare a salt bridge, using a U-tube (bent from 6 to 8-mm tubing or obtained from your instructor) filled with 1.0 M KCl solution (available in the laboratory) and stoppered (not too tightly) with corks wrapped with filter paper. In another beaker obtain about 40 ml of the 1.0 M KCl solution. The ends of the salt bridge should be dipped in this solution each time the bridge is shifted from one half-cell to another. Omitting this rinsing operation may result in substantial errors.

Add to each of the three buffer solutions about 0.1 gm of *quinhydrone*. (Your instructor will show you a test tube containing 0.1 gm of quinhydrone so you may estimate 0.1 gm by eye.) Stir or swirl each of the solutions to promote solution of the quinhydrone, which must be present in excess, i.e., some solid quinhydrone must remain undissolved in each beaker. (If this is not the case, add more quinhydrone as required.)

You will use either potentiometers or vacuum-tube voltmeters (you can use the pH meter, a VTVM, as a millivoltmeter) to measure the potentials of your cells. Before using either instrument, be certain you understand its operation; if you are puzzled by it, ask your instructor for an explanation. Obtain two platinum electrodes from your instructor. (One common way of making a platinum electrode involves sealing a short length of platinum wire in one end of a piece of soft glass tubing, placing some mercury in the sealed tube, and dipping a long piece of copper wire into the mercury. The copper wire is the lead from this electrode. Do not turn this type of electrode upside down or the mercury will run out, obviating the electrode's usefulness and creating a hazard from the mercury vapor.) Dip one electrode into your pH 1 buffer solution and the other into the pH 7 buffer solution. Connect the two half-cells with the salt bridge and use the potentiometer or VTVM to measure and record as accurately as you can the potential of this cell. Record which electrode is positive. Shifting the salt bridge as necessary, repeat the measure-

ments for the pH 1 buffer connected to the pH 4 buffer and the pH 4 buffer connected to the pH 7 buffer.

Make up three acetate buffer solutions as follows:

1) 10 ml of 0.10 M NaOAc + 10 ml of 0.10 M HOAc,

2) 20 ml of 0.10 M NaOAc + 2 ml of 0.10 M HOAc,

3) 2 ml of 0.10 M NaOAc + 20 ml of 0.10 M HOAc.

(NaOAc is sodium acetate and HOAc is acetic acid.) Add excess quinhydrone to each of these three acetate buffers. Taking each of the solutions in turn and shifting the electrodes (platinum) and the salt bridge as required, use the potentiometer or VTVM to measure the cell potential when each of the acetate buffers is connected with the pH 7 buffer solution to form a cell. In each of the three cases, record the cell potential and also which one of the electrodes is positive.

In a test tube mix 1 ml of 0.1 M $AgNO_3$ solution with 1 ml of 1.0 M KCl solution. Swirl until the precipitate coagulates and drain off the supernatant liquid as completely as possible. Wash the precipitate with two or three 1 to 2 ml portions of the 1.0 M KCl solution, draining the precipitate as completely as possible after each wash. Add the precipitate to about 25 ml of 1.0 M KCl solution in a small beaker; stir or swirl this mixture for a few minutes. Obtain a short length of silver wire from your instructor. Rinse the wire with a little distilled water and dip it in the suspension of precipitated AgCl in 1.0 M KCl. Measure the potential of the cell made when this silver half-cell is connected by means of a salt bridge with the pH 7 buffer half-cell. Record the potential and also which one of the electrodes is positive.

Calculations

Compute the potential you would predict for each of the cells created from known buffers. Do these potentials and the predicted positive electrodes agree with those you measured? To what might you ascribe any discrepancies? Are your data internally consistent? (From two of your measurements you ought to be able to predict the third.)

From your measurements on the acetate buffer solutions, compute three values of pK_a for acetic acid. What is the mean deviation? How does this compare with the propagated error in the measurements?

From your measurement on the silver-silver ion couple, compute the solubility product of AgCl, i.e., K_s for the reaction $AgCl(s) \rightleftharpoons Ag^+ + Cl^-$. To do this you will have to write the cell potential in terms of the half-cell potentials (or electrode potentials) and then solve the resulting expression for $[Ag^+]$. Since you know $[Cl^-] = 1.0\ M$ you will immediately be able to calculate K_s.

Further Experimental Problems

Carry out a potentiometric titration to observe for yourself how well such titrations work. In particular you might like to try titrating a mixture of Sn^{++} and Fe^{++} with an oxidizing titrant such as MnO_4^- or $Cr_2O_7^=$ to see what happens. Try to predict the result first. Conditions for doing such titrations will be found in the analytical chemistry textbooks listed in the references.

How does the presence of ions other than H^+ affect the potential of the quinhydrone electrode?

Another potentiometric titration that could yield interesting structural data is a titration of the chloride ions in the $(Coen_2Cl_2)Cl$, which you prepared in Experiment 3, with a standardized $AgNO_3$ solution. Using a silver electrode in the solution to be titrated and any convenient reference half-cell, you can follow the course of this titration potentiometrically. This titration is impossible by any of the techniques discussed in Chapter 4. (Why?) Try this titration on a freshly made solution of the cobalt compound and then on one that has stood for a day or so. Is there any difference? To what factors might you ascribe any difference? What information concerning the structure of the compound do these data provide?

A number of other suggestions for further experiments are given in the articles listed in the references.

EXPERIMENT 22. *The Potentiometric and Analytic Determinations of the Equilibrium Constant of an Ionic Reaction*

Introduction

The equilibrium constant of an ionic reaction may be determined either analytically or potentiometrically. When the first method is used, the constituents of the reaction mixture are allowed to stand at constant temperature until equilibrium has been attained and their concentrations are then determined by analysis. When the potentiometric method is used, an appropriate electrochemical cell is constructed, the potential of the cell is measured, and from the potential the standard free energy change for the reaction and, hence, the equilibrium constant is calculated. The applicability of the electrometric method presumes the availability of reversible electrodes that give correct measurements of the electrode potential. When the potentiometric method is applicable, it is often preferable since it is usually faster and easier than the analytical method. Moreover, as we have previously pointed out, it can readily be used to study reactions with very large or very small equilibrium constants (in which case some of the constituents of the equilibrium mixture will be present only in trace amounts, and will be difficult, if not impossible, to determine accurately).

Finally, by making potentiometric measurements over a range of temperatures we can calculate not only ΔG^0 but ΔH^0 and ΔS^0 for the reaction of interest. Before relying fully on the potentiometric method we should check it against the more direct analytical method, choosing a reaction with an equilibrium constant near unity so the analytical method may be readily applied.

Let us use the reaction*

$$2Ag(s) + 2H^+ + \text{(Q)} \rightleftharpoons 2Ag^+ + \text{(H}_2\text{Q)} \quad (10\text{--}12)$$

The Potentiometric Method. The two half-reactions involved in the overall reaction to be studied are

$$Q + 2H^+ + 2e^- = H_2Q, \qquad 2Ag^+ + 2e^- = 2Ag,$$

which on subtraction yield the overall reaction

$$Q + 2Ag + 2H^+ = 2Ag^+ + H_2Q.$$

The electrochemical cell for the study of this reaction is represented (in our cell shorthand) as

Pt | Quinhydrone (sat'd),
    $HNO_3(0.1\ M)$ | $HNO_3(0.1\ M)$ | $HNO_3(0.1\ M)$,
                                        $AgNO_3(0.001\ M)$ | Ag.

Because the concentration of HNO_3 is the same in both half-cells and the "salt" bridge and the concentration of $AgNO_3$ in the silver half-cell is relatively small, the "liquid junction potential" in this system is relatively

---

* This reaction proceeding from right to left is that which makes hydroquinone useful as a photographic developer.

small.* The cell potential $\Delta\varepsilon$ is then given accurately by the Nernst equation

$$\Delta\varepsilon = \Delta\varepsilon^0 - \frac{2.303RT}{n\mathfrak{F}} \log \frac{(a_{Ag^+})^2 a_{H_2Q}}{(a_{H^+})^2 a_Q} \, .$$

(The activity of solid Ag metal is, by definition, unity and is not included.) The ratio of activities in this expression may be expressed in terms of molar concentrations and activity coefficients:

$$\frac{(a_{Ag^+})^2 a_{H_2Q}}{(a_{H^+})^2 a_Q} = \frac{[Ag^+]^2 (\gamma_{Ag^+})^2 [H_2Q] \gamma_{H_2Q}}{[H^+]^2 (\gamma_{H^+})^2 [Q] \gamma_Q} \, .$$

Because the silver and hydrogen ions are both univalent and because the ionic strength is almost constant throughout the system, we may assume, without appreciable error, that $\gamma_{H^+} = \gamma_{Ag^+}$ (see Section 9–1). Furthermore, in the *quinhydrone* half-cell (see Section 10–5) $[H_2Q] = [Q]$ and at the low ionic strength of this solution we may assume that the activity coefficients of uncharged species are the same, $\gamma_{H_2Q} = \gamma_Q$. Hence the ratio of activities can be reduced to a ratio of concentrations, and because we are using the quinhydrone half-cell, it can be further simplified to give

$$\Delta\varepsilon = \Delta\varepsilon^0 - \frac{2.303RT}{n\mathfrak{F}} \log \frac{[Ag^+]^2 [H_2Q]}{[H^+]^2 [Q]}$$

$$= \Delta\varepsilon^0 - \frac{2.303RT}{n\mathfrak{F}} \log \frac{[Ag^+]^2}{[H^+]^2} \, .$$

Given the actual concentrations of Ag^+ and H^+ and a measurement of the magnitude and sign of $\Delta\varepsilon$, we can at once calculate $\Delta\varepsilon^0$. Knowing $\Delta\varepsilon^0$ we can calculate ΔG^0 and K for the reaction (10–12) as described in Section 10–1.

The Analytical Method. In this case we prepare a mixture containing known initial concentrations of hydroquinone, nitric acid, and silver nitrate. Because the initial concentrations, c_{H_2Q}, c_{H^+}, and c_{Ag^+}, are known, it is only necessary to analyze for one component to determine the equilibrium concentrations of all the reactive species; it is most convenient to analyze for quinone. We will use an iodometric titration: the quinone is reduced (to hydroquinone) by iodide ion in a strongly acid solution with the liberation of an equivalent amount of iodine. We titrate the iodine thus produced with standard thiosulfate

---

* At each point in a cell where two different phases meet, there will, in general, be a potential difference, a junction potential, between the two phases. This is true at the opposite ends of a salt bridge, for example, so the cell potential we measure is not due wholly to the potentials at the metallic conductors but also has contributions from these liquid junction potentials. If the two liquids are very similar in composition, as in the present case, then the liquid junction potential will be very small.

to a starch endpoint. The reactions are

$$Q + 3I^- + 2H^+ = H_2Q + I_3^-,$$
$$I_3^- + 2S_2O_3^= = S_4O_6^= + 3I^-.$$

(What is the standard free-energy change for each of these reactions? Use the data in this chapter and in Appendix G.) Wait for just a moment, though; how do we know that the quinone we determine is only that present as such in the equilibrium mixture? After all, as the quinone is used up in the oxidation of I^-, we would expect additional quinone to be formed when reaction (10–12) proceeds to the left. Certainly such an expectation is in perfect accord with LeChatelier's principle and, more quantitatively, with thermodynamic arguments. Our analytical procedure, however, actually guards quite effectively against this possible complication. The large excess of I^- added to react with the quinone also immediately precipitates essentially all the Ag^+ present as the very insoluble AgI. Thus the addition of I^- "freezes" the equilibrium situation: The equilibrium cannot shift to the right because the quinone is used up and cannot shift to the left because the free silver ion is removed from the solution.

Let $[Q]$ be the analytically-determined concentration of quinone in the final equilibrium mixture; $[H_2Q]$, $[Ag^+]$, and $[H^+]$ are the other concentrations we must know to compute the equilibrium constant. For every mole of quinone formed a mole of hydroquinone must have reacted, so we can write $[H_2Q] = c_{H_2Q} - [Q]$. For every mole of quinone formed two moles of silver ion react, so $[Ag^+] = c_{Ag^+} - 2[Q]$. This same line of argument leads to $[H^+] = c_{H^+} + 2[Q]$. Thus from our knowledge of the initial concentrations and a measurement of the final quinone concentration we can readily establish the concentrations of all the other components present. Substitution of these values into the equilibrium-constant expression for reaction (10–12) immediately gives us the equilibrium constant.

Procedure

Work with a partner for the potentiometric determination, but do the analytical determination individually.

Stock solutions of 0.200 M HNO_3, 0.100 M $AgNO_3$, and 0.005 M $Na_2S_2O_3$ (the exact concentrations will be on the labels) will be available in the laboratory. Take enough of each of these solutions at the beginning of the experiment so you will not get confused if a new stock solution of a different concentration is later placed in the laboratory. Adequate amounts, each to be taken in a clean, dry, labeled, stoppered bottle, are: 250 ml of HNO_3, 150 ml of $AgNO_3$, and 200 ml of $Na_2S_2O_3$. (Store the $AgNO_3$ solution away from the light.)

The Potentiometric Method. Place a small amount of quinhydrone (*not* hydroquinone) in a clean dry test tube. Fill the test tube about three-quarters full with 0.1 M HNO_3. (This solution is to be prepared by a determinate dilution of the stock 0.200-M solution; the diluted solution need not be accurately 0.1 M, but the actual concentration must be known *accurately*. Use pipets for this dilution.) Fill another clean dry test tube about three-quarters full with a solution 0.1 M in HNO_3 and 0.001 M in $AgNO_3$. (This solution is to be prepared by determinate dilution and mixing of appropriate quantities of the HNO_3 and $AgNO_3$ stock solutions; again the solution need not have exactly the nominal concentrations indicated, but the actual concentrations of both species must be known *accurately*.)

Mount your test tubes for ease of handling. Cut a piece about six inches square from the side of an expanded foam acid case and trim the inner side so that the worst ridges are removed. You can punch three holes in this sheet of foam as shown in Fig. 10–5 with a triangular file or a Swiss Army knife. The geometry of your Y-tube (see below) determines the distance between the two larger holes. The smaller hole is for a thermometer. The test tubes and thermometer should fit snugly in the holes so they will be held in position without slipping. This assembly can now be placed on top of a beaker to form a steady support for the cells.

Obtain a Y-tube from your instructor and make sure it is clean and dry. To the two corresponding arms of the tube attach, with *short* Tygon sleeves, two 16-cm lengths of glass tubing with an outside diameter of about 6 mm. These tubes must also be clean and dry, with their ends fire-polished until the openings are reduced to a diameter of about 1 mm. To the third arm of the Y-tube attach a length of rubber tubing (which must fit snugly) to link it with the aspirator (through a trap), and place a screw pinchclamp on this hose very close to its overlap with the Y-tube. Mount your test tubes and thermometer in their holder and insert the two extended legs of the Y-tube into the two test tubes as indicated in Fig. 10–6. The pinchclamp should be open and the tubing should not yet be connected to the aspirator. Use a rubber band to anchor the Y-tube to the thermometer in such a way that the end of the extended leg in the quinhydrone half-cell is well clear of the bottom of the test tube and the solid quinhydrone collected there. If any solid quinhydrone is sucked up into the "salt" bridge, the experiment will be ruined and you will have to start again. Now close the pinchclamp tight and connect the tubing to the aspirator trap with the aspirator going gently. Open the pinchclamp *very slowly* until the solutions begin to be drawn into the Y-tube. Continue until the Y-tube is filled and the liquid is *just* above the pinchclamp and then immediately tighten the clamp firmly. Detach the assembly from the aspirator by cutting off the hose (with scissors) about 2 cm above the pinchclamp. (*It is imperative* that the solutions in the two half-cells remain uncontaminated by the mixed solution in the Y-tube bridge. Do not allow the solution to subside from the bridge into the cells; do not change the relative juxtaposition of the cells once they have been linked through the bridge. This is where your foam support will be very handy.)

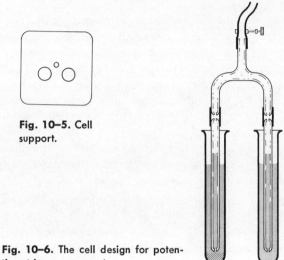

Fig. 10–5. Cell support.

Fig. 10–6. The cell design for potentiometric measurements.

Taking care to avoid shaking, which might contaminate the solutions in the half-cells, carry your cell assembly to a potentiometer set for a full-scale reading of 0.100 v. (This measurement requires a potentiometer capable of registering accurately a few millivolts; the usual pH meter VTVM is inadequate, since its accuracy is usually only about 3 mv.) The beaker in which your cells are placed should be filled with water to act as a temperature bath. Check with your instructor concerning the use of the potentiometer if it is unfamiliar to you. He will give you a platinum electrode to be placed in the quinhydrone half-cell and a silver electrode for the silver-silver ion half-cell. Using your potentiometer, note and record the polarity of your cell. Measure the potential it delivers at 5 to 10 minute intervals for about 20 to 30 minutes or until a steady reading is obtained; record the measured voltages and temperature. Return the electrodes and Y-tube to your instructor.

The Analytical Method. Prepare by determinate dilution and mixing of suitable portions of the stock solutions 200 ml of a solution that is 0.025 M in $AgNO_3$ and 0.1 M in HNO_3. Weigh out accurately and add to this solution sufficient hydroquinone (*not* quinhydrone) to make the solution 0.025 M in hydroquinone, molecular weight 110. (None of the three indicated concentrations need have exactly the indicated nominal values, but all three of the concentrations must be *accurately* known.) Transfer this solution to a clean dry flask. With a clean dry pipet, take a 5-ml aliquot of the solution from the flask and titrate it as described in the paragraph below; since it takes some time for the reaction to proceed to a detectable extent, essentially no quinone should be found in this sample. Stopper the flask with a clean dry stopper and, taking care not to splash the solution on the stopper, which might react with it, store the flask (away from the light) in your desk for about 48 hours. Do not leave this solution for more than two days as side reactions will begin to occur that will change the concentrations. Store a thermometer in the desk alongside the flask and take care to record the temperature reading when you first open your desk to withdraw the flask at the end of the equilibration period. Use a pipet to take a 5-ml aliquot of the solution and immediately treat this sample as described in the next paragraph. Then take a second 5-ml aliquot of the solution and treat it likewise; continue in this fashion until you are satisfied that you have established the quinone concentration in the equilibrium mixture.

The titration procedure is as follows: Immediately before removing each aliquot from the reaction mixture, prepare in a clean 250-ml flask a mixture of 10 ml of 10% KI solution (freshly made by dissolving about 1 gm of KI in 10 ml of H_2O) and 10 ml of 3 M HCl. Add the aliquot of your reaction mixture to this mixture. Immediately, AgI will precipitate and quinone will be reduced to hydroquinone, producing iodine. Titrate the liberated iodine (I_3^- in the presence of excess I^-, as we saw from the equations above) at once with standard 0.005 M thiosulfate. When the orange-red color fades to yellow, add 2 to 5 ml of starch indicator and titrate until the solution is colorless.

In a strongly acid solution like this, I^- can be rapidly oxidized to I_3^- by reaction with the air, $O_2 + 4H^+ + 6I^- \rightarrow H_2O + 2I_3^-$. (What is the standard free-energy change for this reaction?). Inaccuracies resulting from this side reaction can be minimized by preparing each iodide-acid mixture just before it is used and by titrating it immediately after the addition of the reaction-mixture aliquot. To correct for any residual air-oxidation of I^-, a blank determination should be run. Perform the titration exactly as above, except that you will use a 5-ml aliquot of 0.1 M HNO_3 as the sample instead of an aliquot of the reaction mixture. The starch indicator will have to be added immediately in this case. The volume of thiosulfate used in this blank run (in which any I_3^- formed is only that produced by air oxidation) should then be subtracted from the volume of thiosulfate used in the actual sample titrations.

Calculations

Calculate $\Delta \mathcal{E}^0$, ΔG^0, and the equilibrium constant for reaction (10–12) from your potentiometric data. Calculate the equilibrium constant from your analytical data and compare it with that obtained potentiometrically. Are they the same within experimental error?

Further Experimental Problems

Determine the temperature dependence of the potential of the quinhydrone-silver cell in the temperature range 0°C to 30°C. Use one section of an expanded foam acid carton as a water bath at the desired temperature; place your cell assembly in this bath and repeat the potentiometric measurements described above until another steady reading is obtained. Repeat for your other temperatures. From a plot of $\Delta \mathcal{E}$ versus T for this cell you can find $d(\Delta \mathcal{E})/dT$, the slope of the tangent to the curve at any temperature. [From only two measurements you can approximate: $d(\Delta \mathcal{E})/dT \approx \Delta(\Delta \mathcal{E})/\Delta T$.] From these data calculate ΔH^0 and ΔS^0 for reaction (10–12).

REFERENCES

Anson, F., "Electrode Sign Conventions," *J. Chem. Ed.* **36,** 394 (1959) gives a clear exposition of the cause of much of the confusion regarding sign conventions in electrochemistry. If you understand the causes, perhaps the cure will be more easily found.

Bard, A. J., and S. H. Simonsen, "General Equation for the Equivalence Point Potential in Oxidation-Reduction Titrations," *J. Chem. Ed.* **37,** 364 (1960).

Chesick, J. P., and A. Patterson, Jr., "Potentiometric Measurements of Equilibria," *J. Chem. Ed.* **36,** 496 (1959) describes an inexpensive potentiometer and some experi-

ments to show how it is used to determine equilibrium constants potentiometrically.

Dillard, C. R., and P. H. Kammeyer, "Experiment with Galvanic Cells," *J. Chem. Ed.* **40,** 363 (1963) suggests a very simple and convenient combination salt bridge and half-cell that could be used as a reference electrode in a number of different systems.

Goldman, J. A., "Potentiometric Titration Curves for Simple Ion Combination Reactions," *J. Chem. Ed.* **40,** 519 (1963) gives the exact equation for a titration between ions of the same absolute magnitude and opposite sign.

KOLTHOFF, I. M., and E. B. SANDELL, *Introduction to Quantitative Inorganic Analysis*, Macmillan, New York, 1952, Chapters 31, 36, 38, and 39.

LATIMER, W., *Oxidation Potentials*, 2nd ed., Prentice Hall, Englewood Cliffs, N.J., 1952.

LICHT, T. S., and A. J. DE BÉTHUNE, "Recent Developments Concerning the Signs of Electrode Potentials," *J. Chem. Ed.* **34**, 433 (1957) discusses the international recommendations for electrochemical conventions and gives many illustrations of their application.

LIVINGSTON, R., and J. J. LINGANE, "An Experiment Illustrating the Relation Between E.M.F. and the Equilibrium Constant," *J. Chem. Ed.* **15**, 320 (1938) is the source from which Experiment 22 was derived.

LOCKWOOD, K. L., "Redox Revisited," *J. Chem. Ed.* **38**, 326 (1961) discusses a first approach to redox reactions.

MAHAN, B. H., *Elementary Chemical Thermodynamics*, W. A. Benjamin, New York, 1963, pp. 99–103.

NASH, L. K., *Elements of Chemical Thermodynamics*, Addison-Wesley, Reading, Mass., 1962, pp. 81–82.

SKOOG, D. A., and D. M. WEST, *Fundamentals of Analytical Chemistry*, Holt, Rinehart & Winston, New York, 1963, Chapters 17, 18, 19, 20 and 21.

WASER, J., *Basic Chemical Thermodynamics*, W. A. Benjamin, New York, 1965, Chapter 7.

WASER, J., *Quantitative Chemistry*, revised ed., W. A. Benjamin, New York, 1964, Chapters 14 and 15.

11 ATOMIC AND MOLECULAR PROPERTIES

Most of the chapters in this book present a general discussion of some chemical question, followed by suggestions for experiments utilizing the chemical principles explained in the first part of the chapter. Such a method is feasible because some common observations and your previous training have given us enough background for a general discussion of certain points. Two assumptions we have thus made are that atoms and molecules exist and that the atoms of a given element are all identical and, in particular, that each element has a characteristic atomic weight. We have used this Daltonian model to develop stoichiometric relationships.

Although these particular ideas are powerful and quantitatively predictive (in a large, although limited, area of chemistry), they leave many questions unanswered. One of the most interesting of these is: Why do certain atoms combine to form certain molecules but not others, e.g., why do N and O form NO_2, N_2O, NO, and N_2O_3, but not NO_4 or N_3O? An even more funda-

mental problem is: What holds the atoms in molecules together? Also, the Daltonian picture does not mention the shape of atoms and molecules. Do atoms and molecules have definite shapes in space? (This question only has meaning if there is some way to experimentally verify the shape or predict properties of the species that depend on their having or not having a definite shape.) Surely you can think of more questions about atomic and molecular properties that our first assumptions do not answer.

At no place in the field of chemistry or physics does the interplay of experiment, development of models, prediction, further experiment, refinement of models, etc., become so apparent as in the study of atomic and molecular properties. All the tools at our disposal are brought to bear in this study. Therefore in this chapter let us try to interweave principles and experimental problems as we go.

EXPERIMENT 23. The Temperature of the Sun

Planck's Hypothesis

By the end of the nineteenth century the classical theories of electromagnetic radiation (radio waves, light rays, infrared, visible, and ultraviolet, and x-rays) were completely worked out, as were the explanations for a number of the features of the discrete spectra emitted by low-pressure gases when electric discharges are passed through them (like the "neon" lights that are too prevalent today). The seemingly simple phenomenon of radiation from a black body, however, had not yet been explained. A perfect black body is one that, at 0°K., ab-

sorbs all the radiation that strikes it.* A black body at a

---

* A perfect black surface does not exist, but a very good approximation to a black body can be constructed by cutting a small hole in the wall of a hollow opaque vessel. Since the hole is so small compared with the inner surface area of the vessel, almost no radiation that enters the hole, the black body, will escape and all of it will eventually be absorbed by the walls. To perform emission measurements, the radiation that escapes through the hole, the black body, while the vessel is held at a constant temperature is analyzed. Such a "black body" is called a *hohlraum* (German, hollow cavity).

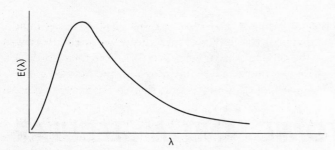

Fig. 11–1. The black-body radiation spectrum.

particular temperature also emits radiation; this emission is continuous, i.e., it includes all wavelengths of electromagnetic radiation. When the energy emitted by a black body at each particular wavelength is plotted as a function of wavelength, a plot like that shown in Fig. 11–1 is obtained. All black bodies at the same temperature emit exactly the same distribution of energy with wavelength, so the black-body radiation spectrum is a function of the temperature alone. However, classical theory did not predict the shape of the black-body radiation spectrum correctly. Wien's prediction that the wavelength of maximum emission, λ_m, would be inversely proportional to the absolute temperature of the black body, the Wien displacement law,

$$\lambda_m = \text{const} \ (1/T),$$

was experimentally verified in 1900 by Lummer and Pringsheim, who found Wien's constant = 0.294 cm-deg, the *shape* of the curve could not be predicted on the basis of classical electromagnetic radiation theory. The theory predicted a continuous increase in the energy emitted as the wavelength decreased and did not predict the observed fall-off at shorter wavelengths, called by some wags the "ultraviolet catastrophe" ("ultraviolet" here is synonymous with "short-wavelength").

In 1900 Planck proposed an "explanation" for the black-body radiation spectrum. Planck's approach was simple: He found an equation that fit the experimental results and then searched for a physical relationship that would yield an equation of the proper form. The physical relationship Planck proposed was that the energy emitted by an oscillator is directly proportional to the frequency of the oscillator:

$$\epsilon = h\nu. \tag{11–1}$$

(The oscillators in a black body are atoms or molecules vibrating about their equilibrium positions in the solid.) This equation implies that an oscillator can emit radiation of only a certain energy, i.e., that the energy is quantized. The relationship between the frequency of emitted radiation, determined by the frequency of the radiating oscillator, and the wavelength of the emitted

radiation is $\nu = c/\lambda$, where c is the speed of light (see Appendix E), so that

$$\epsilon = hc/\lambda. \tag{11–2}$$

When Planck used this relationship to derive the black-body radiation spectrum he found that the energy density per unit wavelength, $E(\lambda)$, for a black body is given as a function of wavelength by the equation

$$E(\lambda) = \frac{8\pi ch}{\lambda^5} \frac{1}{e^{ch/k\lambda T} - 1}, \tag{11–3}$$

where k is Boltzmann's constant. There are two terms in Eq. (11–3) that depend on λ. How do these vary as λ decreases? The first term is inversely proportional to λ^5, so it increases as λ decreases. The second term is inversely proportional to $e^{ch/k\lambda T}$, so as λ decreases the exponential gets larger and the term decreases. The exponential term will dominate the λ^5 term when λ is small enough, so that $E(\lambda)$ decreases as λ decreases beyond a certain λ_m, where a maximum occurs in the $E(\lambda)$ versus λ curve. That this is exactly the behavior of the black-body radiation spectrum is not surprising, since Planck set out to fit the curve. What is surprising and a complete break with the past is the quantum hypothesis, Eq. (11–1), *required* to obtain the correct result. It was not long before further experimental facts, for example, the photoelectric effect (see Shamos' book, pp. 232–237), were explained on the basis of Planck's quantum hypothesis and lent more support to this radical departure from past thought.

It is simple for you to find from Eq. (11–3) the wavelength at which $E(\lambda)$ is a maximum. We know from the calculus that we can find the maximum in such a curve by setting the derivative of $E(\lambda)$ with respect to λ, $dE(\lambda)/d\lambda$, equal to zero and then solving the equation for λ equal to λ_m:

$$\frac{dE(\lambda)}{d\lambda} = 0 = \left(1 - \frac{ch}{5k\lambda T}\right) e^{ch/k\lambda T} - 1, \tag{11–4}$$

$$\left(1 - \frac{ch}{5k\lambda_m T}\right) e^{ch/k\lambda_m T} = 1. \tag{11–5}$$

Now, solve Eq. (11–5) for $ch/k\lambda_m T$.

We can solve this transcendental equation most easily by using the following procedure.

1) Let $ch/k\lambda_m T = x$.

2) Take logarithms of both sides of the equation. Call the left-hand side of the resulting equation $f(x)$, that is, a function of x.

3) Plot $f(x)$ versus x. (Choose arbitrary values for x, e.g., 0, 1, 2, . . . , calculate $f(x)$, and then draw a smooth curve through the points.)

4) The value of x at the point where $f(x)$ is equal to the right-hand side of the equation obtained in step 2 is the solution.

This method can be applied to solve a great many transcendental equations.

From the solution of Eq. (11–5) and the values for h (6.625 × 10^{-27} erg-sec), k (1.38 × 10^{-16} erg/deg), and c (3.00 × 10^{10} cm/sec), determine the theoretical value of the constant in the Wien displacement law. (A translation of part of Planck's original paper is presented on pp. 301–314 of the book edited by Shamos.)

A Thermometer for Black Bodies

Armed with this knowledge of black-body radiation, let us consider how to construct a thermometer to measure the temperature of a black body. The black-body radiation spectrum is a function only of the absolute temperature and the dependence of $E(\lambda)$ on λ is known, Eq. (11–3). Thus we should be able to measure the temperature of a black body by measuring $E(\lambda)$ as a function of λ and determining what T would have to be to yield this particular curve.

How are we to determine $E(\lambda)$ versus λ? First we must have some means of selecting particular wavelengths of radiation. For this purpose we can use a monochromator ("one-color" device) containing a prism or diffraction grating that will separate radiation into its separate wavelengths (see Appendix E). The most common monochromators allow a selection of wavelengths somewhere in the range 2000 to 8000 Å.

Next we need some means of determining the amount of energy emerging from the monochromator at each of the wavelengths we select. Two types of detector can be used. One is the *thermopile*, a device consisting essentially of a large number of thermocouples connected in series with their hot junctions in thermal contact with a blackened piece of metal that is an approximation to a black body. Almost all the radiation striking the blackened metal is absorbed and converted to heat, which warms the metal and hence the thermocouples, so that a voltage is produced. The thermopile must be calibrated so that the amount of energy corresponding to a particular voltage is known; the calibration is usually done at the factory before the instrument is delivered. Thermopiles have several disadvantages: they react slowly, they produce very small signals, and they are very sensitive to changes in the temperature of their surroundings. The other type of detector, the *phototube*, is probably much more familiar. The circuitry necessary for a photocell is indicated schematically in Appendix E, Fig. E–6. When light strikes the photocathode, electrons are emitted (the photoelectric effect), are repelled by the

negative charge, and travel to the anode. Hence, light impinging on the photocathode causes current to flow in the circuit. The voltage drop, V, across the resistor is directly proportional to this current, i, and thus the meter reading, $M(\lambda)$, is proportional to the current, that is, $M(\lambda) \propto V \propto i$. How does the current, i, vary with the energy of the radiation impinging on the photocathode? At a particular wavelength the current is directly proportional to the total energy flux per second, $U(\lambda)$, that is, to the total number of photons per second impinging on the photocathode.* The proportionality constant varies with wavelength, so we can write

$$i = c'(\lambda)U(\lambda),$$

and therefore

$$M(\lambda) \propto c'(\lambda)U(\lambda).$$

Thus the meter readings are directly proportional to the energy flux per second. It is also reasonable to conclude that the energy flux, $U(\lambda)$, from a black body is directly proportional to the energy density per unit wavelength, $E(\lambda)$, so we could transform this last equation to

$$M(\lambda) = c(\lambda)E(\lambda), \tag{11–6}$$

where all the proportionality factors we have discussed are lumped together into $c(\lambda)$.

Should we use a thermopile or a phototube to detect our energy flux? It might seem that the thermopile would be more convenient and more direct, and it has the advantage of being precalibrated. However, we are overlooking the fact that the thermometer we construct will still have to be calibrated. It may have occurred to you already that we have assumed that all the energy entering the monochromator at a particular wavelength will also leave the exit if the monochromator is set at this wavelength; this is not true. Some radiation will be absorbed by the prism or scattered by the grating and will be lost, and the amount lost depends on the wavelength, so we shall have to calibrate our thermometer against a known black body no matter which detector we use. Thus we can use the more convenient phototube and simply let any attenuation of the radiation by the monochromator be combined into the wavelength-dependent proportionality factor $c(\lambda)$ in Eq. (11–6).

Construct a black-body thermometer by attaching a phototube to the exit of a monochromator which covers

---

* The linear response of a phototube does not continue indefinitely. As the energy flux per second increases the phototube overloads and the response begins to fall off. If we use a phototube in our thermometer, we must take care not to work outside the linear response region of the tube as indicated by the specifications furnished by the manufacturer.

at least the range 3500 to 7000 Å so that the radiation leaving the exit falls on the photocathode. (The photocell should be enclosed to protect it from receiving any radiation except that from the monochromator.) A 90-volt dry cell will serve as a satisfactory power supply for most phototubes. The resistance of the variable resistor and the galvanometer or milliammeter used as a meter should be such that the limiting current that can flow in the circuit will be within the linear response portion of the phototube used, usually less than 0.1 amp.

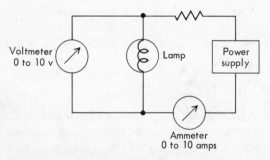

Fig. 11–2. Circuit for operation and control of the black-body thermometer calibration lamp (power supply capable of producing 6.6 amps at 6.83 volts).

This thermometer must be calibrated with the emission from a black body at a known temperature before it can be used to obtain the temperature of any other black body. What can we choose as a convenient reference black body? Fortunately there is a readily available light source which, according to the National Bureau of Standards, is a very good approximation to a black body emitting at 3100°K: this is a 45-watt iodine-filled tungsten filament lamp, often called a quartz-iodine lamp.* Figure 11–2 shows a diagram of the circuit you will need to adjust the lamp to operate at the current and voltage specified on the information sheet that comes with it. When operated at the specified voltage and current this lamp will emit a spectrum of energy that is almost identical to that of a black body at 3100°K. (This does not mean that the filament is actually at 3100°K. In fact, it is at a somewhat lower temperature, but the surface emissivity is such that it is effectively a 3100°K black body. See the article by Stair, *et al.*)

---

* These lamps are made in a variety of sizes and voltages by Sylvania and General Electric. You have probably noticed that light bulbs usually darken as they grow older. The iodine in this kind of bulb keeps the walls of the bulb clean by scavenging tungsten from them. At the high temperature in the lamp the iodine is atomized and reacts with the tungsten atoms that evaporate from the filament. The tungsten iodides are relatively volatile and remain in the gas phase until they come in contact with the hot filament, where they decompose, leaving the tungsten on the filament and releasing the iodine to react with more of the evaporating tungsten atoms.

To calibrate your thermometer, place it so that radiation from the lamp falls on the entrance of the monochromator. (Be careful to shield the lamp in some way so that you do not look directly at it. It is very bright and might damage your retina.) Take meter readings at a number of wavelengths over the range covered by your monochromator. From Eq. (11–3) you can calculate $E(\lambda)$ at each of these wavelengths for a 3100°K black body. By combining these values of $E(\lambda)$ with the meter readings $M(\lambda)$ at the same wavelengths, you can calculate $c(\lambda)$ for each wavelength. Plot $E(\lambda)$, $M(\lambda)$, and $c(\lambda)$ as functions of λ on the same graph.

The Temperature of the Sun

Go outdoors on a clear day, aim your thermometer at the sun, and take meter readings at a number of wavelengths over the range covered by the monochromator. Convert these meter readings to values of $E(\lambda)$ for the sun by using the conversion factor you obtained from the calibration and plot $M(\lambda)$ and $E(\lambda)$ as functions of λ on the same graph. Compute the temperature of the sun from the wavelength of the maximum in the $E(\lambda)$ versus λ curve and your computed value of the Wien displacement law constant. Use Eq. (11–3) to compute $E(\lambda)$ as a function of λ for a black body at the temperature you obtained for the sun. Plot these values on the same graph you made for the experimental values of $E(\lambda)$ for the sun. How do the theoretical and experimental curves compare? Is it valid to consider the sun as a black body?

Perhaps some questions occurred to you about various parts of the procedure in this experiment. Let us list a few important points and questions for you to consider.

1) How are you to go about "aiming" the thermometer at the sun? What sort of setup is required? Should it be fixed or adjustable?

2) How many wavelengths should be examined? In what order? Should any be repeated?

3) The meter readings can be changed by varying the variable resistance in the phototube circuit. Must the setting be kept the same throughout the experiment? Could the setting be changed between the time the thermometer is calibrated and the sun's temperature is taken? How would this affect the calculations you are to do?

4) The meter readings can be changed by varying the slit widths at the entrance and exit of the monochromator. Must the slit widths be kept constant throughout the experiment? What could be the effect of changing the slit widths between the time the thermometer is calibrated and the sun's temperature is taken?

5) It is necessary for the thermometer to be calibrated before it is used to take $M(\lambda)$-versus-λ readings on the sun?

How many more problems of this kind can you think of? Think through the answers to your own and the above questions before doing this experiment. Ask your instructors for aid with any aspect of the experiment that puzzles you.

Questions

1) Is a piece of metal that is "white-hot" hotter or cooler than a "red-hot" piece of the same metal? Explain your answer with reference to the black-body radiation "spectrum."

2) What are the units of $c(\lambda)$ in Eq. (11–6)?

3) What are the units of $E(\lambda)$? Do these make sense in terms of the verbal definition of $E(\lambda)$?

EXPERIMENT 24. Spectroscopy

Only a very cursory look at atomic and molecular spectra will be presented in this experiment. For further explication you should consult the references, especially Herzberg and Shamos on atomic spectra and Barrow on molecular vibration spectra.

The Contribution of Bohr: Quantum Theory of the Atom

When Planck began his analysis of the black-body radiation spectrum he had a substantial background of experimental data to ponder. The same was true for Niels Bohr when he began to consider the problem of the structure of atoms. In fact, there were so many disparate facts that Bohr had to step somewhat outside the framework of conventional ideas to tie them together, just as Planck had done.

What were some of the facts that Bohr had to contend with? He knew, having worked with Rutherford, that the atom is mostly empty space with almost all its mass concentrated in a very small core of positively charged material. Presumably, the negatively charged material of the atom took up the rest of the volume of the atom and was highly dispersed. (Rutherford had, in fact, proposed that the negative particles, electrons, circulated about the nucleus in orbits much like the planets in solar systems. The trouble with this "solar-system" model was that classical physics predicted that such an atom would collapse in very short order, and this was obviously not happening.) Bohr also knew about the quantum theory of Planck and Einstein and how successfully it appeared to explain black-body radiation and the photoelectric effect. Finally, he was aware of the results of atomic spectroscopy. In particular, he knew that the radiation emitted by hydrogen atoms that had been created by discharging electricity through hydrogen gas was not continuous but occurred only at certain wavelengths (or frequencies), as in Fig. 11–4. He was aware of Balmer's mathematical analysis of the hydrogen atom emission spectrum in the visible and near ultraviolet region of the spectrum.

Balmer's result (written as it usually is now) was

$$\bar{\nu} = R\left(\frac{1}{4} - \frac{1}{n_1^2}\right), \qquad (11\text{–}7)$$

where $\bar{\nu}$ is the wave number of the emission (see Appendix E for the relationships of wavelength, frequency, and wave number), R is a constant, the Rydberg constant, with a value 109,678 cm^{-1}, and n_1 takes the values 3, 4, 5, . . . , ∞.

To explain all these results Bohr postulated a model for the hydrogenlike atom (i.e., an atom with one electron). The assumptions of his model were as follows.

1) The Rutherford "solar system" atom is correct.

2) The electrons move about the nucleus in fixed orbits. (Initially Bohr said the orbits were circles, but later refinements allowed elliptical orbits as well.) The electron has a definite fixed energy when it is in a particular orbit.

3) When an electron is moving in a particular orbit, no energy is radiated. (This is a direct contradiction of classical physics.)

4) Energy is emitted or absorbed only when an electron goes from one orbit to another of a different energy (in a process we call a "quantum jump").

5) The orbits allowed to the electron are those in which the electron angular momentum, mvr, is an integral multiple of $h/2\pi$, i.e.,

$$mvr = \frac{nh}{2\pi}, \qquad (11\text{–}8)$$

where m is the electron mass $= 9.108 \times 10^{-28}$ gm, v is the velocity of electron, r is the radius of the orbit, h is Planck's constant $= 6.625 \times 10^{-27}$ erg-sec, and n is an integer (the quantum number) $= 1, 2, 3, \ldots$ This last, quantum, assumption was a guess on Bohr's part, although an educated guess, to provide the correct final result. When Bohr solved the physics and mathematics of this model to give the energies of an electron in the allowed orbits, the result was

$$E = -\frac{2\pi^2 mZ^2 e^4}{n^2 h^2}, \qquad (11\text{-}9)$$

where Z is the number of positive charges on the nucleus and e is the electronic charge $= 4.8029 \times 10^{-10}$ esu. The relative values of these energy levels are shown in Fig. 11-3 for a hydrogen atom ($Z = 1$).

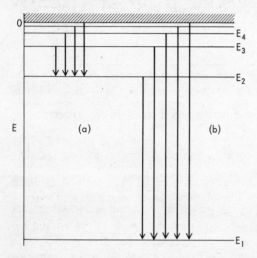

Fig. 11-3. Relative energy levels for the hydrogen atom from Bohr's theory. The transitions shown are (a) those observed and analyzed by Balmer and (b) those predicted by Bohr and found by Lyman.

If an electron is initially in an orbit described by the quantum number n_1, with an energy E_1, and then makes a transition to an orbit described by n_2 with an energy E_2, the energy difference between these two states and, hence, the energy that will be emitted or absorbed in the process can be determined by applying Eq. (11-9):

$$E_2 - E_1 = \Delta E = -\frac{2\pi^2 mZ^2 e^4}{n_2^2 h^2} - \left(-\frac{2\pi^2 mZ^2 e^4}{n_1^2 h^2}\right),$$

$$\Delta E = -\frac{2\pi^2 mZ^2 e^4}{h^2}\left(\frac{1}{n_2^2} - \frac{1}{n_1^2}\right). \qquad (11\text{-}10)$$

The negative sign on the right-hand side of (11-10) reflects the fact that ΔE is negative (energy is emitted) if $n_1 > n_2$ and ΔE is positive (energy must be absorbed) if $n_2 > n_1$. However, we wish to relate ΔE to a frequency through the Planck equation (11-1); we must then use the absolute value of ΔE, since h and ν are always positive. If radiation, energy, is emitted, ν is the frequency of radiation emitted; if radiation must be absorbed to cause the transition, ν is the frequency of radiation absorbed

$$h\nu = |\Delta E| = \frac{2\pi^2 mZ^2 e^4}{h^2}\left(\frac{1}{n_2^2} - \frac{1}{n_1^2}\right). \qquad (11\text{-}11)$$

Let us convert ν to the corresponding $\bar{\nu}$ and rearrange (11-11) slightly to get

$$\bar{\nu} = \frac{\nu}{c} = \frac{2\pi^2 mZ^2 e^4}{h^3 c}\left(\frac{1}{n_2^2} - \frac{1}{n_1^2}\right). \qquad (11\text{-}12)$$

Note the resemblance between (11-7) and (11-12); we can thus identify the Rydberg constant as

$$R = \frac{2\pi^2 mZ^2 e^4}{h^3 c}. \qquad (11\text{-}13)$$

What is the calculated value of the Rydberg constant? How does this compare with the experimental value? (See Problem 1 at the end of the experiment.)

For the emission analyzed by Balmer, $n_2 = 2$ and $n_1 > 2$. According to Bohr there should be other series of spectral lines, for example, if $n_2 = 1$ and $n_1 > 1$, we would predict a series

$$\bar{\nu} = \frac{2\pi^2 mZ^2 e^4}{h^3 c}\left(1 - \frac{1}{n_1^2}\right).$$

These predicted series were sought and found *after* Bohr had predicted exactly where they would be (see Fig. 11-3).

Since Bohr's theory was so successful in explaining and predicting some aspects of atomic spectra, there was strong reason to believe that it was at least partially correct. Unfortunately the theory was (and is) powerless to explain the spectra of atoms with more than one electron, that is, it was limited to H, He^+, Li^{++}, Be^{+3}, etc., which are interesting but not terribly important chemically. An essential feature of the model, however, that electron energies are quantized and that energy is emitted or absorbed by electrons changing quantum states, seems to be at least qualitatively true for all atoms. Figure 11-4 shows the spectra of a number of atoms to indicate that atomic emission and absorption spectra are discrete, not continuous, even though more than one electron is present in the atom.*

Thus, while we find it impossible to analyze the absorption spectrum of sodium (Fig. 11-4) quantitatively using Bohr's theory, we might expect that a series of energy levels (similar to Fig. 11-3) does exist in the

_____

* The wave-mechanical treatment of atoms formulated by de Broglie, Schrödinger, Dirac, Heisenberg, and others gives exactly the same results for hydrogenlike atoms as does Bohr's quantum treatment. It goes far beyond the quantum treatment, however, to yield information about many-electron atoms (and, in principle, any atomic or molecular system). In particular, it predicts the quantization of electronic energy levels for any atomic or molecular system, just as is observed spectroscopically.

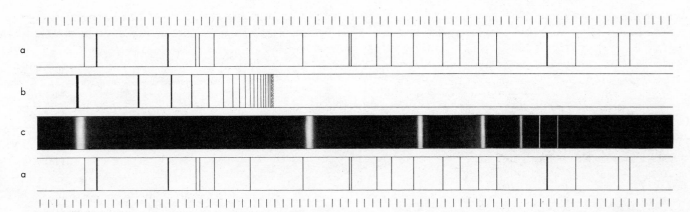

Fig. 11–4. Atomic spectra: (a) emission spectra of Hg for calibration purposes, (b) emission spectrum of H, (c) absorption spectrum of gaseous Na. The H and Na spectra have been simplified to eliminate the spectral features that arise from molecular emission or absorption. The Hg lines that appear are at the following wavelengths (left to right): 5780, 5460.7, 4358.3, 4077.8, 4046.6, 3906.4, 3652, 3341.5, 3131.6, 3125.7, 3022, 2967.3, 2893.6, 2804, 2752.8, 2698.9, 2653, 2536.5, 2482, 2399.4, 2378.3 Å.

sodium atom. We might couple this expectation with our knowledge of the way atoms are built up from protons, neutrons, and electrons (in general, this means our knowledge of the energy levels, guessed at from the hydrogen atom case, and an application of the Pauli Exclusion Principle) to say something about the sodium atom absorption spectrum. Ten of the electrons in the sodium atom are in states that are, on the average, very close to the nucleus.* The state of the eleventh electron, however, is such that it is on the average relatively far from the nucleus. Thus we might imagine that this electron is more or less effectively "shielded" from the nuclear charge by the inner ten electrons, i.e., it moves in a potential field that is much like that from a single positive charge. If this is a valid model, we should expect to find emission or absorption series similar to those for the hydrogen atom. We see (Fig. 11–4) that these qualitative ideas seem to be borne out in the absorption spectrum of sodium atoms. Perhaps the agreement can be made more quantitative.

The Analysis of Atomic Spectra

A few atomic spectra are presented in Fig. 11–4. We shall suggest here some analyses you might perform on these data.

Determine the emission wavelengths for the hydrogen atom spectrum and convert these to wavenumbers. How would you go about finding out what sort of a series would describe these frequencies? (In effect, you are being asked to reconstruct the reasoning of Balmer and Rydberg.) If the electron is in the state for which

---

* In terms of the Bohr theory, the radii of the orbits are small. In terms of wave mechanics, the probability of finding these electrons far from the nucleus is very small.

$n = 2$, how much energy is required to remove it from the atom to form the hydrogen ion, H^+? If $n = 1$, how much energy is required?

Determine the wavelengths at which sodium atoms absorb radiation and convert these to wavenumbers. Try to find a series expression that will describe this sequence of frequencies. Since we cannot expect this atom to act precisely like a hydrogen atom, we must be prepared to find that the numerical factors in this Rydberg type formulation may not be ratios of integers. What interpretation might you give to the results you obtain? What is the ionization potential of the sodium atom, i.e., how much energy is required to remove the outermost electron to infinity?

Vibrational Spectra of Molecules

Our procedure in the preceding sections has been to develop a model of nature to explain experimental observations. In this section let us reverse the procedure just a bit and propose a model and then see what it predicts. (This is, of course, not really different from our previous approach since every model we construct must be tested by comparing its predictions against experiment. The real test of a model is its ability to predict or explain phenomena that it was not devised to explain.)

Let us consider a diatomic molecule. We know from a number of sources that the nuclei of the two atoms are relatively far apart in space (an angstrom or so) compared to the dimensions of the nucleus. Some force must hold the atoms together, a force which is presumably provided by the electrostatic interaction of the nuclei with the electrons that surround them, particularly those that spend a good deal of time between the nuclei. Now the question arises: Is the "connection" between the nuclei a rigid one or do the nuclei move with respect to each

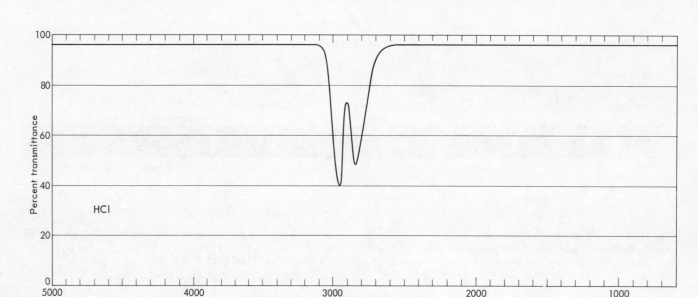

Fig. 11–5. The infrared spectrum of HCl gas.

other along their line of centers? It seems very reasonable to postulate that the nuclei will move with respect to each other. Since the nuclei do not fly apart (unless the molecule absorbs a very substantial amount of energy) nor do they coalesce, this motion must be a vibratory one. The simplest model for such a molecule is to imagine one that consists of two masses held together by a massless spring. If we assume a perfect spring, then the vibratory motion is that of a harmonic oscillator and we can call on our knowledge of physics to give us the force, F, between the atomic nuclei and the frequency of the vibration:

$$F = -k(r - r_e) = -kx,$$

$$\nu = \frac{1}{2\pi} \sqrt{\frac{k}{\mu}},$$

where r is the internuclear distance, r_e is the equilibrium internuclear distance, k is the force constant of the spring (the "strength" of spring), and μ is the reduced mass of the nuclear system $= m_1 m_2/(m_1 + m_2)$. If we knew the value of k for a molecule, we could predict ν and then look for absorption of radiation at this frequency.* We can make a crude calculation of the value of k if we draw on some other facts about diatomic molecules. Energies in the range 25 to 200 kcal/mole are required to dissociate most common diatomic molecules. Let us

take 100 kcal/mole as the dissociation energy for our diatomic molecule (this is about right for HCl). Let us assume that if the bond is stretched by one angstrom, i.e., that $r - r_e = 1$ Å, the bond is essentially broken. The work (energy) required to effect this bond breaking will be $-Fx = kx^2 = 100$ kcal/mole. Thus we can calculate k, since we have assumed $x = 1$ Å $= 10^{-8}$ cm;

$$k = \frac{10^5 \text{ cal/mole} \times 4.2 \times 10^7 \text{ erg/cal}}{(10^{-8})^2 \text{ cm}^2 \times 6 \times 10^{23} \text{ molecules/mole}},$$

$$\approx 10^5 \text{ dyne/cm-molecule},$$

and hence

$$\bar{\nu} = \frac{\nu}{c} = \frac{1}{2\pi c} \sqrt{\frac{10^5}{\mu}}.$$

For a molecule like HCl, $\mu = m_H m_{Cl}/(m_H + m_{Cl}) \approx m_H$ (Why?) so we have

$$\bar{\nu} = \frac{1}{2\pi 3 \times 10^{10}} \sqrt{\frac{10^5}{1/(6 \times 10^{23})}}$$

$$\approx 10^3 \text{ cm}^{-1},$$

which is in the near-infrared region of the spectrum.

Thus we predict that a molecule like HCl should interact with radiation in the near-infrared region of the spectrum. (We should also search the infrared since our calculation is really only indicative of the order of magnitude of the expected frequency.) Figure 11–5 shows the absorption of radiation by HCl in the infrared. The absorption is centered at 2900 cm^{-1}. Using this value we can work backwards through the sort of calculation just

---

* Why should electromagnetic radiation be absorbed at all by a vibrating molecule? The reason is that if the atoms are different, the molecule will have a dipole moment and the vibration will create a changing dipole moment that can interact with the radiation.

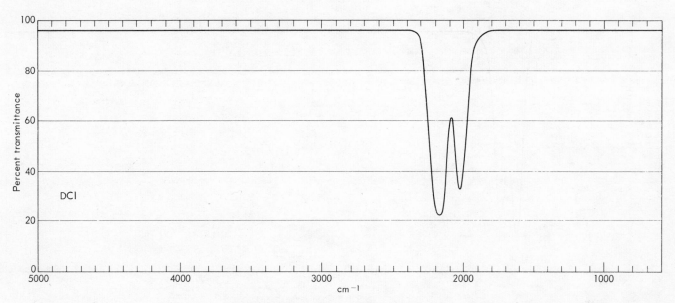

Fig. 11–6. The infrared spectrum of DCl gas.

made to obtain the correct value of k based on this model.*

The Analysis of Molecular Vibration Spectra

Figures 11–5 through 11–11 are infrared spectra of a number of diatomic molecules. Calculate k for each of these molecules and compare them. What conclusions can you draw about the effect of isotopic substitution? Is there any correlation between the "strength" of a bond and the "type" of bond? What sort of variation might you expect a priori?

Figures 11–12 and 11–13 are the infrared spectra of linear triatomic molecules. The analysis of these spectra is not nearly so simple as that for a diatomic molecule, for there are four possible vibrations of the molecule.

After thinking about these spectra for an hour or so and trying to draw your own conclusions about them, take recourse to the article by Little.

quantized. See the article by Little for an exposition of some of the interactions of vibrational and rotational motion and the information to be gleaned from vibration-rotation spectra. (The absorption "envelopes" of Fig. 11–5 through 11–13 occur as a result of the absorptions from the various closely spaced rotational energy levels of one vibrational state to those of the next higher vibrational state.) Little proposes some further problems based on the spectra he gives.

Little presents a method for calculating thermodynamic quantities directly from spectral data for a linear triatomic molecule. The analysis is even easier for a diatomic molecule. Write the formulas for a diatomic molecule and use the data from Fig. 11–14 and 11–15 to calculate the absolute entropies for HCl and DCl at 25°C. Compare your calculated value for HCl with that which you can find tabulated in most recent textbooks or paperbacks on thermodynamics.

Further Problems

Not only do molecules vibrate, they also rotate in space. As you must expect by now, the rotational motion is also

---

* A wave-mechanical treatment of diatomic molecules yields essentially the same model we have just built up by intuition. An interesting feature of the wave-mechanical treatment is that it predicts that the possible energies the vibrating molecule can take are quantized. For a harmonic-oscillator model the energies are $\epsilon = h\nu(v + \frac{1}{2})$, $v = 0, 1, 2, \ldots$ Thus even in the lowest possible state ($v = 0$) the molecule still vibrates with an energy $\epsilon_0 = \frac{1}{2}h\nu$, the zero-point energy. There is no classical analogy for this result.

Questions

1. Bohr originally assumed that the light electron circulated about the stationary heavy nucleus of the atom. A more exact description (which Bohr introduced in his second paper on the subject) is to consider that both masses move with respect to their center of mass. The change this makes in the problem is to substitute the reduced mass of the system, $m_e m_n / (m_e + m_n)$, where m_e and m_n are the electron and nuclear masses, respectively, in (11–9) through (11–13). What effect does this substitution have on the value of the Rydberg constant?

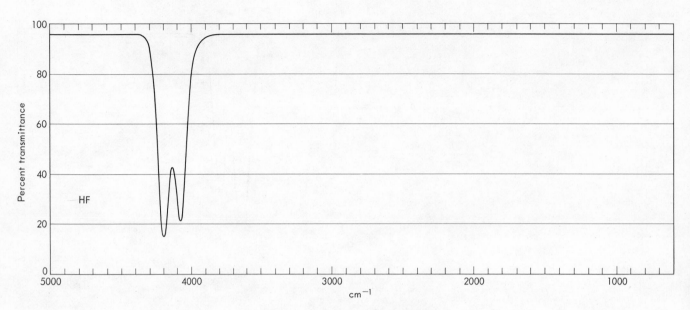

Fig. 11–7. The infrared spectrum of HF gas.

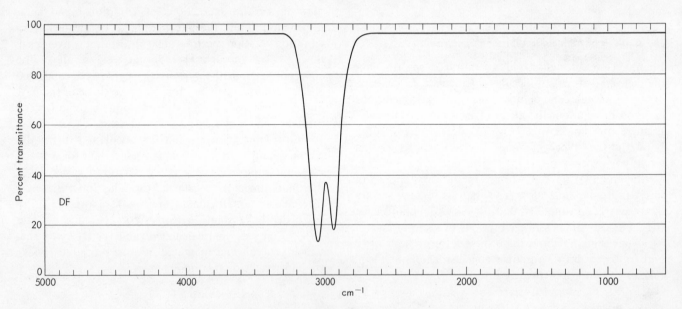

Fig. 11–8. The infrared spectrum of DF gas.

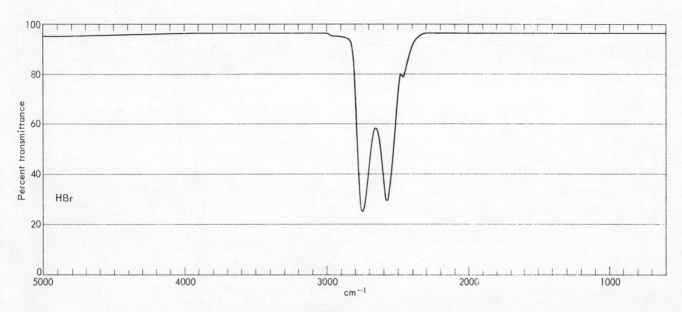

Fig. 11-9. The infrared spectrum of HBr gas.

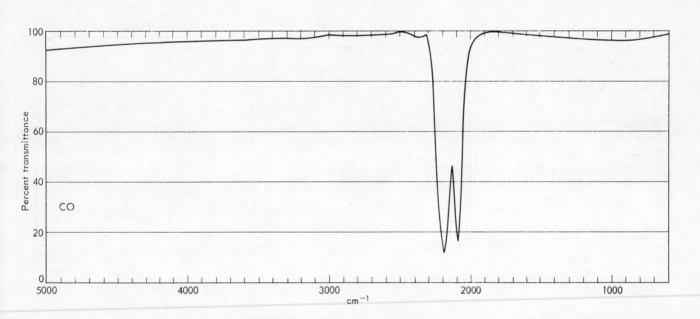

Fig. 11-10. The infrared spectrum of CO gas.

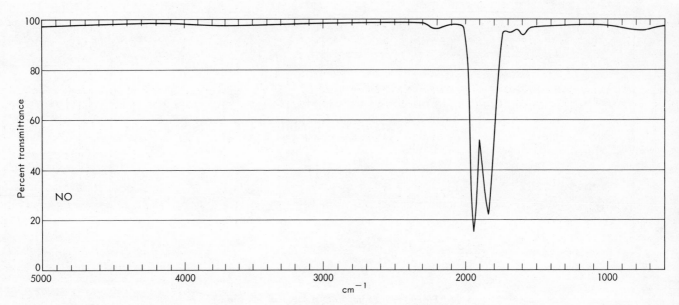

Fig. 11–11. The infrared spectrum of NO gas.

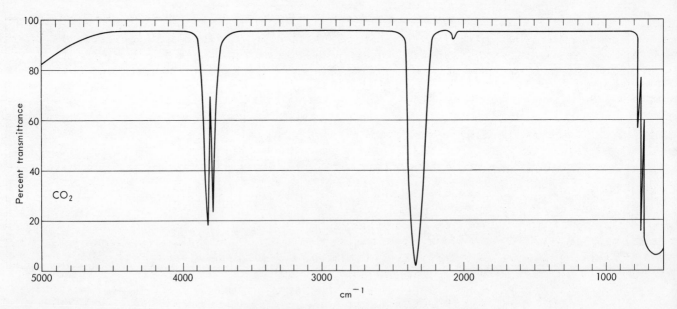

Fig. 11–12. The infrared spectrum of CO_2 gas.

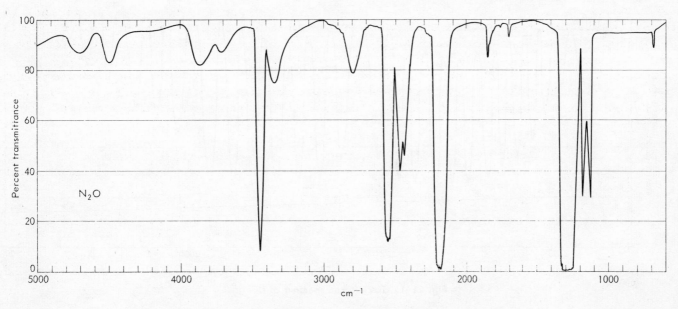

Fig. 11–13. The infrared spectrum of N_2O gas.

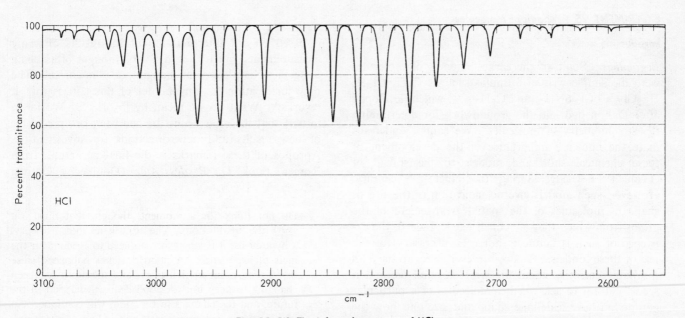

Fig. 11–14. The infrared spectrum of HCl gas.

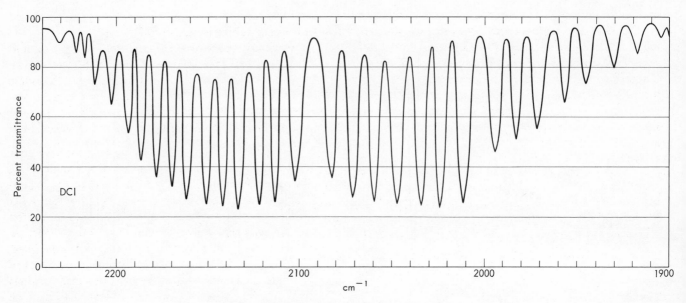

Fig. 11-15. The infrared spectrum of DCl gas.

EXPERIMENT 25. Models of Molecules

Introduction

Beginnings. Some of the earliest models of molecules were the simple written formulas such as CH_4, Cl_3H, Hg_2Cl_2, $CoCl_3 \cdot 6NH_3$, and $C_6H_{12}O_6$, which developed after Dalton had laid the groundwork for determining the stoichiometry of molecules. We cannot underestimate the immense importance of the development of these chemical shorthand models to the spread of chemical knowledge during the nineteenth century. However, such models give no indication of the size or shape of molecules or the spatial arrangement of the atoms from which they are constructed. Indeed, the existence of such structure is not even necessary for the use of these models. We do, however, seem to have an insatiable curiosity about the world around us, and it seems natural to ask whether molecules of a particular compound have a definite shape and size and how the particular atoms that make up the molecule influence its shape and size. In Experiment 24 we found that postulating a simple structure for diatomic molecules enabled us to interpret their infrared spectra in a consistent and wholly reasonable manner. In the same way, on the basis of an enormous number of chemical and physical measurements and arguments, detailed models of molecular structure have been developed.

We must insert here a caveat concerning molecular models. Models of molecules are just that, *models*. Just as a model railroad train is not *the* railroad train, a model of a molecule is not the molecule. The model is based on our interpretation of the results of many measurements, but it should not be thought of as being altogether complete or unchanging or even correct. The only justification for any model of this sort is that it "works." What do we mean by "works"? We mean in part that the model must be heuristic, i.e., predictive of new results and new directions for investigation. Apropos of these remarks is the final paragraph from Romer's book, *The Restless Atom* (Doubleday, Garden City, N. Y., 1960):

Do not think for a moment, though, that now you know the "real" atom. The atom is an idea, a theory, a hypothesis; it is whatever you need to account for the facts of experience. A good deal has happened since the closing point of this story, and the atom has been changing to keep up. A good deal will happen in the future, and the changes in the atom will continue. An idea in science, remember, lasts only as long as it is useful.

Types of Models. A great variety of model types is available. Some of these are quite expensive and are precision-made; others, just as useful in their own way, might consist of the simplest materials (gum drops and toothpicks, for example). We shall list here a few of the types of models that are particularly useful and will refer below by number to the type most useful for a particular experiment.

1) "Accurate" bond angle-bond distance models. In this class are Dreiding-type models and framework

molecular models. The original models designed by A. S. Dreiding are very expensive precision-machined metal models. An inexpensive (relatively) plastic variation of these models has been designed by L. F. Fieser.* Another interesting plastic variation on the Dreiding model is that introduced by J. C. Godfrey.† Framework molecular models using metal nuclei and plastic connectors were described by G. C. Brumlik, E. J. Barrett, and R. L. Baumgarten.‡

2) "Accurate" bond angle models. These are the usual "ball-and-stick" models that consist of a set of color-coded wooden or plastic balls (or other geometric shapes) drilled with holes at the proper locations to represent the bond angles between atoms in molecules and some sort of rigid (wooden or plastic) or flexible (spring) connector to represent the "bond." Almost every scientific equipment distributor has one or more model kits of this type available.

3) Accurate size space-filling models. The best-known set of this type is the Fisher, Hirschfelder, Taylor models. These models are usually molded of plastic and are constructed to show accurately the relative sizes of the atoms (usually, 1 cm = 1 Å). Flat "faces" are left on each atom to represent its valence positions and the atoms are snapped together face-to-face with metal connectors. Most scientific equipment distributors also carry this type of model kit.

A large number of implicit assumptions are made in constructing and using any of the above model kits to construct models of molecules from atomic building blocks. Can you list at least three such assumptions?

4) Completely flexible models. Your imagination and ingenuity are the only limits to the discovery, construction, and use of material for these models. The most common materials are styrofoam, cork, and plastic balls, pipe cleaners, wire, toothpicks, and so on ad infinitum. Sources of supply and additional ideas for construction materials can be gleaned from the advertising pages of journals like the *Journal of Chemical Education.*

5) Geometric-arrangement models. Although all the above models can show the geometric arrangement of atoms in many molecules, sometimes even more flexibility is required or only the geometrical features of a molecule are desired. For these purposes a set of

* Available from the Rinco Instrument Co., Greenville, Illinois.

† Available from the Bronwill Scientific Division of Will Scientific, Inc., Rochester, New York 14601.

‡ Available from Prentice-Hall, Inc., Englewood Cliffs, New Jersey 07632.

flexible plastic connectors of various types combined with plastic tubing is very useful.§

Obviously the basis of these models (and their applications beyond this experiment) must not be forgotten. Many books and articles are now available which discuss the foundations for these models and may suggest new experiments with models for you to undertake. Some of these are listed in the references at the end of the chapter.

Your Report. Record all your observations in your notebook, making sketches where desirable and including all the information asked for in the text of the experiment. At the end of the experiment you will find a list of some of the important terms used in the discussion which may be unfamiliar to you now. Your report on this laboratory will consist of your answers to the questions asked so far, definitions (by word or example) of the terms listed at the end, and information and drawings from any other part of the experiment that may be requested by your instructor.

The Experiment

Regular Polyhedra. The symmetries of many molecules and crystals are based on those of the regular polyhedra. Use type 5 models to construct the regular polyhedra. The characteristics of the regular polyhedra are: a) all faces are the same and are composed of regular polygons, and b) the number of polygons that meet at each vertex is the same for all the vertices of a particular polyhedron. The regular polygons are the equilateral triangle, square, regular pentagon, regular hexagon, etc. Consider first the equilateral triangle as the face of a polyhedron. If only two triangles come together at a vertex, then the sides of the triangles leaving the vertex must be coincident, and no solid structure will be created. Let us then consider the case of three equilateral triangles meeting at a vertex. Cut a number of two- or three-inch lengths of the plastic tubing. (The tubing is easily cut to size by scoring it with a knife or file and then snapping off the desired length.) Insert three of these pieces of tubing into one of the flexible connectors. This represents one vertex of a possible regular polyhedron. Add flexible connectors at the ends of the three pieces of tubing. Can you see how to complete the construction so all faces and vertices are identical? Do so. What is this polyhedron called? Continue this process as far as possible with equilateral triangles; then go on to squares and higher regular polygons. Make a tabulation of the regular polyhedra you find

§ The connectors and tubing can be obtained from (Geodestix) Northwest Vocational Sales, Spokane, Washington or, at a slight premium in price, from Edmund Scientific Co., Barrington, New Jersey 08007.

with columns showing the polygon used for the faces, the number of faces, the number of vertices, the number of edges, and the name of the polyhedron. Can you see a general relationship among columns two, three, and four of your table? How many regular polyhedra are there? Is this a surprising number? If the stability of molecular structures depended solely on the rigidity of their geometric form, which of the regular polyhedra would be favored? Look in Pauling to see if you can find an example of a compound that has the geometry of the least rigid polyhedron.

Geometry of the Tetrahedron. One way of constructing a simple model of a tetrahedral molecule is to begin by placing a styrofoam or cork ball inside a cube made from flexible connectors and plastic tubing. Insert the connectors you will use with the ball through four non-adjacent vertices of the cube (i.e., either those vertices represented by open circles or those represented by shaded circles in Fig. 11–16). Disassemble the cube. You now have a ball with four connectors directed toward the vertices of a regular tetrahedron. By adding four more balls to the free ends of the connectors, you will form a model of a tetrahedral molecule. This might represent methane, CH_4, silicon tetrachloride, $SiCl_4$, ammonium ion, NH_4^+, or many others.*

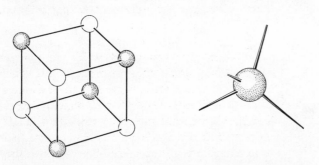

Fig. 11–16

The height of a regular tetrahedron is $\sqrt{\frac{2}{3}}$ as long as its edge, and a central atom is $\frac{3}{4}$ of the distance between the apex and the opposite face. By using trigonometry, determine the angle between any two bonds. For this purpose, *assume* that bonds lie in a straight line between the nuclei of the atoms that are bound together. (You may find it helpful to reconstruct the body-centered cube to see the relationships necessary for this calculation.)

The tetrahedral arrangement is only one of many which can satisfy the formulas CH_4, CCl_4, etc. The

---

* Tetrahedral carbon forms such a wide variety of compounds that it is often studied as a separate branch of chemistry, organic chemistry. This is part of an unhappy and unnatural, but historical, division of little pedagogical value in chemistry.

atoms could conceivably be arranged in a square planar configuration with the carbon at the center of the square and the other atoms (chlorine, for example) at the corners. The arrangement might also be that of an irregular tetrahedron, with each chlorine atom closer to one other chlorine than to the remaining two. There is "direct" experimental evidence (as direct as such evidence ever is, since the results still depend on our interpretation of some sort of "dial readings") which helps to decide the point. In an electron-diffraction study of carbon tetrachloride gas (because of their wave nature a beam of fast electrons is scattered by the CCl_4 molecules, and the angular distribution of the scattered electrons is analyzed and interpreted to determine the interatomic distances in the molecules), only two interatomic distances were found, and their ratio was determined to be 1.64 ± 0.01. Does this result exclude an irregular tetrahedral structure? Calculate the ratio of the Cl–Cl to the C–Cl distance, assuming that the molecule has the square planar configuration and then assuming that it is a regular tetrahedron. Compare these values with the results of the electron-diffraction study. Other "direct" evidence for the tetrahedral arrangement is the measurement of bond angles (by electron or x-ray diffraction or microwave spectroscopy). In the hundreds of molecules studied, observed bond angles lie within about 2° of the value corresponding to the tetrahedral arrangement (which you calculated). Are these measurements good enough to completely exclude the possibility of the square planar configuration even without the data on CCl_4 cited above?

Construct a model of chloroform, $CHCl_3$, using type 3 models. If a slight deviation from tetrahedral angles is permitted, how would you expect the Cl–C–Cl angle to deviate? Construct and examine methane, CH_4, and bromochloroiodomethane, $CHClBrI$. Given the value 1.95 Å for the atomic radius of bromine, determine the atomic radii of chlorine and iodine by measuring the halogen atoms of your model. [Compare the ratio volume I/volume Cl with the ratio atomic number I/atomic number Cl. What does this imply about the packing of "inner shell" (nonvalence) electrons?]

Remove one of the outer atoms on your model of a tetrahedral molecule. The remaining structure might represent the ammonia molecule, NH_3, which has nearly tetrahedral bonding angles (see Pauling, p. 110) with a nonbonding pair of electrons concentrated in the fourth tetrahedral bond direction. Remove a second outer atom. The resulting model has the geometry of the water molecule. What do the two unoccupied connectors *represent*? In fact, one quantum-mechanical theory of bond orbitals predicts that the H–N–H and H–O–H angles in ammonia and water, respectively, should be nearly 90° (see Pauling, p. 123). In these molecules the hydrogen atoms are expected to bear a partial positive charge and the central atom, a partial negative charge. How and why might this affect the bond angles?

Construct a model of ethane, C_2H_6. The distance between the two carbon atoms in this molecule is 1.533 Å, equal within probable error to the C—C distances in diamond, 1.542 Å, and in a number of hydrocarbons (see Pauling, p. 222). The C—H bond distance is 1.095 Å (see Pauling, p. 226). Measure the C—C and C—H bond distances in a type 1 model of ethane and see how their ratio compares with the experimental value. What is the scale of "magnification" of your model?

The nature of a single bond, such as that connecting the two carbon atoms, allows "free rotation" of one methyl group, —CH_3, with respect to the other. There is some residual repulsion, however, probably between the electrons in the C—H bonds of one-half the molecule with those of the other half and also, perhaps, between the corresponding hydrogen nuclei. Rotate your model so that this repulsion is minimized; this is a *staggered configuration*. Now rotate it so that repulsion is maximized; this is an *eclipsed configuration*. The two configurations differ in energy by several kilocalories per mole (3 kcal/mole in ethane) but they have never been separately isolated. Why not? Make an end-on line sketch (the perspective looking down the axis of the C—C bond) of the two configurations. Consider a single C—H bond as it makes one complete revolution with respect to the methyl group in the other half of the molecule. Sketch a plot of the magnitude of the repulsion energy vs. angle (from 0 to 360°) as this rotation is made.

Construct a model of propane, C_3H_8, using type 3 models; then continue adding carbon atoms to make larger molecules. What do you notice about the number of ways you can add on the next carbon atoms? Construct and draw structural formulas for the different ways you can make butane, C_4H_{10}, and pentane, C_5H_{12}. An example of a structural formula is

$$\begin{array}{ccc} H & H & H \\ | & | & | \\ H-C-C-C-H \\ | & | & | \\ H & H & H \end{array}$$

for propane.

Now, instead of making longer and longer chains, connect the two ends of a chain together to make a cyclic structure. What is the smallest number of carbon atoms that can be linked together into a ring without straining the models significantly? The resulting compound is called cyclopentane. Try to make cyclobutane and cyclopropane from type 3 models. These molecules

actually exist; try to construct them using type 2 models. What would you predict about the relative reactivity of cyclopropane, cyclobutane, and cyclopentane toward some chemical reagent which broke a C—C bond to open the ring? Note the relative positions of the C—H bonds in these ring compounds. Is the repulsion maximized or minimized? What is this configuration called?

Using type 1 models, construct cyclohexane, C_6H_{12}. Examine the model carefully and make a sketch of it. Move it and twist it gently to see how easily you can change the relative positions of the atoms. Note the arrangement of the C—H bonds with respect to their neighbors. Now break one of the C—C bonds, pull apart the ends of the chain, and then reconnect them. Carefully examine the model again. Is it exactly the same as the one you had before? Break and reconnect one of the C—C bonds several times or until you have convinced yourself that you have discovered all the possible ways to construct cyclohexane. Draw line sketches of all the different ways and predict which you think should be the most stable configuration. Find out from your instructor the relative stabilities and names of the various configurations. Is there any one of these that has different kinds of hydrogen atoms (that is, hydrogen atoms which are fixed in a different environment from others in the same molecule)? Try to interconvert the configurations without breaking a bond. Record your observations.

Structural Isomers. Two compounds which are different in at least one measurable physical property but which have the same molecular formula are said to be isomers. Thus ethyl alcohol, CH_3CH_2OH, and dimethyl ether, CH_3OCH_3, have the same molecular formula, C_2H_6O, but their properties are decidedly different. Since their component atoms are arranged in different ways, they are called structural isomers. Note that the ways they are written give clues to their structures. The different forms of butane and pentane which you have already constructed are structural isomers. Make models of all the possible isomers of $C_2H_4Cl_2$ and CH_2Cl_2 and draw their structural formulas. How many isomers of the last compound could exist if carbon were to form four bonds directed toward the corners of a square? Stereochemical arguments of this sort were the basis for the historical discovery of tetrahedral bonding. What does the existence of two isomers of $Pt(NH_3)_2Cl_2$ tell us about the probable structure of this molecule? Use your type 4 models to make a model of each of the isomers.

Structural isomers can also exist in substituted cyclic structures. Draw structural formulas and make models (use type 2 models) of all the possible isomers of dichlorocyclobutane, $C_4H_6Cl_2$, and trichlorocyclobutane, $C_4H_5Cl_3$.

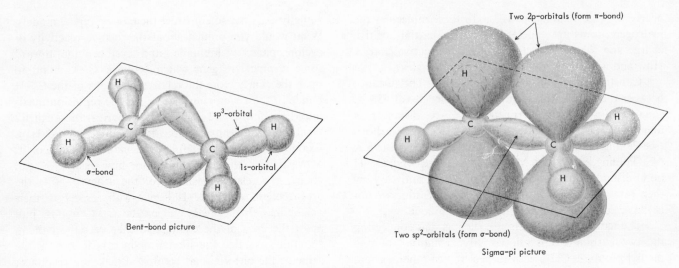

Two 2p-orbitals (form π-bond)

sp³-orbital

σ-bond

1s-orbital

Bent-bond picture

Two sp²-orbitals (form σ-bond)

Sigma-pi picture

Fig. 11–17

Multiple Bonds and Geometrical Isomers. Using type 4 models, insert four connectors at approximately tetrahedral angles into each of two atoms. Attach other atoms to the ends of two bonds on each. Now, instead of adding more atoms, bring the two groups together so that both the unoccupied connectors on each group are shared. The atoms are now arranged as they would be about a double bond. (Replace the four connectors forming the double bond by two bent connectors to hold the atoms in place.) The model would represent a molecule of ethylene, C_2H_4. Note that the atoms are coplanar. The idea of tetrahedral bonding allows us to visualize a double bond as resulting from two tetrahedra sharing a common edge to form two "bent" single bonds.*

In the quantum-mechanical description of the tetrahedral carbon atom, the bonding electrons are concentrated in four equivalent sp^3 hybrid orbitals directed toward the vertices of a regular tetrahedron. (If you have not yet learned about orbitals, they may be described for the moment as standing waves which represent regions of electron density, whose shape is predicted from quantum-mechanical calculations.) Bonding results from the "proper" overlap of these orbitals with orbitals of other atoms. In the "bent-bond" picture of ethylene, the double bond is formed by the overlap of two sp^3 hybrid orbitals of one carbon atom with two of another carbon atom, and the remaining four form bonds by overlap with the $1s$-orbitals of hydrogen atoms. (Most of the assumptions, usually left implicit in beginning textbooks, of the quantum-mechanical treatment of bonding are lurking in this very offhand description and that below. Do not be misled; this is in no sense any "explanation" of bonding, only a very crude hint. Pore through the references at the end of the chapter for further elucidation.)

An alternative picture of the double bond is one in which each carbon forms three planar sp^2 hybrid orbitals connecting with two $1s$-orbitals on the two hydrogens and an sp^2-orbital on the other carbon. The "other part" of the double bond is formed by overlap of two $2p$ carbon orbitals to form what is called a π-bond (pi bond). The other C—C bond and the C—H bonds are termed σ-bonds (sigma bonds). Compare the arrangement of atoms predicted by the two pictures in Fig. 11–17.

Rotations around double bonds occur only with extreme difficulty. (The energy required is about 65 kcal/mole for many double-bonded compounds.) (Why?) Under these conditions how many isomers are possible for 1,2-dichloroethylene, $C_2H_2Cl_2$? Draw their structural formulas and make models. How many isomers would be possible if free rotation occurred about the double bond? Structural isomers which result from restricted rotation about the double bond are called geometrical isomers. The isomer with both Cl atoms on the same side of the molecule is called the *cis* isomer (e.g., *cis*-1,2-dichloroethylene), and the other form is referred to as the *trans* isomer. The *cis* and *trans* nomenclature is used in an analogous fashion in cyclic structures.

---

* Calling these bonds "bent" is a singularly unfortunate choice of terms since it implies that this model is somehow different from others for the same molecule, and this is not true. We do not know where the electrons are in a molecule such as ethylene, nor, indeed, at the present time, in any other molecule. It is only to distinguish bonding *pictures* that we resort to names that are descriptive of what we write on a piece of paper or construct from styrofoam and pipe cleaners but are only perhaps vaguely related to the actual situation in the molecule. Regardless of what we in our partial ignorance decide to call its bond, ethylene will go on having the properties peculiar to it and its bonding.

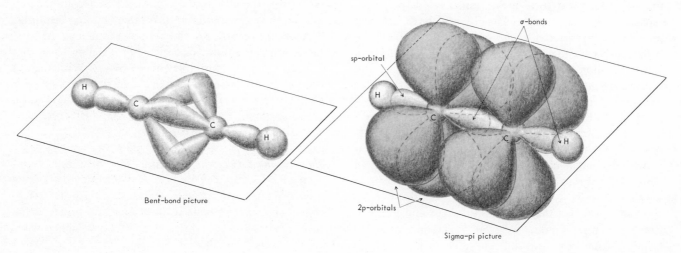

σ-bonds
sp-orbital
H
C
C
H
Bent-bond picture
2p-orbitals
Sigma-pi picture

Fig. 11–18

Label the *cis* and *trans* forms of dichlorocyclobutane, whose isomers you have already drawn.

Insert four bonds in approximately tetrahedral directions into each of two atoms. Attach one other atom to each, leaving three connectors unoccupied. Note that it is possible to bring these groups together so that all three vacant connectors of each group are shared. Replace the connectors by three bent connectors to form a triple bond. The structure could represent the molecule acetylene, C_2H_2. Note that again the tetrahedral bonding formulation ("bent bonds") leads to the correct molecular shape, linear. The bonding in acetylene can also be described in terms of a combination of sigma and pi bonds, with the triple bond comprised of two π-bonds and one σ-bond formed by the overlap of two sp-orbitals (Fig. 11–18).

So you will not think we have exhausted all the possible bonding pictures here you should read about at least three others. The first, suggested by R. J. Gillespie and R. S. Nyholm and later outlined again by Gillespie, emphasizes the obvious electrostatic repulsion between "valence-shell" electrons of atoms to predict the geometry of molecules. This may be called the valence-shell electron-pair repulsion (VSEPR) model. The second model (see Linnett) suggests that both the charge and spin of electrons are very important in determining the geometry of molecules. Finally, H. Bent has suggested a tangent-sphere model of chemical bonding in which the electrons are constrained to stay strictly out of one another's way. (One might say, to use a very moth-eaten pun, that these are truly "Bent bonds.") Bent suggests many model-building exercises utilizing cork or styrofoam balls to rationalize molecular structure on the basis of his model. Naturally, all our models have one thing in common: they predict the correct structures for most

of the known simple molecules of the first three periods of the periodic chart, H through Ar. As you have the time and inclination, study all of these models and compare and contrast them, make appropriate physical models, and try to discover for yourself the strengths and weaknesses of all these models.

Optical Isomers. Construct a molecule similar to methane or carbon tetrachloride but in which all four atoms attached to the central carbon are different. Set this model aside and construct another which is a mirror image of the first (see Fig. 11–19). Satisfy yourself that these molecules are really not the same although the groups and bond distances are the same. Neither can be superimposed on the other or turned into such a position as to completely coincide with the other. They are analogous to the right and left hands, which are mirror images of each other and which cannot be superimposed. Pairs of molecules which differ only in this subtle way are called optical isomers, or mirror-image isomers. As you

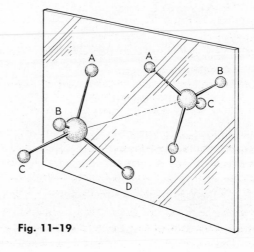

Fig. 11–19

might expect from their great similarity, they can be separated only with some difficulty and have identical physical properties, with one notable exception. The property which allows optical isomers to be distinguished is their rotation of plane-polarized light (see Shurcliff and Ballard) in equal and opposite directions, the angle of rotation for a particular wavelength of light being proportional to the concentration of the isomer in solution and the length of the solution through which the light is passed. What would you say about the rotation of plane-polarized light by a solution which contained equal amounts of the two isomers? A predominance of one over the other?

Satisfy yourself that it is impossible to make optical isomers from your model unless all four groups attached to the carbon atom are different. These groups need not be single atoms. Dextrose is one of the isomers of a compound with the structure

$$H-\underset{\underset{OH}{|}}{\overset{\overset{H}{|}}{C}}-\underset{\underset{OH}{|}}{\overset{\overset{H}{|}}{\overset{*}{C}}}-\underset{\underset{OH}{|}}{\overset{\overset{H}{|}}{\overset{*}{C}}}-\underset{\underset{OH}{|}}{\overset{\overset{H}{|}}{\overset{*}{C}}}-\underset{\underset{OH}{|}}{\overset{\overset{H}{|}}{\overset{*}{C}}}-\overset{\overset{O}{\parallel}}{\underset{\underset{H}{}}{C}}$$

Each of the starred carbon atoms has four different groups attached to it. How many optical isomers are possible for a compound of this structure? If carbon formed compounds with a square planar configuration, could there be optical isomers of a compound such as CHClBrI, for example?

The helix is another geometric construction which can exist in two different forms which are mirror images. Make the two different helices by wrapping copper wire around a pencil. Remove the helices from the pencil and trim excess wire from the ends. Are your two helices mirror images? Are they distinctly different? Convince yourself that they cannot be superimposed. Look down the axis of one helix. Then turn it end-to-end. Does the appearance of the helix change? The inherent left- or right-handedness of the helix is independent of orientation. The helix is the principal structural feature of many polypeptides and proteins (see Pauling, pp. 499–500).

Nontetrahedral Structures. Atoms containing *d*-electrons commonly use these, together with their *s*- and *p*-electrons, to form bonds which make other than tetrahedral angles with one another. The ions of the transition series of elements quite characteristically tend to form six bonds directed toward the vertices of a regular octahedron. These bonds are made by the overlap of d^2sp^3 hybrid orbitals of the central metal atom with orbitals of six atoms which lie at the corners of the octahedron. This model might represent such molecules as $CrCl_6^{-3}$, for example. The attached atoms or groups must be

sufficiently small that six of them may be accommodated around the central atom at favorable bonding distances. The atoms bonded to the central atom may be part of a larger molecule or ion. For example, nitrogen is bonded to chromium in $Cr(NH_3)_6^{+3}$. With the aid of models, determine how many isomers are possible for $Cr(NH_3)_5Cl^{++}$, $Cr(NH_3)_4Cl_2^+$, and $Cr(NH_3)_3Cl_3$. Draw structural formulas of the possible isomers. Are optical isomers possible for any of these?

Introduction to Crystal Structure. The arrangements of atoms and molecules in a crystal may very often be approximated by spheres packed into a box. Use styrofoam or cork balls in the lucite box provided for this experiment to examine the ways in which spheres can be packed together.

Arrange the balls in a single layer in the bottom of the box in such a way that the greatest possible number can be fitted in without deforming the balls. Note that in addition to the unsymmetrical arrangements which you might try, there is more than one way in which they can be arranged symmetrically. With how many neighbors does each ball come in contact in each symmetrical arrangement? When you think you have found the arrangement which packs the largest number of spheres into the available space, put another layer on top of the first. How many different ways can you do this so that you use up the greatest amount of available free space? Now fill in a third layer. Note the position of the spheres in this layer with respect to those in the first layer. Are there other ways of filling in the third layer which would be different from the first way you tried? Now fit spheres into the box until it is full. Examine the arrangement carefully. How many nearest neighbors does each sphere have? This type of arrangement is called "closest packed." Find out the names of the variations of closest packing and the shorthand for designating the layer sequence. Make sketches of the various arrangements. Carefully examine the position of the nearest neighbors with respect to a central sphere. Is there more than one arrangement?

Examples of substances which crystallize in closest-packed arrays are all the noble gases (He, Ne, Ar, Kr, and Xe; these are especially good approximations of spheres), molecular hydrogen, HCl, HBr, HI, H_2S, H_2Se, CH_4, and SiH_4. A large number of metals crystallize in the same arrangement.

Terms to Be Defined. Define the following by word or example in your laboratory report: isomer, structural isomer, geometrical isomer, optical isomer, staggered configuration, eclipsed configuration, cubic closest packing, hexagonal closest packing, *cis*-isomer, *trans*-isomer, bond angle, bond length.

Further Experimental Problems

Geometrical Isomerism. Construct models of the *cis* and *trans* forms of HOOC—CH=CH—COOH; —COOH is the carboxyl group

Prepare a model of the *anhydride* (without water) of this dicarboxylic acid. Acids of this type form their anhydrides by loss of a molecule of water (the OH from one —COOH and the H from the other) and the formation of the structure

Why is it assumed that hydrolysis (reaction with water) of the anhydride yields the *cis*-acid? The common names of these two acids are maleic and fumaric acid. On being heated to 135°C maleic acid decomposes, but fumaric acid is stable. Which acid has which structure? What do you suspect are the decomposition products from the heated maleic acid? Can you test your suggestion easily experimentally? Why not try it?

Structural Isomerism. Use type 3 models to construct all possible isomers of dichlorobenzene. (Remember there are special carbon atoms for benzene rings in this sort of model kit.) Before the advent of all sorts of sophisticated physical methods for such determinations, Körner devised a method for proving which of the actual chemical compounds had which of these structures by reacting each further to form the trichloro isomers and finding out the number of trichloro isomers formed from each one. Can you see how this could be done? In other words, try to reconstruct Körner's reasoning.

Polyhedra. The regular polyhedra by no means represent all the ways that molecules and crystals may be put together. In fact the regular dodecahedron occurs only rarely, one sample being the arrangement of water molecules in the chlorine hydrate crystal (see Pauling, p. 470). Other arrangements include the trigonal bipyramid, pentagonal bipyramid, trigonal prism, and square antiprism. Construct models of these polyhedra (and more complicated ones if you are so inclined) and obtain examples of compounds which exist in these arrangements (Pauling is a good reference source).

Crystals with Tetrahedral Arrangements. Many substances, including C (diamond), Si, Sn, ZnO, ZnS, CuCl, and AgI (see Pauling, pp. 244–248), form crystals in which each atom is surrounded by four other atoms arranged in a tetrahedron. There are two arrangements which achieve this result; they are designated as the sphalerite and wurtzite arrangements after the two crystal modifications of zinc sulfide.

Models of the two forms may be made fairly easily with type 3 tetrahedral atoms. (Please do this kind of experiment only when no one else wants to use the models for the required section.) Construct two or three layers of fused cyclohexane rings (the more stable kind) making sure that all the unoccupied connectors on each side of a layer are of the same variety. Now stack the layers, adding the third in the same way as the second. Note that there are two ways to add a layer, each resulting in a different arrangement. The all-staggered arrangement represents sphalerite (diamond has this structure), and the other wurtzite. Note that some of the bonds in wurtzite are eclipsed. Make a sketch of the two forms or, better yet, construct permanent models out of cork balls or styrofoam.

Cubic and Hexagonal Closest Packing. The two closest packing arrangements which you discovered using styrofoam balls in a lucite box are called cubic and hexagonal closest packing. Construct permanent models of cubic and hexagonal closest packing to show clearly the unit cells involved in each. For a good discussion and help in locating the unit cells, see Holden and Singer, pp. 180 ff. This reference will also suggest some experiments in crystal growing which may interest you.

EXPERIMENT 26.   *The Preparation and Optical Resolution of Tris-Ethylenediamine Cobalt(III) Ion*

Introduction

In this experiment you will prepare and resolve into its optical isomers a salt of the tris-ethylenediamine cobalt(III) complex. To show that there is indeed a difference between the two isomers and to give you an indication of your success in resolving the two isomers, you will make solutions of each isomeric salt and observe their effect on plane-polarized light with a polarimeter. If a spectro-polarimeter is available, you should use it to obtain the optical rotation of your solutions as a

Threefold   Twofold   Tartaric acid

function of wavelength. A plot of optical rotation vs. wavelength is known as an optical rotatory dispersion (ORD) curve. For comparison with your ORD curve, you should also obtain the absorption spectrum of each sample.

In Experiment 25 you were told that compounds which could exist in two nonsuperimposable mirror-image forms were optically active. That is, these compounds have the effect of rotating the plane of plane-polarized light. Let us examine the structure of the tris-ethylenediamine cobalt(III) ion. As with a great many of the transition series metals, Co(III) has six coordination positions directed toward the corners of a regular octahedron. Each ethylenediamine, $H_2NCH_2CH_2NH_2$, takes up two of these positions (two adjacent ones). You can make a model of this compound by using styrofoam or cork balls and grouping six of them about a central ball (the cobalt) in an octahedral arrangement. Now use tape or some other marking device to show that these six balls are grouped in pairs. Construct the mirror image of this system. Are they superimposable? These molecules are said to be disymmetric, i.e., they are not so symmetric as to have superimposable mirror images, but on the other hand, they do not completely lack symmetry. To see this, note that there is a threefold rotational axis in these models as shown in the structural formulas above. Find this axis in your models. There are also three twofold rotational axes, each passing through opposite "edges" of the "octahedron." (A threefold axis is an axis such that a rotation of 120° about it yields another view of the

molecule that is superimposable on the original. The same is true for a twofold rotational axis, with a rotation of 180°.) Note that in the structural formulas shown above the lines between the N's do not represent bonds but are inserted only to show where the "faces" of the octahedron are.

Optical isomers, *enantiomorphs*, are almost identical in their physical properties (except, notably, in their interaction with plane-polarized light), so a fairly subtle effect must be utilized to separate them. A by-product of the fermentation of grape juice, *d*-tartaric acid, is a readily available and inexpensive disymmetric substance used as a resolving agent in this experiment. [The *d* stands for *dextro* (Latin, right) and refers to the sign of rotation of polarized light, *vide infra*. The other isomer, the mirror image, is called *l*-tartaric acid, where *l* stands for *levo* (Latin, left).] Show why this compound is disymmetric. (±)-Tris-ethylenediamine cobalt(III) chloride (+)-tartrate are salts which are formed by the tris-ethylenediamine cobalt complex and the dianion of the tartaric acid (+ and − have the same meaning as *d* and *l*, respectively). Compounds such as this, formed from parts that are optically active molecules (or ions), by themselves, are called *diastereoisomers* (often shortened to *diastereomers*). In this case there is enough difference in solubility between the salts formed by the + and − cobalt complexes to make the diastereomers readily separable. The cobalt(III) complex is prepared initially by air oxidation of the Co(II) species (see Experiment 3). The reaction sequences so far discussed are:

$$\tfrac{1}{2}O_2 + 2\,Co(H_2O)_6{}^{++}SO_4{}^= + 6H_2NCH_2CH_2NH_2 + 2HCl \rightarrow$$
$$2(+)\text{-}(Coen_3)^{+3}SO_4{}^=Cl^- + 13H_2O$$

$$Ba(+)\text{-tartrate (s)}$$

$(+)\text{-}(Coen_3)^{+3}Cl^-(+)\text{-tartrate}^= + BaSO_4(s) \qquad (-)\text{-}(Coen_3)^{+3}Cl^-(+)\text{-tartrate}^= + BaSO_4(s)$

Since barium sulfate is very insoluble in water, the final solution contains nothing but the desired compound and traces of byproducts.

After separating the diastereoisomers left behind by this procedure, we are faced with the problem of generating the pure enantiomorphs of the cobalt complex from the separated diastereomers. This is accomplished by displacing the following equilibrium to the right by the addition of a large excess of iodide ion:

$$3I^- + (+)\text{-}(Coen_3)^{+3}Cl^-(+)\text{-tartrate}^= \rightleftharpoons$$
$$(+)\text{-}(Coen_3)^{+3}I_3^{-3} + Cl^- + (+)\text{-tartrate}^=$$

and similarly for $(-)\text{-}(Coen_3)^{+3}Cl^-(+)\text{-tartrate}^=$.

Procedure

Set up the apparatus shown in Fig. 11–20, using a 125-ml flask for the reaction vessel. Measure exactly 0.10 mole of ethylenediamine (a standardized solution that is about 40% ethylenediamine will be available in the laboratory) into the reaction flask, dilute with 17 ml of water and cool in ice. Add 0.033 mole of HCl (as 10 M HCl), a solution of 0.033 mole $CoSO_4 \cdot 7H_2O$ in 17 ml of water, and 1.3 gm of charcoal (What is this for?). Allow the mixture to warm to room temperature and suck air through the solution for four hours (or overnight, if this is more convenient).

Filter the solution through a small Buchner funnel (available from your instructor) with suction and wash the collected charcoal with 1 to 2 ml of water. Adjust the pH of the solution to 7.0 to 7.5 (use pH paper) by adding acid or base as necessary.

Prepare separate concentrated aqueous solutions of 8.1 gm $BaCl_2 \cdot 2H_2O$ and 9.4 gm sodium potassium (+)-tartrate tetrahydrate, which has the formula $(+)\text{-}NaOOCCH(OH)CH(OH)COOK \cdot 4H_2O$. Heat these solutions to 90°C and mix them. Allow the resulting suspension to cool, collect the crystals on a Buchner funnel, and wash them with a *small* amount of water.*

Add the barium tartrate (with the filter paper) to the cobalt complex solution and heat the mixture for thirty minutes on a steam bath (rig one from a beaker and wire gauze, if necessary) with occasional stirring. Filter off the suspension of barium sulfate, wash it with a few milliliters of hot water, and concentrate the filtrate on the steam bath to a volume of 20 to 25 ml. A stream of air blown or sucked gently over the surface of the hot liquid will hasten evaporation. What sort of container

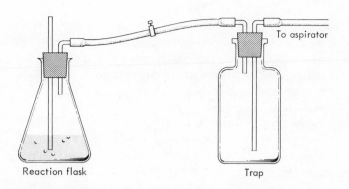

Reaction flask   Trap

To aspirator

Fig. 11–20

should you use at this point? Allow the hot concentrated solution of the chloride tartrate salt to cool slowly overnight.

Collect the crystals on a Buchner funnel and transfer the filtrate to a 50-ml flask. Label this flask (−) or *levo*. Wash the crystals with a 40% ethanol-water mixture, transfer them to a 50-ml flask, and dissolve them in 10 ml of hot water. Allow this solution to cool to room temperature slowly. Label this flask (+) or *dextro*.

To the *levo* filtrate, add 0.1 ml of concentrated ammonia, heat the solution to 80°C, and add 12 gm of sodium iodide. Cool the mixture in ice. Filter the resulting yellow-orange suspension and wash the collected solid with 8 ml of 30% sodium iodide solution. Dissolve the crude (−) triiodide in 22 ml of water at 50°C, and filter the solution while hot through a small folded filter paper.† (You do this without suction so the solution will not cool off by fast evaporation.) Add 3 gm of sodium iodide to the heated (50°C) filtrate and allow the solution to cool. Collect the crystalline solid, wash with 4 ml of 30% sodium iodide in 2-ml aliquots and then with 95% ethanol, and allow it to dry thoroughly. This is *levo* tris-ethylenediamine cobalt(III) triiodide.

Cool the solution of the *dextro* chloride tartrate in ice (after it has cooled to room temperature) and collect the crystals. Wash the crystals with 40% ethanol, then with 95% ethanol. Dissolve the solid in 10 ml hot water and add 0.1 ml concentrated ammonia and 12 gm sodium iodide dissolved in 5 ml hot water. Allow the solution to cool to room temperature, then to 0°C in an ice bath. Collect the crystals and wash them with 6 ml of 30% sodium iodide solution in 2-ml aliquots, followed by 40% and 95% ethanol. Allow the solid to dry thoroughly. This is *dextro* tris-ethylenediamine cobalt(III) triiodide.

Determine the optical rotation of both your *dextro* and *levo* samples at the wavelength of the sodium D line (this is an atomic emission "line" which is in actuality

---

* Note that you can start the cobalt oxidation and the preparation of the barium tartrate during the same laboratory period. At the start of the next period you can filter the cobalt solution and collect the barium tartrate crystals. Thus you will be using your time and the equipment relatively efficiently.

---

† The solution is filtered at this point to remove the insoluble *racemic* salt (the salt of the other optical isomer).

a closely spaced doublet, two lines, at 5896 and 5890 Å) using a sodium vapor lamp. (Some manual polarimeters have a built-in filter that passes only wavelengths that are close to the sodium D lines. Any source of white light can be used with such an instrument and the rotation will closely approximate that obtained with a sodium vapor lamp.) For this measurement, a solution 2% by weight in water is satisfactory. If a polarimeter is unavailable, the articles by Nechamin and Garvin give suggestions for constructing simple polarimeters using Polaroid® films and easily obtained glassware. These designs are easily modified and improved to fit individual needs.

Calculate the specific rotation, $[\alpha]$ from the formula:

$$\alpha = [\alpha] lc / 100,$$

where α is the observed rotation, l is the length of cell in decimeters, and c is the concentration in gm solute/100 ml solution. The rotation is recorded as $+$ if the solution rotates the plane of polarized light in a clockwise direction, with the viewer facing the light beam as it emerges from the sample; a counterclockwise rotation is designated $-$. The specific rotation is recorded with notations for temperature and the wavelength of light employed, the concentration of the solution and the nature of the solvent, or the fact that a pure liquid was employed. For example, $[\alpha]_D^{25} -11.3 \pm 0.3°$ (c 1.47, acetic acid) means that a counterclockwise rotation was measured at 25° using the sodium D line (the usual light source) with a sample having a concentration in acetic acid of 1.47 gm/100 ml of solution. What was the observed rotation in a 1-dm cell? If a pure liquid is employed, the *observed rotation* is given with a notation for the path length: for example, $\alpha_{5460}^{25} +28.6 \pm 0.1°$ (neat, $l = 1$ dm). Note that the wavelength used for this sample is not the sodium D line (it is one of the emission lines of the electronically excited Hg atom).

If a spectropolarimeter is available, use it to determine the optical rotation of your sample as a function of wavelength. The spectropolarimeter has a light source and monochromator like a spectrophotometer, but in addition the wavelengths of light selected by the monochromator are now polarized before passing through the sample. Usually the angle and sign of rotation are determined photoelectrically and read from a dial in this type of instrument. These readings are recorded as a function of wavelength. A plot of *specific rotation* as a function of wavelength is an *optical rotatory dispersion* (ORD) curve. Solutions that are about 0.2% by weight should be used to measure the ORD curve. Measurements of ORD curves are of great utility in biochemical research as well as in inorganic studies such as ours.

® Polaroid is a registered trademark of Polaroid Corp.

If you have ORD curves for your isomeric complex salts, it is also interesting to record optical absorption spectra to compare with the ORD curves.

The Report

Calculate your percentage yield of each optical isomer based on the amount of cobalt(II) with which you began. Calculate the specific rotation for each isomer. Which of your isomers do you think is more pure? Is your answer borne out by the specific rotation data?

If you obtained ORD curves, compare them with those in Basolo and Pearson, p. 294. To what might you attribute any differences? Compare the ORD curves with the optical absorption spectra. What correlations do you find?

Further Experimental Problems

Analysis of the Complexes. Up to this point you have no assurance, outside the assumption that you are not being deceived either deliberately or through ignorance on the part of the designers of this experiment, that the compound described is actually tris-ethylenediamine cobalt(III) triiodide. It would not be unreasonable to suspect, for example, that the complex contained one or more tartrate anions chelated to the cobalt (in place of one of the ethylenediamines). After all, tartrate and oxalate, $^-OOCCOO^-$, do complex with metal ions. To examine the assertion that the tris-ethylenediamine complex was actually prepared, the percent iodine might be determined and compared with the value expected for $Co(en)_3I_3$.

Weigh accurately 0.20 to 0.25 gm of sample and transfer it to a 250-ml iodine flask (obtained from the stockroom). After dissolving the sample in about 35 ml of H_2O, add 1 gm of urea, swirl, and then add 5 ml of 0.5 of $NaNO_2$ followed by 3 ml of 2 M H_2SO_4. Iodine will appear immediately after addition of acid. Insert the lightly greased stopper and add a few milliliters of water above the stopper. Shake the flask occasionally over a fifteen-minute period and then cool it in an ice bath. Note that during the fifteen-minute period, gas is being evolved; to prevent the build up of pressure, the stopper should not be jammed tight. A few milliliters of water should always be above the stopper so that any escaping gas is scrubbed by liquid. After the solution is cooled (all the iodine vapor will have condensed), add first 2 gm of sodium acetate and then 1 gm of potassium iodide with swirling. Rinse down the sides of the flask by adding water above the stopper and then lifting the stopper momentarily. Swirl until the iodine is dissolved. Then titrate with standard 0.05 M sodium thiosulfate (see Experiment 17 for the standardization procedure) adding starch indicator near the endpoint. Add the starch when the red-brown color is nearly gone. Remember that the solution, when the starch-iodine color is discharged, is yellow in this case. Why?

Calculate the percent iodine in the sample and compare it with the theoretical value. Run a duplicate analysis as a check.

Read Kolthoff and Sandell, pp. 585–604, before carrying out this procedure. Oxygen error (Kolthoff and Sandell, p. 588) is apparently strongly catalyzed by $Co(en)_3^{+3}$ and this is the reason the pH was changed to that of acetate buffer from that of sulfuric acid solution. At about pH 4 the fading of the endpoint is very slow.

A few questions to consider concerning this determination are: What gas is evolved in this procedure? Doesn't the addition of a large amount of KI cause an error in the determination of I^- in this procedure? Suppose your analysis does not agree with the theoretical value for percent iodine; what are some possible reasons for the discrepancy and what are some ways in which your hypotheses could be checked? Can you suggest other chemical and/or physical methods which could be used to verify the composition and structure of the complex?

Other Optically Active Species. Two references in the list below will help you to get started on a study of other optically active inorganic compounds. The article by Kauffman and Takahashi outlines a very nice experiment in which one optically active compound is resolved and then used to resolve another optically active compound. Unlike the complexes we prepared, one of these complexes is relatively labile (meaning?) and *racemizes* (what does this mean?) relatively quickly in solution. The course of the racemization could perhaps be studied (how?) to obtain its rate. This compound is also light-sensitive and perhaps its interaction with light, photochemistry, would be interesting to study. A number of experiments that are concerned with optical rotation are suggested or suggest themselves in Holden and Singer's little book on crystals.

Questions

1. Which tris-ethylenediamine cobalt(III) chloride tartrate diastereomer is most soluble? Which of the triiodides is most soluble?

2. What percentage of the original sulfate remains in solution after the chloride sulfate is treated with barium tartrate? The solubilities of barium sulfate and tartrate are:

$BaSO_4$ 1.67×10^{-5} moles/liter,

Ba(tartrate) 2.24×10^{-3} moles/liter.

3. Let us suppose that you are doing research on complexes of cobalt and you have published an article in which you have proposed an octahedral structure for the arrangement of nitrogen atoms about the cobalt atom in tris-ethylenediamine cobalt(III) ion on the basis that all six nitrogens appear to be chemically equivalent.

Your theory has been attacked by scientist X and scientist Y, who presented the following arguments:

X: Far from being octahedral, metal complexes in general and $Co(en)_3^{+3}$ in particular are loose aggregates of ligands surrounding a central atom. The relative ligand positions shift continuously and it is meaningless to talk of structure in such situations.

Y: The data given thus far are consistent with any of four arrangements: planar hexagonal, octahedral, trigonal prismatic, or trigonal antiprismatic.

Now that you have succeeded in resolving $Co(en)_3^{+3}$ into optical isomers, how would you use this new evidence to refute the critics of your previous, somewhat hasty, publication?

4. By the method of resolution we have used, it is possible to achieve at best a 50% yield of either the *dextro* or *levo* enantiomorph of tris-ethylenediamine cobalt(III) triiodide (yield based on the amount of Co(II) salt originally used). By a modification of reaction conditions, however, one may obtain a greater than 50% yield of one isomer. Outline a procedure for doing this (tell which isomer you will get) based on the following facts.

a) The ligands of tris-ethylenediamine cobalt(II) are labile, so that the enantiomorphs rapidly interconvert in solution.

b) Electron transfer between the tris-ethylenediamine complexes of cobalt(II) and cobalt(III) occurs rapidly in solution. That is, the reaction

$$Co^*(en)_3^{+3} + Co(en)_3^{++} \rightleftharpoons$$
$$Co^*(en)_3^{++} + Co(en)_3^{+3}$$

is rapid.

c) The *dextro* diastereomer of tris-ethylenediamine cobalt(III) chloride (+)-tartrate is only sparingly soluble in 25 to 30% aqueous ethanol, whereas the *levo* diastereoisomer is relatively quite soluble.

Perhaps you would like to carry out your procedure in the laboratory: the acid test of your suggestions.

5. In the standardization titration of ethylenediamine with standard acid, methyl orange was used as the indicator. Why was this indicator used rather than, for example, phenolphthalein? For enH_2^{++}, $pK_{a1} = 6.85$ and $pK_{a2} = 9.93$; you can look up indicator pK's in Chapter 7.

REFERENCES

BARROW, G., *The Structure of Molecules*, W. A. Benjamin, New York, 1963.

BASOLO, F., and R. G. PEARSON, *Inorganic Reaction Mechanisms*, John Wiley & Sons, New York, 1958.

BENT, H., *J. Chem. Ed.* **40**, 446, 523 (1963); **42**, 302, 348 (1965) is a series of articles on the "hard-sphere-electron" model of molecular structure.

BRUMLIK, G. C., E. J. BARRETT, and R. L. BAUMGARTEN, *J. Chem. Ed.* **41**, 221 (1964) describes framework molecular models.

COMPANION, A. L., *Chemical Bonding*, McGraw-Hill, New York, 1964.

COULSON, C., *Valence*, 2nd ed., Oxford, Fairlawn, N.J., 1961.

DREIDING, A. S., *Helv. Chim. Acta.* **42**, 1339 (1959) describes the molecular models now known as Dreiding models.

EDWARDS, R. K., W. W. BRANDT, and A. L. COMPANION, "Simple and Inexpensive Student Spectroscope," *J. Chem. Ed.* **39**, 147 (1962). This simple apparatus can be constructed in a couple of hours and is useful for semi-quantitative study of emission spectra. S. D. HARRIS, *J. Chem. Ed.* **39**, 319 (1962) has suggested some improvements in the original design.

FIESER, L. F., *J. Chem. Ed.* **40**, 457 (1963); **42**, 408 (1965) describes the uses of inexpensive Dreiding-type molecular models.

GARVIN, J. E., "Inexpensive Polarimeter for Demonstrations and Student Use," *J. Chem. Ed.* **37**, 515 (1960).

GATES, D. M., "Spectral Distribution of Solar Radiation at the Earth's Surface," *Science*, **151**, 523 (1966), particularly Figure 8, may be of interest in your analysis of Experiment 23.

GILLESPIE, R. J., and R. S. NYHOLM, *Quarterly Reviews* (London) **11**, 339 (1957) begins the development of the valence-shell electron-pair repulsion model for molecular structure.

GILLESPIE, R. J., "The Valence-Shell Electron-Pair Repulsion (VSEPR) Theory of Directed Valency," *J. Chem. Ed.* **40**, 295 (1963) contains many references to work done between this and his 1957 article.

GODFREY, J. C., "Stereo Molecular Models," *J. Chem. Ed.* **42**, 404 (1965) introduces an interesting and relatively inexpensive molecular model set.

HERZBERG, G., *Atomic Spectra and Atomic Structure*, Dover, New York, 1944.

HOLDEN, A., and P. SINGER, *Crystals and Crystal Growing*, Doubleday Anchor, Garden City, New York, 1960.

The Journal of Chemical Education is usually packed with goodies in the area of chemical bonding and the structure of molecules. A few of these are referenced here, but you are urged to peruse this journal for yourself.

KAUFFMAN, G. B., and L. T. TAKAHASI, "Resolving Optically Active Coordination Compounds," *J. Chem. Ed.* **39**, 481 (1962) discusses two very interesting experiments which are connected because the optically active product of the first experiment is used in the resolution of the second compound synthesized.

KOKES, R. J., M. K. DORFMAN, and T. MATHIA, "Cloud Chamber, Molecular Film, and Atomic Weight of Silver," *J. Chem. Ed.* **39**, 18 (1962) presents a connected series of experiments to get Avogadro's number and hence atomic weights.

KOLTHOFF, I. M., and E. B. SANDELL, *Textbook of Quantitative Inorganic Analysis*, 3rd ed., Macmillan, New York, 1952, Chapter 39.

LINNETT, J., *The Electronic Structure of Molecules*, Wiley, New York, 1964.

LITTLE, R., "Molecular Structure and Thermodynamic Properties of HCN and DCN, *J. Chem. Ed.* **43**, 2 (1966) is an excellent introduction to the power and methods of spectroscopy combined with statistical mechanics.

NECHAMKIN, H., "A Student Polarimeter," *J. Chem. Ed.* **31**, 579 (1954).

PAULING, L., *The Nature of the Chemical Bond*, 3rd ed., Cornell University Press, Ithaca, N.Y., 1960.

PAULING, L., and R. HAYWARD, *The Architecture of Molecules*, Freeman, San Francisco, 1965.

SCHOENBECK, R., and F. D. TABBUTT, "Inexpensive Spectrograph of Moderately High Resolving Power," *J. Chem. Ed.* **40**, 452 (1963) describes the construction of a spectrograph for under one hundred dollars. Such an instrument should be invaluable for anyone desiring to follow up on the ideas presented in Experiment 24.

SEBERA, D. K., *Electronic Structure and Chemical Bonding*, Blaisdell, New York, 1964.

SHAMOS, M. H., ed., *Great Experiments in Physics*, Holt, Rinehart & Winston, New York, 1959. Chapters 16 and 17 and Appendixes 2 and 4.

SHURCLIFF, W. A., and S. S. BALLARD, *Polarized Light*, Van Nostrand, Princeton, N. J., 1964, is a good short introduction to the subject.

STAIR, R., W. E. SCHNEIDER, and J. K. JACKSON, *Applied Optics*, **2**, 1151 (1963) is a reference giving information about the quartz-iodine standard lamps we use in Experiment 23.

WILLIAMS, F. T., "Resolution by the Method of Racemic Modification," *J. Chem. Ed.* **39**, 211 (1962) points up the use of the right hand–left hand analogy for optical isomers to suggest quite graphically how diastereoisomers could differ markedly in their properties.

12 NUCLEAR MAGNETIC RESONANCE

12–1 THE ORIGIN OF NUCLEAR MAGNETIC RESONANCE

There are many ways that a molecule can absorb energy. We have discussed several of these ways and the spectroscopic methods based on them in other chapters: absorption by electrons in molecules (or atoms) going from one electronic energy state to another, absorption that makes a molecule vibrate more violently, and absorption that causes a molecule to rotate more rapidly in space. All these forms of energy absorption (and the corresponding emissions) occur whether or not the molecules are being acted on by external electric or magnetic fields. To be sure, the effects of such perturbations on absorption or emission spectra often tell us a great deal about the atom or molecule under study, but the important point is that these spectra appear even in the absence of such fields. On the other hand, in magnetic resonance spectroscopy, an important recent addition to the scientists' bag of tricks for studying molecular structure and molecular interactions, no absorption of energy occurs unless the system under study is in a magnetic field.

Protons and neutrons as well as electrons have "spin," and as with electrons, this spin has a magnetic moment associated with it. (We will consider only the proton, the hydrogen nucleus, during this discussion, since a great deal of nuclear-magnetic-resonance spectroscopy deals with hydrogen-containing molecules.) When no external magnetic field is applied, the proton magnetic moment (a vector quantity) has no preferred orientation in space, or, to put it another way, all its orientations are of equal energy. When the proton is placed in a magnetic field the situation changes markedly. Its magnetic moment can now take only two orientations (as with electron spin), which we characterize by saying the proton can have a nuclear spin quantum number, I, of $+\frac{1}{2}$ or $-\frac{1}{2}$. Figure 12–1 shows the "splitting" of the degenerate energy levels in the presence of the

magnetic field. In the figure, μ_H is equal to the magnetic moment of the proton (the Hydrogen nucleus), 14.1×10^{-24} erg-gauss^{-1}, and H is the magnetic field "felt" by the nucleus, about 14,000 gauss in most of the instruments that make use of this effect. When a difference in energy levels has been established, the system can absorb electromagnetic radiation which will cause protons in the lower energy state to be "excited" to the upper state. The energy difference between the two states is $2 \Delta\epsilon = 2\mu_H H$, and, by Planck's quantum hypothesis, the frequency of radiation that can be absorbed is

$$\nu = \frac{2\mu_H H}{h}$$

$$= \frac{2 \times 14.1 \times 10^{-24} \times 1.4 \times 10^4}{6.6 \times 10^{-27}} = 6.0 \times 10^7 \ \text{sec}^{-1}$$

$$= 60 \ \text{Mc/sec.} \tag{12–1}$$

Thus if we had a spectrometer that could be used in the frequency region around 60 Mc (in the radio frequency part of the electromagnetic spectrum), we could put a sample containing hydrogen nuclei into a 14,000-gauss field and analyze it with this spectrometer. The above calculation indicates that we should find a very sharp absorption at 60 Mc; such absorption does occur. (We say then that the system is "in resonance with" this frequency.) The absorption and reemission of energy by nuclei that possess magnetic moments, such as hydrogen, are the basis of the technique we are describing, nuclear magnetic resonance spectroscopy, NMR.

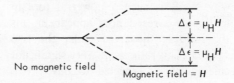

Fig. 12–1

Current for small variations in magnetic field

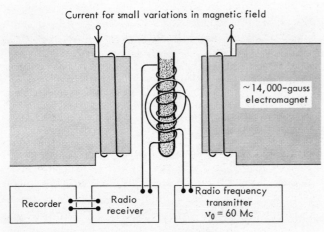

Fig. 12–2. The NMR apparatus (block diagram).

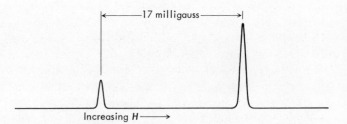

Fig. 12–3. NMR spectrum of CH_3OH at 60 Mc with a magnetic field of about 14,000 gauss.

Experimental arrangements like the one shown schematically in Fig. 12–2 are used for actual NMR work. It is very much easier experimentally to keep ν fixed at one radio frequency and to vary H. From Eq. (12–1) you can see that if ν is held constant at ν_0 (60 Mc in commercial instruments for studying proton magnetic-resonance absorption), H can be varied until the equation is satisfied, at which field the system will resonate with the fixed frequency. When this resonance occurs, some of the protons in the lower level will be excited to the upper level; since this disturbs the equilibrium, they will return to the lower state, emitting radiation of frequency ν_0. In the experimental setup there are two coils placed at right angles to each other; one, the receiver, is wrapped around the sample, and the other, the transmitter, is placed parallel to the sample tube and emits radiation ν_0. Since the coils are at right angles to each other, no radio radiation is detected by the receiver when the sample is not emitting energy. When the system is in resonance, the sample will emit radiation of frequency ν_0 in all directions, so the receiver coil will detect radiation; its signal can be amplified by the receiver and displayed on a recorder or oscilloscope.

12-2 THE CHEMICAL SIGNIFICANCE OF NMR

At this point you should be wondering, "What good is all this?" After all, we can already calculate all the quantities in Eq. (12–1), so what can we learn from these experiments? Looking at the NMR spectrum of, for example, the compound methanol, CH_3OH, Fig. 12–3, will show you why NMR is such a powerful tool in chemistry. Note that two resonances appear in this spectrum, and the ratio of the areas under the two absorption peaks is 1:3. This ratio seems very significant since this molecule might be expected to have "two kinds of hydrogen," i.e., the H attached to the O and the three H's attached to the C, in the ratio 1:3. But

why should there be two resonances for the hydrogens? The answer is not hard to find; return to Eq. (12–1) and look again at the definition of H, the magnetic field *felt by the nucleus*. We have assumed that the field felt by the nucleus is that impressed on the system by our large magnet. Indeed, most of the field felt by the nucleus comes from this source, but the field from the magnet is "tempered" somewhat by the electrons which surround the nuclei. Thus the field at the nucleus is different for nuclei in different electronic environments.

This very subtle effect, which shifts the resonance frequencies from where we would expect them to be (if we assume that the field at the nucleus is created with the magnet alone), is called the "chemical shift" (since the electronic interactions are thought to be in the chemists' domain). What is the direction of this chemical shift? To make clearer both the direction of the chemical shift and its origins, let us refer to the *schematic* Fig. 12–4, which shows a proton with one electron in a Bohr-like orbit about it. The motions of the electrons in molecules produce magnetic fields as indicated in the figure. Now, when the external field is applied, the magnetic fields created by the electronic motions tend to line up as shown, in opposition to the applied field, since this is the configuration of lowest energy under this circumstance. Thus, as indicated by the "vector diagram," the magnetic field at the nucleus is less than the external field, and we will have to apply slightly higher external

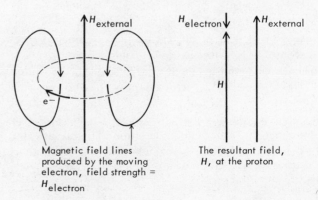

Fig. 12–4. A schematic representation of the origin of nuclear magnetic shielding.

fields than we would have anticipated to put the system in resonance. The higher the field we have to apply, the more "shielded" we say the nucleus is.* In the CH_3OH spectrum presented in Fig. 12–3, you can see that the CH_3 hydrogens are more shielded than the OH hydrogen. (Note, however, that this difference is very small, since the change in field necessary to bring the CH_3 hydrogens into resonance is only about one millionth of the total applied field.)

Chemical shifts are usually stated in terms of the difference between the field required to bring the system of interest into resonance and the field required for some standard substance. (This standard can be any hydrogen-containing compound, but one that is widely used now is tetramethylsilane, $(CH_3)_4Si$, TMS.) The chemical shift is defined as

$$\delta = \frac{H_{sample} - H_{reference}}{H_{reference}} \times 10^6. \qquad (12\text{-}2)$$

The 10^6 is inserted because the field differences are so small compared with the total field and we like to work with numbers in the neighborhood of unity, a human foible made more imperative by the widespread use of computers. It is easy to convert the chemical shift, δ, in parts per million, ppm, to the difference in frequency between the sample and the reference which would have been observed if we had varied ν at constant H instead of doing the experiment as we actually do:

$$\Delta\nu = \delta \times \nu_0, \qquad (12\text{-}3)$$

where ν_0 is given in megacycles (60 for most NMR instruments) but $\Delta\nu$ is obtained in cycles/sec because of the 10^6 in δ. You will find chemical shifts reported both in ppm and in cycles/sec, cps, in the literature.†

Before going on to discuss the interpretation of NMR spectra we must note two items briefly. First, the hydrogen nucleus is not the only nucleus examined by NMR spectroscopy. In fact, any nucleus that does not contain

---

* There is a notable exception to this general picture. The resonances of the hydrogens in benzene and the ring hydrogens of other similar molecules appear at fields lower than we would have anticipated for a "bare" proton. You should be able to see at least qualitatively why this is true if you treat the pi-electron system as though it were a wire loop through which current is flowing, creating a magnetic field. Draw the magnetic field lines associated with such a current and see whether they will add to or subtract from the external applied field at the hydrogen nuclei that lie about the periphery of this "loop."

† Note that δ and $\Delta\nu$ can be negative. Indeed, with TMS as the reference standard most hydrogen nuclei chemical shifts are negative, since the shielding in TMS is quite large. Often, however, you will find the chemical shift given as a positive number even when it should be negative. Be careful; the context should make clear what is meant

an even number of both protons and neutrons should be observable (but at different frequencies than hydrogen, since μ will be much different than for the proton). Other nuclei which are extensively studied are ^{11}B, ^{13}C, ^{15}N, and ^{19}F. We must also realize that not only electrons but also other nuclei with magnetic moments can alter the field felt by a particular nucleus. Since nuclear magnetic moments are much smaller than electronic magnetic moments, this effect will be correspondingly smaller, but it is readily observable. An example of the result of such nuclear spin-nuclear spin interactions is shown in the high resolution NMR spectrum of CH_3CH_2OH, Fig. 12–5. The ratio of areas under the three absorption peaks is $1:2:3$, but the peaks for what are presumably the CH_2 and CH_3 hydrogens are split into a "quartet" and a "triplet," respectively, by this "spin-spin coupling" of the hydrogen nuclei. This effect is unimportant for the experiment we are going to perform, but it is of immense diagnostic value when evaluating what an NMR spectrum tells you about the structure of a molecule.

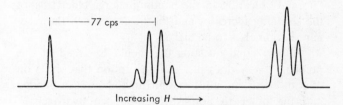

Fig. 12–5. NMR spectrum of CH_3CH_2OH (at high resolution) at 60 Mc in a magnetic field of about 14,000 gauss.

Now we should examine in a bit more detail what the NMR spectrum of CH_3OH, Fig. 12–3, tells us. We first note that the OH hydrogen is less shielded than the CH_3 hydrogens. (We see the same thing in CH_3CH_2OH.) This may be interpreted as indicating that the average electron density about the OH hydrogen nucleus is lower than that about the CH_3 hydrogens. Qualitatively, perhaps, this is understandable, since oxygen is more electronegative than carbon and it might be expected that the electron-density distribution making up the bond between O and H would be shifted toward the O, leaving that H less shielded than the ones bonded to the less electronegative carbon.

Appealing as this very simple picture is, it is marred by further experimental facts. When CH_3OH is diluted by some nonpolar NMR-inert solvent such as CCl_4, the peak due to the OH hydrogen shifts to higher fields until it is actually found on the high-field side of the CH_3 peak; under these circumstances, the OH hydrogen is more shielded than the CH_3 hydrogens. To what can we ascribe this behavior? It seems certain that there must be intermolecular effects at work as well as the intramolecular effects we have previously discussed. The interaction that you should most readily think of when we discuss molecules containing the —OH grouping is hydrogen bonding. We know this has very profound effects on the physical properties of water, the alcohols, and organic acids. When a hydrogen bond is formed, the hydrogen nucleus, the proton, is drawn a bit farther away from the atom to which it is bonded, due to the electrostatic interaction of its positive charge with the negative "charge cloud" of the atom (usually oxygen or nitrogen) with which the hydrogen bond is formed. The hydrogen does not take up a position half-way between the two atoms but remains closer to the atom to which it was originally bonded. If you have been following the arguments closely, you will now see that if the proton is actually drawn slightly farther out of its bonding-electron density distribution, it will be less shielded from external magnetic fields and will be in resonance at "low field." As the system is diluted, the possibilities for hydrogen bonding decrease, since not all the neighboring molecules are alcohol, and the OH hydrogen on the average finds itself less hydrogen-bonded and more at its "normal" location in the bonding charge cloud; hence the shielding increases and the field at which the resonance occurs has to be higher.

A very good question that could be asked at this point is, "Why does just one absorption that shifts on dilution occur and not two, one due to hydrogen-bonded and the other to non-hydrogen-bonded hydrogens?" Briefly, if a changing interaction of a hydrogen puts it in two different magnetic environments (e.g., H-bonded and non-H-bonded) and the rate of change from one environment to the other is fast compared with the time resolution of the NMR technique, then the instrument will detect only an average of the signals from the two different environments. The average will be weighted by the average mole fractions of hydrogens in each of the two environments, and the observed chemical shift will be given by

$$\delta = X_1 \delta_1 + X_2 \delta_2, \qquad (12\text{-}4)$$

where X is the mole fraction of hydrogens in a given environment denoted by the subscripts and δ_1 and δ_2 are the shifts that would be observed if all the hydrogens were in environment 1 or 2, respectively. Measurements of effects such as these can be readily correlated with the equilibrium constant for the change of hydrogens from one environment to the other, as we shall see in the next section.

Thus we have seen that the NMR technique allows us to probe very sensitively into the structure and interaction of molecular systems containing nuclei with magnetic moments. Results of this technique can readily be seen by opening almost any scientific journal; you will find that more than half the research utilizes NMR in some way, usually just as an analytical device, but more and more often to study very subtle intra- and intermolecular interactions.

12-3 AN APPLICATION OF NMR TO AN EQUILIBRIUM SYSTEM

Let us now examine further the consequences of Eq. (12–4). Suppose that one of the hydrogens in a molecule C can interact to form a hydrogen bond with an electronegative atom in a molecule A, but that there is very little interaction between molecules of C. In this circumstance we will probably find that the NMR chemical shift, δ_c (relative to some reference), of this hydrogen nucleus (proton) in the pure compound is different from the NMR chemical shift, δ, of this proton in a mixture of c moles of C and a moles of A. (From our discussion above you ought to be able to develop an argument to show that the NMR signal for this proton in the pure compound spectrum will appear at a higher field than in the mixture.) Let us describe the hydrogen bonding interaction by an equilibrium reaction,

$$A + C \rightleftharpoons A \cdots C. \qquad (12\text{-}5)$$

To apply Eq. (12–4) we have to define the states in which the proton may be found. We shall call the proton in its non-hydrogen-bonded situation state 1 and the proton in the hydrogen-bonded complex ($A \cdots C$, which we shall denote as X for simplicity) state 2. If we have x moles of X in the equilibrium mixture, then, from the stoichiometry of Eq. (12–5), we will have $c - x$ moles of free C at equilibrium. We can write (12–4) as

$$\delta = \frac{c - x}{c} \delta_c + \frac{x}{c} \delta_x,$$

or

$$\delta - \delta_c = \frac{x}{c} (\delta_x - \delta_c), \qquad (12\text{-}6)$$

where δ_x is the NMR chemical shift of the proton in the hydrogen-bonded complex. (What further criterion must be met by the reactions in Eq. (12–5) for (12–4) to be applicable?)

We may write the equilibrium constant for (12–5) using mole fractions as the concentration "unit":

$$K = \frac{x/[(a - x) + (c - x) + x]}{\dfrac{a - x}{(a - x) + (c - x) + x} \cdot \dfrac{c - x}{(a - x) + (c - x) + x}}$$

$$= \frac{x(a + c - x)}{(a - x)(c - x)}. \qquad (12\text{-}7)$$

The experimentally observable properties of the system we are considering are δ, δ_c, a, and c. Thus we have two equations, (12–6) and (12–7), in three unknowns, δ_x, x, and K. You might suggest that we could make up a new and different mixture of A and C which would yield us another equation like (12–6) with a different value of δ. Unfortunately x will, of course, also be different in this new situation since it, naturally, varies with changes in the ratio of the reactants, A and C.

This is, however, the correct approach to solving our dilemma. We make up a number of mixtures of A and C with varying ratios of a to c. Our task will be easier in the succeeding computations if we vary the *ratio* of a to c while holding the *sum* $(a + c)$ constant, which is easy to do experimentally. The simplest choice for this sum is unity. With this choice Eq. (12–7) becomes

$$K = \frac{x(1 - x)}{ac - x + x^2}. \qquad (12\text{--}8)$$

Show how. We then plot $(\delta - \delta_c)$ versus $c/(a + c)$, and extrapolate this experimental plot to get $(\delta - \delta_c)$ in the limit that c goes to zero, i.e., the intercept at

$$c/(a + c) = 0$$

on our plot. Let us call this extrapolated value $(\delta - \delta_c)_0$, referring to the fact that "zero c" is present at this point. As c approaches zero, i.e., as the mixtures get closer and closer to being pure A, $(a + c - x)$ will approach the value $(a - x)$ and we can write

$$K = \frac{x(a + c - x)}{(a - x)(c - x)} \lim_{c \to 0} \frac{x}{c - x}, \qquad (12\text{--}9)$$

which can (in the limit) be rearranged to give

$$\frac{x}{c} = \frac{K}{1 + K}. \qquad (12\text{--}10)$$

Substitute (12–10) into (12–6) to get

$$(\delta - \delta_c)_0 = \frac{K}{1 + K}(\delta_x - \delta_c). \qquad (12\text{--}11)$$

(This substitution is proper because both equations refer to the same "mixture" of A and C, the limiting mixture, as c approaches zero.)

Now note that Eqs. (12–6), (12–8), and (12–11) are independent equations containing the three unknowns, δ_x, x, and K. Thus we should be able to solve them simultaneously to obtain the values of these three unknowns. The most important of these is K, the equilibrium constant that describes the molecular interaction of A with C. The solution for K is*

$$K = \frac{1 - N}{N - 1 + M} = \frac{1 - N}{M - (1 - N)}, \qquad (12\text{--}12)$$

where

$$N = a\frac{(\delta - \delta_c)_0}{(\delta - \delta_c)},$$

$$M = c\frac{(\delta - \delta_c)}{(\delta - \delta_c)_0}.$$

Thus once we have obtained a value for $(\delta - \delta_c)_0$ by extrapolation of the $(\delta - \delta_c)$ data for a series of mixtures, we can calculate N and M for each mixture from the appropriate values of a and c (whose sum is unity) and $(\delta - \delta_c)$, and hence get a value for K.

---

* You can show this for yourself by eliminating $(\delta_x - \delta_c)$ between (12–6) and (12–11), solving the resulting equation for x, substituting this in (12–8), and solving the quadratic equation for K (dropping zero and negative roots of equations).

EXPERIMENT 27. The Acetone-Chloroform System; Part II: An NMR Study

Background

The result of the simple experiment of mixing equal volumes of acetone and chloroform together in a test tube certainly testifies that some very substantial interaction between chloroform and acetone occurs. (Is this single test enough to show that such an interaction exists?) On the basis of our previous knowledge we might be led to expect that hydrogen bonding, through the chloroform hydrogen, is the cause of this interaction. The above discussion of NMR suggests a possible way of testing this hypothesis. If we were to examine the NMR spectra of pure chloroform (which is assumed not

to be hydrogen-bonded†) and of a mixture of chloroform and acetone, we would expect to see the resonance due to the chloroform hydrogen shift relative to the reference standard if the hydrogen atom spends some average portion of its time in a hydrogen bond with the acetone. In which direction (to lower or higher fields) would you expect such a shift to be?

In this experiment we shall examine the NMR spectra of a series of acetone-chloroform mixtures rang-

---

† Mahan, p. 138, says that no hydrogen-bonding interaction exists in pure chloroform. If you have done Experiment 8, can you cite evidence to refute or support this statement?

ing from 100% chloroform to about 2% chloroform. (Each solution will also contain less than 0.01 mole fraction of TMS, tetramethylsilane, as a reference standard.) If the postulated shifts in the NMR signal from the chloroform hydrogen actually materialize, we can use the analysis suggested in Section 12–3 to obtain the equilibrium constant for the reaction

$$CH_3\overset{O}{\overset{\|}{C}}CH_3 + CHCl_3 \rightleftharpoons \overset{CH_3}{\underset{CH_3}{>}}C{=}O \cdots HCCl_3. \qquad (12\text{--}14)$$

Procedure

Make up about a dozen mixtures of chloroform and acetone that cover the range of concentration 100 to 2 weight percent chloroform. The chloroform and acetone used for these mixtures must be very dry. (The article by Huggins, Pimentel, and Shoolery gives methods for freeing the reagents of water.) The following procedure is recommended for making up your samples.

1) Weigh a capped NMR sample tube.

2) Use a dropper with a long tip to place approximately the correct amount of chloroform in the NMR tube. (These tubes are very uniform in dimension and you will find that it is easy to calculate from the tube dimensions and the density of the reagents the height to which you should fill the tube to obtain a particular mass of that reagent. Hold the tube against a piece of graph paper when filling it and you will be able to estimate the correct quantity of reagent closely.)

3) Weigh the capped tube and its contents.

4) Use another dropper with a long tip to place approximately the correct amount of acetone in the tube.

5) Weigh the capped tube and its contents.

6) Add a *very small* drop of TMS, tetramethylsilane, to the tube.

7) Weigh the capped tube and contents.

These mixtures have a high vapor pressure and tend to escape unless the NMR tubes are sealed. If you are going to use your samples once within a very few days, a seal of electrical tape around the cap is probably sufficient. For longer periods of storage or a more extended set of runs (see below for additional experiments) it is wise to seal the tubes permanently. To seal off a tube, freeze the contents of the capped tube by immersing the tube in liquid nitrogen, remove the cap, and immediately attach the tube by means of a short piece of Tygon tubing to a vacuum line or vacuum pump (*not* a water aspirator), evacuate the tube (still held in liquid nitrogen), and finally, heat the tube carefully as near as possible to the top (without setting fire to the Tygon) with a very small flame from a gas-oxygen

torch. As the glass gets hot it will be sucked in and if you are skillful, will seal without cracking. Anneal the sealed end of the tube in a sooty flame and allow it to cool completely before removing the tube from the liquid nitrogen and allowing the contents to melt. As a check on your work, weigh the sealed tube, cap, and remaining open end of the tube to see that no weight has been lost in the sealing process. The weight should check within a few milligrams with the weight before the seal was made.

Take the NMR spectra of your solutions at 25°C. Your instructors will explain the operation of the particular NMR instrument that you will use for this experiment.

If for some reason you do not have access to a nuclear-magnetic-resonance spectrometer, you will find spectra given in the article by Bell and Snider which were obtained on samples made just as the above procedure directs. You can use the data from this article to complete the calculations for this experiment.

Calculations

Compute the number of moles of acetone, a, and the number of moles of chloroform, c, in each of your mixtures. Measure the chemical shift of the chloroform hydrogen resonance in each of your mixtures relative to the TMS resonance. Compute $(\delta - \delta_c)$, where δ_c is the chemical shift for pure chloroform, for each of your mixtures and plot $(\delta - \delta_c)$ versus $c/(a + c)$. Draw a smooth curve through your points and extrapolate the curve to $c/(a + c) = 0$ to obtain $(\delta - \delta_c)_0$. Compute what the values a and c would have been in each of your mixtures if you had made exactly 1 mole of a mixture with the same ratio of a to c. Tabulate these values. In the same table, also give your calculated values of M and N, Eq. (12–12), for each mixture and the value of K computed for each mixture.

In what range of concentration do you obtain the most consistent values of K? Take the average of these values, choose about a dozen arbitrary values of $c/(a + c)$ in the range zero to unity, and calculate x, the mole fraction of the hydrogen complex, for each value using Eq. (12–8). Calculate $(\delta_x - \delta_c)$ from Eq. (12–11) and your average value of K. Now calculate the theoretical $(\delta - \delta_c)$ for each value of $c/(a + c)$ you have chosen and plot these theoretical points on the graph containing the experimental data. Do the theoretical and experimental curves agree? If they disagree, where is the disagreement worst? (Can you think of any reason why the theoretical and experimental values might disagree?)

If you have done the first part of the investigation of the acetone-chloroform system, Experiment 8, you can now use the equilibrium constant derived in this experiment to calculate how many moles of reaction actually took place in your calorimetric experiments. From this information and the calorimetric data you can compute ΔH^0 for the formation of one mole of hydrogen bonds, if there are any, between chloroform and acetone. You can also compute ΔG^0 and ΔS^0 for this reaction.

Further Experimental Problems

To check the direct calorimetric measurement of ΔH^0 for this reaction you can obtain ΔH^0 indirectly by measuring K as a function of temperature. This simply requires running the whole set of NMR spectra over again at a series of temperatures. Three or four temperatures in the range $-40°C$ to $+25°C$ should be adequate to obtain the temperature dependence. How does ΔH^0 obtained from a log K versus $1/T$ plot compare with the "directly" measured ΔH^0?

A number of other suggestions for further work as well as some data to implement these suggestions are given in the article by Bell and Snider. Primarily, these are suggestions for testing various hypotheses concerning the discrepancies between the theoretical and experimental results of this experiment. Perhaps you can suggest other tests that you would like to carry out in your own laboratory.

Questions

1. Calculate the energy separation, ΔE, between the two states of the hydrogen nucleus in a 14,000-gauss field. The Boltzmann distribution law tells us that the ratio of the number of nuclei in the upper level, n_u, to that in the lower level, n_l, will be

$$n_u/n_l = \exp{(-\Delta E/kT)}.$$

Since all the nuclei have to be in one state or the other, you can calculate the percentage that are in the lower level and the percentage in the upper level. Do this for a system at 300°K.

2. Using the resonance of the OH hydrogen as your reference, calculate δ for the CH_3 hydrogens of

CH_3OH and the CH_2 hydrogens of CH_3CH_2OH. Would you have anticipated the result you obtain?

3. Given the nuclear magnetic moments and spin quantum numbers in the table below, calculate the frequency at which each of the nuclei would be in resonance in a 14,000-gauss field.

Nucleus	Nuclear magnetic moment $\times 10^{-24}$ erg-gauss^{-1}	I
^{13}C	3.55	$\frac{1}{2}$
^{15}N	1.43	$\frac{1}{2}$
^{19}F	13.3	$\frac{1}{2}$

4. Equivalent hydrogens (such as the three CH_3 hydrogens in CH_3OH) appear at the same field in low-resolution NMR where spin-spin coupling effects are not observed. This is why it is fairly easy to correlate the relative areas under the peaks with the numbers of hydrogens giving rise to that particular resonance.

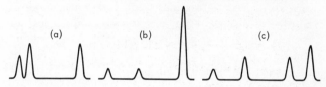

Fig. 12–6

Three isomers of the formula C_3H_8O can be written

$$CH_3CH_2CH_2OH \qquad CH_3{-}O{-}CH_2CH_3 \qquad CH_3\overset{\displaystyle CH_3}{\underset{\displaystyle H}{C}}OH$$

$$\text{I} \qquad\qquad\qquad \text{II} \qquad\qquad\qquad \text{III}$$

Match these compounds with the low-resolution NMR spectra shown in Fig. 12–6 and indicate why you make the choices you do. (The field increases to the right as usual.)

REFERENCES

BELL, J. A., and W. H. SNIDER, "The Acetone-Chloroform System: An NMR Study," *J. Chem. Ed.* **44,** 200 (1967).

HUGGINS, C. M., G. C. PIMENTEL, and J. N. SHOOLERY, *J. Chem. Phys.* **23,** 1244 (1955) is the original NMR study of the acetone-chloroform system.

JACKMAN, L. M., *Applications of Nuclear Magnetic Resonance Spectroscopy in Organic Chemistry*, Pergamon, London, 1959, is a short introduction to NMR.

MAHAN, B. H., *University Chemistry*, Addison-Wesley, Reading, Mass., 1965.

PIMENTEL, G. C., and A. L. McCLELLAN, *The Hydrogen Bond*, Freeman, San Francisco, 1960, pp. 142–157. This whole book is worth perusing; the pages indicated contain a discussion of the use of NMR to study hydrogen-bonded systems.

ROBERTS, J. D., *Nuclear Magnetic Resonance*, McGraw-Hill, New York, 1959, is an interesting little book containing a great deal of information regarding the uses of the NMR method.

Almost any recent physical chemistry textbook will have a section on the NMR technique and the information obtainable from the results. Many of the new organic chemistry textbooks also discuss NMR.

KINETICS: REACTION RATES
13 AND MECHANISMS

Many of the experiments described in this text enable us to obtain thermodynamic information, directly or indirectly, about the reactions studied. It must, however, be pointed out again that this knowledge does not necessarily tell us what will happen in a given system not studied experimentally, for all thermodynamics can tell us is what the situation will be *if* (and this is a big if) equilibrium is attained. For, even if a reaction is thermodynamically favored to proceed to a measurable extent (which we can often predict from tabulated values of thermodynamic functions), it may not do so; often a more important factor in determining the actual reactions we will observe is the speed or rate at which the reaction proceeds. Some reactions are almost immeasurably rapid, such as

$$H^+(aq) + OH^-(aq) \rightarrow H_2O,$$
$$\Delta G^0 = -19.095 \text{ kcal/mole},$$

while others (with a larger driving force) are immeasurably slow at room temperature, like

$$H_2 + \tfrac{1}{2}O_2 \rightarrow H_2O, \qquad \Delta G^0 = -54.636 \text{ kcal/mole}.$$

Thus, after determining that a given reaction is thermodynamically favorable, we still must inquire: how fast does the reaction proceed toward equilibrium?

13-1 EMPIRICAL KINETICS: RATES AND DIFFERENTIAL RATE LAWS

Unfortunately, this question cannot at present be answered a priori. Our knowledge of molecular interactions, while quite detailed in some very subtle aspects, tends to break down completely when the molecules under study obtain large amounts of energy and their intra- and intermolecular motions become violent enough to make and break bonds, i.e., undergo chemical reaction. Thus we must have recourse to empirical deter-

minations to obtain information about rates of reaction. This situation is certainly not intolerable, since the study of the kinetics of a reaction can provide extremely interesting and valuable information about the reaction. One can often infer from the kinetics a microscopic picture of the molecular dynamics (see Section 13-2); these rate studies may enable us, in the future, to predict the kinetic behavior of unstudied systems.

Let us illustrate the kind of information that kinetic studies can provide by examining the general reaction of compound A, which reacts to yield the products B and C. The first item of information we need is the overall stoichiometry of this reaction, which is expressed in a *stoichiometric equation*. Let us suppose that the reaction we are studying is described by the stoichiometric equation

$$2A = B + C. \tag{13-1}$$

The *rate of a reaction* is defined as the rate of change with time of the concentration of one of the products, e.g., $d[C]/dt$, or the rate of change of a reactant concentration with a minus sign inserted, e.g., $-d[A]/dt$. (The minus sign is inserted so that all rates will be positive.) We can use the stoichiometric equation for the overall reaction to obtain the relationships among the various changing concentrations. For the reaction whose overall stoichiometry is given by Eq. (13-1) we see that the following equalities hold among the possible expressions for the rate of the reaction:

$$\frac{d[B]}{dt} = \frac{d[C]}{dt} = -\frac{1}{2}\frac{d[A]}{dt}.$$

(Why do these equalities hold? In particular, where does the factor of one-half come from in the last term?) We can use any of these three time derivatives as the rate of the reaction. The choice of the concentration change we use to express the rate of a particular reaction depends on which is the most convenient for the purpose we have in mind. It makes no difference how we express the rate, for if we know the stoichiometric equation, we can rewrite the rate in terms of any of the other concentrations we desire.

Since molecules presumably have to come together to react and since the probability of molecules encountering one another is proportional to the concentrations of the molecules, we should certainly postulate that the rates of chemical reactions would depend in some way on the concentrations of the reactants. This hypothesis is easy to check experimentally; the rate of the reaction is determined and then, in another experiment, the initial concentration of one of the reactants (or products) is changed while all the others are held constant, and the rate is again determined. A series of such experiments with varying initial concentrations of all species that are thought to affect the reaction is described in Section 13–4. The results show that rates are usually proportional to some power of one or more of the concentrations of the species in the system. The *differential rate law*, i.e., the dependence of the rate of reaction on the concentrations, for the reaction represented by the overall stoichiometry of (13–1), can in general be written

$$\frac{d[C]}{dt} = k[A]^a[B]^b[C]^c[E]^e, \qquad (13\text{–}2)$$

where the proportionality constant, k, is called the *rate constant*. (The symbol E is simply a general symbol for the one or more compounds that may affect the rate of the reaction but do not appear in the stoichiometric equation, such as a catalyst which accelerates the reaction but is not consumed.) The appropriate concentrations to be inserted into the rate-law expression are those of the system at the moment the rate, $d[C]/dt$, was measured. The sum of the exponents on the concentration factors is called the *order of the reaction* (which equals $a + b + c + e$ in this case). The exponent on any one of the concentrations is called the *order with respect to that compound*, e.g., this reaction is ath order in [A]. These exponents, which may have any value (usually in the range -2 to $+2$, since exponents greater than two are almost never found), must be determined experimentally.

In general, rate constants for different reactions are different. In the following discussions, we will often use subscripts on rate constants to distinguish them from one another. Note that rate constants have units; if the differential-rate-law expression is nth order overall, then the units of k are $\sec^{-1}$ concentration$^{-(n-1)}$. Why?

Let us suppose that in our experiments on the reaction of A to yield B and C we find that the rate of reaction is directly proportional to [A] and not at all dependent on [B], [C], or any other species in the

system. Then we have $a = 1$, $b = 0$, $c = 0$, and $e = 0$, so the experimentally determined differential rate law is

$$\frac{d[B]}{dt} = \frac{d[C]}{dt} = -\frac{1}{2}\frac{d[A]}{dt} = k[A]. \qquad (13\text{–}3)$$

This reaction is first order overall, first order with respect to A, and zero order with respect to all other species.

It is very important to note here that the *rate law has no necessary relationship to the overall stoichiometry of the reaction.* Two expressions of this fact are the possible appearance of the concentration of species in the rate law which do not enter into the overall stoichiometry and the discovery in this case that the rate law is first order in A, whereas the stoichiometric equation requires that the overall reaction involve two molecules of A. "To add verisimilitude to an otherwise bald and unconvincing narrative," let us look at an actual reaction. The decomposition of N_2O_5 in carbon tetrachloride solution is described by the stoichiometric equation

$$2N_2O_5 = 2N_2O_4 + O_2$$

and the rate law for the reaction (followed by measuring the rate of oxygen evolution) is

$$\frac{d[O_2]}{dt} = k[N_2O_5].$$

The *thermodynamics* of a particular reaction are, of course, determined solely by the state of the reactants and products that enter into the stoichiometric equation for the reaction. The *kinetics* of a reaction, in particular the dependence of the rate on the concentrations of reactants and/or products, the rate law, are determined by the actual molecular interactions which occur. It is only rarely that one can deduce the dependence of the rate of a reaction on the concentrations by considering the equilibrium expression. The converse, however, is possible; under certain conditions* the combination of the overall rate-law expressions for the forward and reverse directions of a reaction gives the equilibrium-constant expression.

Experimental proof of this statement was obtained by Roebuck from an experimental study of the equilibrium reaction

$$H_3AsO_4 + 3I^- + 2H^+ \rightleftharpoons H_3AsO_3 + I_3^- + H_2O,$$

which has a forward-reaction rate law

$$\frac{d[I_3^-]}{dt} = k_f[H_3AsO_4][I^-][H^+]$$

---

* This statement is true under the conditions that the reaction is reversible and that the rate laws for the forward and reverse reactions are the same close to and far from equilibrium.

and a reverse-reaction rate law

$$- \frac{d[I_3^-]}{dt} = k_r \frac{[H_3AsO_3][I_3^-]}{[I^-]^2[H^+]}.$$

(The forward reaction is third order overall and the reverse reaction is minus first order.) At equilibrium, the rates of the forward and reverse reactions must be equal (since no net concentration changes are occurring), i.e.,

$$\frac{d[I_3^-]}{dt} = - \frac{d[I_3]}{dt}$$

or

$$k_f[H_3AsO_4]_e[I^-]_e[H^+]_e = k_r \frac{[H_3AsO_3]_e[I_3^-]_e}{[I^-]_e^2[H^+]_e}$$

where the subscript e reminds us that the concentrations are those of the system at equilibrium. Rearranging this last equation yields

$$\frac{k_f}{k_r} = \frac{[H_3AsO_3]_e[I_3^-]_e}{[H_3AsO_4]_e[I^-]_e[H^+]_e[I^-]_e^2[H^+]_e}$$

$$= \frac{[H_3AsO_3]_e[I_3^-]_e}{[H_3AsO_4]_e[I^-]_e^3[H^+]_e^2}.$$

The ratio of concentrations on the right-hand side of this expression is simply the equilibrium-constant expression for the reaction of interest. Hence

$$k_f/k_r = K. \qquad (13-4)$$

Suggestions for an experimental study of this reaction and, hence, the comparison of the equilibrium constant with the rate-constant ratio are given in the article by Britton and Hugus.

13-2 THEORETICAL KINETICS: MECHANISM AND RATE LAWS

The more or less detailed molecular description, the reaction *mechanism*, determines what rate law will be observed experimentally. What is the relationship between the mechanism and the rate law for a reaction? Conceptually, you might feel that the mechanism should be deduced from the experimentally observed rate law. In general, however, it is a much easier task to use our chemical intuition to guess at a mechanism for a reaction, then deduce the rate law that would be observed experimentally if this mechanism were correct, and compare the predicted and experimentally observed rate laws. If they are the same, we can say that this mechanism is consistent with the observed data. If they are different, we are forced to reject this mechanism and try another.

For the reaction represented by the stoichiometric equation (13-1) and the rate law (13-3), we could first choose the simplest possible mechanism, i.e., the re-

action of two A molecules yielding a B and a C molecule as products,

$$A + A \xrightarrow{k_5} B + C. \qquad (13-5)$$

A reaction written to represent the actual interaction that occurs between or among molecules is called an *elementary process*. Knowing (or postulating) the elementary process (or processes) we can immediately write the predicted rate law as

$$\frac{d[B]}{dt} = \frac{d[C]}{dt} = - \frac{1}{2} \frac{d[A]}{dt} = k_5[A]^2.$$

You might ask why it is that we can deduce this rate law from (13-5) but not from the formally similar (13-1). This is because (13-1) represents only the stoichiometry of the reaction, whereas we are postulating that the elementary process (13-5) really represents the molecular event that occurs when reaction takes place. We make this distinction even more vivid by discussing elementary processes in terms of their *molecularity*, the number of molecules that come together in a particular elementary process. From the molecularity of the elementary process, we can immediately predict the order of the rate law: a unimolecular process gives a first-order rate law, a bimolecular process gives a second-order rate law, a termolecular process gives a third-order rate law, etc. (The converse, that an observed second-order rate law, for example, implies an elementary process that is bimolecular, is not true.) Our analysis thus far has led to the prediction that the reaction of A to yield B and C will be second order in A. Experimentally, we found that the reaction is first order in A, Eq. (13-3), so this mechanism, Eq. (13-5), must be rejected.

Suppose then that two molecules of A interact to form a molecule X with which the A molecules are in very rapid equilibrium and that X can also dissociate into B and C,

$$A + A \underset{}{\overset{K_6}{\rightleftharpoons}} X, \qquad \text{Rapid equilibrium,} \qquad (13-6)$$

$$X \xrightarrow{k_7} B + C, \qquad \text{Slow.} \qquad (13-7)$$

Reaction (13-7) must be slow so that the equilibrium (13-6) is not disturbed by the occasional loss of an X molecule. We can write the rate of this reaction in terms of [B] as

$$d[B]/dt = k_7[X].$$

What is [X]? If the equilibrium is always maintained, we can write

$$K_6 = [X]/[A]^2, \qquad [X] = K_6[A]^2$$

so

$$d[B]/dt = k_7K_6[A]^2.$$

Again we predict that the rate of the reaction will be second order in A. (Does the product k_7K_6 have the correct units to be a second-order rate constant?) Thus we again have chosen a mechanism that incorrectly predicts the observed order of reaction.

Let us try again by assuming that an energetic A molecule (some highly energetic molecules will always be present if there is a Boltzmann distribution of energies in the sample, i.e., if thermal equilibrium is maintained in the reacting system) dissociates to yield B and Y and that Y very rapidly reacts with a molecule of A to form C,

$$A \xrightarrow{k_8} B + Y, \quad \text{Slow,} \tag{13-8}$$

$$Y + A \xrightarrow{k_9} C, \quad \text{Rapid.} \tag{13-9}$$

So long as A molecules remain in the system, reaction (13-9) will occur essentially every time reaction (13-8) occurs. Thus reaction (13-8) is called the *rate-determining step* in this sequence of elementary processes and we can write the rate as

$$\frac{d[C]}{dt} = \frac{d[B]}{dt} = k_8[A].$$

Thus we have finally found a mechanism that predicts a first-order rate law for the reaction and is therefore consistent with the experimentally determined rate law.

"But wait," you might be tempted to say, "It seems reasonable that $d[C]/dt = d[B]/dt$ from the arguments we gave, but also $d[C]/dt = k_9[Y][A]$ from (13-9). How can these two expressions be reconciled?" To answer this criticism we must invoke an assumption often made in problems like this called the *steady-state approximation*. In essence, the argument is that after the reaction has gone a very short way, the rate of formation of the intermediate Y, $(d[Y]/dt)_f = k_8[A]$, and the rate of disappearance of Y, $(-d[Y]/dt)_d = k_9[Y][A]$, will be equal. At this point the net rate of change of [Y] will be

$$\frac{d[Y]}{dt} = \left(\frac{d[Y]}{dt}\right)_f - \left(-\frac{d[Y]}{dt}\right)_d = 0,$$

since the rates of formation and disappearance are equal. We write this equation in terms of concentrations as

$$\frac{d[Y]}{dt} = 0 = k_8[A] - k_9[Y][A],$$

and we can solve the equation for [Y],

$$[Y] = \frac{k_8[A]}{k_9[A]} = \frac{k_8}{k_9}.$$

It should not be surprising to find [Y] equal to a constant, since that is part of the input data to the problem. The constant itself is interesting, however, for we can

use this to find that

$$\frac{d[C]}{dt} = k_9[Y][A] = k_9 \frac{k_8}{k_9}[A] = k_8[A] = \frac{d[B]}{dt},$$

as we also derived on somewhat more qualitative grounds above.

What would have happened if we had chosen the mechanism

$$A \xrightarrow{k_{10}} B + Z, \tag{13-10}$$

$$Z + B \xrightarrow{k_{11}} A, \tag{13-11}$$

$$Z + A \xrightarrow{k_{12}} C? \tag{13-12}$$

When confronted with a series of elementary processes like this we almost always have recourse to the steady-state approximation, $d[Z]/dt = 0$, which we write here as

$$\frac{d[Z]}{dt} = \left(\frac{d[Z]}{dt}\right)_f - \left(-\frac{d[Z]}{dt}\right)_d = 0$$

$$= k_{10}[A] - (k_{11}[Z][B] + k_{12}[Z][A]) = 0$$

and solve for [Z],

$$[Z] = \frac{k_{10}[A]}{k_{11}[B] + k_{12}[A]}.$$

The rate of formation of C is then

$$\frac{d[C]}{dt} = k_{12}[Z][A] = \frac{k_{12}k_{10}[A]^2}{k_{11}[B] + k_{12}[A]},$$

and the net rate of formation of B is

$$\frac{d[B]}{dt} = k_{10}[A] - k_{11}[Z][B]$$

$$= k_{10}[A] - \frac{k_{11}k_{10}[A][B]}{k_{11}[B] + k_{12}[A]}.$$

At this point we must ask: "Under what, if any, conditions is this mechanism compatible with the experimental rate law, (13-3)?" If $k_{12}[A] \gg k_{11}[B]$, the equations for the rates of formation of C and B become

$$\frac{d[C]}{dt} \approx \frac{k_{12}k_{10}[A]^2}{k_{12}[A]} = k_{10}[A]$$

and

$$\frac{d[B]}{dt} \approx k_{10}[A] - \frac{k_{11}k_{10}[A][B]}{k_{12}[A]} = k_{10}[A]\left(1 - \frac{k_{11}}{k_{12}}\frac{[B]}{[A]}\right)$$

$$\approx k_{10}[A],$$

since $k_{11}[B]/k_{12}[A] \ll 1$. These equations are identical in form with the experimental rate law, (13-3). What does this imply about reactions (13-10), (13-11), and (13-12)? It means that the steady-state approximation for this mechanism will only yield the rate law that is observed experimentally if reaction (13–12) is rapid compared with reaction (13–11). This can occur in two ways: 1) if [A] and [B] are comparable then k_{12} must be much larger than k_{11}, which is rather like saying that reaction (13–11) can be neglected [and then the mechanism is the same as (13–8) and (13–9)], or 2) if k_{11} and k_{12} are comparable, then [A] must be much larger than [B], i.e., the rate law

$$d[\text{C}]/dt = k_{10}[\text{A}]$$

will be valid only in the initial stages of the reaction before much B is formed.

This example illustrates at least two important points. First, a particular experimental rate law may be predicted correctly by a number of different mechanisms for the reaction in question. In this situation the rate law alone is powerless to aid you in narrowing the choice of mechanisms to a "correct" one. (You can never be certain that any one is "correct," since you may not even have thought of the actual mechanism.) Second, however, this predicament has in it the seeds of a method for selecting among the various possible mechanisms. For the mechanisms not to be simply redundant there must be some differences among them, and these differences will often be the key to the design of critical experiments to test the possible mechanisms. Let us, for example, look back on the two possible mechanisms for the reaction of A giving B and C. Mechanism I [reactions (13–8) and (13–9)] and mechanism II [reactions (13–10), (13–11), and (13–12)] are really different only in the case that $k_{11} \approx k_{12}$. Under these circumstances we see that $d[\text{C}]/dt$ and $d[\text{B}]/dt$ should become rather complex functions of [A] and [B] if there is appreciable B present in the system. How well have we tested this possibility? We said above, Section 13–1, that we had found that the rate of the reaction was not affected by the presence of B. Have we investigated a large enough concentration range of B? Have we carried the reaction far enough toward completion to discover whether the first-order dependence of the rate on A is followed throughout the reaction? If the answers to these questions are "yes," then we can with some confidence eliminate mechanism II, but if the answers are "no," then we had better carry out the experiments to find out whether the results are consistent with mechanism I or mechanism II.

This kind of variation of reaction conditions to yield more information about the rate law, hence allowing a more definite decision to be made about the mechanism of the reaction, is only one of many variations that are possible. Substituting one reactant for another, isotopic labeling experiments, temperature studies, ionic strength variations in solution reactions that are thought to involve ions, and many other variations suggested by the possible mechanisms to be tested have all and can all be used to produce information besides just the rate law (although these variations sometimes change the rate law) to decide among the alternative mechanisms.

13-3 INTEGRATED RATE LAWS

The usual data of chemical kinetics are the concentrations of one or more species in the reaction at various times during the reaction. Although it is possible to make the approximation

$$\frac{d[\text{C}]}{dt} \approx \frac{\Delta[\text{C}]}{\Delta t},$$

where C is the species whose concentration is being determined, this is not very satisfactory, particularly if the time intervals are long or if [C] is changing very rapidly. A better recourse is to integrate the differential-rate-law expression so that we can use the actual data in a completely valid way. In this section we shall integrate three differential rate laws that cover a substantial number of reactions. (For a more comprehensive coverage you might begin with King's book and proceed to Frost and Pearson.)

First let us integrate a zero-order differential-rate-law expression,

$$-\frac{d[\text{A}]}{dt} = k_0[\text{A}]^0,$$

where we are assuming that A is one of the reactants and that 1 mole of A disappears per mole of reaction. (How would this expression be changed if 2 moles of A disappeared per mole of reaction, i.e., if a reaction like (13–1) were occurring?) We separate the variables and solve the differential equation:

$$-\frac{d[\text{A}]}{dt} = k_0,$$

$$d[\text{A}] = -k_0 \, dt,$$

$$\int_{[\text{A}]_1}^{[\text{A}]_2} d[\text{A}] = [\text{A}]_2 - [\text{A}]_1$$

$$= -\int_{t_1}^{t_2} k_0 \, dt = -k_0(t_2 - t_1), \quad (13\text{–}13)$$

which is the *integrated form of the zero-order differential rate law*. If we start at $t = 0$ and let $[\text{A}]_0$ be the initial concentration of A and [A] be the concentration at time t, then we can write this as

$$[\text{A}] - [\text{A}]_0 = -k_0 t. \quad (13\text{–}14)$$

Now let us integrate a first-order differential rate law,

$$-\frac{d[A]}{dt} = k_1[A],$$

where the same assumptions hold as before. We proceed as before:

$$\frac{d[A]}{[A]} = -k_1\,dt,$$

$$\int_{[A]_1}^{[A]_2} \frac{d[A]}{[A]} = \ln[A]_2 - \ln[A]_1$$

$$= -\int_{t_1}^{t_2} k_1\,dt = -k_1(t_2 - t_1), \quad (13\text{-}15)$$

and where $[A]_0$ corresponds to $t_1 = 0$ and $[A]$ to t we get $\ln[A] - \ln[A]_0 = -k_1 t$ or

$$\ln\frac{[A]}{[A]_0} = -k_1 t. \quad (13\text{-}16)$$

Finally, let us integrate a second-order differential rate law:

$$-\frac{d[A]}{dt} = k_2[A]^2,$$

$$\frac{d[A]}{[A]^2} = -k_2\,dt,$$

$$\int_{[A]_1}^{[A]_2} \frac{d[A]}{[A]^2} = -\frac{1}{[A]_2} + \frac{1}{[A]_1}$$

$$= -\int_{t_1}^{t_2} k_2\,dt = -k_2(t_2 - t_1), \quad (13\text{-}17)$$

$$\frac{1}{[A]_0} - \frac{1}{[A]} = -k_2 t. \quad (13\text{-}18)$$

What do we learn by studying Eqs. (13–13) through (13–18)? We note first that each differential rate law gives rise to an integrated rate law of a different form from the others. We also see that each integrated rate law has the form of the equation for a straight line if the appropriate concentration variable is plotted as a function of time. This immediately gives us a powerful tool for investigating the order of a reaction. We take our data, coordinate concentration and time values, and plot the concentration vs. time, the logarithm of the concentration vs. time, and the reciprocal of the concentration vs. time. If the reaction is zero, first, or second order, one of these plots (corresponding to the actual order of the reaction) will be linear. This procedure not only gives us the order of the reaction, but the slope of the straight-line plot also tells us the rate constant, k, for the reaction.

13-4 THE EXPERIMENTAL DETERMINATION OF A RATE LAW

To make the preceding discussion more concrete, let us apply it to a specific example, the reaction studied in Experiment 30,

$$I_3^- + RC\!\!\underset{R_1}{\overset{O\quad H}{\underset{|}{\overset{\|\quad|}{C}}}}\!\!R_2 \rightarrow RC\!\!\underset{R_1}{\overset{O\quad I}{\underset{|}{\overset{\|\quad|}{C}}}}\!\!R_2 + H^+ + 2I^-,$$

where

$$RC\!\!\underset{R_1}{\overset{O\quad H}{\underset{|}{\overset{\|\quad|}{C}}}}\!\!R_2$$

represents cyclohexanone. From the rate law we obtain for this reaction we will attempt to infer a mechanism for the reaction. How do we determine the rate law?

Test-tube reactions (which you can carry out if you desire) indicate that the action of I_3^- (and I_2) on cyclohexanone in dilute aqueous solution is exceedingly slow but becomes much more rapid in the presence of acids. The accelerating effect is much the same with any of the strong mineral acids but is less pronounced in the case of weaker acids like acetic acid. Neutral salts of strong acids and bases (such as KCl or NaBr) in general do not exert any marked accelerating or hindering influence on the rate of the reaction. We infer from these results that it is the hydrogen ion coming from the acids that is producing the rate effects observed. The rate of the reaction run in diffused sunlight is not sensibly different from that of the reaction run in darkness, so we conclude that the reaction is not "catalyzed" by absorption of light. These preliminary tests *suggest* that the differential rate law might be expressed as

$$\frac{-d[I_3^-]}{dt} = k[H^+]^a[C_6H_{10}O]^b[I_3^-]^c. \quad (13\text{-}19)$$

We shall try to test this expression further.

To study the kinetics of any reaction, we must devise means to monitor the concentration changes of the reactants and/or products. The techniques used may be chemical or physical or both. Whenever possible, the physical changes accompanying the reaction are monitored, since this method usually means that the system is not disturbed while the reaction is in progress. In the system we shall study, I_3^- is the only colored species present in solution (see Experiment 30 for a qualification of this statement), so the rate can be very conveniently followed by monitoring the change in absorbance of the I_3^- as a function of time.

To simplify the interpretation of the experimental data, we shall employ the technique of "flooding." If the reaction is carried out so that the cyclohexanone and acid concentrations are very large relative to the iodine species concentration, then during the course of the reaction, while I_3^- is being depleted, it will be justifiable to assume (from the stoichiometry) that the cyclohexanone and acid concentrations remain approximately constant. Under these conditions the rate law can be simplified:

$$-\frac{d[I_3^-]}{dt} = k[H^+]_0^a[C_6H_{10}O]_0^b[I_3^-]^c \qquad (13\text{-}19a)$$

$$= k'[I_3^-]^c, \qquad (13\text{-}20)$$

where*

$$k' = k[H^+]_0^a[C_6H_{10}O]_0^b. \qquad (13\text{-}21)$$

$[H^+]_0$ and $[C_6H_{10}O]_0$ designate the initial concentrations of acid and cyclohexanone which will be "constant" throughout a given reaction and can therefore be lumped together with the rate constant.

Now we proceed to use the method discussed in Section 13–3 to obtain c. First we assume a number of possible values of c, say 0, 1, and 2, and then we integrate the differential rate law (13–20) for each of these choices. The results are:

$$[I_3^-]_0 - [I_3^-] = k't, \qquad \text{for } c = 0,$$

$$\ln[I_3^-]_0 - \ln[I_3^-] = k't, \quad \text{for } c = 1,$$

$$\frac{1}{[I_3^-]} - \frac{1}{[I_3^-]_0} = k't, \qquad \text{for } c = 2.$$

Thus, if we plot our experimental values of $[I_3^-]$ versus t and obtain a straight line, we can infer that $c = 0$. Similarly, if a plot of $\ln[I_3^-]$ versus t is a straight line, we infer that $c = 1$, and, likewise, $c = 2$ if $1/[I_3^-]$ versus t is linear. By plotting various functions of $[I_3^-]$, namely $[I_3^-]$, $\ln[I_3^-]$, and $1/[I_3^-]$, versus time, we can then obtain k' (that is, $k[H^+]_0^a[C_6H_{10}O]_0^b$) from the slope of the plot that is linear.

To determine a, we can run the reaction at a given initial concentration of cyclohexanone and iodine for two or three initial concentrations of H^+. These runs will provide different values of k', namely

$$k'_i = k[H^+]_{0i}^a[C_6H_{10}O]_0^b,$$

where the subscript i denotes the various values of $[H^+]_0$. To obtain a we take the logarithm of both sides of this expression,

$$\log k'_i = a \log[H^+]_{0i} + \log(k[C_6H_{10}O]_0^b),$$

and note that a plot of $\log k'_i$ versus $\log[H^+]_{0i}$ should be a straight line of slope a and intercept

$$\log(k[C_6H_{10}O]_0^b).$$

A similar method of procedure, with the concentration of hydrogen ion kept constant and the concentration of cyclohexanone varied, may be used to obtain b.

We think now that we have varied all the relevant parameters, we have "completed" the determination of the differential rate law. If further experiments were to show that the concentration of some other species in the solution affects the rate, we would then have to test it as we have tested $[I_3^-]$, $[H^+]$, and $[C_6H_{10}O]$ to correct the value we determined earlier.

13-5 THE TEMPERATURE DEPENDENCE OF REACTION RATES

Completely empirical observations led Arrhenius to propose that the dependence of reaction-rate constants on temperature should be expressed as†

$$k = Ae^{-\Delta_a E/RT}. \qquad (13\text{-}22)$$

(Since k is not strictly a constant but varies with T as shown here, it is sometimes called the *reaction-rate coefficient*.) The *frequency factor*, A, is a crude measure of the entropy effect on the reaction. If two molecules, for example, have to come together in a certain orientation with respect to each other for reaction to occur, then the reaction will be less likely to occur for any given random collision because of this strict *steric* requirement. Such a reaction will have a low frequency factor, reflecting the low probability that in a given collision the molecules will have the correct orientation. The *activation energy*, ΔE_a, for the reaction is the amount of energy the reactants must possess in excess of their ground-state energy before they can react.‡ The energy enters into the rate constant in an exponential fashion as a result of the Boltzmann distribution of energies (an exponential distribution) in the reaction system. The higher the temperature, the greater the number of molecules that will possess energy ΔE_a or higher above the ground state of the reactants, as you can see by examining Boltzmann distribution curves.

The activation energy and frequency factor for a reaction can be obtained by measuring the rate constant

---

* This is a *pseudo* "cth" *order reaction* since the actual reaction is probably not "cth" order but other concentration dependencies are washed out by the "flooding" technique.

† A clue to the temperature dependence was also given by Eq. (13–4), which was known to Arrhenius. Can you show how Eq. (13–22) is compatible with (13–4) and the temperature dependence of equilibrium constants?

‡ Although we shall use ΔE_a rather than ΔH_a in this discussion, it would be just as valid to discuss activation enthalpies as activation energies.

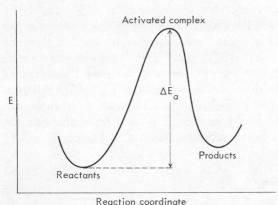

Fig. 13–1

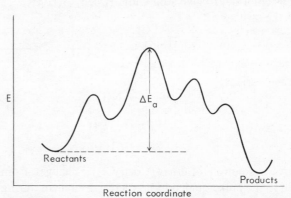

Fig. 13–2

at different temperatures and utilizing the following formulation of the Arrhenius equation:

$$\log k = -\frac{\Delta E_a}{2.3R}\frac{1}{T} + \log A. \qquad (13\text{–}23)$$

A plot of $\log k$ versus $1/T$ should yield a straight line with a slope $-\Delta E_a/(2.3R)$ and an intercept, at $1/T = 0$, of $\log A$.

A *schematic* representation of the energetics of a reaction is provided by a *reaction coordinate diagram* (Fig. 13–1). This diagram indicates the relative energies of the system as it passes from reactants to products. (Although it would be more appropriate to plot relative free energies, it is conventional to show only the energy and to disregard the entropy term in these diagrams.)

The configuration of the reactants at the top of the barrier is called the *activated complex*. (The atoms and molecules that enter into the activated complex are those that appear in the rate law for the reaction.) Such a diagram is valid only for an elementary process in a reaction mechanism. The change from reactants to products in a complex system has a reaction-coordinate diagram that is composed of a number of such curves (Fig. 13–2).

Sometimes the intermediate products can be isolated and shown to participate in the reaction, but more often than not they have only transient existence and must be inferred from other evidence, including the rate law. The observed activation energy will be the energy difference between the reactants and the highest point on the reaction-coordinate diagram.

EXPERIMENT 28.   *A Kinetic Study of a Reaction of trans-dichloro-bis-ethylenediamine cobalt(III) chloride*

Introduction

In this study you will measure the rate of a reaction at different temperatures to determine how such a change in reaction conditions affects the reaction. The result typifies what would happen with most chemical reactions; we have picked this reaction because it is very convenient to follow visually.

One of the reactants in the reaction you will study is *trans*-dichloro-bis-ethylenediamine cobalt(III) chloride.* The directions for synthesizing this compound and analyzing it are presented in Experiments 3 and 4. The ion $(Coen_2Cl_2)^+$ (en is used to represent $H_2NCH_2CH_2NH_2$, ethylenediamine) is green and has

the structure

where the nitrogens and cobalt all lie in a plane with the two chlorine-cobalt bonds extending above and below this plane. This compound is called *trans* because the chlorines are opposite to each other. When dissolved in water, $(Coen_2Cl_2)^+$ undergoes a reaction in which water replaces one of the chlorines (which goes off into the solu-

---

* Thanks are due to Professor C. H. Langford, Amherst College, for suggesting the use of this compound and for discussing some of its chemistry.

tion as chloride) to give a pink ion, $(Coen_2Cl(H_2O))^{++}$, with the structure.*

As a solution of *trans*-$(Coen_2Cl_2)^+$ changes from green to the pink aquated form, there is a moment during which it appears gray. You should probably take the time to become familiar with the appearance of these solutions by dissolving a small amount of $(Coen_2Cl_2)Cl$ in water and heating aliquots of this solution in a flame or hot-water bath. You will also want to convince yourself that the gray color can be produced by a mixture of the green and pink complexes by mixing the green and pink solutions while they are cold (so the reaction will be slow enough not to interfere with the observations).

The fact that the solution turns gray for a moment part way through the reaction provides a simple method for determining the rate of the reaction or at least of comparing rates under different conditions. To compare the rate of the reaction at various temperatures, for example, we simply compare the lengths of time that it takes for the solution to turn gray at each temperature. In such a series of experiments we must, of course, hold all other relevant reaction conditions constant.

Before doing the experiments, it is worthwhile to examine how the concentration of $(Coen_2Cl_2)^+$ might enter into the rate law for the reaction and hence how the rate will depend on this concentration. This information is necessary to determine how carefully the solutions must be made up to obtain data of the desired accuracy. Although many other choices are possible, let us assume that the rate law for the reaction may be written as

$$\frac{-d[(Coen_2Cl_2)^+]}{dt} = k_1'[(Coen_2Cl_2)^+][A]^a[B]^b \ldots,$$

or

$$\frac{-d[(Coen_2Cl_2)^+]}{dt} = k_2'[(Coen_2Cl_2)^+]^2[A]^a[B]^b \ldots,$$

---

* If a solution of *trans*-$(Coen_2Cl_2)Cl$ is evaporated on a steam bath, reddish-purple crystals will remain when the water is gone. This is *cis*-$(Coen_2Cl_2)Cl$ (formed as the concentration of Cl^- gets high enough to "reverse" the aquation reaction). Make models of the *trans* and *cis* complexes. Can you detect a molecular property of the *cis* isomer that cannot occur in the *trans* isomer?

that is, as either first or second order in $[(Coen_2Cl_2)^+]$. If we hold the concentrations of all other species in the solution constant from one run to another then the factors $[A]^a$, $[B]^b$, ..., will be constant and can be lumped into the rate constants to make the equations easier to write. From this point on $k_1 = k_1'[A]^a[B]^b_b \ldots$ and $k_2 = k_2' [A]^a[B]^b \ldots$ Integration of these differential rate laws (one a pseudo first-order and the other a pseudo second-order rate law) gives

$$\ln \frac{[(Coen_2Cl_2)^+]}{[(Coen_2Cl_2)^+]_0} = -k_1 t, \qquad (13\text{--}24)$$

$$\frac{1}{[(Coen_2Cl_2)^+]_0} - \frac{1}{[(Coen_2Cl_2)^+]} = -k_2 t. \qquad (13\text{--}25)$$

(See Eqs. (13–16) and (13–18).)

Now the observation we make is the time it takes a given solution to turn gray, t_g; we must ask how this time will depend on $[(Coen_2Cl_2)^+]_0$, the initial concentration of the green complex, the other observable parameter of our system. The solution is gray only when the ratio $[(Coen_2Cl_2)^+]/[(Coen_2Cl_2)^+]_0$ has a particular value, which we shall call R_g. Now we shall substitute R_g and t_g into Eqs. (13–24) and (13–25). Equation (13–24) becomes, after a simple rearrangement,

$$t_g = -\ln R_g / k_1, \qquad (13\text{--}26)$$

in which there is no dependence of t_g on $[(Coen_2Cl_2)^+]_0$.† Thus if Eq. (13–24) is valid, it will not be necessary to make up all the solutions for the experiments in such a way that they have the same initial concentrations; indeed, it is not even necessary to know what the initial concentrations are.

Equation (13–25) requires a bit more manipulation; first we multiply through by $[(Coen_2Cl_2)^+]_0$,

$$1 - \frac{[(Coen_2Cl_2)^+]_0}{[(Coen_2Cl_2)^+]} = -k_2 t[(Coen_2Cl_2)^+]_0,$$

and then substitute R_g and rearrange to get the equation for t_g,

$$t_g = -\frac{1 - 1/R_g}{k_2[(Coen_2Cl_2)^+]_0} = \frac{1 - R_g}{R_g k_2[(Coen_2Cl_2)^+]_0}. \qquad (13\text{--}27)$$

In this case, the time it takes for the solution to turn gray, t_g, is inversely proportional to the initial concentration of the green complex, $[(Coen_2Cl_2)^+]_0$. Thus if Eq. (13–25) is valid, it will be necessary always to use

---

† This is a general result for reactions that are first order in a particular species; the time required for a certain fraction of this reaction to occur is independent of the concentration of this species.

the same $[(Coen_2Cl_2)^+]_0$ or, at least, to know what this concentration is in each run.

Procedure

This experiment, requiring only very simple manipulations, demands very careful observations. Continue the observations suggested in the next paragraph until you are sure you can reliably distinguish the gray reference color. The color is most readily recognized if the initial concentration of reactant, cobalt complex, is within the range 0.03 to 0.04 M, but acceptable observations are possible in the wider range of 0.025 to 0.05 M. Since the molecular weight of the complex is 285 (check this), the addition of 0.14 to 0.28 gm to 20 ml of water will produce solutions having concentrations in this wider range. (If you find that accurate concentration measurements are unnecessary, you will save time by keeping before you a weighed 0.20 gm sample so you can use a simple visual estimate of the amount of complex needed.)

Weigh out about 1.0 gm of $(Coen_2Cl_2)Cl$ and dissolve the solid in about 80 ml of ice-cold distilled water in a small flask, swirl, and immerse the flask in an ice bath at once. Transfer about half the solution to another small flask and heat this portion to 75 to 85°C. (At this temperature the aquation reaction is rapid and essentially quantitative in a few moments.) Cool the pink solution to room temperature and charge a buret with this solution. Carefully measure (pipet or small graduate) 10 ml of the green solution into a clean test tube and, with this test tube in a cold-water bath (near 0°C), add pink solution from the buret until the mixture assumes a neutral gray color when viewed against a white background. (In these initial trials you may find it helpful to record the buret readings corresponding to the last distinct green color, to the appearance of the most neutral gray, and to the first detectable trace of pink.) Add another 5 ml of the green solution to the test tube and, by adding pink solution from the buret, again produce a mixture showing the gray reference color. Do the total-volume green-to-pink ratios agree in the two mixtures you have observed as gray? Discard the solution and repeat the preparation of gray mixtures until you can, within reasonable limits, reproduce the green-to-pink ratio (*without* looking at the buret as you make up the mixtures).* Make one last run in which you mix 10 ml of green solution with 10 ml of cold water and then add pink solution from the buret until the gray reference color is obtained. If our previous arguments and assumptions are correct, you should find the green-to-pink volume ratio unchanged, implying that the gray color

*You may wish to keep your last mixture as a reference standard for the kinetic runs; if so, be sure to keep the test tube in an ice bath until it is needed.

is characteristic of the *ratio*, R_g, of concentrations and quite independent of their individual magnitudes. Since the pink and green solutions are identical in molar concentration, the concentration ratio is simply equal to the volume ratio, i.e.,

$$R_g = \frac{\text{volume green solution used}}{\text{volume pink} \atop \text{solution used} + \text{volume green} \atop \text{solution used}}.$$

Into four dry identical test tubes place the quantities of reactant, cobalt complex, that will be sufficient to produce 20 ml of each of four solutions with molarities about 0.025, 0.033, 0.042, and 0.050. To each of the test tubes add 20 ml of ice-cold distilled water and place all the tubes in an ice bath at once. In an 800-ml beaker prepare a water bath at 55 to 60°C. Transfer all the test tubes simultaneously from the ice bath to the warm water bath. Starting at the same temperature, and in the same environment, these similar tubes should warm up at exactly the same rate. Observe the tubes against a white background. The results of this test should enable you to decide whether Eq. (13–24) or (13–25) is valid for this reaction. (Of course, neither might be valid, but you can go through the same sort of analysis we did above for other orders such as zero, three-halves, etc., and predict how t_g will vary with $[(Coen_2Cl_2)^+]_0$ for these cases and compare them with the experimental observations.) The interpretation of these results is an important step in the experiment, since, if the reaction is first order in $(Coen_2Cl_2)^+$, then you will be able to save a great deal of time that you would otherwise have to spend weighing out samples.

The temperature dependence of this reaction is determined as follows. Hold your water bath steady at some temperature in the range 50 to 75°C, and put into it a test tube containing 20 ml of distilled water. From this point on do not remove the test tube from the bath and maintain the bath temperature constant to at least ±1°C. On a dry spatula, take up enough of the solid reactant to produce a concentration within the range of acceptability, transfer the sample to the test tube, and stir the solution violently with the spatula or a stirring rod for two to three seconds. Start timing the reaction (use a stopwatch or watch with a sweep second hand) as the crystals drop into the water; the solution process is completed within a few seconds. Watch the solution carefully and record the time at which it shows the gray reference color. (In addition to recording the time at which a solution appears gray, it is also wise to record the last time the solution is definitely green and the first time it is definitely pink, thus giving a range of uncertainty in the gray time. The range of uncertainty in the temperature should also be estimated for each experiment.) As always, look at a white background for accuracy and minimize eye fatigue by occasionally looking away for a moment and then refocusing on the solution. (Using an already prepared reference tube may improve the accuracy of your observation, especially at the lower temperatures where the gray color is only gradually developed.)

Take data at six or more temperatures in the easily-studied temperature range 50 to 75°C. Collect the data in tabular form to make it easier to see what you have left to do. Making a rough plot of the data as they are taken will help in deciding where more data are necessary.

Calculations

When you have collected sufficient data you should try to find an equation that will fit your results, i.e., will give the temperature dependence of the rate of the reaction. The function that provides a description of the temperature dependence of the rate of a reaction is the rate constant (see Section 13–5). Let us then look again at Eqs. (13–26) and (13–27) to see what they tell us about the rate constant. Note that you can rewrite either equation in the form

$$k = \frac{1}{t_g} Y,$$

where Y is some function of R_g and $[(Coen_2Cl_2)^+]_0$. For example, in Eqs. (13–26) and (13–27), respectively,

$$Y_1 = -\ln R_g$$
$$Y_2 = \frac{1 - R_g}{R_g[(Coen_2Cl_2)^+]_0}.$$

(What is Y for a zero-order reaction?) If $[(Coen_2Cl_2)^+]_0$ is constant in your experiments, then Y will be constant also.* Hence $1/t_g$ will be directly proportional to the rate constant. Plot an appropriate function of $1/t_g$ versus an appropriate function of temperature (where "appropriate" in this case means that you should plot functions which are predicted to give a linear plot) to obtain the activation energy, ΔE_a.

Average your results to obtain a value for the ratio R_g. What, then, is the Arrhenius frequency factor for this reaction? What is the range of uncertainty of ΔE_a and A?

What is the half-life of each of your reaction runs, i.e., how long did it take in each case for exactly one-half of the initial amount of reactant to react?

---

* Naturally, Y_1 is constant whether or not $[(Coen_2Cl_2)^+]_0$ is constant, since this factor does not enter into Y_1. If the reaction is second order and $[(Coen_2Cl_2)^+]_0$ was not the same in all your experiments, you can obtain the ratio of the various Y_2 values and then correct them all to a standard value.

Further Experimental Problems

To further test the temperature dependence of this reaction, you could carry out reactions at temperatures nearer to room temperature. These reactions will take a considerable length of time to go to the gray point. These slower reactions may conveniently be followed spectrophotometrically rather than by eye, but you must take care to remember that both the reactant and product absorb throughout the visible region of the spectrum so that you must make corrections for build-up of product or decay of reactant to turn absorbance readings into concentrations. (The room-temperature reaction may take longer than three hours to go to the gray point, so you may have to take it home with you to observe this point.)

A "Proof." More evidence that a reacting solution of $(Coen_2Cl_2)^+$ is always a mixture of only the green reactant and pink product might be obtained as follows. First, record absorption spectra (see Appendix E) of the green and pink solutions. Since the green solution changes even at room temperature, it is imperative to do this with a freshly made solution and it is best to use a recording spectrophotometer, if one is available. Next record the absorption spectrum of a mixture of the green and pink solutions. Now you will find, if our assumptions are correct and if you know the total concentration of cobalt species in each of the three solutions, that the spectrum of any synthetic mixture or partially completed reaction mixture can be synthesized from the individual spectra by assuming that a certain fraction of the total cobalt is in the green form and the rest in the pink form. The concentration of free chloride ions in a solution containing the green or pink complex or a mixture can be determined by cooling them in an ice bath to slow the reaction rate and then titrating the mixture with standard silver solution (see Chapters 4 and 10). This gives an independent measure of the extent of the reaction (or the proportion of green to pink complex in a synthetic mixture), which can be checked against that obtained from the spectrum of the mixture.

We have proposed, without evidence (perhaps you would like to think of a way to get some), that the pink color is due to the monoaquo complex. Certainly, if one of the chlorines can be replaced by water, it seems reasonable that the other might also, and this could interfere with the reaction we think we are studying. Perhaps you could use the silver titration technique to attempt to find out whether the second chlorine is displaced and, if so, how rapidly, compared with the first displacement.

Base Catalysis. It is very easy to show that base catalyzes the reaction we studied above; simply add some basic solution to freshly made solution of *trans*-$(Coen_2Cl_2)^+$ in a test tube. It is interesting, however, to inquire whether this is a specific effect of added hydroxyl ion or whether any Brönsted base will do. This latter case is called *general base catalysis.** A simple way to test these two alternatives is to use a buffer solution to control the basicity of the solution. The concentration of hydroxyl ion will be constant in such a solution as long as the ratio of the acidic to the basic form of the buffer species is constant. We can, however, vary the actual concentration of the basic form of the buffer without changing this ratio, if at the same time we vary the concentration of the acidic form. Develop from these general ideas an experiment to determine whether the aquation reaction shows general or specific base catalysis. Perhaps a phosphate buffer system would be suitable for this experiment.

Other Solvents. The reaction we have studied here can be profoundly changed by a change in solvent. This should be natural, since the reaction is a sort of solvolysis where a solvent molecule displaces a species already in the complex. You might, for example, try the reaction in methanol. It is interesting in this case to make some of the *cis*-$(Coen_2Cl_2)Cl$ and see what it does when dissolved in water and in methanol. (See the article by Brice.)

Isotopic Exchange. You can use your $(Coen_2Cl_2)Cl$ as the starting material to synthesize $(Coen_2CO_3)^+$ and, hence, to study the exchange reaction

$$(Coen_2CO_3)^+ + {}^{14}CO_3{}^= \rightleftharpoons (Coen_2{}^{14}CO_3)^+ + CO_3{}^=.$$

Consult the article by Barton and Winter for more details and Experiment 32 for a discussion of isotopic exchange reactions.

EXPERIMENT 29.   *Kinetics of Decomposition of Ethyl Diazoacetate*

Introduction

The reaction that you will study is the hydrolysis of the liquid ethyl diazoacetate (also often called diazoacetic ester), represented by the stoichiometric equation,

$$N{=}N{=}CHC{-}OCH_2CH_3 + HOH =$$
$$\overset{O}{\overset{\|}{}}$$

$$N_2(g) + HOCH_2C{-}OCH_2CH_3. \qquad (13{-}28)$$

After the rate law for this reaction has been established you will draw some conclusions about the rate expression for the reverse reaction by combining the rate-law expression for the forward reaction with the equilibrium-constant expression. (See Section 13–1.)

The choice of ethyl diazoacetate as a reactant in this study has not been made to confuse you inordinately, but rather to introduce you to a new technique. Since the reaction evolves nitrogen gas, the extent of the reaction can be continuously monitored by collecting the nitrogen in a gas buret. The amount of nitrogen collected at any time compared to the amount present when the reaction is complete is a measure of the extent of the reaction.

Although the reaction's proceeding as written is thermodynamically favored by the continuous loss of one of the products, the nitrogen gas, from the solution, the reaction is nevertheless quite slow if the ethyl diazoacetate is simply dissolved in water. If acid is added to

the mixture, the reaction proceeds quickly. You might do a few simple test-tube experiments to show this for yourself. If you write the equilibrium-constant expression for the reaction represented by Eq. (13–28), you will confirm that the equilibrium expression reveals nothing about the role of the acid in the reaction, which is why the acid is called a catalyst.

On the basis of these remarks, let us conjecture about the form the differential-rate-law expression for the forward reaction might take. We can write a general expression for the disappearance of the ester, ethyl diazoacetate, as

$$-d[ester]/dt = k'[ester]^m[HOH]^n[H^+]^p \cdots \qquad (13{-}29)$$

It is difficult to see from a molecular viewpoint how m could be zero or greater than one (although such assumptions must be experimentally tested before they can be accepted) so for the sake of concreteness, let us assume that $m = 1$, i.e., that the reaction is first order in ester. If water, the solvent, is present in large excess, then its concentration will remain essentially constant throughout the reaction; and if H^+ serves simply as a catalyst, then its concentration is not altered during a run. We can combine these constant quantities with k' to yield a new rate constant k,

$$k = k'[HOH]^n[H^+]^p.$$

The rate law then becomes

$$-d[ester]/dt = k[ester] \qquad (13{-}30)$$

for a given concentration of solvent and hydrogen ion. [Equation (13–30) is an example of pseudo first-order

---

* There is, of course, a corresponding definition of specific, as opposed to general, acid catalysis.

kinetics.] Let the number of moles of ester be A at time $t = 0$ and let x be the number of moles of nitrogen produced in time t; then [ester] $= (A - x)$ at time t and (13–30) becomes

$$-d(A - x)/dt = dx/dt = k(A - x),$$

which can be rearranged to

$$dx/(A - x) = kt. \qquad (13\text{--}31)$$

Now let us relate Eq. (13–31) to the experimentally measurable variable, the volume of nitrogen gas. Assuming that nitrogen acts as an ideal gas, we can write

$$x = PV/RT, \qquad (13\text{--}32)$$

$$dx = (P/RT)dV. \qquad (13\text{--}33)$$

When all the ester has reacted, we will have obtained a volume of gas we shall call V_∞. This volume represents the total number of moles of gas available from the sample, and, from the stoichiometry of the reaction,

$$A = PV_\infty/RT. \qquad (13\text{--}34)$$

When (13–32), (13–33), and (13–34) are substituted into (13–31) we obtain

$$dV/(V_\infty - V) = kt, \qquad (13\text{--}35)$$

which on integration yields

$$\ln (V_\infty - V) = -kt + \text{Const.} \qquad (13\text{--}36)$$

(The constant of integration may be evaluated from the condition $V = 0$ at $t = 0$. What is the constant?) The volume of gas V_∞ cannot be simply calculated from the amount of "ester" with which you begin because the ester as obtained is not pure; V_∞ must, therefore, be determined by actually allowing the reaction to go to completion. A plot of $\ln (V_\infty - V)$ versus t should be a straight line with a slope $-k$, the rate constant for the reaction, if the reaction is first order in ester. Indeed, if the plot is linear, it verifies our original assumption that the reaction is first order in ester. On the other hand, curvature of the plot will indicate that the reaction cannot be described by first-order kinetics, in which case further analysis of the problem will be required. If the reaction is second order in ester, what function of V_∞ and V will you have to plot versus t to obtain a straight line?

The Guggenheim Method

Sometimes it is inconvenient or impossible to obtain a value corresponding to V_∞ for a reaction. (Although the Guggenheim method is applicable to any first-order reaction, not just those that evolve gases, we shall

develop it for our particular case; you can easily generalize the argument for other cases.) In these cases a method devised by Guggenheim can often be employed to advantage for first-order reactions. The method requires that the time intervals between readings of the variable be constant; let us call this interval Δt. Now take exponentials of both sides of Eq. (13–36), after evaluating the constant, to get

$$V_\infty - V = V_\infty e^{-kt}. \qquad (13\text{--}37)$$

If we take two successive readings at times t and $t + \Delta t$, we can write

$$V_\infty - V_t = V_\infty e^{-kt}$$
$$V_\infty - V_{t+\Delta t} = V_\infty e^{-k(t+\Delta t)}.$$

Subtracting the second equation from the first yields

$$V_{t+\Delta t} - V_t = \Delta V = V_\infty(e^{-kt} - e^{-k(t+\Delta t)})$$
$$= V_\infty e^{-kt}(1 - e^{-k\Delta t}).$$

Now if we take logarithms of both sides of this equation, we obtain

$$\ln (\Delta V) = -kt + \ln V_\infty(1 - e^{-k\Delta t}). \qquad (13\text{--}38)$$

Note that the final term in (13–38) is a constant for any run, if Δt is a constant. Thus k can be obtained from a plot of $\ln (\Delta V)$, i.e., the logarithms of successive increments in volume, versus t, the initial times for each volume increment, without our having actually to measure V_∞. A linear plot in this case is an indication that the reaction is first order, as we assumed to obtain Eq. (13–30).

Although it is not difficult to obtain V_∞ in this reaction, you might find it interesting to try the Guggenheim method as a second independent test of the first-order assumption we have made. If the reaction is first order, you even have another method of calculating k from the intercept of the $\ln (\Delta V)$-versus-t plot, Δt, and the value you determine for V_∞.

Procedure

You should work with a partner for this experiment. *Caution.* Although ethyl diazoacetate is a particularly convenient substance for rate studies, it is a member of a class of compounds, diazo-compounds, which have bad reputations for unpredictable explosive decomposition as well as high toxicity. You must therefore handle the diazoacetic ester with great care, being particularly careful to avoid contact with flames, concentrated acids, and strong oxidizing agents. All glassware used should be scrupulously clean. Your instructor will give you only a small amount, about 0.5 gm, of the ester at a time to minimize any hazard.

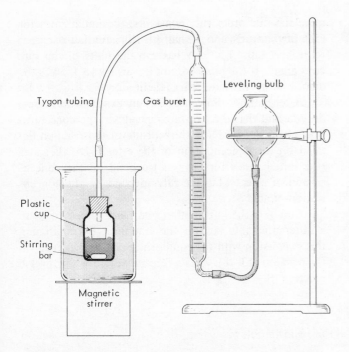

Fig. 13–3. Apparatus for following the rate of decomposition of ethyl diazoacetate.

The apparatus you should use is shown in Fig. 13–3. With the exception of the beaker for the water bath, the apparatus will be supplied by your instructor. For each run the proper amounts of water and 0.010 M HNO$_3$ are pipetted into the small reaction bottle. The proper portion of ester is put into the previously weighed polyethylene cap by drops and weighed again on the analytical balance. The dropper and the polyethylene cap must be completely dry before you use them, acetone may be used to hasten the drying if necessary. Firmly clamp the reaction bottle at a suitable height on a ringstand. With everything in readiness, grasp the polyethylene cap containing the ester with tweezers and carefully lower it into the reaction bottle without spilling any ester. The cap and its contents will float.* Place the stopper firmly in the reaction bottle and level the water in the buret again by adjusting the height of the leveling bulb. Be certain the ester does not come into contact with the acid solution until you are ready to begin the run. Adjust the temperature of the water bath to 25°C. Have some hot water and some ice handy for

* An alternative method is to place the ester and a small Teflon or glass-covered magnet in a small glass or plastic vial and "attach" these to the inside wall of the reaction bottle by using a second small magnet on the outside of the reaction bottle. When you are ready to start the reaction, simply turn the vial over by manipulating the external magnet. The inner magnet in this case can even be the stirring bar.

any temperature adjustments you find necessary during the run. Place the water bath on the stirrer, move this setup under the reaction bottle, carefully lower the reaction bottle into the water bath, and support it by placing a clamp around the glass tubing above the stopper.

Note how sensitive the level of water in the buret is to the position of the leveling bulb. It will be necessary to level carefully for each volume reading. Reading the leveled gas volume in the buret during the course of the reaction will be a problem. Since the gas is being continuously evolved, you have no time for trial-and-error adjustments. Instead, you should purposely lower the leveling bulb stepwise to preselected readings and then record the time at which the water level passes each of these points. For the reactions with high initial concentrations of reactants, these volume intervals should be about 2 ml; for the reactions with lower initial concentrations, the interval should be reduced to about 1 ml.† All runs should be continued until there are no further significant changes in volume.

Before beginning your reaction, test the system for leaks by raising and lowering the leveling bulb two or three times (to water-saturate the air left in the apparatus). Support the leveling bulb at a low position and record the buret water level for five minutes. If the system is leak-free and at temperature equilibrium, changes in the water level will correspond to volumes of less than 0.01 ml.

With acid and ester in the flask, the Tygon tubing connected, and the system checked for leaks, record the initial volume reading, lower the leveling bulb to the first preselected volume, start the magnetic stirrer, and begin recording time as the ester is upset into the solution. Record the time when the water levels are equal at the preselected volume reading and reset the leveling bulb; continue in this manner until the reaction is complete. Maintain the water bath at 25°C, throughout the run. You will note that the rather insoluble ester does not dissolve immediately but requires continued stirring, which is also necessary throughout the reaction to minimize supersaturation of the solution with nitrogen gas. Clean out and dry the reaction bottle, polyethylene cap, and stirrer between runs.

When measuring the rates of reactions, you must have the experiments carefully planned with tables and graphs prepared for data before beginning the reactions. Remember, once the reaction starts, it continues in-

† If you wish to test the Guggenheim method also, you will have to change this procedure and continuously move the leveling bulb to keep the water levels equal, reading the buret quickly at equal time intervals. Time intervals of 30 to 60 seconds are convenient.

exorably on its course. As a guide to planning your procedure you will find that acid concentrations in the range 0.0025 M to 0.005 M and amounts of ester in the range 0.09 gm (about 4 drops) to 0.20 gm (about 8 drops) give conveniently measurable rates. The total volume of the acid and water in each run should be the same (20 ml is good). Plan to do enough experiments to enable you to answer the questions posed below. (In fact, if you plan correctly, only three runs, provided they are all good ones, are required, although you might like to make more as confirmatory evidence for your answers.)

Calculations

On the same graph, plot log $(V_\infty - V)$ versus time in minutes for each run. Are the plots linear? If so, deter-

mine the first-order rate constants, the initial rates for each of your runs, and the half-life (time for half-reaction) for each of the runs. What are the units of the rate constants? If the plots are not linear, try to analyze the data in terms of some other reaction order.

After making allowances for any experimental error, do you find that the half-life depends on the concentration of the acid? Does the half-life of the reaction depend on the concentration of the ester? Do the rates (the initial rates, for example) depend on the concentration of ester? Do the rates depend on the concentration of acid?

Combine the information you have gained to write a differential rate law for the reaction. By combining this expression with the equilibrium-constant expression for reaction (13–28), write a rate equation for the reverse reaction.

Two possible mechanisms which may fit the rate data are shown below.

Mechanism I

$$N{=}N{=}CHC\overset{\overset{\textstyle O}{\|}}{}{-}OC_2H_5 + H^+ \rightarrow [N{=}N{-}\overset{\overset{\textstyle H}{|}}{C}H\overset{\overset{\textstyle O}{\|}}{C}{-}OC_2H_5]^+,$$

$$[N{=}N{-}\overset{\overset{\textstyle H}{|}}{C}H\overset{\overset{\textstyle O}{\|}}{C}{-}OC_2H_5]^+ \rightarrow N_2 + {}^+CH_2\overset{\overset{\textstyle O}{\|}}{C}{-}OC_2H_5,$$

$\Big\}$ Slow;

$$HOH + {}^+CH_2\overset{\overset{\textstyle O}{\|}}{C}{-}OC_2H_5 \rightarrow [H\overset{\overset{\textstyle H}{|}}{O}CH_2\overset{\overset{\textstyle O}{\|}}{C}{-}OC_2H_5]^+,$$

$$[H\overset{\overset{\textstyle H}{|}}{O}CH_2\overset{\overset{\textstyle O}{\|}}{C}{-}OC_2H_5]^+ \rightarrow HOCH_2\overset{\overset{\textstyle O}{\|}}{C}{-}OC_2H_5 + H^+,$$

$\Big\}$ Rapid.

Mechanism II

$$N{=}N{=}CHC\overset{\overset{\textstyle O}{\|}}{}{-}OC_2H_5 + H^+ \rightleftharpoons [N{=}N{-}\overset{\overset{\textstyle H}{|}}{C}H\overset{\overset{\textstyle O}{\|}}{C}{-}OC_2H_5]^+,$$

$\Big\}$ Rapid equilibrium;

$$[N{=}N{-}\overset{\overset{\textstyle H}{|}}{C}H\overset{\overset{\textstyle O}{\|}}{C}{-}OC_2H_5]^+ + HOH \rightarrow [N{=}N\cdots\overset{\overset{\textstyle H}{|}}{C}H\overset{\overset{\textstyle O}{\|}}{C}{-}OC_2H_5]^+,$$
$$H\cdots\overset{\cdot\cdot}{O}H$$

$$[N{=}N\cdots\overset{\overset{\textstyle H}{|}}{C}H\overset{\overset{\textstyle O}{\|}}{C}{-}OC_2H_5]^+ \rightarrow N_2 + HOCH_2\overset{\overset{\textstyle O}{\|}}{C}{-}OC_2H_5 + H^+$$
$$H\cdots\overset{\cdot\cdot}{O}H$$

$\Big\}$ Slow.

Do your results verify that these mechanisms fit the dependence of the rate on the concentration of the ester and the acid?

Further Experimental Problems

This reaction is acid catalyzed. Is it base catalyzed? You might investigate this problem, keeping in mind that ester hydrolysis, represented by the stoichiometric equation

$$\underset{\text{RCOR}'}{\overset{\displaystyle O}{\|}} + \text{HOH} = \underset{\text{RCOH}}{\overset{\displaystyle O}{\|}} + \text{R}'\text{OH},$$

is also base catalyzed and might cause problems as a result of the production of the carboxylic acid, RCOOH, during the reaction. How? The hydrolysis is acid catalyzed as well. Why didn't we take it into account in our analysis of the acid-catalyzed decomposition of diazoacetic ester? Have we made a substantial blunder in our analysis? Can you think of ways to test any hypotheses you might have on this point?

EXPERIMENT 30.   *The Iodination of Cyclohexanone* *

Introduction

The purpose of this experiment is threefold. We wish to determine the rate law, the rate constant, and the mechanism (insofar as this is possible) for the reaction of iodine (I_2 and I_3^-) with cyclohexanone in the presence of acid.

The overall stoichiometry of the reaction we wish to study is

$$I_3^- + \text{(cyclohexanone)} \rightarrow \text{(2-iodocyclohexanone)} + H^+ + 2I^-.$$

Substitution reactions in a group of organic compounds of the general formula

$$\underset{\underset{\displaystyle R''}{|}}{\overset{\displaystyle H \quad O}{R'\text{---}C\text{---}C\text{---}R}}$$

such as ketones (e.g., cyclohexanone, acetone), aldehydes (where R is H), and carboxylic acids are of interest and have aroused much discussion. There is a possibility that these substitutions, i.e., replacement of a hydrogen atom on the carbon next to the carbonyl, C=O, group (this is called the alpha, α, position and,

hence, these are α-hydrogens) *may not* be a direct displacement process but may be due to the initial formation of the enolic (from *-ene* designating a double bonded carbon system and *-ol* designating an -OH group attached to carbon) form of these compounds,

$$\underset{\underset{\displaystyle R''}{|}}{\overset{\displaystyle OH}{R'\text{---}C=C\text{---}R}}$$

The I_3^- might then attack this species rapidly and the rate-determining step of the reaction could be enol formation.

In a solution containing I_2 and I^-, the following equilibrium is very rapidly established:

$$I_2 + I^- = I_3^-, \qquad K = 710 \text{ liter mole}^{-1}.$$

Both I_2 and I_3^- are effective iodinating agents for the ketone, so we have to know how much total $I_2 + I_3^-$ is present. Since I_2 and I_3^- absorb light in the same region of the spectrum, the total absorbance will always be due to contributions from both species. Therefore it might appear that it would be impossibly difficult to follow the course of this reaction. However, a solution to this problem can be derived from an examination of the plot of absorptivities for I_3^- and I_2 as a function of wavelength, Fig. 13–4. Note that at 565 mμ the absorptivities are the same (an isosbestic point) for I_3^- and I_2, so we can write the absorbance of a solution at this wavelength as

$$A_{565} = a_{I_2}b[I_2] + a_{I_3^-}b[I_3^-] = a_{I_2}b([I_2] + [I_3^-]).$$

Thus A_{565} is directly proportional to the sum of the concentrations of I_2 and I_3^-, exactly the information we desire. (The same arguments could be advanced for $\lambda = 610$ mμ and 468 mμ. However, the sensitivity at the former wavelength would be lower than at 565 mμ and the form of the absorption curves in the region near 468 mμ is not conducive to good analysis by a spectrophotometer with a wide "band pass." Why not?) The

---

* It is a pleasure to acknowledge the suggestion of Professor M. F. Hawthorne, University of California, Riverside that cyclohexanone would be a good choice for this study.

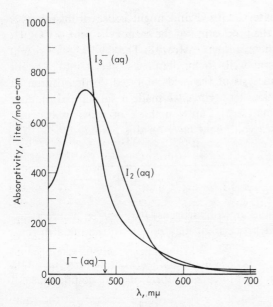

Fig. 13-4. Absorptivities of I_3^- and I_2 vs. wavelength.

solution of iodine and iodide is made up with a tenfold excess of I^- so that the great majority of the I_2 is present in the form of I_3^-. (This is because free I_2 in water tends to escape into the gas phase, thus changing the concentration of the solution.) We thus dispose of the complications in analytical technique by a judicious choice of analysis wavelength.*

Procedure

Work with a partner on this experiment. There will be available in the laboratory 2.3×10^{-1} M cyclohexanone in water, 5.0×10^{-1} M HCl, and a solution that is 3.60×10^{-2} M in I_2 and 3.60×10^{-1} M in KI; thus it can be said to be about 3.6×10^{-2} M in I_3^-. Obtain enough of each solution in clean, dry, labeled containers to last for one laboratory period of work. The containers for the cyclohexanone and "iodine" solutions must be stoppered. A test tube will be fine for the "iodine" solution. Prepare a bath at about room temperature by filling one section of an expanded foam acid case with water and suspend your solutions in it so they will all be at the same temperature. Also suspend a 25-ml graduate, a 50-ml beaker, and a spectrophotometer sample cuvette in this bath so they will come to the same temperature as the solutions. It will be accurate enough to make up your solutions for the experiment in the graduated cylinder. Suggested recipes for solutions

---

* It is not at all necessary to use a spectrophotometer to follow this reaction. Make up a series of test tubes containing decreasing known concentrations of the I_3^- solution used for the experiment and then as the reaction proceeds, simply note the times when the color in the reaction test tube matches that in each of the standards. Thus you obtain coordinated concentration and time values.

to be used to determine the coefficients a, b, and c in the suggested rate law, Eq. (13–19), are given below.

The general procedure to be followed is to add the acid, ketone, and water to the graduate, mix with a stirring rod, and transfer to the 50-ml beaker. The "iodine" solution is most easily added with a pipet (*do not*, under any circumstances, pipet this solution by mouth). Start the addition about five seconds before the time you will call $t = 0$. When the "iodine" solution has all been added, stir the solution and transfer enough to the sample cuvette to fill it adequately. Take an absorbance reading a minute or two after the reaction has started and each minute or two thereafter until the absorbance reading is zero or until twenty minutes have elapsed, whichever comes first. Note that you can run two or three reactions simultaneously by simply measuring the absorbances of the solutions in succession, one every thirty seconds or so. (Good record keeping is a must for such a procedure.) A solution that is 2 parts cyclohexanone solution to 3 parts acid solution is a good reference standard for zeroing the spectrophotometer. Leave your sample cuvette in the spectrophotometer a minimum amount of time, since it may heat up inside the instrument. Between readings, keep the cuvette in the temperature bath. When a reading is to be taken, remove the cuvette, wipe it dry, take the reading, and immediately return the cuvette to the bath. It is not a bad idea to have a few pieces of graph paper already labeled with time and absorbance axes so that you can plot your data as they are obtained.

You will find that absorbance vs. time plots will look like Fig. 13–5. Note that there is some curvature during the first three or four minutes of the reaction. This seems to be typical of these reactions and probably arises from the small amount of peroxides that are usually found in oxygenated hydrocarbons (such as ketones and ethers). These peroxides react with the I^- to produce a small amount of I_2, thus producing I_2 (I_3^-) at the same time that it is being used up in the main reaction. The peroxides are soon destroyed and the remainder of the plot is linear, as shown in the figure.

Suggested solutions to be used to determine c are indicated in the table on p. 191. All volumes are given

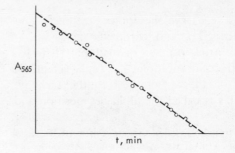

Fig. 13-5. Absorbance vs. time for a cyclohexanone iodination run.

in milliliters. (Cogitate upon Fig. 13–5.)

	Ketone	H^+	H_2O	"Iodine"
C1	10.0	5.0	8.0	2.0
C2	10.0	5.0	7.0	3.0

Suggested solutions to be used to determine a are:

	Ketone	H^+	H_2O	"Iodine"
C1	10.0	5.0	8.0	2.0
A2	10.0	3.0	10.0	2.0
A3	10.0	7.0	6.0	2.0

Suggested solutions to be used to determine b are:

	Ketone	H^+	H_2O	"Iodine"
C1	10.0	5.0	8.0	2.0
B2	7.0	5.0	11.0	2.0
B3	13.0	5.0	5.0	2.0

Calculations

From the data, calculate a, b, c, and the rate constant, k. Use seconds as the unit of time and moles/liter for concentrations. Is the condition for "flooding" fulfilled in these runs within 5%?

A mechanism proposed for this reaction is

Step 1

Step 2

Step 3

Step 4

What does your experimentally determined rate law tell you about the relative speeds of these various reactions? For example, is the forward rate of Step 2 faster or slower than Step 3? How about Steps 1 and 2?

Further Experimental Problems

The Activation Energy. Make a convenient temperature bath (ice and water in one of the sections of an expanded foam acid case will do nicely). Mix 13 ml of cyclohexanone solution and 10 ml of HCl solution and allow them to come to the bath temperature. Also cool the spectrophotometer sample cuvette and some I_3^- solution to the bath temperature. Add 2 ml of the I_3^- solution to the acid-ketone mixture, noting the time of mixing and record absorbance-vs.-time readings as described for the room temperature runs. (Water vapor will condense rapidly on the sample cuvette at the low temperature if you wipe it dry as described for the room temperature runs. Therefore instead of wiping it dry, take it from the bath, let it drain for three or four seconds, remove the drop of water from the bottom, take a reading as rapidly as possible, and return the cuvette to the bath.) Note that the concentrations you use are higher than those used at room temperature. Why? Repeat the experiment at a temperature between 10 to 15°C, using the knowledge you already have gained to choose concentrations that will give a convenient reaction time.

What is ΔE_a? What is A? What would be the rate constant for the reaction at 50°C? At 50°C, how long would it take to decolorize a solution in which the initial concentrations are $[C_6H_{10}O] = 10^{-2}\ M$, $[H^+] = 10^{-2}\ M$, and $[I_3^-] = 10^{-3}\ M$?

The Bromination of Cyclohexanone. From the data gathered in the first part of this experiment and the rate law (and mechanism?) derived from the data, you probably ought to be able to predict the effect of substituting Br_3^- for I_3^- in this reaction. A solution of Br_3^- will be available to anyone who desires to test his prediction experimentally by making the substitution. (If you have to make up your own Br_3^- solution, see your instructor first for directions on handling bromine. It is a viciously corrosive and volatile liquid.) The wavelength of the isosbestic point for Br_3^- and Br_2 in aqueous solution is 448 mμ.

The Kinetic Isotope Effect. You probably have a good idea from the work already carried out that the iodination of ketones (at least cyclohexanone) may involve an enol that reacts rapidly with the iodine species present. But as yet you have no information whether Step 1 or 2 of the possible mechanism suggested above is rate controlling. Information on this point can be obtained by studying the effect which substitution of deuteriums for the α-hydrogens has on the rate of the iodination.

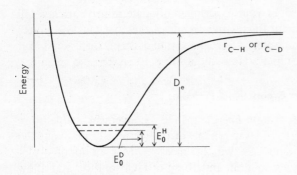

Fig. 13–6. Potential-energy diagram for C—H or C—D.

To see how this substitution could have an effect on the reaction rate, let us consider the potential-energy diagram for the molecule C—H, Fig. 13–6. The diagram would be identical for the molecule C—D, the only change being a difference in the quantized vibrational energy levels for CH and CD. If we make the approximation that the vibrational motion of this molecule is like a harmonic oscillator (two weights connected by a perfect spring), we can immediately write, from our knowledge of physics, that the frequency of such oscillations will be

$$\nu = \frac{1}{2\pi}\sqrt{\frac{k}{m}}.$$

For our derivation we assume that we are observing the motion of one atom, the hydrogen or deuterium, relative to the other, the carbon. Hence the mass, m, in this equation is the mass of the H or D. The constant, k, is the force constant of the "spring" holding the two particles together. This force constant is related to the bonding characteristics of the molecule and is identical for CH and CD. The energy of the vibration, ϵ_v, is given by (Planck's equation)

$$\epsilon_v = h\nu = \frac{h}{2\pi}\sqrt{\frac{k}{m}},$$

and we see that the energy will get smaller if m gets larger. One of the interesting properties of the vibrational motion of molecules is that the vibrational energy never goes to zero, but has a definite lower limit that is $\frac{1}{2}h\nu$ above the very bottom of the potential curve. Let us compare, then, the *zero-point vibrational energy*, E_0 (per mole), for CH and CD:

$$\frac{E_0^H}{E_0^D} = \frac{\frac{1}{2}h\nu_H}{\frac{1}{2}h\nu_D} = \frac{\frac{1}{2}(h/2\pi)\sqrt{k/m_H}}{\frac{1}{2}(h/2\pi)\sqrt{k/m_D}} = \sqrt{\frac{m_D}{m_H}} = \sqrt{2}.$$

Thus we see that the lowest vibrational energy level of CH will be higher in energy than the lowest level of CD, as shown in the potential diagram, Fig. 13–6. Next let us compare the dissociation energies of CH and CD. These energies are $D_e - E_0^H$ and $D_e - E_0^D$, respec-

tively. Since $E_0^H > E_0^D$, we immediately see that

$$D_e - E_0^D > D_e - E_0^H,$$

so that it will take more energy to dissociate a CD bond than a CH bond. Thus a reaction of CH that involves the breaking of the CH bond as the rate-determining step will be slowed down (at the same temperature) by the substitution of D for H, since more energy will be required for the bond breaking. (There is also an effect of the substitution of D for H on the frequency factor for a reaction. It is in the same direction but is somewhat more complicated to analyze than the effect on the activation energy.)

All the above arguments can be carried over to more complicated molecules like cyclohexanone with the understanding that predictions can be made about the *direction* of the effect on replacing H with D, but predictions about the magnitude will necessarily be crude due to the large number of interactions within such a molecule. As at least partial confirmation of this picture, you might, during the course of this experiment, take infrared spectra of cyclohexanone and 2,2,6,6-cyclohexanone-d_4. (The numbering system for cyclohexanone calls the carbon atom with the oxygen attached 1 and continues numbering clockwise about the ring.) The -d_4 indicates that deuterium atoms rather than hydrogens occupy the four designated positions. You should be able to calculate, from the equation for the frequency, the ratio of the vibrational frequencies expected for CH and CD bonds. You can see how well this is confirmed in your infrared spectra since vibrational energies are in the infrared region of the electromagnetic spectrum.

To return to our main problem, if Step 1 is the rate-determining step in the iodination reaction, then we see that it is very unlikely that substitution of deuterium at the α-positions would have any effect on the rate. On the other hand, we see that in Step 2, one of the α-C—H bonds is broken and we would expect, if this is the rate-determining step, that the rate would be appreciably slowed down by deuterium substitution. A rate determination with 2,2,6,6-cyclohexanone-d_4 will thus be a diagnostic test to help us decide which step might be rate determining. You will have to run this reaction in a somewhat different fashion from your others because you cannot make up stock solutions of the deuterated cyclohexanone in water, since the deuteriums would be slowly replaced by hydrogens from the water as a result of the following equilibria:

$$C_6H_6D_4O + H_2O = C_6H_7D_3O + HOD,$$
$$C_6H_7D_3O + H_2O = C_6H_8D_2O + HOD, \text{ etc.},$$

which are driven far toward the right and down the series of reactions because of the great excess of water present.

Indeed, it is the reverse of these reactions that you use to deuterate the cyclohexanone in the first place. Cyclohexanone and D_2O are mixed together and refluxed (boiled with a cold condenser so arranged that all vapors condense and return to the pot to be boiled again) for 24 hours in the presence of a basic catalyst (CaO or $CaCO_3$) which creates OD^- ions by reaction with D_2O. The mixture is cooled and the cyclohexanone layer (it is only slightly soluble in water) is separated and treated again in the same way. At equilibrium, the mole fraction of deuterium in the α-positions of the cyclohexanone should be quite close to the mole fraction of deuterium remaining in the water. Repetition of the exchange process a few times is a much more efficient use of D_2O than is an attempt to exchange most of the hydrogens in one reaction. After the final exchange the cyclohexanone should be distilled to rid it of as much water as possible. The equilibria that are set up are similar to the following:

As a check on the deuteration procedure, obtain an NMR spectrum of cyclohexanone and the 2,2,6,6-cyclohexanone-d_4 you have prepared. Since deuterium does not show up on the hydrogen NMR spectrum, you can attribute differences in the spectra to the deuterium substitution. Ask your instructor about the interpretation of these NMR spectra, especially the position of the resonances and the isotopic purity of the deuterated cyclohexanone.

To run a reaction, first weigh a small capped sample vial on the analytical balance, place about 0.4 gm of the

deuterated cyclohexanone in the vial, and reweigh the vial and its contents. The following are suggested as suitable initial conditions to start the investigation of the deuterated cyclohexanone. Proceeding as quickly as possible, pour the ketone into a 25-ml graduate, using a previously measured 12 ml of acid to rinse the vial a few times placing the rinsings in the graduate. Fill to the 23-ml mark with water, mix, pour into a beaker, add 2 ml of the I_3^- solution, noting the time of addition, and proceed as with all your other runs, with the exception that this run should be followed until the absorbance goes to zero. Before beginning, of course, the acid, water, and I_3^- solution should be brought to the temperature of the bath used to keep the temperature constant during the reaction.

Calculate the rate constant, k_D, for this run, assuming (you might use other runs to check this assumption) that the *rate law* is the same for the deuterated ketone as for the nondeuterated ketone. Usually, the results of experiments such as these are presented as k_H/k_D. What is your value of k_H/k_D? What do your results indicate concerning the rate-determining step in the reaction?

Other Ketones. It is certainly possible that the rate law and mechanism we have derived for cyclohexanone are unique to this ketone. To test this you might try the experiment with another ketone. If you find that the rate law is the same, try to correlate the difference in rate constants, if any, for the two ketones on the basis of their respective molecular structures. Possible choices for other ketones to study are cyclopentanone and acetone.

Questions

1. If one mole of cyclohexanone and two moles of D_2O are equilibrated, we would expect one-half the replaceable hydrogens (those in the 2- and 6-positions) in the ketone to be replaced by deuterium and one-half the deuteriums in the water to be replaced by hydrogen. This is because there are 4 moles of deuterium atoms in 2 moles of D_2O, and at equilibrium we expect the mole fraction of D in each component to be the same as the overall mole fraction of D in the whole system (one-half). Calculate the mole fraction of D that would be introduced into cyclohexanone if 1 mole of the ketone and 6 moles of D_2O were equilibrated. Calculate the mole fraction of D that would be introduced into cyclohexanone by the following process. One mole of the ketone is first equilibrated with 2 moles of D_2O and then separated from the water; this partially exchanged ketone is mixed and allowed to equilibrate with 2 additional moles of D_2O and again separated from the water;

finally the process is repeated with 2 more moles of D_2O. A total of 6 moles of D_2O are used in each of the above procedures. Which is the more efficient technique for introducing a maximum amount of D into the cyclohexanone?

2. We have assumed that only 1 iodine atom becomes attached to a cyclohexanone molecule. Might not further iodination of the C_6H_9IO occur? How would this affect the results? How might you test for the possible occurrence of such a reaction?

EXPERIMENT 31. *Kinetics of Enzymatic Reactions; The Invertase-Catalyzed Hydrolysis of Sucrose*

An Hypothesis and Some Experimental Observations

We shall here postulate and attempt to prove in the discussion and experiment that follow that enzymatic reactions (e.g., the fermentation reaction that Pasteur regarded as an intrinsically vital phenomenon) are not, in fact, fundamentally different in kind from many more familiar catalytic reactions. The enzyme, E, is simply a particular (exquisitely complex) molecular structure that, at some one or several "active sites," forms with the reactant, S (called the substrate), a transient intermediate, ES. The rapid conversion of this intermediate to the final product, P, then frees the active site for combination with another molecule of reactant which is also at once converted into product. We can represent the situation by the following two stoichiometric equations:

$$E + S = ES, \qquad ES = E + P.$$

The overall reaction, the sum of the two individual reactions, is then

$$S = P.$$

Because the enzyme molecule is regenerated and recirculated, a few molecules of enzyme are capable of bringing about the conversion of a comparatively immense number of reactant molecules to product.

In the absence of the enzyme the overall reaction may be so slow as to be experimentally undetectable. The enzyme acts, in this model, simply by opening up a new route for the reaction. In order for this new pathway to

produce such an immense increase in the rate of the reaction, it must be true that the activation energy for the enzyme-catalyzed reaction is much lower than the uncatalyzed reaction. This is the first prediction of the model we are developing for enzymatic reactions. Table 13–1 presents data that confirm this prediction and show the profound reduction in activation energy brought about by the enzymatic catalysts. The activation energies are obtained, as outlined in Section 13–5, by measuring the rate of reaction at various temperatures and plotting the logarithm of the reaction rate versus $1/T$. Since the slope of the line so obtained is directly proportional to the activation energy, one can see at a glance from such a plot, Fig. 13–7, the effect of adding catalyst to a reaction.

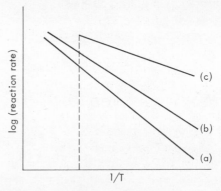

Fig. 13–7. Graphical comparison (not to scale) of reaction rates for the same reaction: (a) uncatalyzed, (b) catalyzed ("weak" catalyst), (c) enzymatically catalyzed.

Our hypothesis thus far predicts that enzymatic reactions are qualitatively exactly like any other catalyzed (or uncatalyzed) reaction. There is, however, one aspect in which enzymatic reactions differ markedly from the great majority of other reactions. As the temperature increases in an enzyme-catalyzed reaction, the rate increases, Fig. 13–7, although slowly since the activation energy is low. However, above some more or less sharply defined temperature, the activity of the enzymatic catalyst drops off sharply toward zero as indicated by the dotted line in the figure. Is this effect explicable on the basis of our model? Yes, if we remember that enzymes are thermally sensitive protein compounds, and at even slightly

Table 13–1

COMPARISON OF UNCATALYZED, CATALYZED, AND ENZYME-CATALYZED REACTIONS

Reaction and conditions	ΔE_a, kcal/mole
Decomposition of hydrogen peroxide, H_2O_2, in the presence of	
No catalyst	18
Colloidal platinum catalyst	12
The enzyme "catalase"	2
Hydrolysis of sucrose in the presence of	
No catalyst	Huge*
Mineral acid catalyst	26
The enzyme "invertase"	9

* Reaction too slow to measure

elevated temperatures the catalytic protein undergoes chemical denaturation and loss of activity. In more graphic terms, the enzyme is cooked like the protein of an egg or meat at elevated temperatures. Thus the fall-off in the rate of enzymatic reactions at elevated temperatures simply reflects the destruction of the catalyst.

Thus far our hypothesis concerning the mechanism of enzymatic catalysis is in complete qualitative accord with the results we have quoted. Since this hypothesis is central to much of modern biochemistry, it would certainly be desirable to test whether quantitative predictions made on the basis of this model can be confirmed by experiment. There are many avenues of experimentation we might examine, but let us limit our considerations to the general form of the quantitative dependence of the rate of enzymatic reactions on the concentration of the substrate and the enzyme, i.e., the rate law for the reaction.

Let us put some limits on the problem we have set ourselves, so that we will find it reasonably tractable. We shall restrict our attention to experiments carried out at a single constant temperature and, further, shall consider only measurements of the *initial* rates at which the reaction proceeds in each case. This latter restriction enables us to avoid two nonfundamental complications: depletion of the substrate concentration and the back reaction. Thus we can consider [S] a constant throughout the (short) time any reaction is run.* Since [P] will thus be very small, we can neglect the reformation of the intermediate, ES, by the reaction of E with P, and this considerably simplifies the mechanism we must write for the reaction. A great many other "complicating factors" could conceivably arise in an enzymatic system; there might be two intermediate stages in the reaction or there might be more than one "active site" on the enzyme and hence more than one pathway for the reaction. In our analysis we will disregard such complications and then test our predictions against the experimental data to see how close our "ideal" model approaches the actual situation.†

---

* The measurement of initial rate demands that we have available a method for accurately determining the very small amount of P formed in the first few minutes of the reaction. For, if we have to await the accumulation of a substantial quantity of P, there will be a corresponding substantial diminution of S which is just what we want to avoid. Fortunately, there are often methods available for the determination of small amounts of products and in these cases the *initial rate* of the enzymatic reaction can be easily measured.

† This is rather analogous to Boyle's law which provides a very simple expression for the dependence of the volume of a gas on its pressure if the pressure is not too high, the temperature is not too low, the gases are not reactive, or any number of other complications. Boyle's law is a limiting law and we propose to deal with a similar limiting rate law for enzymatic reactions.

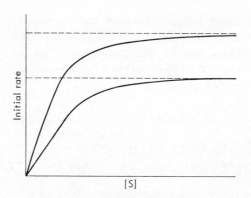

Fig. 13–8. Typical experimental results for an enzymatic reaction.

Before proceeding to our mathematical analysis of the mechanism we have postulated for enzymatic reactions, let us look at one further kind of experimental result. When we determine the initial rates at various substrate concentrations with a fixed concentration of enzyme present, we find that a plot of the data has the form shown in Fig. 13–8. If we then perform the series of experiments again with another fixed concentration of enzyme, we obtain another curve of the same general form, as shown in the figure. There is such a curve for each concentration of enzyme we choose. We must now show that our postulated mechanism is consistent with these results or we shall have to discard it, even though it seems consistent with the experimental data we have presented in preceding paragraphs.

Kinetic Analysis of Our Postulated Enzymatic Reaction Mechanism

The reaction mechanism we hypothesize for enzymatic systems is

$$E + S \underset{k_2}{\overset{k_1}{\rightleftharpoons}} ES,$$
$$ES \overset{k_3}{\longrightarrow} E + P, \tag{13-39}$$

where the k's are the rate constants for the indicated reactions. The back reaction, $E + P \rightarrow ES$, has been omitted since we are considering only the initial stages of the reaction. The rate law for formation of the product based on this mechanism is

$$\frac{d[P]}{dt} = v = k_3[ES], \tag{13-40}$$

where v symbolizes the initial rate or velocity of the reaction. As an example of a case covered by this simple law, consider the conversion of sucrose into invert sugar in the presence of the enzyme invertase. We hypothesize that an intermediate complex ES is formed between a molecule of sucrose and a molecule of invertase. An encounter between this complex and a molecule of water may then yield the reaction product, invert sugar. The actual rate of this reaction will then be

$$v = k'_3[ES][H_2O].$$

But in dilute aqueous solution the concentration of water is a constant that we can incorporate with the rate constant k'_3 to give a single constant, k_3, which permits us to write the rate law in the simple form:

$$v = k_3[ES].$$

The overall reaction has the form, $S + B = P$, but the concentration of B does not appear in the rate law when [B] is a constant, as it is in the case of water. To be sure, in many enzymatic reactions B may represent a molecular species variable in its concentration. In that case we find a more complex rate law, involving [B], but we have already waived consideration of cases involving any such complicating factor.

We have no way of measuring [ES] so we must somehow express this concentration in terms of measurable quantities, initial (constant) concentration of substrate and initial enzyme concentration. Since during the short period over which we measure the rate it is essentially constant, it is reasonable to expect that the concentration of the reaction intermediate, ES, is also constant. This *steady-state assumption* was the key innovation made in 1912, by Michaelis and Menten, which permitted them, and us, to proceed with the analysis. We can write the rate of formation of ES as

$$\left(\frac{d[ES]}{dt}\right)_f = k_1[E][S]$$

and the rate of destruction as the sum of two processes

$$\left(\frac{-d[ES]}{dt}\right)_d = k_2[ES] + k_3[ES].$$

The steady-state assumption requires that the rate of formation equal the rate of destruction, so we find

$$k_1[E][S] = k_2[ES] + k_3[ES].$$

At first sight, it appears that we are no better off than before, because we do not know [E], the instantaneous concentration of enzyme. We do, however, know $[E]_0$, the initial concentration of enzyme, and we must conserve enzyme so we can write,

$$[E]_0 = [E] + [ES]$$

and substitute for [E] in the preceding equation to give

$$k_1\{[E]_0 - [ES]\}[S] = k_2[ES] + k_3[ES].$$

Now collect terms and factor

$$[ES]\{k_2 + k_3 + k_1[S]\} = k_1[E]_0[S]$$

and solve for [ES] to give

$$[ES] = \frac{k_1[E]_0[S]}{k_2 + k_3 + k_1[S]} = \frac{[E]_0[S]}{(k_2 + k_3)/k_1 + [S]}.$$

All we know about k_1, k_2, and k_3 is that, at a given temperature, they are constants. Thus we might as well combine them into a single unknown constant, K_m (the Michaelis-Menten constant), and write

$$[ES] = \frac{[E]_0[S]}{K_m + [S]}.$$

Now we substitute this expression for [ES] into Eq. (13–40) to give

$$\frac{d[P]}{dt} = v = \frac{k_3[E]_0[S]}{K_m + [S]}. \tag{13–41}$$

Usually the analysis is carried a step further by asking: What is the maximum possible rate, V_{max}, at which the reaction can be made to go at a given temperature? From Eq. (13–40) we see that as [ES] increases, the rate increases, but what is the limit of this increase, i.e., what is $[ES]_{max}$? Obviously, in any given system the maximum possible amount of enzyme in the complex is limited by the total amount of enzyme present, $[E]_0$, and the maximum possible value for the complex concentration is therefore $[ES]_{max} = [E]_0$. Hence we can write

$$V_{max} = k_3[ES]_{max} = k_3[E]_0$$

and substitute this in (13–41) to yield

$$v = \frac{V_{max}[S]}{K_m + [S]} \tag{13–42}$$

the Michaelis-Menten equation.

Testing This Solution. Analysis of the Michaelis-Menten equation immediately indicates that it is just the form we need to fit the curves of Fig. 13–8. Observe, first, that at sufficiently low substrate concentration $K_m \gg [S]$. In this range of low S concentrations we can neglect [S] compared to K_m in the denominator of (13–42) and obtain

$$v \approx \frac{V_{max}[S]}{K_m},$$

which predicts a linear dependence of v on [S] in this region. This is just the behavior we see in Fig. 13–8 at low [S]. The slope of the line will depend on the particular values of V_{max} and K_m for the enzyme under study.

Note, second, that at sufficiently high substrate concentration $[S] \gg K_m$ and K_m may then be neglected in the denominator of (13–42) to yield

$$v \approx \frac{V_{max}[S]}{[S]} = V_{max}.$$

Thus, at sufficiently high values of [S], the initial rate makes an asymptotic approach to a maximum rate value V_{max}, just as indicated in Fig. 13–8. Finally, observe that the maximum rate is $V_{max} = k_3[E]_0$ so that the maximum rate which is approached by the curves in Fig. 13–8 will be directly proportional to the initial concentration of enzyme, just as is observed.

Quantitative Predictions Based on Our Mechanism

Since the Michaelis-Menten equation is so successful in at least qualitatively rationalizing the kinetic data obtained in enzymatic reactions, such reactions are almost always discussed in terms of the parameters that enter into the equation, K_m and V_{max}. So far, however, we have not indicated how we might evaluate K_m and V_{max}. A direct determination of V_{max} is often impossible because we cannot go to high enough substrate concentrations without denaturing the enzyme, and extrapolation of curved plots like Fig. 13–8 is dangerous. This problem is easily overcome by rearrangement of the Michaelis-Menten equation.* We merely invert the equation to yield

$$\frac{1}{v} = \frac{K_m}{V_{max}} \frac{1}{[S]} + \frac{1}{V_{max}}, \qquad (13\text{–}43)$$

which is the equation of a straight line on a $1/v$-versus-$1/[S]$ graph. Therefore, when initial rate data for an enzymatic reaction at a constant temperature and a given initial concentration of enzyme are plotted on such a graph, we predict that a linear plot should be obtained. From the extrapolated intercept on the ordinate ($1/v$ axis) we will obtain $1/V_{max}$, and K_m can readily be obtained by dividing the slope of the line by the intercept. Moreover, this method of plotting the data allows us to see at a glance whether the Michaelis-Menten equation fits our data not merely qualitatively but quantitatively also.

What further tests of our hypothesis, now based on our kinetic analysis of the mechanism, expressed by the Michaelis-Menten equation can we devise? Let us investigate the mechanism of the action of antimetabolites ("poisons") that are often useful as chemotherapeutic agents. We shall restrict our attention to inhibitors, I, that do not denature the enzyme, but rather can complex

---

* One can compare the analogous case of Boyle's Law: $PV = b$ ($b = $ constant). If we plot P versus V and wish to extrapolate our data to lower pressures than we can conveniently attain, we find that this is difficult to do reliably along the hyperbolic curve we have obtained. However, the simple expedient of replotting the data as P versus $1/V$ yields a straight line (the equation of the line being $P = b/V$) that is easy to extrapolate and, as a bonus, the constant b is immediately obtained from the slope of the line.

with it at the active site in an equilibrium reaction

$$EI \rightleftharpoons E + I,$$

$$K_I = \frac{[E][I]}{[EI]}. \qquad (13\text{–}44)$$

Such agents act as inhibitors of enzymatic reactions by competing with the normal substrate for the "active site(s)" on the enzyme molecule. To the extent that the inhibitor monopolizes the "active sites," there are fewer such sites available for the formation of ES.

Let us see what effect the inhibitor will have on our kinetic predictions. The rate expressions for the formation and destruction of the intermediate, ES, will remain the same; on the basis of the steady-state approximation for [ES] we will still obtain

$$k_1[E][S] = k_2[ES] + k_3[ES].$$

In this situation, however, we have to account for [EI] in our equation for the conservation of enzyme,

$$[E]_0 = [E] + [ES] + [EI].$$

Substitution for [E] in the steady-state equation yields

$$k_1\{[E]_0 - [ES] - [EI]\} = k_2[ES] + k_3[ES],$$

which can be solved for [ES] and then substituted into Eq. (13–40) to give

$$\frac{d(P)}{dt} = v = \frac{k_3\{[E]_0 - [EI]\}[S]}{K_m + [S]}. \qquad (13\text{–}41a)$$

Comparing this expression with (13–41), we see that the term [EI] simply represents the amount of enzyme that is inaccessible to the substrate because it is combined with inhibitor. How much is this? The concentration of enzyme-inhibitor complex, [EI], can be evaluated in terms of K_I, the dissociation constant for the complex, Eq. (13–44). After considerable algebraic manipulation (which you should check) we can arrive at the equation

$$v = \frac{V_{max}[S]}{K_m + [S] + \dfrac{K_m}{K_I}[I]}. \qquad (13\text{–}42a)$$

Equation (13–42a) differs from Eq. (13–42) only in the presence of the last term in the denominator. Clearly, the tighter the enzyme-inhibitor complex (i.e., the smaller the value of K_I) and/or the larger the inhibitor concentration, [I], the smaller will be the v, the rate of reaction, just as we should expect from our mechanism.

Now we can rearrange Eq. (13–42a) just as we formerly did with (13–42) to obtain

$$\frac{1}{v} = \left\{ \frac{K_m}{V_{max}} \left(1 + \frac{[I]}{K_I}\right) \right\} \frac{1}{[S]} + \frac{1}{V_{max}}. \qquad (13\text{–}43a)$$

At a given temperature, a given concentration of a particular inhibitor, and a given enzyme concentration, all the terms within the braces are constant, and we again have an equation for a straight-line plot on a $1/v$-versus-$1/[S]$ graph. We would thus predict that under the restrictive conditions just specified, a plot of the experimental values of $1/v$ versus $1/[S]$ would fall on a straight line. Furthermore, if we make another series of trials with a higher concentration of the inhibitor (or with the same concentration of some other inhibitor that forms a tighter complex, smaller K_I, with the enzyme), we would expect to find again that the values of $1/v$ versus $1/[S]$ would fall on a straight line, but one of greater slope since the value of the term in the braces,

Eq. (13–43a), will now be greater. Since in both these cases the enzyme concentration is constant we would expect V_{max} ($k_3[E]_0$) to be the same and hence would predict that the extrapolated intercepts of the two plots at $1/[S] = 0$ would be the same and would be the same as the intercept in the absence of inhibitor. That is to say, we predict that the limiting value for the maximum reaction velocity remains the same whether or not an inhibitor is present. At lower substrate concentrations the inhibitor may greatly reduce the rate of reaction, but by sufficiently increasing the substrate concentration, we can minimize, and even entirely overcome the effect of the inhibitor.*

Experimental Procedures for Testing our Predictions

Introduction. The enzyme invertase (technically β-fructo-furanosidase) catalyzes the reaction shown below.

Like a number of other enzymatic reactions, this one can also be carried out without the enzyme by using H^+ as a (notably less efficient) catalyst. The most striking consequence of the reaction is a large change in the optical rotatory power of the solution as the sucrose is progressively converted to glucose and fructose. The conversion actually produces a change in the direction in which the plane of polarization of the light is rotated by the solution and it is from this "inversion" that the enzyme derives its name. (The products are sometimes called "invert sugars.") The inversion of sucrose in the presence of yeast was noted as early as 1832 by Persoz. Michaelis and Menten used the enzyme extracted from yeast in their studies of the mechanism of enzymatic action, following the reaction by observing the change of optical rotation that accompanies the reaction.

In the present series of experiments we shall use a different, but at least as accurate, way of following the progress of the reaction. The method hinges on the fact that glucose and fructose (like all other monosaccharides) are active reducing agents, while the sucrose from which they are formed is not a "reducing sugar." Thus any

measure of the reducing capacity of a reaction mixture becomes, in effect, a measurement of the extent to which the conversion of sucrose to glucose and fructose has proceeded in that mixture. In our experiment we shall use 3,5-dinitrosalicylate reagent in assaying the reducing capacity of various reaction mixtures:

3,5-dinitrosalicylate acid anion

Our general procedure will be to set up some particular system containing sucrose, let the hydrolysis reaction proceed in it for some specified time, "quench" the reaction by an addition of sodium hydroxide (contained in the 3,5-dinitrosalicylate reagent added at this point), heat to "develop" the color produced by the reagent in the presence of reducing activity in the solution, and measure the absorbance of the solution with a spectrophotometer. After calibration, the absorbance reading at once establishes the number of moles of fructose and glucose present in the solution. Combining this information with the reaction time, we can readily establish the average net rate at which sucrose was converted to glucose and fructose.

---

* It is found that the bacteriostatic effect of the sulfonamides is wiped out if the concentration of *p*-aminobenzoic acid is sufficiently increased. It was this observation that furnished the first solid clue to the mechanism by which sulfanilamide acts as a chemotherapeutic agent; it is an antimetabolite, blocking an enzyme whose normal function is to bring *p*-aminobenzoic acid into a synthetic sequence producing folic acid. See the interesting article by Roblin.

Techniques. Since there are a large number of repetitive operations in this experiment you will find it profitable to work in groups of three or four dividing the work among you.

Success in this experiment demands extremely careful technique, and exact adherence to the prescribed procedure. Some pointers on technique include the following:

1) When first using a pipet, rinse it with a small portion of the solution to be delivered from it, and make sure the pipet drains cleanly. As far as possible, always use the same pipet for the same solution. The pipets required for this experiment are as follows:

two 1-ml transfer pipets for dispensing the standard amounts of the sucrose solution and the enzyme solution (It is imperative that the pipet used for the enzyme *never* be used with any of the other solutions.),

one 2-ml transfer pipet to be used exclusively for dispensing the dinitrosalicylate reagent,

one 5-ml transfer pipet to be used exclusively for dispensing the NaOH solution required in the last part of the experiment (optional),

one 1-ml graduated pipet to be used for dispensing buffer solution and distilled water,

one 2-ml graduated pipet to be used for dispensing non-standard amounts of enzyme solution.

The pipets you do not have in your desk are to be obtained from your instructor to whom they must be returned at the end of each laboratory period.

2) Take care that you make all the additions called for in each trial; check them off in the lists below as you go along.

3) Swirl the assay tube thoroughly immediately before and after the addition of the last reagent required to initiate the reaction; swirl thoroughly again immediately after adding the dinitrosalicylate reagent.

4) To avoid needless expenditure of time, you will carry out several runs concurrently. Do not, however, undertake so many that you are unable to stop the reactions at precisely the correct times. If you have to make several runs of equal duration, a staggered schedule is optimal. Set up all the assay tubes for a given set of trials containing all but the last solution that will initiate the reaction. Add the prescribed amount of this last solution to the first tube; exactly one minute later add the prescribed amount of solution to the second tube and so on. You will then be able to quench the reactions at one minute intervals with all times precisely controlled.

5) The enzyme, a protein, is susceptible to attack by airborne microorganisms. Obtain it from your instructor only in the amount needed for the runs you expect to be able to complete that day. Obtain the enzyme in a clean test tube, sterilized by boiling water in it for a few minutes and then cooled (after pouring out the water) with a cotton plug in its mouth. When you have obtained your enzyme solution (or suspension), immediately cover it with a thin layer, a few drops, of toluene, keep the cotton plug in place as much of the time as possible, and keep the tube in a beaker of ice to retard bacterial spoilage. Before pipetting an aliquot of the enzyme, swirl the tube a few times to produce a uniform suspension, and when pipetting, take care not to deliver any toluene to the assay tube.

The Reagents. Although all the solutions you will require for this experiment will be available in the laboratory, you might like to know how the nonconventional ones are prepared. We shall give here the recipes for making enough 3,5-dinitrosalicylate reducing-sugar reagent, glucose-fructose standard solution, acetate buffer, and enzyme suspension for twenty complete performances of this experiment.

The reducing-sugar reagent is made up by mixing two solutions: a solution of about 25.0 gm of 3,5-dinitrosalicyclic acid in 1000 ml of warm 1 M NaOH and one of 750 gm of sodium potassium tartrate, $NaKC_4H_4O_4 \cdot 4H_2O$ (Rochelle salt) in 750 ml of warm distilled water. These solutions are mixed slowly and diluted to a total volume of 2500 ml with warm distilled water.

The glucose-fructose standard solution contains exactly 0.090 gm of glucose and 0.090 gm of fructose in 100 ml of distilled water made up in a volumetric flask.

The acetate buffer solution contains 4.10 gm of sodium acetate, $NaC_2H_3O_2$, in 1000 ml of distilled water; 2.65 ml of glacial acetic acid is added to this solution. What is the pH?

The enzyme solution must be prepared with great care. All apparatus that will come in contact with the enzyme is first sterilized. Then about 0.50 gm (precisely weighed) of powdered invertase (available from most biological supply houses) is suspended in 2000 ml of boiled distilled water. Once made up, the enzyme is kept chilled at all times and a thin layer of toluene is poured over the surface of the suspension to keep out bacteria. When the enzyme is dispensed to you, it should be stirred to homogenize it before being dispensed. This is more readily accomplished by having a magnetic stirring bar in each bottle of enzyme so that it can be easily stirred without introducing any contamination.

The Standard Assay Procedure. The standard procedure to be used (with variations as indicated) in all runs is as follows.

1) Into a clean test tube pipet, in order,

1.0 ml of enzyme solution,

0.5 ml of distilled water,

0.5 ml of buffer solution,

1.0 ml of 0.3 M sucrose solution.

2) Begin timing as the sucrose is added and let the reaction proceed for *exactly* 5.0 minutes.

3) At the end of the allotted period, "quench" the reaction by adding 2.0 ml of dinitrosalicylate reagent (containing NaOH as the active quenching agent).

4) Immerse the test tube in a boiling water bath for five minutes.

5) Cool the reaction tube by running cold tap water down the outside of it while holding the tube in a slanted position.

6) Dilute with 15.0 ml of distilled water carefully dispensed from a graduate.

7) Using a spectrocolorimeter, read the absorbance of the solution at 5400 Å against a distilled water blank.

The Specific Experiments and Calculations. The experiments to be performed are grouped into six categories, each denoted by a capital letter. Each group contains questions that should be answered, plots that should be constructed, and calculations that should be indicated in your final report of this experiment.

A The Blank Trials. Our first concern is to establish that the dinitrosalicylate reagent gives no appreciable test in the absence of reducing sugars. To establish this point, we systematically examine the results of the action of the reagent on each of the other substances present in the reaction mixture. The makeup of the solutions to be tested is indicated below.

Run	Enzyme, ml	Water, ml	Buffer, ml	0.3 M sucrose, ml
B1	0.0	2.5	0.5	0.0
B2	0.0	1.5	0.5	1.0
B3	1.0	1.5	0.5	0.0
B4	1.0	0.5	0.5	(1.0)

In the first three trials, mix the indicated reagents, wait 5.0 minutes, and then pick up the standard assay procedure at step 3. In trial B4, add the enzyme, water, and buffer solutions; then add 2.0 ml of the dinitrosalicylate reagent, swirl, and only then add the 1.0 ml of sucrose solution. Wait 5.0 minutes after the last addition and then pick up the standard assay procedure at step 4. Trial B4 constitutes a so-called "zero-time assay," since the sucrose is added only after the reagent that, allegedly, completely halts the enzymatic reaction, and is a particularly searching blank trial. (Why?) None of the blank trials should develop any appreciable absorbance at 5400 Å. Compare these results with those now to be obtained in the trials in which the effect of the reagent is to be standardized.

B The Standardization Trials. We must establish the absorbance (at 5400 Å) produced by the action of our reagent in the presence of known amounts of glucose and fructose. The reagent offers an exceedingly delicate test, and to standardize such a reagent we use a very dilute aqueous glucose-fructose solution (GFS) containing only 0.9 gm of glucose and 0.9 gm of fructose per liter. Three standardization trials should be sufficient.

Run	Enzyme, ml	Water, ml	Buffer, ml	0.3 M sucrose, ml	GFS, ml
S1	0.0	1.1	0.5	1.0	0.4
S2	0.0	0.7	0.5	1.0	0.8
S3	0.0	0.3	0.5	1.0	1.2

In each case, make up the indicated mixture and then pick up the standard assay procedure at step 3.* Blank B2 should have convinced you that, in the absence of the GFS, the mixture of reagents used in the standardization trials yields no test. The tests actually obtained in these trials can then be properly attributed to the action of the reagent on the GFS. Plot the results obtained in trials S1, S2, and S3 on a graph showing observed absorbance vs. micromoles of glucose and fructose present. (The GFS contains 0.005 moles of glucose + fructose *per liter*.)

C Standard Assay Procedure. Carry through the standard assay procedure, described above, with the enzyme solution that has been issued to you. The observed absorbance should fall in the range 0.6 to 0.9: if it does not do so, *complain*. You will be given the exact concentration of the enzyme solution in grams per liter. Using the standardization curve prepared under B, calculate from the result of your standard assay the "specific activity" of the enzyme, that is, the number of micromoles of sucrose hydrolyzed per minute per gram of enzyme present. (The specific activity of an enzyme preparation is, of course, a function of the purity of the enzyme. As inactive protein is removed from the preparation, the specific activity will rise. When the specific activity can no longer be increased by any purification method, a homogeneous enzyme preparation may have been achieved, but proof of this depends on other criteria.) The exact chemical composition of invertase is still unknown, but its molecular weight has been estimated as 100,000. Combining this datum with your calculated specific activity, calculate the "turnover number" for the enzyme, i.e., the number of molecules of sucrose hydrolyzed per second per molecule of enzyme present. Considering that the enzyme preparation used in your

---

* The standard assay called for under C can be conveniently conducted at the same time as the three standardization trials. However, take care that the standard assay is run for exactly 5.0 minutes.

solution is not 100% pure, and considering further that the entire invertase molecule apparently contains only one (perhaps doubtful) catalytically active site, you should find the turnover number a rather impressive reflection of the enormous catalytic activity of an enzyme.

D *Progress of the Reaction in Time.* For the first of the following two sets of trials, prepare some 0.03 *M* sucrose solution by diluting 1 ml of the 0.3 *M* stock solution with 9 ml of distilled water.

Run	Enzyme, ml	Water, ml	Buffer, ml	0.03 *M* (N.B.) sucrose, ml	Time, min
TC0	1.0	0.5	0.5	(1.0)	0
TC1	1.0	0.5	0.5	1.0	1
TC3	1.0	0.5	0.5	1.0	3
TC5	1.0	0.5	0.5	1.0	5
TC10	1.0	0.5	0.5	1.0	10
TC20	1.0	0.5	0.5	1.0	20

Run	Enzyme, ml	Water, ml	Buffer, ml	0.3 *M* sucrose, ml	Time, min
TD0	0.2	1.3	0.5	(1.0)	0
TD1	0.2	1.3	0.5	1.0	1
TD3	0.2	1.3	0.5	1.0	3
TD5	0.2	1.3	0.5	1.0	5
TD10	0.2	1.3	0.5	1.0	10
TD20	0.2	1.3	0.5	1.0	20

Trials TC0 and TD0 are zero-time blanks in which the sucrose addition is made only *after* inactivation of the enzyme by the addition of 2.0 ml of dinitrosalicylate reagent. In all other trials, begin timing when the sucrose solution is added, and let the reaction proceed for *precisely* the time indicated in each case. Then pick up the standard assay procedure at step 3.

If the reaction were zero order in sucrose, it would be the case that $x = kt$, where x stands for the number of micromoles of sucrose hydrolyzed (= one-half the micromoles of glucose and fructose produced). (Why?) Prepare a graph of the results obtained in the above two series of trials, plotting x versus t, and indicate whether your data are consistent with the hypothesis that the reaction is zero order in sucrose.

If the reaction were first order in sucrose, then it would be the case that $\ln [a/(a - x)] = kt$ where a stands for the number of micromoles of sucrose originally present. (Why?) Prepare a graph of the results obtained in the above two series of trials, plotting $\log [a/(a - x)]$ versus t, and indicate whether your data are consistent with the hypothesis that the reaction is first order in sucrose.

Can we properly regard the average rate measured over the first 5.0 minutes of reaction as an acceptable approximation to the true *initial* rate of reaction?

E *Dependence of the Initial Rate on Substrate Concentration.* Prepare, from the 0.3 *M* stock solution of sucrose, another 10 ml of 0.03 *M* sucrose solution. Taking care to use the sucrose solution called for in each case, proceed to the following trials, all of which are to be run for the standard time of 5.0 minutes, except that run E0 is a zero-time blank.

Run	Enzyme, ml	Water, ml	Buffer, ml	Sucrose, ml
E0	1.0	0.5	0.5	(1.0), 0.3 *M*
E1	1.0	0.5	0.5	1.0, 0.3 *M*
E2	1.0	1.3	0.5	0.2, 0.3 *M*
E3	1.0	0.5	0.5	1.0, 0.03 *M*
E4	1.0	1.0	0.5	0.5, 0.03 *M*
E5	1.0	1.3	0.5	0.2, 0.03 *M*
E6	1.0	1.4	0.5	0.1, 0.03 *M*

From your results, determine the initial velocity, v, at each concentration of sucrose. Prepare a (Lineweaver-Burk) plot of $1/v$ versus $1/[S]$. Are your results consistent with the Michaelis-Menten equation? If so, from your plot, determine the values of the maximum velocity, $V_{\max}$ and the Michaelis-Menten constant, K_m.

F *Dependence of the Initial Rate on Enzyme Concentration.* Use the stock (0.3 *M*) sucrose solution in all the following trials, which are to be run for the standard time of 5.0 minutes except that run F0 is a zero-time blank.

Run	Enzyme, ml	Water, ml	Buffer, ml	0.3 *M* sucrose, ml
F0	1.0	0.5	0.5	(1.0)
F1	1.5	0.0	0.5	1.0
F2	1.0	0.5	0.5	1.0
F3	0.5	1.0	0.5	1.0
F4	0.2	1.3	0.5	1.0
F5	0.1	1.4	0.5	1.0

From your results, prepare a plot of initial reaction rate vs. enzyme concentration. Comment on the consistency of your data with the requirements of the Michaelis-Menten equation.

Further Experimental Problems

Dependence of the Rate on Temperature. Use one section of an expanded foam acid case as a constant-temperature bath. Convenient temperatures are 0° (ice bath), 12°, 25°, 35°, and 45°C, approximately. In each case, prepare the standard enzyme-water-buffer mixture in the assay tube, put about 2 ml of the sucrose stock solution in another test tube, and immerse both tubes in the chosen water bath for a few minutes to secure temperature equilibrium. Then pipet 1.0 ml of the equilibrated sucrose solution into the assay tube. Leave the assay tube in the constant-temperature bath until exactly 5.0 minutes after the addition of the sucrose solution; the reaction is terminated by the addition of 2.0 ml of dinitrosalicylate reagent. Then finish the assay as usual. Determine v for each temperature, and prepare a plot of $\log v$ versus $1/T$ for all your trials. From the slope of the line defined by your experimental points, you can determine ΔE_a. Ordinarily ΔE_a is calculated from a plot of $\log k$ versus $1/T$; what basis have we to establish ΔE_a from a plot of $\log v$ versus $1/T$?

The Nonenzymatic Hydrolysis of Sucrose, with H^+ as Catalyst. The basic procedure here runs as follows.

1) Pipet the indicated volume of 0.3 M sucrose solution into the assay tube.

2) Add sufficient distilled water to hold the final volume of reaction mixture steady at 4 ml (not 3 ml, as in all preceding trials).

3) Add the indicated volume of 1 M HCl solution to initiate catalytic hydrolysis, starting your timing as the acid is added.

4) After exactly 5.0 minutes, stop the reaction by adding 5 ml of 1 M NaOH, which at once soaks up the bulk of the catalytically active H^+ present.

5) Add 2.0 ml of dinitrosalicylate reagent and heat in a boiling water bath for five minutes.

6) Cool the reaction tube and dilute by adding 9 ml of distilled water (not 15 ml, as in earlier runs) so that the final volume is, as before, 20 ml.

7) Read the absorbance of the solution at 5400 Å.

The following is a set of suggested concentrations at which the above procedure can be carried out.

Run	Sucrose, ml	Water, ml	1 M HCl, ml
H1	1.0	2.0	1.0
H2	1.0	1.0	2.0
H3	2.0	1.0	1.0
H4	2.0	0.0	2.0
HB	2.0	2.0	0.0

Trial HB is a blank, which will allow you to see how much (if any) hydrolysis takes place in the absence of any catalyst. From trials H1 through H4 you can estimate the rate constant, for the reaction, on the assumption that the rate law has the form

$$-\frac{d[S]}{dt} = k[S][H^+].$$

Are your data generally consistent with this assumption? Also, calculate a turnover member for the H^+-catalyzed reaction, i.e., calculate the number of molecules of sucrose hydrolyzed per second per H^+ ion present, and compare this value with the turnover number calculated for the enzyme-catalyzed reaction. Comment.

Other Problems. By a series of trials at different temperatures, determine ΔE_a for the H^+-catalyzed reaction and compare this value with ΔE_a for the enzyme-catalyzed reaction.

Determine the temperature at which the enzymatic reaction reaches a maximum velocity. This is the temperature just below that at which the enzyme begins to be denatured. In such studies take care that the solutions have really reached temperature equilibrium before the sucrose is added to initiate reaction.

Determine the pH at which invertase functions most effectively as a catalyst. Is the reaction rate highly dependent on pH? Why should pH have anything to do with the catalytic activity of invertase?

Investigate the inhibition of the enzymatic reaction by p-mercuribenzoate at concentrations of about 10^{-5} M. Show how an investigation of inhibition or "poisoning" of the catalyst might be used to establish the number of catalytically active sites on an invertase molecule.

If you would prefer to follow up the sucrose inversion, acid-catalyzed, in more detail you might get some ideas from the article by Dawber, et al. You can use the assay method developed in this experiment in place of the polarimetric technique described in the article.

EXPERIMENT 32.   The Rate of Exchange of Iodine Between Inorganic and Organic Iodides

Introduction

Most reactions involve reactants and products of differing formulas and geometries; the effects of these differences may obscure some smaller influences which are interesting. Consider, however, an *exchange reaction* such as

$$I^{*-} + RI \rightleftharpoons I^- + RI^*, \tag{13-45}$$

where the iodine initially present as iodide ion is "exchanged" for the iodine initially bonded to the organic group, R. If we can study the rate of this exchange reaction for a number of different organic iodides, the only change from one reaction to the next will be the structure of the organic group; perhaps we can correlate differences in exchange rates with differences in the structure of the organic group.

You might object that it is impossible to study a reaction like (13–45) because no changes in concentrations occur during the course of the reaction. However, if we label one of the forms of iodine to begin with, we can follow the path of this labeled iodine as a function of time. The most convenient labeling method is to use a radioactive isotope of iodine, I^{131}. Until the radioactive decay occurs, the only difference between I (the nonradioactive isotope) and I* (the radioactive isotope) is a small difference in mass; chemically they are the same.† Naturally, then, as the reaction proceeds, the gross concentrations of the inorganic and organic iodides do not change, and what at first appeared to be an obstacle actually makes the results of exchange reactions comparatively simple to analyze.‡

The integration of a second-order rate expression that is first order in each of two changing concentrations is somewhat complicated. Let us take as our example the reaction we will study, reaction (13–45); the experiment consists of taking a known amount of RI in a suitable solvent and then adding a known amount of inorganic iodide ion. Some of the iodide is radioactive; it is used as a "tracer" for the bulk of the iodide, which is inactive. All the iodide reacts in the same manner, whether radioactive or not, and the course of the reaction is followed by separating the organic iodide from the iodide ion and determining the amount of radioactivity left as inorganic iodide. We know the following quantities:

$[I^{*-}]_0$ = radioactive iodide ion concentration, $t = 0$,

$[RI]_0$ = organic iodide concentration, $t = 0$,

$[I^-]_0$ = total iodide concentration, any time,

$[I^{*-}]$ = radioactive iodide concentration, $t = t$,

$[I^-]_0 \gg [I^{*-}]_0$.

If we take reaction (13–45) as a representation of the actual mechanism of the reaction, then we can write the rate expression for the forward reaction as

$$\left(-\frac{d[I^{*-}]}{dt} \right)_f = k_f [I^{*-}][RI].$$

After the reaction has proceeded to some extent, we

---

† Recall that we showed in Experiment 30 that a kinetic isotope effect would exist and would affect the rate of a reaction. Such effects are very roughly proportional to $\sqrt{m'/m}$, where m' is the mass of one isotope and m is the mass of the other. Thus for deuterium and hydrogen we get $\sqrt{2/1} = 1.41$, but for I^{131} (radioactive) and I^{127} we get $\sqrt{131/127} = 1.01$. The kinetic isotope effect for iodine is negligible in comparison to other uncertainties in the experimental procedure.
‡ A radioactive tracer is also used in Experiment 2, but there it is a convenience, not a necessity. In this experiment labeling is a necessity.

shall have to take into account the reverse reaction that will form I^{*-},

$$\left(\frac{d[I^{*-}]}{dt} \right)_r = k_r [I^-][RI^*].$$

The overall rate of change of the $[I^*]$ will be given by the difference between the forward and reverse expressions,

$$\left(-\frac{d[I^{*-}]}{dt} \right)_f - \left(\frac{d[I^{*-}]}{dt} \right)_r = -\frac{d[I^{*-}]}{dt},$$

$$-\frac{d[I^{*-}]}{dt} = k_f [I^{*-}][RI] - k_r [I^-][RI^*].$$

This expression can be simplified somewhat by noting that since (chemically) the forward and reverse reactions are the same, $k_f = k_r = k$:

$$-\frac{d[I^{*-}]}{dt} = k\{[I^{*-}][RI] - [I^-][RI^*]\}. \qquad (13\text{–}46)$$

Of the quantities on the right-hand side of Eq. (13–46), k is to be determined and $[I^{*-}]$ is to be measured. Since only minute amounts of RI* are ever formed, [RI] is essentially equal to $[RI]_0$. Similarly, $[I^-] \simeq [I^-]_0$. Thus $[RI^*]$ is conveniently expressed as $[I^{*-}]_0 - [I^{*-}]$. When these relationships are substituted into Eq. (13–46), we obtain

$$-\frac{d[I^{*-}]}{dt} = k\{[I^{*-}][RI]_0 - [I^-]_0([I^{*-}]_0 - [I^{*-}])\}.$$

To simplify our notation, let us make the substitutions: $x = [I^{*-}]$, $a = [RI]_0$, $b = [I^-]_0$, $c = [I^{*-}]_0$. Then the preceding equation becomes

$$-\frac{dx}{dt} = k\{ax - b(c - x)\}$$

or

$$-\frac{dx}{ax - b(c - x)} = k\,dt,$$

$$\left(\frac{1}{a+b} \right)\left(\frac{dx}{x - bc/(a+b)} \right) = -k\,dt. \qquad (13\text{–}47)$$

Equation (13–47) can be integrated to give (see a table of integrals)

$$\frac{1}{a+b} \cdot \ln\left\{ x - \frac{bc}{a+b} \right\} = -kt + C; \qquad (13\text{–}48)$$

C can be evaluated by noting that, when $t = 0$, $x = c$:

$$C = \frac{1}{a+b} \cdot \ln\left\{ \frac{c(a+b) - bc}{a+b} \right\}$$

$$= \frac{1}{a+b} \cdot \ln\left\{ \frac{ac}{a+b} \right\}.$$

Substituting this result into (13–48) and simplifying, we obtain

$$k = \frac{2.303}{(a+b)t} \log \left\{ \frac{a}{(x/c)(a+b) - b} \right\},$$

and returning to concentration symbols this becomes

$$k = \frac{2.303}{([RI]_0 + [I^-]_0)t}$$
$$\times \log \left\{ \frac{[RI]_0}{([I^{*-}]/[I^{*-}]_0)([RI]_0 + [I^-]_0) - [I^-]_0} \right\}.$$
$$(13-49)$$

All of the quantities on the right-hand side of (13–49) are either known or measured, so we can determine values of k for various organic iodides. (Note that it is only the *ratio* of amounts of I^{*-} at $t = 0$ and $t = t$ that is involved in this determination.)

Variations of exchange rates with changes in the structure of the reactants arise from a variety of effects, such as inductive effects, resonance effects, and steric factors; we shall be most concerned with *inductive effects*. Organic molecules can be viewed, as can all molecules, as collections of nuclei held together by electrons (Experiments 24 and 25). Some of these electrons, especially those in the innermost orbitals, will be very closely bound to a nucleus and will be little affected by any other nuclei. The spatial distribution of the electrons, however, may be influenced by two or more nuclei; a change in the position or nature of one of these nuclei will thus change the electronic distribution around the other, an induced (or inductive) effect. Let us examine the molecules acetic acid and chloroacetic acid to see how this effect operates.

Acetic acid   Chloroacetic acid

All of the $1s$-electrons on the carbons, oxygens, and the chlorine are closely bound and will not be considered further. The $2s$- and $2p$-electrons of the carbons and oxygens and the electrons from the hydrogens, which form the bonds between all these atoms, are less tightly held.

Let us focus on the O—H bond in each molecule. The electronegativity of oxygen is greater than that of hydrogen, so the electron pair which forms this bond will be closer to the oxygen atom. However, the bond is still quite strong; the proton is rather tightly held, which means that acetic acid is a weak acid. Substitution of a chlorine atom for a hydrogen atom causes the O—H

bond to become weaker; the acidic ionization constant of chloroacetic acid is 85 times as large as the constant for acetic acid. The reason that the O—H bond is weaker is that the electrons forming the bond are affected by the chlorine atom.

Since the Cl is more electronegative than the H it replaced, the bonding electrons in the C—Cl bond will be, on the average, closer to the Cl than to the C, thus producing a slight positive charge at the C. This charge in turn tends to distort the electron distribution in the C—C bond, moving electron density toward the C attached to the Cl. The loss of electron density from the C of the carboxyl group distorts the electron density in the C—O bonds, resulting in a slight loss of electron density about the oxygens and, hence, an even greater tendency to draw the electrons in the O—H bond away from the H. The overall effect is a slight shift of electron density in the molecule toward the Cl, so that the bond between O and H is not as strong and the proton ionizes more easily.

Before we go merrily on our way thinking we have thus explained the increase in acidic ionization constant for chloroacetic as opposed to acetic acid, we should examine the further implications of our ideas. If one chlorine is good, replacing two or all three hydrogens by chlorine should increase the ionization constant even more. Such is the case; trichloroacetic acid is a moderately strong acid, more than 10,000 times stronger than acetic. However, the change in ionization constant reflects a change in the free energy for the ionization reaction, but all our arguments have revolved about the energy or enthalpy changes in the reaction. Trying to correlate a free-energy-dependent function with an energetic argument might lead us into trouble; in particular, when we examine the enthalpy changes for the ionization of acetic and trichloroacetic acids, we find that they are almost the same. It is a very large difference in the entropies for these two reactions that accounts for the difference between their ionization constants. This does not vitiate the inductive-effect argument, for the same solvation effects that cause the large change in entropy probably ought to increase the enthalpy of the ionization reaction for trichloroacetic acid; thus, perhaps, the inductive effect is just strong enough to balance out the solvation effects and cause a net zero effect in going from acetic to trichloroacetic acid. This note is added here to make you aware that you must be on your toes and not accept glib and facile explanations for phenomena until you have thought through their implications and tested these.

Many other examples of the inductive effect are known; in particular, different kinds of organic groups will have different effects. It is this latter effect we may study in this experiment.

Procedure

Before continuing this discussion (and before entering the laboratory) turn to Appendix F and familiarize yourself with the discussion of radioactivity and the proper precautions to be observed for safe handling of radioactive isotopes.

The procedure outlined in this section is used for counting with a well-type scintillation counter. (Here and there throughout the procedure modifications will be suggested that would be applicable to an end-window Geiger tube. A great advantage of the scintillation counter is its relatively high efficiency so that the required activity of the sample is lower: a desirable safety feature. The advantage of the Geiger counter is its much lower cost.)

The background counting rate, from cosmic rays and stray radiation, should be determined each day so that it may be subtracted from the observed counting rate for your samples. It is convenient to determine the background while you are preparing the exchange solutions. Before turning on your counter, consult the instruction manual or your instructor. Turn on your counter and put a clean sample tube in the scintillation well (or a clean planchet and filter paper in front of the Geiger tube).* Set the register, decades, and the timer to zero. Since as large a total count as possible is desirable for the background reading, you should begin counting and timing (without limit) as soon as possible and continue until you have a sample to count. At that time, stop the counting and record the total time and total number of counts. This will probably be much less than 10,000 counts, but sufficient accuracy can be obtained by counting background whenever you are not counting a sample. The background rate should be at most 300 cpm; if it reaches 500 cpm, the scintillation well, or the sample tube (planchet), is almost surely contaminated. *Take care not to contaminate the detector*; a high background reduces the precision of the sample measurements.

The reaction will be carried out in acetonitrile, $CH_3C{\equiv}N$, a flammable and slightly toxic liquid (and vapor). Technical grade acetonitrile may be used but is sometimes contaminated; use only solvent that is clear and "water-white." Do not have any flames in the laboratory, avoid breathing the vapors, and always work in the hoods except when actually counting a

sample. Acetonitrile is a fairly good solvent for both inorganic and organic iodides (Why might this be? What are the physical properties of acetonitrile compared to water?) and it does not seem to interfere with the exchange reaction.

Prepare two reaction mixtures as follows.† Pipet 50 ml of 0.1 M NaI in acetonitrile into a 125-ml flask. Add 1.0 ml of radioactive NaI solution, using the proper (micro)pipet. (This solution is 0.10 M NaI in acetonitrile; it contains small amounts of H_2O, NaOH, Na_2SO_3, and enough (a minute amount) I^{131} to give an initial, time zero, counting rate of 1000 to 2000 cpm. The contaminants are present because labeled sodium iodide is obtained as an aqueous solution containing a small amount of sodium sulfite.) Swirl the mixture to make sure it is well mixed. Place 5.0 ml of CCl_4 and 7.0 ml of H_2O in a small separatory funnel; remove 4.0 ml of solution from the reaction flask and run it into the separatory funnel. Treat the mixture in the separatory funnel according to the procedure described in the next paragraph. Pipet (micropipet) 0.5 ml of one of the available organic iodides into the 125-ml reaction flask. Swirl the mixture until it is homogeneous (about five seconds) and record the time; this is t_0. (Some organic iodides that are suitable for this experiment are n-propyl, n-butyl, isobutyl, sec-butyl, isopropyl, n-pentyl, and n-hexyl; your instructor will tell you which one to use in your experiment.)

Stopper the separatory funnel, invert it, shake once, and open the stopcock to vent it. Close the stopcock, shake again, and vent again. Close the stopcock, turn the funnel right side up, and set it in a ring to allow the two layers to separate. The organic iodide, when it is present, will be concentrated in the CCl_4 layer, while the NaI will be almost entirely in the upper aqueous layer. (What proof can you devise for these assertions?) Open the funnel and drain off the CCl_4 layer; put it into the plastic waste jar *immediately*. Take two sample tubes and pipet 4.0 ml of the aqueous layer into each. (For planchet counting, pipet 0.2-ml portions of the aqueous layer into filter paper circles in aluminum planchets.) Insert one tube into the detector well carefully and record the time for 10,000 counts. (Counting more than 10,000 counts is rarely necessary in kinetic studies; the factors that limit the ultimate accuracy of the experiment are usually other variables.) This can usually be done automatically by presetting the counter for a given number of counts, setting the register, decades,

---

* The tube (or planchet) is inserted even while counting background to make all conditions as much as possible identical to those you will use in counting samples. Relative counting rates can only be compared if they are obtained on the same equipment with the samples in the same position and constant voltage on the photomultiplier (or Geiger tube). If these conditions are met, relative counting rates can be accurate to within about a percent.

---

† If this is the first time you are carrying out the procedure, prepare only one mixture and use 1.0 ml of *inactive* 0.1 M NaI solution. Practice the entire procedure with this solution, including the "counting," to develop your technique. This *must* be done before you handle radioactive solutions.

and the timer to zero, and then counting; the count and timer will both stop at the preset (10,000 count) figure. Record which reaction mixture the sample came from, at what time it was delivered into the CCl_4-H_2O mixture, the total number of counts, and the time required for those counts. (If it takes more than ten minutes to reach 10,000 counts, it is wise to stop and accept lower accuracy for the sake of obtaining more measurements. Discard the sample into the plastic waste container and rinse the sample tube twice with decontaminating solution (0.1 M NaI in acetonitrile), then twice with water. Invert it to dry. Repeat the count with the second sample tube.

Follow this procedure with both reaction mixtures. At 15 to 25 minutes after t_0, remove a 4.0-ml aliquot from each reaction mixture and run it into a CCl_4-H_2O mixture exactly as described above. Follow the procedure for obtaining a count, being careful to record the relevant data. In the same way, try to obtain a third count from each reaction mixture at 45 to 60 minutes after t_0. Then discard the second reaction mixture and follow the activity decrease in the first for as long as possible. Stop in plenty of time to clean up. Rinse all glassware that contained radioactive solutions once or twice with decontaminating solution and once with water. Be careful not to splash the rinse liquids; deliver them into the waste container. Leave all glassware as you found it (or cleaner). Discard your plastic gloves into the "radioactive waste" basket.

Calculations

The raw counting rates you have collected must be corrected for *coincidence loss* (dead time of the apparatus) and the background rate. The dead time correction, Eq. (F–6), which is discussed in Appendix F should be used to correct your counting rates. Your instructor will tell you what the dead time of your equipment is (for a Geiger detector, 200 microseconds is a good figure); ignore the correction if it results in less than 1% change. Subtract the background rate (corrected, if necessary) from the corrected rates to get the true rates for the samples.

Calculate the various initial concentrations, assuming that the alkyl iodide is 100% pure, that all volumes are additive, and that NaI is ionized completely in 0.1 M acetonitrile solutions. The ratio $[I*^-]/[I*^-]_0$ can be replaced by the ratio of (corrected) counting rates at t and t_0. Calculate k, Eq. (13–49), in units of liter/mole-second for each counting rate you have; average these for each sample. (Do t_0 and $[I*^-]_0$ have to be those of the initial reading?)

When the results of everyone's runs have been posted, note the average rate constant for each of the organic iodides studied. What conclusions can you draw about the effect of the structure of the reactant on the rate of exchange?

Further Experimental Problems

Exchange reactions of organic iodides with I^- have been studied in a variety of solvents and the results reported in the literature. Very few reports have been made of exchange studies in acetonitrile. It might be very interesting to compare your results in this aprotic (i.e., without protons) solvent to those obtained in other solvents, e.g., acetone (also aprotic), acetone-water, and alcohol-water mixtures. The absence of protons (and hydroxyl groups) may have a large influence on the relative rates of these reactions. Such influences are certainly implied by the finding that solvents containing water often produce some alcohol from the original iodide:

$$RI + H_2O = ROH + H^+ + I^-.$$

(Interfering reactions like this make interpretation of the exchange results harder, but not impossible.) This solvent-effect study could be either an experimental or a library problem. (You might begin by reading the article by Schaefer and glancing at the review by Streitwieser.)

Rate constants for ionic reactions are, in general, dependent on the ionic strength of the solution. This effect is due in part to the lowering of the activity of ions by other ions (see the discussion of the Debye-Hückel theory in Section 9–1). Most physical chemistry textbooks discuss this point, as do kinetics textbooks like Frost and Pearson. You might like to test the effect of ionic strength by running a series of exchanges at different ionic strengths and comparing the results.

Temperature, of course, may be an important variable in this reaction. It is easy to run the reaction at a series of temperatures to test this point.

The analysis we have presented for exchange reactions rests on a number of assumptions, the most important of which is the assumed validity of Eq. (13–45). What if this reaction does not truly represent the sole, or even most important, mechanism for exchange? Then our analysis leading to Eq. (13–49) is incorrect and the rate constants you have calculated are meaningless. In particular, suppose the following mechanism is important:

$$RI \rightarrow R^+ + I^-, \quad \text{Slow,}$$
$$R^+ + I* \rightarrow RI*, \quad \text{Rapid.}$$

Then this first-order reaction would have to be accounted for in the analysis of the data. How can you test for such a reaction (or any first-order reaction involving the organic iodide, but not the inorganic iodide)?

Try varying the initial concentration of organic iodide at constant ionic strength and calculate the exchange-rate constant under these new conditions. What result would you expect if first-order processes are negligible? If not?

A further assumption you have made is that the molarity of NaI is the molarity of I^-. This will not be true unless the NaI is completely dissociated into its ions. In solvents of relatively low dielectric constant (such as acetonitrile) dissociation may not be complete so $[I^-]$ will be lower than your calculated value. Studies of these *association effects* are not easy to carry out, but you might do some library work and perhaps be able to design an experiment that would test for ion association.

REFERENCES

BALDWIN, M. E., S. C. CHAN, and M. L. TOBE, "The Mechanism and Steric Course of Octahedral Aquation. Part IV. The Aquation of *cis-* and *trans-*Dichloro and *cis-* and *trans-*Chlorohydroxo-bis (ethylenediamine) cobalt(III) salts," *J. Chem. Soc.* (London) **1961,** 4637 presents a detailed study of the reaction we outlined in Experiment 28; the reaction is actually a great deal more complex than our simple outline indicates.

BARROW, G. M., *The Structure of Molecules,* W. A. Benjamin, New York, 1963, Chapters I, III, and IV.

BARTON, D., and K. WINTER, "Ligand Exchange Kinetics by the Radioactive Tracer Technique," *J. Chem. Ed.* **43,** 93 (1966).

BRICE, L. K., "A First-Order Rate of Isomerization," *J. Chem. Ed.* **39,** 634 (1962) discusses the $Coen_2Cl_2{}^+$ system in methanol.

BRITTON, D., and Z. Z. HUGUS, JR., "Static and Kinetic Measurements of an Equilibrium Constant," *J. Chem. Ed.* **40,** 607 (1963).

BURR, J. G., JR., *Tracer Applications for the Study of Organic Reactions,* Interscience, New York, 1957, Chapters 2 and 4.

CHESICK, J. P., and A. PATTERSON, JR., "Determination of Reaction Rates with an A. C. Conductivity Bridge," *J. Chem. Ed.* **37,** 242 (1960) describes an inexpensive, transistorized A. C. bridge for conductivity measurements and a kinetics experiment to use it. Such a tool might be useful for many other studies as well; consider Experiments 28 and 30, for example.

DAWBER, J. G., D. R. BROWN, and R. A. REED, "Acid-Catalyzed Hydrolysis of Sucrose," *J. Chem. Ed.* **43,** 34 (1966) develops the acid-catalyzed counterpart of Experiment 31.

FROST, A. A., and R. G. PEARSON, *Chemical Kinetics,* 2nd ed. John Wiley & Sons, New York, 1961.

GREENBERG, D. B., "Reaction Kinetics from Conductivity Data," *J. Chem. Ed.* **39,** 140 (1962) presents the construction and use of a conductivity apparatus for following the course of a hydrolysis reaction.

JONES, P., and K. B. OLDHAM, "Theory of the Formaldehyde Clock Reaction," and with M. L. Haggett, "Flowing Clock Reaction," *J. Chem. Ed.* **40,** 366 and 367 (1963) presents the formaldehyde clock reaction ($HCHO + HSO_3{}^-$) adapted for a simple flow system. See also, R. L. Barrett, "The Formaldehyde Clock Reaction," *J. Chem. Ed.* **32,** 78 (1955).

The Journal of Chemical Education usually averages one or two kinetics experiments per issue. A few are listed in these references; however you should go to the journal yourself for further ideas if this area of study is interesting to you.

KING, E. L., *How Chemical Reactions Occur,* W. A. Benjamin, New York, 1963.

KREEVOY, M. M., "The Exposition of Isotope Effects on Rates and Equilibria," *J. Chem. Ed.* **41,** 636 (1964).

LEISTEN, J. A., "Homogeneous Catalysis," *J. Chem. Ed.* **41,** 23 (1964) reexamines the old definitions and proposes a new one.

McCOOL, W. J., and R. R. HENTZ, "Two Experiments for the Radiochemical Laboratory," *J. Chem. Ed.* **32,** 329 (1955) suggests tests for the equivalence or nonequivalence of the sulfurs in $S_2O_3{}^=$ and for finding out whether exchange occurs between $S_2O_3{}^=$ and $S_4O_6{}^=$ [erratum: **32,** 455 (1955)].

ROBBIN, R., "The Imitative Drugs," *Scientific American,* April 1, 1951, p. 60.

SCHAEFER, W. P., "A Kinetics Experiment for First Year Chemistry," *J. Chem. Ed.* **41,** 558 (1964) is the work upon which Experiment 32 is based; it presents the experiment as carried out at Caltech.

SCHWEITZER, G. K., and I. B. WHITNEY, *Radioactive Tracer Techniques,* D. Van Nostrand, Princeton, N.J., 1949.

SHAW, W. H. R., "Kinetics of Enzyme Catalyzed Reactions," *J. Chem. Ed.* **34,** 22 (1957).

WHITAKER, R. D., "Kinetics Experiment for the Physical Chemistry Laboratory," *J. Chem. Ed.* **40,** 264 (1963) suggests measuring the rate of dissociation of the complex Ni (o-phen)$_3{}^{++}$ spectrophotometrically.

ZOLLINGER, H., "Lecture Demonstration of a Kinetic Isotope Effect," *J. Chem. Ed.* **34,** 249 (1957) is an excellent experiment that you can probably develop even further if you are interested in studying isotope effects.

14 THE FINAL PROBLEM

Because we began this peregrination through the practice of chemistry with a quotation from Arthur Conan Doyle's Sherlock Holmes stories, it seems appropriate that the final chapter should have the title "The Final Problem." Let us hope that you, like Holmes, have learned a great deal about the art and practice of observation and deduction during this journey. Further, let us hope that you will put this knowledge to appropriate use in solving the experimental problems posed in this chapter, rather than, like Holmes, attemping a brute force solution to "the final problem."*

14-1 RATIONALE FOR THE N-SOLUTION PROBLEM

It has been traditional in introductory chemistry courses to spend a rather substantial amount of time doing qualitative analysis, i.e., identifying the components in a mixture (usually inorganic cations and anions in aqueous solution). Such formal exercises are missing from this textbook for two reasons: (1) these exercises often form a portion of secondary school chemistry laboratory problems and (2) we felt that less formal presentation of the chemical reactions of the ions involved in your experiments would prompt you to read and experiment further on your own concerning the typical chemistry of some of the compounds you studied. Now the questions arise: How successful has such an approach been? How observant were you in your laboratory work? How well have you learned to use resource material to find out about reactions you have not actually performed in the laboratory?

To answer these questions we propose here an experiment in which such background information (or the ability to find it) along with the application of your deductive reasoning is of key importance. This experiment may be carried out any number of times in the course of your laboratory experience with an emphasis on different kinds of chemically reacting systems each time, e.g., precipitation reactions one time and redox reactions another.

14-2 THE N-SOLUTION PROBLEM STATED

Suppose you are confronted with N test tubes, numbered one through N, each containing a colorless aqueous solution and you are told the composition of the N solutions but not which composition corresponds to which test tube. Your problem is to find out which solution is in which test tube by intermixing aliquots of solutions from the test tubes only, i.e., no external reagents are allowed. This is the N-solution problem. The original suggestion for this problem and some good problems are given by MacWood, *et al.*

14-3 AN N-SOLUTION PROBLEM SOLVED

To make this problem more concrete let us consider a five-solution problem. Suppose that you have five numbered test tubes each of which contains one of the following aqueous solutions: 0.1 M AgNO$_3$, 0.1 M KI, 0.05 M KIO$_3$, 0.2 M HNO$_3$, and H$_2$O. How should we proceed to discover which solution is in which test tube without using external reagents? If we have learned anything from the experiments in this textbook we realize that some planning before simply barging ahead with indiscriminate solution mixing is always a wise idea.

---

* If, however, you should, by some quirk of fate, end like Holmes, we will hope that you too may be brought back for an encore as Holmes was from his seemingly fatal Swiss meeting with Professor Moriarty.

Therefore let us first sit back and consider what will happen when we intermix equal portions of each pair of these solutions. A table like Table 14–1 is useful in making such a comparison. Armed with such a tabulation we can begin our experimental work and will be able to compare our results with those in the table.

Table 14–1

RESULTS OF SOLUTION MIXING; REDUNDANT DATA ARE NOT GIVEN

	KI	KIO$_3$	HNO$_3$	H$_2$O
AgNO$_3$	AgI[a] Yellow solid	AgIO[b] White solid	–	–
KI		I$_2$ formed[c] Reddish brown	–	–
KIO$_3$			–	–
HNO$_3$				–

[a] $pK_s = 16.1$
[b] $pK_s = 7.5$
[c] The reaction I$^-$ with IO$_3^-$ is quite slow in neutral solution since the reaction is

$$5I^- + IO_3^- + 6H^+ \rightarrow 3I_2 + 3H_2O,$$

and H$^+$ will speed up the reaction (see Experiment 17).

Let us place about 0.5 ml of solution 1, i.e., the solution in test tube 1, in each of four small test tubes. Now add to the first of these small test tubes about 0.5 ml of solution 2, to the second about 0.5 ml of solution 3, and so on. Note the results. Let us suppose that no visible change occurs in any of the test tubes. What can we conclude? Evidently solution 1 does not react to cause a visible change with any of the other solutions. Which of our solutions would behave in this manner? Our table indicates that neither water nor HNO$_3$ will react to cause a visible change with any of the other solutions. Hence, solution 1 is either H$_2$O or 0.2 M HNO$_3$.

Continue the problem by placing about 0.5 ml of solution 2 in each of three small test tubes and add about 0.5 ml of solutions 3, 4, and 5, respectively, to the three small test tubes. Note the results. Suppose that solution 2 + solution 3 yields a yellow precipitate and solution 2 + solution 4 and solution 2 + solution 5 yield no visible change. What can we conclude? Since the only yellow precipitate we expect is AgI, either solution 2 or 3 is AgNO$_3$ and the other is KI. Can we tell which is which? We know that either solution 4 or 5 must be KIO$_3$ and, if solution 2 were AgNO$_3$, we would have expected to obtain a white precipitate from one of the other two mixings, but this did not occur. Thus, presumably, solution 3 is AgNO$_3$. But wait, if this is so, should we not have obtained a reaction of solution 2, now presumed to be KI, with either

solution 4 or 5, one of which must be KIO$_3$, to form I$_2$? We see from the footnotes to our table that the iodide-iodate reaction is not fast in neutral solution and we might, therefore, not see any visible change in the few moments we have been waiting. Let us assume this is the case; we now know:

solution 2 is 0.1 M KI,
solution 3 is 0.1 M AgNO$_3$, and
either solution 4 or 5 is 0.05 M KIO$_3$.

Now, mix about 0.5 ml each of solution 3 and solution 4 in a small test tube. Note the results. Suppose no visible change occurs. Since we have presumably already thought to calculate that AgIO$_3$ would indeed precipitate if equal volumes of 0.1 M AgNO$_3$ and 0.05 M KIO$_3$ were mixed (do so now, if you didn't before), we can conclude that solution 4 is not KIO$_3$ and hence, solution 5 is 0.05 M KIO$_3$.

Now we know that either solution 1 or 4 is 0.2 M HNO$_3$. How are we to discover which is which? We have the solution at our fingertips in the mixture of solutions 2 and 5 made above. If acid is added to this solution, the reaction to form I$_2$ ought to take place quite rapidly. Add a few drops of solution 1 to this mixture. Note the results. Suppose that the solution rapidly turns reddish-brown. We then conclude that:

solution 1 is 0.2 M HNO$_3$ and
solution 4 is H$_2$O.

This concludes our problem, since all solutions are now identified. You can run some checks now if you wish. For example, a few drops of solution 4 added to a mixture of 2 and 5 should give no observable change. Further, since HIO$_3$ is only a moderately weak acid we might anticipate that AgIO$_3$, like Ca(IO$_3$)$_2$ (Experiment 17), would be rather soluble in acid solution. Thus we would expect that if a few drops of solutions 3 and 5 were mixed to form some AgIO$_3$ (another test of our solution to the problem), addition of solution 1 would dissolve the precipitate. Can you think of any further checks on our solution?

Observe that only eight binary mixings were necessary to solve this problem. If we had not thought about the problem at each stage of the experiment, but had simply made all the nonredundant binary mixings possible (this is always $\sum_{j=1}^{j=N-1} j$, where j's are integers) we would have had to make ten mixings and still would have had to interpret them. In this particular case such a procedure does not even solve the problem because binary mixings cannot distinguish between the H$_2$O and HNO$_3$ in this problem. Hence, advance planning and careful thought throughout the problem are absolutely essential for efficient use of your laboratory time.

EXPERIMENT 33.   *The N-Solution Problem*

Preparation

The preparation you will need for this experiment will depend on your instructor and his use of the problem. In general, a nine-solution problem is adequate for one laboratory period. One method of presenting such a problem is to provide you with a list of fifteen to twenty solutions from which your nine will be chosen. Such a list should be available two or three weeks before you are to do the experiment. If the chemistry involved in the problem is supposed to be familiar to you from past experiments, you will not require too much time for preparation. On the other hand, you may find that some of the chemistry involved is not familiar, and you will have to spend time searching through the library for the answers to some of your questions. If the chemistry is such that actual experimental familiarity with the systems involved would be very helpful, your instructors will make the chemicals available during the laboratory periods preceding the one when you will tackle the problem. Thus you will be able to carry out any tests you feel will be valuable to your solution to the problem.

Before going to the laboratory for this experiment make a table for your possible solutions similar to Table 14–1 for the hypothetical problem we worked.

Procedure

During the laboratory period before this experiment, clean and dry N six-inch test tubes and label them with your name and the numbers 1 through N. Give the test tubes to your instructor.

When you arrive at the laboratory you will be given a list of the N solutions contained in your N test tubes and one-half to one hour to plan your attack on the problem. You will then have the remainder of the laboratory period to solve the problem.

Reporting the Experiment

Your report will consist, in part, of the solution to the problem, i.e., the matching of the numbers on the test tubes with the solution possibilities. This part of the report will be graded on the basis of speed and accuracy. Usually a certain point score will be assigned for a correct solution within a given time limit and the possible score will decrease with time thereafter. Points will be deducted for incorrect answers and you will have a chance to return to your laboratory bench to continue work toward a correct solution.

The other part of your report and your score will be based on your reasoning in approaching the problem. This will be deduced from your laboratory record of the experiment (including the planning you do at the beginning of the laboratory period) which you will turn in to your instructor before leaving the laboratory.

Further Experimental Problems

Why do the reactions carried out in qualitative analysis work the way they do? Why are some of the ingredients of the "recipe" necessary? Examples of such "recipes" will be found in the qualitative analysis textbooks listed in the references. Some examples of the kinds of questions you might ask and then try to answer are given in the article by Packer.

This concludes "the final problem" and the experiments in this textbook. Your instructors and those of us responsible for this book hope you enjoyed putting chemical principles into practice.

REFERENCES

MacWood, G. E., E. N. Lassettre, and G. Breen, "A Laboratory Experiment in General Chemistry," *J. Chem. Ed.* **17**, 520 (1940).

Packer, J. E., "Research Topics from Qualitative Inorganic Analysis," *J. Chem. Ed.* **43**, 197 (1966).

Ricketts, J. A., "Laboratory Exercise Emphasizing Deductive Reasoning," *J. Chem. Ed.* **37**, 311 (1960) suggests a procedure whereby you work out a qualitative analysis scheme based on your own observations on the individual ions that might be present in an unknown.

Sorum, C. H., *Introduction to Semi-Micro Qualitative Analysis*, 3rd ed. Prentice-Hall, Englewood Cliffs, N. J., 1960.

Swift, E. H., and W. P. Schaefer, *Qualitative Elemental Analysis*, Freeman, San Francisco, 1962.

Vogel, A. I., *A Textbook of Macro and Semi-Micro Qualitative Inorganic Analysis*, 4th ed. Longmans Green, London, 1954.

Zuehlke, R. W., "The Case of the Unlabeled Bottles," *J. Chem. Ed.* **43**, 601 (1966) presents a subtle variation on Experiment 33.

APPENDIX A

TREATMENT OF EXPERIMENTAL DATA

A-1 UNCERTAINTIES

Before launching into a discussion of the sources and treatment of uncertainties in our results, we must first define error and deviation and, concomitantly, accuracy and precision: two terms that are often incorrectly used as synonyms.

The *error* in a measurement or result is the difference between the measured value and the true value of the quantity measured. The smaller the error, the closer the measured value is to the true value and the more *accurate* is the measurement. *Accuracy is a measure of the correctness of a measurement.*

In a sense, the error in a measurement is very difficult to determine because the "true value" of the measured quantity is rarely known. Thus it is often useful to have an expression for the exactness of a measurement that does not depend on a knowledge of the true value of the measured quantity. The *deviation*, δ_i, of a measurement is defined as the difference between the measured value, x_i, and the arithmetic mean, $\bar{x}$, of a number, n, of measurements,

$$\delta_i = x_i - \bar{x}, \qquad (A-1)$$

$$\bar{x} = \frac{\sum_{i=1}^{n} x_i}{n}. \qquad (A-2)$$

The smaller the deviation of a measurement, the more *precise* is the measurement. *Precision is a measure of the reproducibility of a measurement.*

It should be evident that a series of measurements may be very precise but quite inaccurate. For example, your buret may have been mislabeled so that it reads 0, 1, . . . , 10, 11, 13, . . . , 25 ml (this example is not imaginary). You might make three identical titrations, beginning at the same volume near the top of the buret each time, and obtain the same final buret reading,

23.15 ml, in all three runs. The precision of your measurements is very good; the results are reproducible. The accuracy is very low; the actual volume delivered is 1.00 ml less than you read on the buret.

The term "error" is often used in a much looser sense than that defined above to refer to any mistake that is made. Although common in everyday usage, this sense should not be used in referring to laboratory practice. Misreading the mass stamped on a weight, losing solution from "bumping," using the wrong reagents, and so on, are not errors; they are *blunders*. *If blunders are due to carelessness, they are completely inexcusable.* At first, however, you will be somewhat inexperienced in laboratory techniques and operations, so it is not unlikely that you will make mistakes. These may contribute to the error (and deviation) of the final result, but they are not, strictly speaking, errors themselves.

A-2 SYSTEMATIC ERRORS

Errors are of two general types, systematic (determinate) and random (indeterminate). A systematic error has the same directional effect on each measurement that you make of a quantity. If the source of this type of error can be found, it is usually possible to make corrections to take it into account or to change the procedure to eliminate the error.

Methodic Errors

Sometimes the particular method employed for a determination will have an inherent error. For example, under certain conditions the precipitate formed in a gravimetric determination may be somewhat soluble. If you do not realize this and use the method under these particular conditions, your results will always be low because of loss of precipitate. Another example of methodic error is in titrations where the observed endpoint may not correspond to the true equivalence point. The error can be either positive or negative, depending on whether the endpoint comes after or before the true equivalence point.

Methodic errors are probably the worst sort of systematic errors because they are often very difficult to locate and even more difficult (or impossible) to eliminate. Often the only recourse is choosing a completely different procedure for obtaining a particular measurement.

Incorrect Calibrations of Apparatus

If the apparatus you use has not been calibrated or has been calibrated under different conditions than those you are using, your measurements will very probably be erroneous. You should understand the effect on your data of such things as weight calibrations, volumetric glassware calibrations, corrections for buoyancy in weighings, and corrections for temperature in barometric pressure readings.

Personal Errors

There are a number of ways that your personal traits can cause systematic errors in measurements. For instance, one of the most common physical defects, partial color-blindness, can make it very hard to tell the difference between, say, a green solution and a gray-green solution. Another form of personal error is number discrimination: you may, for example, tend to pick odd numbers when you read a scale by interpolation.

A more serious form of discrimination is prejudice based on some knowledge of the expected result. If the best straight line passing through the temperature-vs.-time readings in a calorimetric experiment seems to extrapolate to 35.2°C but you expected it to extrapolate to 35.4°C, you might be tempted to tilt the straightedge just a bit. Scientific results are never completely free of subjectivism, but you should strive to be as objective as possible.

Additive and Proportional Errors

Systematic errors may usually be classified as either additive or proportional. In general, both types will be present in any determination. An *additive* error is one which adds (or subtracts) the same absolute amount of uncertainty to all determinations of a value. For example, if you measure several lengths with a meter stick which has its first centimeter missing, all your measurements will be off by one centimeter (each measured apparent length will be one centimeter greater than the

true length). A *proportional* error is one which adds to (or subtracts from) a determination an uncertainty which varies in proportion to some parameter in the determination. For example, suppose you use a meter stick which has been miscalibrated so that each centimeter division is actually 11 mm long; all your measurements will be off, but the longer the length measured, the greater the absolute error will be (each measured apparent length will be too short by $\frac{1}{11}$ of its true value). Proportional errors are often relatively easy to find by simply varying all the parameters of a determination to see if the variations make any difference in the final result. If a variation does make a difference, there is a proportional error present in the determinations which will have to be controlled and corrected for. Additive errors, on the other hand, are exceedingly difficult to discover. If a determination is made by two completely independent methods in which all proportional errors have been eliminated and the values do not agree, then it is likely that one or both are afflicted with some additive error.

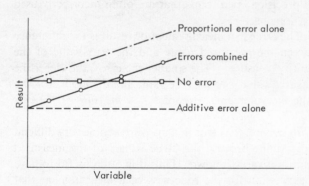

Fig. A–1. Effects of additive and proportional errors (□ true values, ○ values actually measured).

A schematic representation of the effect of additive and proportional errors on a determination is shown in Fig. A–1. The "variable" in the figure is the variable on which the proportional error depends.

A–3 RANDOM ERRORS

Even if all the systematic errors in a measurement are found and eliminated, there will still be a chance that the measurement is in error simply because it is impossible to make any measurement with infinite accuracy. Thus if you make a measurement a great many times you will obtain a range of values, due to the *random errors* inherent in any set of measurements. A number of measures of the spread or uncertainty in the observed values are used, such as mean deviation and standard deviation.

Mean Deviation

The *mean deviation*, *a*, is the average of the absolute values of the deviations from the means

$$a = \frac{\sum_{i=1}^{n} |\delta_i|}{n} = \frac{\sum_{i=1}^{n} |x_i - \overline{x}|}{n}. \tag{A–3}$$

Absolute values must be used in order to eliminate the signs of the deviations or, because of the way they are defined, the sum of all the deviations will be zero.

Standard Deviation

The *standard deviation*, *s*, is the root-mean-square deviation of a set of measurements calculated from the formula

$$s = \left\{ \frac{1}{n-1} \sum_{i=1}^{n} \delta_i^2 \right\}^{1/2}. \tag{A–4}$$

The factor $n - 1$ rather than n is used to correct for the difference between error and deviation (see the footnote at the end of the next column).

Normal Error Distribution

In general, a number of different sources whose identity is almost never known combine to give the total "observed" error. If the assumptions are made that these sources of error are independent of one another, that the individual errors are small compared with the total error, and that the individual errors vary in size and sign in an unpredictable (random) way, then the distribution of the total "observed" error in a series of measurements will be the *normal error distribution* governed by the *normal error probability function*.

$$f(\delta) = (h/\sqrt{\pi})e^{-h^2\delta^2}. \tag{A–5}$$

This is the equation of a Gaussian curve where $f(\delta)$ is the probability that a measurement will deviate from the mean of all the measurements by δ, defined by Eq. (A–1) and (A–2).* For this function to be valid, either the

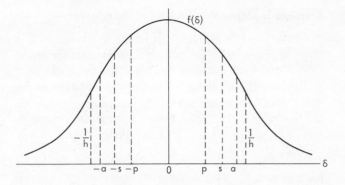

Fig. A–2. The normal error distribution. (The relative sizes of the various error formulations are shown.)

total number of measurements must be infinite or the deviations should be replaced by the true errors in the measurements.† The symbol h, the *precision index*, is a constant for any given set of measurements and is determined by the requirement that the area under the error distribution curve, Fig. A–2, be unity. The larger the value of h, the more precise are the measurements. It is evident from the figure that for the normal error distribution small random errors, small δ, are much more probable, that is, $f(\delta)$ is larger, than are large random errors.

Probable Error

The *probable error*, *p*, is that error such that one-half of all the errors (or deviations, in our approximation) are smaller and one-half larger than *p*. This error is computed with the error function and may be approximated as

$$p = 0.6745s = 0.6745 \left\{ \frac{1}{n-1} \sum_{i=1}^{n} \delta_i^2 \right\}^{1/2}. \tag{A–6}$$

The larger the number of measurements, the better the approximation will be, provided that the measurements are represented by a normal error distribution.

---

* The letter *e* in this equation represents the number 2.71828 . . . , which is the base of natural logarithms just as 10.000 . . . is the base of the so-called common logarithms. The equation is usually read "a function of δ (the error function) equals $h/\sqrt{\pi}$ times *e* to the power minus $h^2\delta^2$." The symbol *e* is also called the "exponential," and equations which contain it are called exponential equations. (This usage can be confusing since any base can be converted to any other by appropriate changes in the exponents, so you should be careful to ascertain what any given author means by "exponential equations.") You may also see exponential equations written in this form:

$$(\delta) = (h/\sqrt{\pi}) \exp(-h^2\delta^2).$$

---

† In this short qualitative discussion we shall ignore the distinction between error and deviation and proceed as if Eq. (A–5) were valid when the deviations are not replaced by true errors. When Eq. (A–5) is used in this way, based on a finite number of measurements and deviations from their mean, it is called *Student's distribution*. ("Student" was the pseudonym used by W. S. Gosset, who derived this distribution.) For very large numbers of measurements, the difference between this distribution and the normal distribution is very small. When only a few measurements have been made, the results need to be corrected to take account of the divergence between the two distributions. Consult one of the texts on statistics or errors listed in the references.

Relationship among the Measures of Uncertainty

To relate the various measures of the uncertainties in a series of observed values, we must assume that the errors follow a normal distribution. This has been observed already for the probable error and the standard deviation. As they are defined in the preceding paragraphs, the precision index, mean deviation, standard deviation, and probable error are related as follows:

$$1/h:a:s:p = 1.000:0.876:0.707:0.477, \qquad (A–7)$$

for a given set of values that are represented by a normal error distribution. This relationship is shown in Fig. A–2.

Relative Uncertainties

Any one of the measures of uncertainty may be converted to a relative value by dividing the uncertainty by the mean value of the measurements, e.g.,

Relative standard deviation = $s/\bar{x}$.

The relative values, as well as the uncertainties themselves, represent the *limits* of the uncertainties and are therefore both $+$ and $-$, since both positive and negative deviations can occur. (Sometimes the value of the uncertainty is called the *absolute uncertainty* to distinguish it from the relative uncertainty. Note that this has nothing to do with the absolute values and the $\pm$ signs are retained.)

A–4 REJECTION OF DISCORDANT DATA

Should you reject a measurement or determination that seems to be far out of line from the rest? This is a severe test of your judgment. No one wants to skew his results by including a "bad" point, but how do you know if it is bad? Obviously, if there is recorded in your notebook some factor that is quite different about this particular determination, then it would be much more valid to consider it separately from the rest of the measurements. By the same token, if an accident occurs which you know makes the result not so reliable as the others, then you must not use it. This of course applies even if the result is very close to the mean of all the measurements and looks "good" to you.

But what about the case when there seems to be no experimental reason to explain the point's difference? There is a criterion called the *Q-test* which can be used for rejection of discordant data. The rejection quotient, Q, is defined as the ratio of the difference between the discordant value and its closest neighbor, d, to the difference between the highest value and the lowest value of the series of measurements, r (the *range* of the measurements),

$$Q = d/r. \qquad (A–8)$$

There is a 90% probability that the discordant value should be rejected if Q is equal to or greater than 0.94 (for 3 measurements), 0.76 (for 4 measurements), 0.64 (for 5 measurements) and 0.56 (for 6 measurements). Remember, however, that there is a 10% chance that the value should be retained, or, stated another way, this test will reject 1 out of 10 valid points. Use it with judgment. It goes without saying that such a rejection of data may be performed only once with any given series of values.

Illustrative Example: Determinations of the equilibrium constant for a distribution equilibrium gave these results: 5.65, 5.71, 5.72, 5.90. Does the Q-test indicate that the value 5.90 has a 90% or greater chance of being in error?

$$d = 5.90 - 5.72 = 0.18,$$
$$r = 5.90 - 5.65 = 0.25,$$
$$Q = 0.18/0.25 = 0.72.$$

For four measurements, Q must be equal to or greater than 0.76 for the probability that the value is in error to be 90% or greater. The Q-test indicates that the probability of error is *not* greater than 90% in this case; this value probably should be retained.

A–5 PROPAGATION OF ERRORS

Maximum Errors

The "result" of an experiment is almost never a directly measured quantity but is computed by means of some functional relationship between it and the measured values. Each of the measured values presumably contains some error. How can we determine the amount of uncertainty due to these errors in the final result? In other words, how do the errors propagate through the functional relationship to the final result?

Since the actual error in a measurement or series of measurements is rarely known, what do we use as the values for the errors we propagate through the calculations? In general, we use simply an estimate of the error. Some authors suggest the use of the standard deviation, calculated by Eq. (A–4), as an estimate of the error, but this is probably unjustifiable if you make fewer than four independent measurements of the quantity. Here we shall suggest two rules of thumb which will, in general, yield estimates of maximum values of error that are probably more realistic than the standard deviation when only a few measurements are made.

1) If only one measurement has been made, then we estimate the error on the basis of the scale reading uncertainties in the experiment. Scale uncertainties are probably best estimated at one-half to one-fifth the size of the smallest graduation, unless other information about the apparatus used suggests a larger error limit.

For example, the smallest graduation on a 25-ml buret is 0.1 ml, and it is possible to estimate the reading to 0.01 ml, but it is probable that a fair estimate of the reading error is 0.02 ml. On the other hand, analytical balances usually have 0.1 mg as the smallest scale division but are usually neither more precise nor more accurate than 0.1 to 0.2 mg. Therefore estimates of readings to a precision greater than this are meaningless and a realistic estimate of the weighing error due to the balance is 0.2 mg.

2) If a series of measurements (fewer than four) has been made, compare their mean deviation with your estimate of error in one of the readings as obtained in the preceding paragraph, and choose the larger as the error to be propagated in the computations. If more than four independent measurements have been made, then using the standard deviation as an estimate of the error becomes realistic.

Addition and Subtraction

Both addition and subtraction of measured quantities to give a final result may be represented by

$$A + B = C, \tag{A–9}$$

where either of the quantities on the left may be negative and the sign of the result is determined by the relative sizes of the positive and negative quantities that are combined. Now we apply the calculus to this equation to give

$$d(A + B) = dA + dB = dC,$$

where d represents the differential operator. Converting differentials to finite differences,* we obtain

$$\Delta A + \Delta B = \Delta C \tag{A–10}$$

and identify the finite differences as the errors in the quantities A, B, and C. Since ΔA and ΔB range from ΔA to $-\Delta A$ and ΔB to $-\Delta B$, the error in the result will range from $(\Delta A + \Delta B)$ to $-(\Delta A + \Delta B)$.

Thus the error in a sum or difference is equal to the sum of the absolute values of the errors in the measured quantities. The error obtained in this way is the *maximum error* in the final result that could arise from the estimated errors in the measured quantities.

Illustrative Example: A weighing bottle containing a sample weighs 28.0365 gm. Some of the sample is transferred to a beaker and the weighing bottle and remaining sample are found to weigh 27.9201 gm. The weighing error in each

---

* This operation is not a simple substitution but really an approximation which is valid if $\Delta A/A$, $\Delta B/B$, and $\Delta C/C$ are small. Consult a calculus text for further elaboration.

weighing is estimated to be ±0.2 mg. What is the error in the mass, M, of the sample transferred?

$$M = 28.0365 - 27.9201 = 0.1164 \text{ gm},$$
Error in sample mass = $\Delta M = 0.0002 + 0.0002$,
$$\Delta M = 0.0004 \text{ gm} = 0.4 \text{ mg},$$
$$M = 0.1164 \pm 0.0004 \text{ gm},$$
$$\frac{\Delta M}{M} = 0.0004/0.1164 = \tfrac{1}{291}.$$

Thus although the relative error in each weighing is about one part in 14,000, the maximum error in the final result is about one part in 300.

The propagation of errors can lead to much larger uncertainties in the results than in any of the individual measurements; for instance, when the difference of two large and nearly equal quantities is taken, as in this example, the relative error in the result is always large compared with the relative errors in the initial quantities.

Multiplication and Division

Multiplication of measured quantities to yield a final result may be represented by

$$A \cdot B = C. \tag{A–11}$$

Application of the calculus to this equation gives

$$d(AB) = B \cdot dA + A \cdot dB = dC$$

and changing to finite differences we obtain

$$B \cdot \Delta A + A \cdot \Delta B = \Delta C. \tag{A–12}$$

Again we identify the finite differences, ΔA, ΔB, and ΔC as the errors in A, B, and C. It is useful in this case to divide Eq. (A–12) by (A–11) to obtain

$$\frac{B \cdot \Delta A + A \cdot \Delta B}{A \cdot B} = \frac{\Delta A}{A} + \frac{\Delta B}{B} = \frac{\Delta C}{C}, \tag{A–13}$$

where ΔA and ΔB range from ΔA to $-\Delta A$ and ΔB to $-\Delta B$, so that the range of the relative error in the final result will be from

$$(\Delta A/A + \Delta B/B) \text{ to } -(\Delta A/A + \Delta B/B).$$

Division is treated in a like manner:

$$\frac{A}{B} = C, \tag{A–14}$$

$$d\left(\frac{A}{B}\right) = \frac{dA}{B} - \frac{A \, dB}{B^2} = dC,$$

$$\frac{B \cdot \Delta A - A \cdot \Delta B}{B^2} = \Delta C,$$

$$\frac{(B \cdot \Delta A - A \cdot \Delta B)/B^2}{A/B} = \frac{\Delta A}{A} - \frac{\Delta B}{B} = \frac{\Delta C}{C}. \tag{A–15}$$

And again the range of ΔA and ΔB is the same, so that the range of $\Delta C/C$ is $(\Delta A/A + \Delta B/B)$ to $-(\Delta A/A + \Delta B/B)$. (Prove this to your satisfaction if it does not seem valid to you.)

Thus *the relative error in a product or quotient is equal to the sum of the absolute values of the relative errors in the measured quantities.* This sum is the maximum error in the result.

Illustrative Example: The density, ρ, of a metal cylinder can be computed from its mass, m, diameter, d, and length, L, with the formula

$$\rho = \frac{m}{\pi(d/2)^2 L}.$$

The results of the measurements and the estimated error in each are $m = 24.4936 \pm 0.0002$ gm, $d = 0.63 \pm 0.01$ cm, and $L = 10.24 \pm 0.01$ cm. What is the error in the density calculated from these data?

$$\rho = \frac{24.4936 \times 2 \times 2}{\pi \times 0.63 \times 0.63 \times 10.24} = 7.669 \text{ gm/cc},$$

$$\frac{\Delta\rho}{\rho} = \frac{\Delta m}{m} + \frac{\Delta d}{d} + \frac{\Delta d}{d} + \frac{\Delta L}{L},$$

$$\frac{\Delta\rho}{7.669} = \frac{0.0002}{24.4936} + \frac{0.01}{0.63} + \frac{0.01}{0.63} + \frac{0.01}{10.24}$$

$$= 0.0000 + 0.0159 + 0.0159 + 0.0010,$$

$$\frac{\Delta\rho}{7.669} = 0.0328,$$

$$\Delta\rho = 0.252.$$

Therefore

$$\rho = 7.669 \pm 0.252 \text{ gm/cc}.$$

On the basis of the rules given in Section A–6 for rounding off and significant figures, this result should be expressed as

$$7.7 \pm 0.3 \text{ gm/cc}.$$

This example illustrates two other points. First, multiplication or division by a constant (2 and π, in this case) has no effect on the error calculation, since the error in the constant is assumed to be zero. Second, the largest fraction of the error in the final result is often determined by the error of just one of the measurements. Error calculations happily reveal which measurement is most responsible for the total error so that you can begin improving your experimental technique and design by examining ways to improve that measurement.

Other Functions

The error propagated in other operations may be treated in exactly the same way as arithmetic operations. The results for two common operations, square root and logarithm, are useful.

Square Root

$$\sqrt{A} = A^{1/2} = B,$$
$$\tfrac{1}{2} dA \cdot A^{-1/2} = dB,$$
$$\frac{\Delta A}{2\sqrt{A}} = \Delta B.$$

Therefore

$$\frac{\Delta A}{2A} = \frac{\Delta B}{B}. \tag{A–16}$$

Logarithm

$$\log A = B.$$

To use the calculus we will have to convert this logarithm to the base 10 to the logarithm to the base e, usually denoted as ln:

$$\ln x = 2.303 \log x,$$
$$(1/2.303) \ln A = 0.434 \ln A = B,$$
$$0.434(dA/A) = dB.$$

Therefore

$$0.434(\Delta A/A) = \Delta B. \tag{A–17}$$

That is, the *error* in the result is proportional to the *relative error* of the measurement.

Other Error Representations

When the number of independent determinations of each measured variable exceeds four and an error analysis based on the statistics of the normal distribution is justified, the error usually calculated is the probable error in the final result. If the final result, R, is a function of a number of measured quantities, $F(A, B, C, \ldots)$ and the errors in these quantities are independent of one another, then the probable error of the result R is

$$p_R = \sqrt{\left(\frac{\partial F}{\partial A}\right)^2 p_A^2 + \left(\frac{\partial F}{\partial B}\right)^2 p_B^2 + \left(\frac{\partial F}{\partial C}\right)^2 p_C^2 + \cdots}, \tag{A–18}$$

where p_A, p_B, p_C, $\ldots$ are the probable errors in each of the measured quantities. This formulation is sometimes used with estimated errors substituted for the probable errors, but this is not strictly correct. (If you are not familiar with partial derivatives, do not be concerned, but return to this formulation when you have been introduced to them.)

A–6 SIGNIFICANT FIGURES AND COMPUTATIONS

The accuracy of a result should be indicated by the number of significant figures quoted for the result. Since we usually do not know the accuracy, we approximate it by using the precision. The number of figures used to express a result should be all the certain figures plus the first one that is uncertain (with the exception noted below). It is poor technique to quote more than the warranted number of significant figures in a result, for it indicates that you have not thought carefully enough about the accuracy and precision of the experiment.

When a result is simply stated without any qualifications, e.g., 13.58 gm, it is assumed that all figures are significant except the last. There is no agreement, however, as to how uncertain the last figure should be assumed to be. Some authors feel that this statement of the result implies that the last digit is uncertain by one unit, i.e., that the result in the example could have been 13.59 or 13.57 gm. Others think that higher uncertainties, 2, 3, or 5 units, are implied.

The best way to circumvent these ambiguities in your work is to state the uncertainty with each result. Do not, however, simply add a new ambiguity by writing 13.58 ± 0.03 gm, since this does not indicate what the origin of this uncertainty might be. Be explicit; note whether this is an estimate on your part of the accuracy of the balance or the mean deviation of a number of readings or the maximum error propagated through a calculation or whatever other uncertainty you are trying to represent.

The digit zero, 0, is a special case, since it may be significant or it may be merely a place-holder to indicate where the decimal point is. All results containing insignificant zeros can be rewritten in exponential notation to remove the zeros. As an example, the result 0.00580 mm may contain 2 or 3 significant figures, depending on whether or not the final zero is significant; the other zeros are obviously simply place-holders. This result may be rewritten as 5.80×10^{-3} or 5.8×10^{-3} mm, depending on whether the final zero is significant or not.

Sometimes the standard deviation of a result is given to two significant figures and the result is given so that the last digit of the result corresponds to the same decimal place as the second significant digit of the standard deviation: for instance,

Avogadro's number
$$= (6.02237 \pm 0.0090) \times 10^{23} \text{ atoms/mole},$$

$(6.052 \pm 0.011) \times 10^4$ calories = a heat of reaction.

(It would not be correct to report the latter result as 60,520 ± 110 calories.)

Rounding Off

Almost always when computations are carried out in longhand or on a desk calculator, more digits will appear

in the result than are significant, so the result must be rounded off. You round off as follows.

1) Determine the number of significant figures that is appropriate and discard the digits beyond the last significant figure.

2) If the first digit discarded is less than five, retain the last significant figure as is; if the first digit discarded is greater than five or is five followed by digits that are not all zeros, then increase the last significant figure by one unit; if the first digit discarded is five followed by zeros (or nothing), then leave the last significant figure unchanged if it is even and increase it by one if it is odd. (The rationale for this last arbitrary rule is that, in the long run, the number of roundings-up will equal the number of values that remain the same. Any consistently applied arbitrary rule that yields this result is all right.)

Addition and Subtraction

When a result is obtained as the sum or difference of a set of values, the value with the largest *absolute* uncertainty (lowest accuracy) governs the uncertainty and thus the number of significant figures that should be reported in the result. When the addition or subtraction occurs before the end of a computation, it is wise to retain more figures than are significant (one or two beyond that justified by the least accurate value) until the final result is obtained, or rounding errors will accumulate which can significantly affect the final value. For example, in rounding off

$$
\begin{array}{r}
203.1 \\
+7.24 \\
+0.3994 \\
-5.58 \\
\hline
\end{array} ,
$$

retaining two extra insignificant digits gives

$$
\begin{array}{r}
203.1 \\
+7.24 \\
+0.399 \\
-5.58 \\
\hline
205.159 ,
\end{array}
$$

which rounds off to 205.2. However, rounding off immediately to the final number of significant digits gives

$$
\begin{array}{r}
203.1 \\
+7.2 \\
+0.4 \\
-5.6 \\
\hline
205.1 .
\end{array}
$$

Thus rounding off too soon, in this case, gives a result that is too small by one unit in the final digit.

Multiplication and Division

The uncertainty in a product or quotient is governed by the term with the largest *relative* uncertainty (least accuracy). The result should not be reported with a relative uncertainty less than the largest relative uncertainty of the values used to calculate it. Again, as with addition and subtraction, more significant figures than are justified should be kept during the computation and only the final result should be rounded off to the correct number of significant figures. The illustrative example on page 216 demonstrates this procedure. You will note that in that example the largest relative error is one part in 63, so the final result cannot have more than two significant figures. (This number of significant figures is also consistent with the calculated error in the result.)

It is convenient to use a slide rule for as many calculations as possible, but sometimes this seems impossible when the numbers involved in a division are very nearly the same. For example, consider this calculation:

$$A = \frac{25.59}{0.2557}.$$

You can, in this case, use a trick to make the calculation much simpler.

$$A = \frac{0.2559 \times 10^2}{0.2557} = \frac{(0.2557 + 0.0002) \times 10^2}{0.2557}$$

$$= \left\{1 + \frac{0.0002}{0.2557}\right\} \times 10^2 = (1 + 0.00078) \times 10^2$$

$$= 100.08.$$

The value $0.0002/0.2557$ was calculated with a slide rule. The same trick may be used if the denominator is the slightly larger number, in which case we remember that

$$(1 + x)^{-1} \approx 1 - x,$$

if x is small compared with unity so that x^2, x^3, etc., may be neglected. Thus

$$B = \frac{0.1156}{0.1167} = \frac{0.1156}{0.1156 + 0.0011} = \frac{1}{1 + (0.0011/0.1156)}$$

$$\approx 1 - \frac{0.0011}{0.1156} = 1 - 0.00952 = 0.9905.$$

The ratio $0.0011/0.1156$ was again calculated easily to the desired accuracy on a slide rule. The result done out longhand is $B = 0.9906$.

Logarithms

The number of significant figures of a result that is a logarithm of some value is determined by the uncertainty calculated from Eq. (A–17). For example,

$$A = \log P_1/P_2,$$

where

$$P_1 = 0.567 \pm 0.003 \text{ atm}$$

and

$$P_2 = 0.290 \pm 0.003 \text{ atm},$$

(The uncertainties are estimated reading uncertainties.)

$$\frac{P_1}{P_2} = \frac{0.567 \pm 0.003}{0.290 \pm 0.003} = 1.955 \pm 0.030,$$

$$A = \log(1.955 \pm 0.030) = \log 1.955 \pm 0.434 \times \frac{0.030}{1.955}$$

$$= 0.2912 \pm 0.0064 = 0.291 \pm 0.006.$$

A–7 GRAPHICAL DATA TREATMENT

Data are often plotted on a graph because it is easier to observe trends and anomalies when they are so presented. A graph is ideally suited for obtaining intermediate values by *interpolation*. If a smooth curve is drawn through a series of data points, then the value of the dependent variable that corresponds to a particular unmeasured intermediate value of the independent variable can be read off the curve. This procedure is often used in calibration and correction procedures.

Illustrative Example: The vapor pressure of ethyl alcohol as a function of temperature is shown graphically in Fig. A–3. What is the vapor pressure of ethyl alcohol at 25°C?

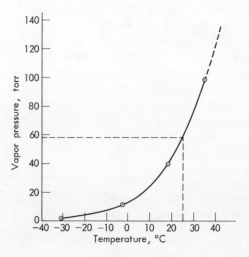

Fig. A–3. Vapor-pressure-vs.-temperature curve for ethyl alcohol.

To read the curve, we follow up vertically from the value of the independent variable on the abscissa, 25°C, until we cross the curve and then follow across the graph horizontally to read the corresponding value of the dependent variable on the ordinate, 58 torr.

Sometimes we desire to know the value of a dependent variable at a point outside the limits of the data used to construct a curve on a graph. Then we have to *extrapolate* the curve, i.e., extend it smoothly beyond its limits. The danger in this procedure is that such an extension may not be valid because the curve changes shape. If we have some physical or theoretical basis for assuming that the curvature does not change, then this procedure is a useful one. For example, we might extend the curve of Fig. A–3 at the high end (dashed line) to find out at what temperature the vapor pressure is atmospheric, i.e., what the boiling point is.

Straight-Line Graphs

Of course, it is difficult to extrapolate a curve such as that in Fig. A–3 accurately simply by eye or even with a French curve. A much easier curve to extrapolate is the straight line. Many sets of experimental points may be plotted so that the plot will be a straight line. If, for example, the vapor pressure, P, of a liquid is determined at a number of different temperatures, T, and a plot of the data is made on a graph of P versus T, the plot will be curved (Fig. A–3). But arguments based on thermodynamics indicate that the logarithm of the pressure should be a linear function of the reciprocal of the absolute temperature, and, indeed, when $\log P$ versus $1/T$ is plotted, the plot is a straight line. Such a plot is very easy to interpolate from and to extrapolate, since we simply extend the straight line. Ease of extrapolation should not, however, lull you into a false sense of security about the validity of the extrapolation. Inherent in every extrapolation is the assumption that the curve continues as it is. The straight-line plot of $\log P$ versus $1/T$ cannot be extrapolated too far in either direction with accuracy, because the plot actually does have some curvature and is only approximately a straight line when the temperature range is not too great.

Equation of a Line.
The equation for a straight line is

$$y = ax + b, \qquad (A\text{-}19)$$

where x is the independent variable, y is the dependent variable, a is the slope of the line, and b is the intercept of the line on the y-axis ($x = 0$). The slope and intercept are easily calculated from the graph on which the line appears. Choose two points far apart on the line, (x_1, y_1) and (x_2, y_2). These, of course, need not be actual data points and in most cases will not be. Each of these points satisfies the equation for the line,

$$y_1 = ax_1 + b,$$

$$y_2 = ax_2 + b,$$

and these two simultaneous equations in two unknowns may be solved to obtain a and b.

$$a = \frac{y_2 - y_1}{x_2 - x_1}, \qquad (A\text{-}20)$$

$$b = y_1 - ax_1 = y_2 - ax_2 = \frac{x_2 y_1 - x_1 y_2}{x_2 - x_1}. \qquad (A\text{-}21)$$

Note that it is not necessary to actually extrapolate the line to $x = 0$ to obtain the intercept, since it is readily calculable once the slope is known. Note also that the slope has a sign. In Fig. A–4, for example, the slope is negative, as you can see by noting that, if $1/T_2 > 1/T_1$, then $\log P_2 < \log P_1$ so Eq. (A–20) gives a negative a. Exercise care in determining the slope of a straight line to see that you obtain the correct sign.

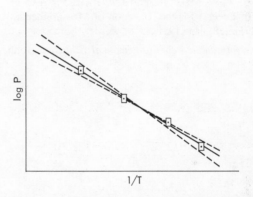

Fig. A–4. Pressure-temperature data for compound X.

Graphical Error Analysis.
If fewer than five points are involved, it is then easiest to draw the "best" straight line through them by eye. The error in the slope and intercept of this line may be estimated by constructing two other limiting lines. The method is best described by an example.

On the graph of Fig. A–4 are plotted the results of a vapor-pressure-vs.-temperature experiment in the form which should yield a straight-line plot. The rectangle drawn about each point is an estimate of the "blurriness" of the point resulting from the errors in the measurements. The estimated error spread in the independent variable is the base of the rectangle and the estimated error spread in the dependent variable is the height of the rectangle. The solid line is the "best" straight line through the points, as judged by eye with the use of a transparent straightedge. The dashed lines are limiting lines drawn with the least slope and the greatest slope possible while still passing through the error rectangles of the points.

To estimate the error, calculate the slopes and intercepts of all three lines. One-half the difference between the two limiting slopes is an estimate of the error in the "best" slope. Similarly, one-half the difference between the two limiting intercepts is an estimate of the error in the "best" intercept.

When a larger number of points is involved, more than five, then it often becomes profitable to use a somewhat more objective method to find the "best" line; in this case the method of least squares is usually used. The experiments in this text are designed not to require such an extensive treatment of data, so we shall not discuss this method. You can find an explanation of the least-squares method and the assumptions involved in its use in the texts on errors and treatment of experimental data listed in the references.

REFERENCES

BEERS, Y., *Introduction to the Theory of Errors*, Addison-Wesley, Reading, Mass., 1957, is a short book that can serve as an amplification of the treatment given in Section A–3 and as an introduction to further study of error analysis.

BLAEDEL, W. J., V. W. MELOCHE, and J. A. RAMSAY, "A Comparison of Criteria for the Rejection of Measurements," *J. Chem. Ed.* **28,** 643 (1951).

HOEL, P. G., *Introduction to Mathematical Statistics*, John Wiley & Sons, New York, 1954.

PINKERTON, R. C. and C. E. GLEIT, "The Significance of Significant Figures," *J. Chem. Ed.* **44,** 232 (1967).

WILSON, E. B., JR., *An Introduction to Scientific Research*, McGraw-Hill, New York, 1952, Chapters 8 through 12.

WORTHING, A. G., and J. GEFFNER, *Treatment of Experimental Data*, John Wiley & Sons, New York, 1943. A very good book that treats both the principles and practice of data analysis.

RECORDING AND REPORTING

... it may be that, for its lack of the fabulous, my work will be counted as less than delightful. But if men who shall want a clear picture of the past as an aid to knowing the future—which in the course of human things will be like or near—if such men judge my work a help, it will be enough.

In short, this history has been written not as some prize essay for the immediate, but as a possession for all time.

Thucydides, *History of the Peloponnesian War.*

B–1 RECORDING

The Laboratory Notebook

All records of laboratory work should be kept in a bound laboratory notebook with numbered pages. The 8 × 10-in. "ledger" type is a convenient size. The page numbers are very useful for referring back to previous work or calculations. Pages should not be removed from the book.

Some workers prefer laboratory notebooks with ruled pages, others like blank white space, and still others use notebooks that are quadrille-ruled (with vertical and horizontal rulings so that rough graphs of data may be made quickly during experiments). This choice is yours to make, although, for a laboratory course such as that outlined in this text, the quadrille-ruled pages will probably be most helpful. It is usually wise to leave the first two or three pages for a table of contents, compiled as you work, which will save you time leafing through to find what you want.

The Record

The record of your laboratory work should be complete and accurate. The only way it can be so is for you to form the habit immediately of noting down what you have done when you do it. Do not trust to memory. Faulty memory has ruined many experiments or made them useless. Write down exactly what you have done and what happens, not what you should have done and what you think should have happened.

All notes in your notebook should be in ink so that they will be permanently legible. Do not erase any entry in your notebook; simply cross out erroneous entries with a single line and explain in a note why the entry was incorrect. Sometimes you will find later that such an entry was not erroneous after all and will want to retrieve the data.

All data and observations should be recorded directly in the notebook without the intermediacy of scraps of paper and the like. Instructors have a habit of confiscating and destroying scraps of paper lying about the laboratory. Do not be a victim of this pillage.

When you begin a new experiment, start the record on a fresh page of your notebook and put the title and number of the experiment at the top of the page. Note below this, in one or two sentences of your own, the purpose of the experiment. This will not only help you initially to define the purpose in your own mind but will keep it before you as you carry through the routine of laboratory work. If you are working with a partner, note his name here also. (Preparing the laboratory notebook, like all preparation for the laboratory, should be done before you come to the laboratory.)

Always record the date that work is done. If an experiment extends over a number of days, begin each day's record with the date. This can be very important if you later find, for instance, that on one particular day a standard solution stored in a stock bottle in the laboratory was contaminated. Such an occurrence, if you have kept proper records, could explain a mystifying discrepancy in your results.

As you prepare for a laboratory, you will often see that the procedure involves repetitive measurements on more than one sample. The obvious form for recording such data is a table. Decide, as you prepare, what data you are going to be taking, and make a table for the results in your notebook. Such a table not only collects all the data in one place in your record but reminds you also of the items that have to be recorded, jarring your memory so you do not forget to record some important parameter. All the data necessary to describe your work completely must be recorded: sample numbers, solution concentrations, weights and measures, and so on.

All calculations that are done in the laboratory or outside *should be done in the notebook*. If, for example, you make an error in calculating how much reagent to add to a solution, you will have a record of where the error occurred so that you can correct it next time and will know which data to trust and which to discard. It is a good idea to record data on one page and reserve the facing page for calculations.

Laboratory notebooks should be neat but not to the point of fetishism. Obviously, the pages in a working notebook are not going to look like the pages from a book, but they still should not be sloppy. (A sloppy notebook connotes something about the thinking habits of the notetaker.) Neatness should not interfere with accuracy, but if you have planned your work well ahead of time, only a small amount of crossing out and redoing will ever be necessary.

A well-kept laboratory notebook is your record of your laboratory experience. It should be a record you can show with pride.

A Sample Notebook Page

On page 223 is reproduced a sample page from a student notebook.

B–2 REPORTING

Laboratory Report Form

A good laboratory report is concise. It should be as brief as possible, consistent with a clear explanation and analysis of the results. It should, if possible, be typed on $8\frac{1}{2} \times 11$-in. paper. The report should be written in a good, clear style, with complete sentences and proper grammar. Your report will be judged on the basis of your ability to express your ideas clearly and to argue for them. A poorly written report may be full of good ideas but so badly expressed that a reader cannot judge their merits. Writing a laboratory report should be looked on in the same light as writing a theme on the interrelationship of Hamlet's soliloquies. The data are different; the technique is the same.

Laboratory Report Content

The content and order of presentation of a laboratory report will vary as the type of results presented varies. The suggestions given here are for a typical experiment. Leaf through a few issues of the standard journals to see how the authors of research articles present their results. However, do not try to emulate all you read, since much of the writing is overdone and some is just plain bad.

Introduction. An introduction to a report should be short, a few sentences at most, unless you are presenting original work that requires more extensive background. The introduction consists of your conception of the purpose of the experiment.

Experimental. In the experimental section of the report you should report what you did in the laboratory and what data were taken. As in the laboratory notebook, data are best presented in tabular form (see below). The instruments which you used should be identified by manufacturer and serial number (or the number assigned in the laboratory) in your notebook and in your report (you need not do this for balances).

In general, only report procedural details which differ from the procedure outlined in the given set of instructions. You may assume that the instructions which you followed are indelibly printed on the minds of your readers as well as on your own and need not be repeated.

Results and Discussion. An analysis of your data is the heart of the report. An experiment is not complete until the data have been analyzed, correlated, and otherwise wrung dry of the information they provide you.

The first thing to present is *the results* of your calculations with the data. The computations themselves should not be presented, except perhaps for a sample calculation in an appendix at the end of the report. The actual computations, done in your laboratory notebook, are part of your permanent record. The equations used in the computations should be given and any assumptions that go into the calculations must be fully explained. The final numerical results should be presented in tabular or graphical form. The errors which propagate through the computations are naturally also reported as part of the final result.

Experiment 1. The Density of Two Metal Bars
September 15, 1966

The object of this experiment is to determine the density of two cylindrical metal bars by two methods: water displacement and calculation of the volume. The procedure is given in the laboratory notes handed out by the instructor.

Measurements:

	282	148
Bar number	282	148
Mass, gm (trial 1)	24.4936 ± 0.0002	27.4142 ± 0.0002
(trial 2)	24.4936 ± 0.0002	27.4143
Volume H$_2$O in graduate, ml	6.38 ± 0.02	6.30 ± 0.02
Volume H$_2$O + bar (trial 1)	9.64	9.60
Volume H$_2$O	misreading 6.28 6.38	6.30
Volume H$_2$O + bar (trial 2)	9.62	9.58
Diameter of bar, cm (trial 1)	0.63 ± 0.01	0.63 ± 0.01
(trial 2)	0.63	0.64
Length of bar, cm (trial 1)	10.24 ± 0.01	10.25 ± 0.01
(trial 2)	10.25	10.25

I noticed droplets of water on the graduate above the meniscus due to faulty cleaning of the glass. Perhaps they make the apparent volume of the water displaced too large. I used vernier calipers to measure the dimensions of the bar. The uncertainties are estimated as reading errors on the apparatus.

Tables again are the most concise way to present numerical data. Some rules for setting up tables are:

1) Tables should be numbered for easy reference in the text.

2) Each table should have a descriptive caption, for example, "Rates of Reaction of Cyclohexanone with Iodine at 20°C." A caption such as "Reaction Rates" conveys almost no meaning; no one should have to look through the text of your report to find the meaning of a table.

3) Each column (or row) in a tabular display of data should have a descriptive heading including the units of the numerical values in the column.

4) The entries in the column (or row) of a table that correspond to the independent variable of the experiment should be arranged in order of increasing or decreasing size, so that trends in the dependent variables can be easily seen by simply following down the other columns.

5) If at all possible, the numerical results in a column (or row) of a table should all be presented as the same power of ten. For example, if the values 3.2×10^{-4}, 4.5×10^{-5}, and 7.9×10^{-3} are listed as 3.2, 0.45, and 79×10^{-4}, their relative sizes are more obvious.

6) Notes or further explanations of certain values in the tables should be put in notes at the bottom of the table.

Graphs are a convenient way of showing trends in data points or their relationship to some theoretical function. A few general rules for preparing graphs for a report are:

1) Graphs, like tables, should be numbered for easy reference.

2) Every graph, like every table, should have a descriptive caption so that it can stand alone.

3) The axes of graphs should be labeled descriptively, and the units of the variables should be given. The axes should be labeled as well with numerical values, so that their scale is easy to read.

4) As much as possible of the graph should be used for the points plotted on it. The ranges of the scales of the axes must be chosen accordingly. For example, if you are plotting $1/T$ on the abscissa and the values of $1/T$ range from 2.2×10^{-3} to 3.3×10^{-3} deg^{-1}, then it is pointless to choose a scale that runs from 0 to 3.5×10^{-3} deg^{-1}, since you will waste two-thirds of the graph by putting no information on it. A better choice would be a scale that runs from 2.0×10^{-3} to 3.5×10^{-3}; this will put the points farther apart, allow a more accurate plot, and use all the informational space on the graph.

5) Each data point represented on the graph should be set off by a circle or some other geometric enclosure around it. In general, the size of this geometric figure should represent the estimated uncertainty in the point (see Section A-7). If more than one set of data is presented on the same graph, the geometric figures chosen to represent points in the different sets should be different to make the graph more readable and comparison between data sets immediately apparent.

6) In general, the independent variable is plotted on the abscissa, while the dependent variable is plotted on the ordinate.

7) If more than one set of data is presented on a graph, there must be a legend telling the reader the different conditions used for the different sets of data. For instance, the variation of the volume of a fixed amount of gas as a function of temperature might be plotted for a number of different constant pressures of the gas in a plot such as Fig. B-1.

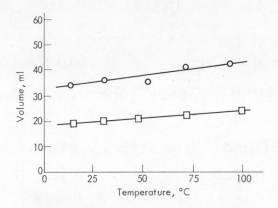

Fig. B-1. Variation of volume with temperature for a sample of air at two pressures; ○ pressure = 0.50 atm, □ pressure = 0.89 atm.

The *conclusions* you draw from your data are the second important part of the Results and Discussion section. The questions presented at the end of each experiment in this text are designed to help you start thinking about your results and the conclusions you can draw from them. These questions are not exhaustive, and you will often be able to obtain more from your data than just their answers. Go as far as you can in milking your data of its content.

The final important item to discuss in the report is the sources of *error* and their effect on the final results. You have some estimate of the trustworthiness of the final result from the error treatment (Appendix A) you have carried out in your calculations. You should, however, examine carefully the experimental method and any assumptions made therein that could cause systematic errors in the result. Give the direction of error in the final result (high or low) due to these causes and try to estimate the magnitude of the effect. Suggest methods to improve the experimental procedure which would eliminate these sources of error and give you a more accurate result. (Mistakes and blunders on your part are *not* to be included as errors, since they are not errors but the results of carelessness and lack of preparation.)

Summary. Short clear reports should be the norm. Sometimes long involved reports will be necessary, however, and a good way to end such reports is by summarizing the major results of the data, including the most important numerical values. Any summary should be only a few sentences long.

A Sample Laboratory Report

A sample laboratory report appears on pages 226 through 228.

THE DENSITY OF TWO METAL BARS

A. Student

INTRODUCTION

The object of this experiment was to determine the density (mass/unit volume) of two cylindrical bars of metal. Each bar was weighed and then two approaches were used to obtain the volume: Method 1, by displacement of water, and Method 2, by calculating the volume from the measured dimensions of the cylindrical bars. The results are compared in Table 2.

EXPERIMENTAL DETAILS

Table 1

Experimental data on the density of two metal bars

Bar number	282	148
Mass, gm (trial 1)	24.2936 ± 0.0002*	27.4142 ± 0.0002
(trial 2)	24.4936	27.4143
Volume H_2O in graduate, ml-cc	6.38 ± 0.03	6.30 ± 0.03
Volume H_2O + bar (trial 1)	9.64	9.60
Volume H_2O	6.38	6.30
Volume H_2O + bar (trial 2)	9.62	9.58
Diameter of bar, cm (trial 1)	0.63 ± 0.01	0.63 ± 0.01
(trial 2)	0.63	0.64
Length of bar, cm (trial 1)	10.24 ± 0.01	10.25 ± 0.01
(trial 2)	10.25	10.25

*The uncertainties listed are estimates of the reading errors of the balance, graduate, and calipers used.

The volume by water displacement, Method 1, was obtained by (a) partially filling a 10-ml graduate and reading the volume, (b) inserting the bar and again reading the volume, and (c) removing the bar, wiping it dry, and then repeating steps (a) and (b).

Table 2

Results of measurements to determine the density of two metal bars

Bar number	282	148
Mass, gm (average of readings)	24.49*	27.41
Volume, ml-cc by Method 1 (trial 1)	3.26 ± 0.06	3.30 ± 0.06
(trial 2)	3.24	3.28
(average)	3.25 ± 0.06	3.29 ± 0.06
Diameter, cm (average)	0.63 ± 0.01	0.64 ± 0.01
Length, cm (average)	10.24 ± 0.01	10.25 ± 0.01
Volume, cc by Method 2	3.2 ± 0.1	3.3 ± 0.1
Density, gm/cc† by Method 1	7.5 ± 0.1	8.3 ± 0.2
Density, gm/cc by Method 2	7.7 ± 0.3	8.3 ± 0.3

*More significant figures are not justified by the remainder of the data.

†The difference between cc and ml, one part in 35,000, is neglibible compared with the uncertainty in the density, greater than one percent.

The equation used to calculate the volume by Method 2 was

$$v = \frac{\pi d^2 L}{4},$$

where d is the diameter and L is the length of the bar. The density is then $\rho = m/v$, where m is the mass of the bar.

All the calculated uncertainties in Table 2 are maximum deviations. Since only duplicate readings were taken, it is doubtful that any more sophisticated error treatment is justified. An example of this type of error calculation is given in Chemical Principles in Practice, Appendix A, Section A-5.

DISCUSSION

The data and results presented in Table 2 clearly show that the measurement of volume is the limiting factor in the precision of this experiment. Although the measurements of the dimensions of the bar are as good or better (in terms of estimated uncertainty) than direct volume measurement with the equipment available, the propagation of error in the calculations makes Method 2 less precise than Method 1. This is well shown by a comparison of the maximum error limits on the densities obtained by these two methods.

A possible error in the volume obtained by displacement would occur if water droplets clung to the side of the graduate. Their volume would not appear in the original reading, but would be indicated in the reading with the bar present. Thus the volume would appear to be larger than it actually should be, and the density would be too small. Small droplets were present in all cases, but it was assumed that this source of error was insignificant. The results do not allow any justification for this assumption, since the droplets could represent a systematic error present in all determinations, leading to the good precision obtained but causing the accuracy to be quite bad. It is possible that the lower density obtained by Method 1 with Bar number 282 is a result of this error.

Better precision might have been obtained by using a graduate with finer divisions to obtain the volume by displacement.

ANALYTICAL BALANCES

A false balance is abomination to the Lord: but a just weight is His delight.

Proverbs 11:1

C–1 THE PRINCIPLE OF THE EQUAL-ARM BALANCE

The balance is in essence a first-class lever, Fig. C–1. Let us place an object of a certain unknown *mass*, m_1 on the left-hand side of the lever. By *mass* we mean a quantity of matter which is defined by Newton's first law: force equals mass times acceleration, $f = ma$. The acceleration acting on the object is that due to the gravitational attraction of the earth and is symbolized as g.

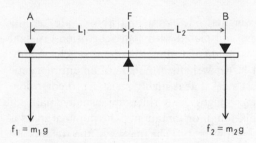

Fig. C–1. The first-class lever and balance principle.

The force $f_1 = m_1g$, due to the acceleration of gravity, is called the *weight* of the object. The weight of the object is exerted at point A. The force, f_1, will tend to make the lever rotate about the fulcrum, F. To counteract this tendency, we shall place some known mass, m_2, on the right-hand side of the lever so that its force, $f_2 = m_2g$, is acting at point B. If we choose m_2 correctly, there will be no tendency for the lever to rotate in either direction about the fulcrum. Under this condition the moments due to the two forces are equal and therefore

$f_1L_1 = f_2L_2$ (equal moments),
$m_1gL_1 = m_2gL_2$,
$m_1L_1 = m_2L_2$.

For the equal-arm balance $L_1 = L_2$, so the masses are equal,

$$m_1 = m_2. \tag{C–1}$$

This very simple result is all-important in emphasizing that the equal-arm balance measures *mass*, not weight. The value of g, the gravitational constant, differs from place to place on earth, so that the weight of an object, mg, is variable. The mass of an object is a constant and *the equal-arm balance compares masses*.

Since weight is proportional to mass and at any one place on earth the proportionality factor, g, is a constant, it is common usage to use the term "weighing" to describe the operation of comparing masses with a balance and to refer to the quantity which is thus determined as the "weight." This usage is found in this text, but you must remember that mass and weight are not the same quantity.

C–2 THE DOUBLE-PAN BALANCE

Figure C–2 shows the beam and knife edges of a double-pan balance. The knife edges are triangular prisms made

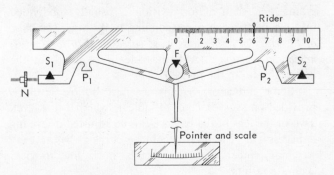

Fig. C–2. The beam of a double-pan balance.

of agate or some other very hard natural or synthetic substance. The central knife edge, F, resting on a flat bearing plate made of the same material, acts as the fulcrum of the lever formed by the beam. The outer knife edges, S_1 and S_2, are at equal distances from the fulcrum knife edge. A stirrup hangs (upside down) from each of the outer knife edges. Contact with the knife edges is again made by bearing plates of the same material mounted in the flat plates of the stirrups. The balance pans hang from the stirrups. A long pointer, attached directly below the fulcrum knife edge, swings past a scale at the base of the balance and indicates the deflection of the beam from its horizontal position. The beam of the empty balance is adjusted so that it is horizontal by the adjusting screw, N, on one end of the beam (some balances have screws on both ends of the beam).

When the balance is not in use or when objects or weights are being placed on or removed from the pans, the knife edges are protected from wear by being separated from the plates. The separation is accomplished by a mechanical linkage (making contact with the beam by two ball-and-socket joints at the projections P_1 and P_2) that raises the beam slightly and the stirrups a bit farther; it holds all moving parts of the balance stationary. This mechanical device, called the *beam arrest*, is usually operated by a knob on the front of the balance base. Another arresting device, the *pan arrest*, prevents the pans from swinging by supporting them from beneath without acting on the beam. The pan arrest is usually operated by a push button on the front of the balance base. The pan arrest also prevents violent motion of the beam and consequent damage to the knife edges if the beam is released when the masses on the pans are very greatly out of balance.

The beam is graduated, sometimes only on the right-hand side, so that weight adjustments less than 10 mg (on some balances, 5 mg) may be made with a *rider*. A rider is a piece of wire that is bent to fit over the beam with a loop projecting above it; it is manipulated with a rider rod, which has a hook to pick up the rider. The numbers of the major graduations correspond to milligrams, and each major division is usually subdivided into ten parts, each corresponding to 0.1 mg. *The mass of the rider in milligrams must correspond to the largest numbered division.* (A 10 mg rider is required for the balance beam in the figure.)

Some indicator, usually a spirit bubble level, is provided on every balance to indicate whether it is level. Two of the legs of the balance can be adjusted if leveling is necessary. The level should be checked before each weighing, since the beam must be horizontal to yield accurate results.

The balance is always enclosed in a glass case with a sliding door to prevent air currents from disturbing the balance and to protect the balance from laboratory fumes. Keep the case closed except when placing objects on or removing them from the pans.

C-3 WEIGHTS

The reference masses used for comparison to obtain the mass of an object are called *weights*. Through a long line of succession, these masses have been compared with the standard mass, the international prototype kilogram, a hunk of very well-protected platinum-iridium kept in a cave at Sèvres, France (at the International Bureau of Weights and Measures). Copies of the standard mass, each directly compared with the prototype, are kept in standards laboratories throughout the world. The National Bureau of Standards has two of these copies, against which are calibrated the sets of weights used as "standards" by manufacturers of weights for laboratories.

The weight sets which are used with double-pan balances commonly contain the following pieces:

> 1, 2, 3, 5, 10, 10, 20, and 50 gm;
>
> 10, 10, 20, 50, 100, 100, 200, and 500 mg;
>
> a rider (usually 10 mg).

The larger weights, one gram and above, are usually made of brass and plated with some corrosion-resistant metal such as gold, platinum, rhodium, or chromium; some sets of larger weights are made of an antimagnetic chrome-nickel steel that is highly resistant to corrosion. The milligram weights and rider are usually made of aluminum, platinum, or tantalum. The nominal mass is stamped on each weight. [The masses of the weights are the masses *in vacuo*, so a correction for air buoyancy (Section C-8) must be made for very accurate work.] Duplicate weights are usually distinguished from one another by a dot or some other characteristic mark stamped on one of them.

Constant use over a period of time causes enough wear on a set of weights that you should recalibrate your weight set when you receive it. Fortunately, you will almost never be interested in absolute masses but in the ratio of two masses. Therefore a set of weights which is internally consistent, i.e., in which the 10 gm weight is 10 times the mass of the 1 gm weight, etc., is completely satisfactory and does not need to be returned to the manufacturer or the Bureau of Standards for absolute calibration. (An outline of the procedure to follow for internal calibration of weight sets is given in Section C-8.)

C–4 WEIGHING WITH A DOUBLE-PAN BALANCE

Precautions to Protect the Balance

Never add to or remove anything from the balance pans unless the beam is arrested. If both the beam and pans are released, *arrest the beam before arresting the pans.* Both these precautions prolong the life of the knife edges (dull knife edges decrease the sensitivity and the accuracy of the balance). *Always leave the beam arrested when you leave the balance.*

Determination of the Rest Point

A good way to obtain the rest point is by the method of *short swings.* This way is quick, and its accuracy is comparable to that of other methods.

The usual balance pointer scale has 10 or 12 divisions on either side of the central mark. Usually the fifth and tenth lines are longer for ease in reading. To avoid any confusion that might arise from using negative numbers, it will be convenient for you to number the scale mentally from left to right: call the first long mark on the left zero and continue numbering to 20 at the last long line on the right. The central mark, the ideal "zero" reading of the balance, is then 10.

Check to be sure the balance is leveled. With the balance unloaded, the case closed, and the rider removed from the beam, release the pans and then slowly release the beam; the knife edges now rest on the bearing plates. The pointer will probably start to swing. [If the pointer does not move after you make sure that the pans have actually been released, arrest the beam and pans (in that order) and then rerelease them. If this procedure does not work, consult the instructor.] It should swing so that it passes through the 10 mark and travels about the same number of divisions on either side.* If the total excursion of the pointer is greater than 5 or 6 divisions, arrest the beam and pans (in that order) and try to release them gently so the swings will not be so wide. When the swings are short, 5 or 6 divisions total, read the scale at the pointer's extreme left-hand position and at its extreme right-hand position for the same swing. Estimate the readings to the nearest 0.1 division. (It does not matter whether you read the right or left first, but it is good to get into the habit of reading the swings in the same order every time you use the balance.) The average of these two readings is the rest point of the

---

* If this is not the case, i.e., if the swings are all on one side of the scale or off the scale, consult an instructor. Do not try to make any of the adjustments on the beam yourself. If anything goes wrong because of someone's putting his hands inside the balance case, let it be the instructor who is culpable.

unloaded balance:

$$p_{RP}^0 = \frac{p_L + p_R}{2}.$$

The rest point of a loaded balance, with the loads closely enough equal that the pointer deflection is on scale, is determined in exactly the same way. In this case, the rest point need not be near the center of the scale. Indeed, its position can be used to estimate the weight, as described below.

Sensitivity

One of the most important characteristics of any balance is its sensitivity. The sensitivity, *s*, is defined as the number of scale divisions the pointer is deflected from its rest position per milligram mass difference between the loads on the pans. Thus, if a mass difference of *w* milligrams causes a scale deflection of *p* divisions, the sensitivity of the balance is

$$s = p/w. \qquad \text{(C–2)}$$

It is important to know the sensitivity of your balance to weigh most efficiently.

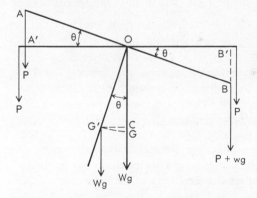

Fig. C–3. Schematic representation of balanced and slightly imbalanced rest position of the balance beam and pointer, θ = angle, in radians, through which the beam (and pointer) is deflected, $\overline{OA} = \overline{OB} = L$ = length of the balance arm (one-half the beam length), $\overline{OG} = \overline{OG'} = h$ = distance of the center of gravity of the beam from the fulcrum, P = weight of the pan and its contents, wg = excess of weight on the right-hand pan, which is causing the deflection, Wg = weight of the beam.

What factors affect the sensitivity of a balance? To answer this question, let us look at Fig. C–3, in which the rest positions of the beam and pointer of an ideal balance are shown schematically both at balance and with an excess of *w* milligrams on the right-hand pan.

Note that the larger the angle of deflection, θ, the greater the deflection of the pointer. The pointer scale on most balances is made so that its readings are directly proportional to the size of the angle of deflection. In this case we can let $p = k\theta$, where k is a constant for a given balance; then the sensitivity is

$$s = p/w = k\theta/w.$$

To determine how θ is dependent on the other parameters of the problem, we note that the beam is at rest, even though it is not quite balanced. The moments about the fulcrum must, therefore, be equal, and we can write

$$P(\overline{OA'}) + Wg(\overline{CG'}) = (P + wg)(\overline{OB'}).$$

From the geometry of the system we know that

$$\overline{OA'} = \overline{OA} \cos \theta = L \cos \theta,$$
$$\overline{OB'} = \overline{OB} \cos \theta = L \cos \theta,$$
$$\overline{CG'} = \overline{OG'} \sin \theta = h \sin \theta,$$

so that

$$PL \cos \theta + Wgh \sin \theta = (P + wg)L \cos \theta,$$
$$Wh \sin \theta = wL \cos \theta$$

or

$$\sin \theta / \cos \theta = \tan \theta = wL/Wh.$$

When θ is very small it is valid to make the approximation

$$\tan \theta \simeq \theta,$$

so that

$$\theta \simeq wL/Wh \qquad (C\text{-}3)$$

and the sensitivity is

$$s \simeq k(wL/Wh)/w = kL/Wh. \qquad (C\text{-}4)$$

Therefore the longer the arms, the lighter the beam, and the closer the center of gravity of the beam to the fulcrum, the larger the sensitivity of the balance is.

The sensitivity formula we have just derived for an ideal balance indicates that the balance's sensitivity is not affected by the size of the load on the pans. In practice this is not the case, for the sensitivity of a double-pan balance usually decreases as the load is increased. The very slight bending of the beam under heavier loads displaces the ends of the beam downward relative to the fulcrum. The consequent downward displacement of the center of gravity increases the length h and thus decreases the sensitivity. Balance design is, therefore, a compromise among the factors of length, rigidity, and mass of the beam that will give the balance the sensitivity required.

To determine the sensitivity of your balance as a function of load use the following procedure.

1) Determine the rest point of the unloaded balance, p_1.

2) Add a 1-mg weight to the right-hand pan or use the rider to add 1 mg to the right-hand arm.

3) Determine the new rest point, p_2. The sensitivity at zero load, s_0, is

$$s_0 = (p_2 - p_1) \text{ divisions/mg.}$$

4) Remove the 1-mg weight. Place 10 gm on each pan and determine the rest point, p_3. If the rest point is not within two divisions of the center of the scale, use the rider to adjust it within these limits.

5) Add 1 mg to the right-hand pan.

6) Determine the new rest point, p_4. The sensitivity at 10-gm load, s_{10}, is then

$$s_{10} = (p_4 - p_3) \text{ divisions/mg.}$$

7) Continue for 20-, 30-, 40-, and 50-gm loads.

8) Plot the sensitivity vs. load and draw a smooth curve through the points. Keep this graph handy when weighing samples by the sensitivity method described below.

Weighing by the Sensitivity Method

Determine the rest point of the balance. Record it. Arrest the beam and pans. Place the object to be weighed on the left-hand pan. (The left-hand pan is conventionally the object pan because right-handed people find it easier to manipulate the weights on the right-hand pan.) Select the weight from your weight set that you think is near the correct mass and place it on the right-hand pan. *Slowly* release the beam while watching the pointer. If it moves resolutely in one direction or the other and shows no sign of stopping, arrest the beam. If the pointer moves to the left, there is too much weight on the right-hand pan; try the next smaller weight. If the pointer moves to the right, the right-hand pan is too light; try the next larger weight. Continue in this way until the pointer does not swing off scale as the beam arrest is being released.

Then, with the beam arrested, release the pans. Wait until they stop oscillating (if necessary, use the pan arrest to help them stop swinging). Slowly release the beam while again watching the pointer. If it begins to go off scale, arrest the beam and then the pans and make the appropriate weight adjustments. Release the pans and again slowly release the beam while watching the pointer. Continue until you are within 10 mg (on the light side) of the balance point. Arrest the beam, close the door of the balance case, release the beam, and continue approaching the balance point using the rider. Use the rider systematically; set it first at 5 and then increase or decrease the setting as necessary. When the deflection of the pointer is on scale, find the rest point of the balance and record it. Arrest the beam and pans. Carefully record each weight on the weight pan and the position of the rider in a column in your notebook and add them; do not just record a total weight added in your head. (If you used one of a pair of duplicate weights, note which one. If you wish to weigh this object again later, use the same weight.) Remove the weights from the pan in ascending order of weight and check to make sure each has been recorded correctly. Also, before removing the rider from the beam, double check its position.

Armed with the rest point of the unloaded balance, p_{RP}^0, the rest point of the loaded balance, p_{RP}, the total mass of the weights plus the rider setting, W gm, and the sensitivity of the balance at a mass W, s_W divisions/mg, you are prepared to find the mass of the object, M gm. The difference in mass between the right-hand pan and the left-hand pan is $(W - M)$ gm. If we assume that at true balance the rest point would be the same as with the balance unloaded, then the deflection of the balance due to this mass difference is $(p_{RP}^0 - p_{RP})$. We can then write the sensitivity as

$$s_W = \frac{p_{RP}^0 - p_{RP}}{(W - M) \times 10^3}.$$

(The factor of 10^3 converts grams to milligrams to be consistent with the units of sensitivity, divisions/mg.) Therefore the mass is given by

$$M = W + \frac{p_{RP} - p_{RP}^0}{s_W} \times 10^{-3}. \qquad \text{(C–5)}$$

Since the sensitivity is a positive number, the sign of the term inside the parentheses will depend on the relative sizes of p_{RP}^0 and p_{RP}.

Illustrative Example: The rest point of an unloaded balance is 10.23. With a beaker on the left-hand pan and a total of 25.3430 gm (including the rider reading) on the right-hand pan, the rest point is 5.64. The sensitivity of the balance is 4.35 divisions/mg. What is the mass of the beaker?

Let us think for a moment about what we should expect before we plug into the formula. The final rest point is to the left of the initial rest point. This means that too much weight is present on the right-hand pan. We therefore anticipate that the actual weight of the beaker will be less than 25.3430 gm.*

Equation (C–5) gives:

$$M = 25.3430 + \frac{5.64 - 10.23}{4.35} \times 10^{-3}$$

$$= 25.3430 - 1.05 \times 10^{-3} = 25.3430 - 0.0011$$

$$= 25.3419 \text{ gm.}$$

---

* "Directional" reasoning like this is valuable in any situation and often helps you catch sign errors in your work.

Weighing by the Exact Balancing Method

The technique in this case is identical to that used in weighing by sensitivity except that the rider is adjusted finally to reproduce the rest point of the unloaded balance. The combined mass of the weights on the pan and the rider reading is then the mass of the object being weighed.

The exact balancing method is slower than the sensitivity method, and beginners often make it even slower by taking the word "exact" too literally. The usual laboratory analytical balance has a precision of about 0.1 mg. This means that if a rider setting of 5.3 mg is too heavy and 5.2 is too light, it does not matter which reading you choose. (You can estimate from the swings whether the true balance position is closer to one than to the other.) It is unnecessary, time-consuming, and indicative of poor technique to try to manipulate and read the rider any closer than this. For a good deal of routine work a precision of 1 mg is sufficient, in which case the "exact" weighing method can be just as rapid as the sensitivity method.

C–5   THE CHAINOMATIC BALANCE

The chainomatic balance is a double-pan balance in which weight adjustments below 100 mg are made with a fine gold chain attached to its right-hand arm. The chain is adjusted from outside the balance case, and the mass added by it is read on a vernier scale (a vernier scale is shown in Fig. C–4). Most chainomatic balances have numbered notches on the top of the beam into which a cylindrical rider fits. The notches are precision ground and are spaced so that the numbers correspond to multiples of 100 mg and the total range is 1 gm. Thus on a chainomatic balance, no weights below one gram need to be placed on the pan and all manipulations for weighings in this range may be done from outside the balance case. The methods of weighing and the precautions are still applicable, but the speed of weighing is much increased.

C–6   THE SINGLE-PAN (AUTOMATIC) BALANCE

Construction and Principles

There is nothing mysterious about the operating principles of the single-pan balance. The beam, knife edges, pointer, one "pan," and the weights are usually hidden from view by the case. The second pan is visible in a clear plastic compartment with sliding doors to allow you to insert and withdraw samples. The movement of the beam is magnified optically (instead of mechanically by a long pointer), and masses less than 100 mg are read on an illuminated ground glass scale on the face of the balance.* Weights greater than 100 mg are manipulated by knobs located on the front or side of the balance. There are usually three of these knobs, for increments of 0.1, 1.0, and 10.0 gm. The values of the masses dialed with these knobs appear in "windows" on the front of the balance. When an object weighing 96.1617 gm is placed on the pan, we will have to turn the knobs to positions 1, 6, and 9, respectively, to bring the optical readout on scale; the optical scale will then read 0.0617. Figure C–4 shows the total readout as it would appear on a Mettler single-pan balance, Model H15. The last digit has to be read with a vernier, as indicated.

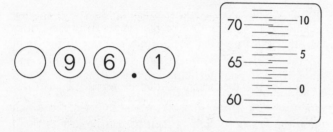

Fig. C–4. Readout on the Mettler H15 balance. The reading is 96.1617 grams. Note carefully how the vernier scale is read.

Substitution Weighing

You will have sensed something wrong here if you have read and understood this appendix from the beginning. As we saw in Section C–4, the sensitivity of a balance changes as the mass on the pans changes. If the sensitivity changes, then the deflection of the beam for a given difference in the masses on the two pans will change. Since mass differences less than 0.1 gm are read from the beam deflection of these balances, we may get the wrong mass because the sensitivity of the balance changes with load. This is not the case, however, because these balances work at *constant load* and hence *the sensitivity is constant.*

Before any object is placed on the sample pan of a single-pan substitution-weighing balance, both the sample and reference ends of the beam already support, effectively, about 200 gm and are balanced, Fig. C–5(a). The reference "pan" is really a fixed counterweight which is an integral part of the beam; the counterweight is designed so that the oscillations of the beam are highly damped, usually by the use of an air dashpot as shown in the figure. The weights on the sample end of the beam, however, are removable, as shown schematically in the figure. (The actual form of these weights, which are

_____

* In some of the more recent models the illuminated scale has given way to a completely digital readout, so that no thinking at all is necessary to read the mass. The last 100 mg (in some cases, 10 mg) is still, however, an optical magnification of the beam movement.

usually made of antiferromagnetic chrome-nickel steel, varies from one manufacturer to another.) Note that these are not equal-arm balances; the fulcrum knife edge is much closer to the sample pan than to the reference counterweight. This arrangement requires a lighter reference counterweight, and the smaller overall weight reduces wear on the knife edge.

When an object is added to the sample pan (sort of a "second sample pan," as shown), the sample end of the beam is heavier than the reference, and we must *remove* some of the removable weights to restore the balance, Fig. C–5(b). (Removal is accomplished by mechanical connections between the external knobs and the weights which are made only when a weight is removed; at all other times the weight is fully supported by the beam.) Obviously, the total of the weights that must be removed equals the weight of the object (to within 0.1 gm). We have *substituted* for some of the original weights (their total weight is shown in the windows on the front of the balance) the object being weighed.

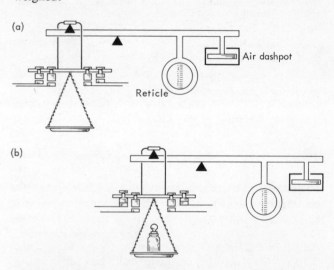

Fig. C–5. Schematic representation of a single-pan balance (a) unloaded, (b) loaded.

Usually the balance will still not be quite balanced because the smallest increment of mass we can remove is 0.1 gm, so the rest position of the beam will be different from what it was when the balance was initially balanced. The reticle† shown in the figure will thus be in a different

_____

† A reticle is a system of lines at the focus of the observer's end of an optical system. In telescopes, the reticle often consists of crosshairs or other sighting aids. In the single-pan balance, the reticle is a scale from zero to 100 (or more to give a longer optical range) with the divisions made so that they correspond to 1-mg imbalances of the balance beam. The reticle scale must be very precisely made, since the accuracy of the readout depends on the divisions being equivalent to exactly 1 mg.

position and a different part of its scale will be projected on the ground glass vernier scale where the mass is read. Thus the deflection of the beam is registered as a mass on the optical scale and, since the load is constant, the deflection of the beam for a given mass imbalance is constant, so the optical scale indicates an accurate mass for the object.

It is evident that the load on the balance is not precisely constant, since there is usually an imbalance in any weighing which must be read optically. The largest imbalance we will ever have, however, is 0.1 gm, for if the imbalance is greater than this we simply remove more weight from the sample end of beam, using the knobs and weights. However, 0.1 gm of the total effective load of about 200 gm is only one part in 2000, so the assumption of constant load is at least this good. Changes in sensitivity for this small deviation from a constant load are negligible, and we can use the balance with confidence.

Other Balance Controls

Besides the weight adjustment (removal) knobs on the single-pan balance, there are two other control knobs: the beam arrest and the zero adjustment.

The *beam-arrest control* has three positions: beam arrested, beam semireleased, and beam fully released. In the beam-arrested position, the knife edges are separated from their bearing plates, the moving parts are prevented from moving, the pan is held still, and the light source for the optical system is off. *The beam arrest must be in the arrest position whenever objects are removed from or placed on the pan.* It is a good idea to get in the habit of arresting the beam whenever the balance case doors are opened. In the semireleased position, the sample pan knife edge contacts its bearing plate, the beam is no longer prevented from moving, the pan is released, and the light source is on; the beam now pivots on an auxiliary fulcrum, however, and does not rest on the fulcrum knife edge and bearing plate, thus lessening wear on the fulcrum knife edge. In this position, changes in weights may be made and their effect observed on the optical scale. In the fully-released position, both knife edges contact their bearing plates, the beam is free to move, the pan is released, and the light source is on. *The beam-arrest control should never be turned to the fully-released position until the imbalance of the balance will be shown on the optical scale.*

The *zero adjustment* is used when the balance pan is empty to adjust the optical scale to read zero. The adjustment does not change any mechanical linkage in the instrument, but slightly adjusts the path of the optical system that projects on the ground glass at the front of the balance. This adjustment is made with the beam in

its fully-released position. If you cannot zero your balance, arrest the beam and check first to see that the balance is leveled. If you still cannot zero the balance, see your instructor. (The long optical lever arm that magnifies the beam movement makes these balances very sensitive to a slight maladjustment of level. Such a maladjustment may even be caused by the "elbow effect." If you lean on the balance table while trying to read the scale, you may get an inaccurate result because you will have changed the leveling of the balance enough to throw the reading off. Try it.)

C–7   WEIGHING WITH A SINGLE-PAN BALANCE

To weigh with a single-pan balance follow the procedure described below.

1) Make certain the beam is arrested and level the balance.

2) Set all the weight knobs to zero. Remove all objects from the pan and close the balance case. Fully release the beam. When the optical scale has come to rest, move the zero mark of the optical scale to coincide with the zero mark on the fixed vernier scale by adjusting the zero adjustment control. Arrest the beam.

3) Place the object to be weighed on the pan and close the sliding doors immediately. Do not keep your hands in the balance case any longer than necessary, to avoid introducing heat and humidity into the weighing chamber.

4) Semirelease the beam. The optical scale will move toward increasing mass and then stop, because full excursion of the beam is not allowed with this setting. Start with the weight knob you think controls the heaviest weights that must be removed to restore the balance and turn it to remove weight from the sample end of the beam. If you are removing increasing amounts of weight and you have chosen the correct knob, the optical scale will eventually move toward zero. Back up one step. Repeat the process with the other weight knobs in descending order. (The weight-setting knobs may also be turned so that decreasing amounts of weight are removed. In this case, resetting by one step when the optical scale moves, toward higher weight in this case, is not necessary.) It is unnecessary to go through this entire operation if you have some knowledge of the weight of the object you are weighing.

5) Arrest the beam and then *slowly* release the beam completely. (It is possible that the removal of weights may have moved the beam slightly, so arrest the beam first to make certain that it will be in the correct position when you set it down on the fulcrum knife edge.) Allow the optical scale to come to rest. Get in the habit of sitting with your hands in your lap while you wait for the beam to come to rest and read the optical scale.

Read and record the mass with your hands off the balance table. Arrest the beam.

6) Unload the pan and clear away any debris you may have scattered in and around the balance. *Please leave the balance clean;* it is bad technique to spill chemicals around the balances, but it is inexcusable not to clean up any mess you cause.

C–8   ERRORS IN WEIGHING

There are a number of possible sources of error in weighing. Some of these, for example, unequal balance arm lengths, buoyancy, and inaccurate weights, may be corrected for; others, such as change of sample during weighing, temperature differences between the sample and the balance, and electrification of the balance or objects to be weighed, must simply be avoided.

Unequal Balance Arms

This source of error is only applicable to double-pan balances, since on substitution-weighing single-pan balances the weights and sample are compared on the same side of the balance beam. Equation (C–1) is valid only if the distance from the fulcrum knife edge to each of the pan support knife edges is identical. If there is any inequality in the lengths of the balance arms, an object placed on the right-hand balance pan will not require the same amount of weight to balance it as when it is on the left-hand pan.

You can test your balance and, if necessary, counter the effect of unequal arm lengths by the following procedure.

1) Weigh some object as described in Section C–4. Designate the sum of the masses of the weights used as W_1 and the length of the balance arm on the same side of the balance weights as L_1.

2) Place the object on the other pan and again weigh it. Designate the sum of the masses of the weights used as W_2 and the length of the balance arm on the same side of the balance as the weights as L_2.

3) Denote the true mass of the object as M_0. The following equations represent the balance conditions in each of the weighings:

$$M_0L_2 = W_1L_1, \tag{C–6}$$

$$M_0L_1 = W_2L_2. \tag{C–7}$$

Multiplying (C–6) times (C–7) gives

$$M_0^2L_1L_2 = W_1W_2L_1L_2,$$
$$M_0^2 = W_1W_2;$$

therefore

$$M_0 = (W_1W_2)^{1/2}. \tag{C–8}$$

Thus the true mass of an object can be obtained from this method of double weighings (the Gauss transposition method) by taking the square root of the product of the two weighing results.

We can make an approximation to simplify this calculation:

$$W_2 = W_1 + (W_2 - W_1),$$
$$W_1W_2 = W_1^2 + W_1(W_2 - W_1),$$
$$W_1W_2 = W_1^2\left[1 + \frac{(W_2 - W_1)}{W_1}\right],$$
$$(W_1W_2)^{1/2} = W_1\left[1 + \frac{(W_2 - W_1)}{W_1}\right]^{1/2}. \tag{C–9}$$

As a consequence of the binomial theorem,* we can write

$$(1 + x)^{1/2} \approx 1 + \tfrac{1}{2}x,$$

if x is small compared with unity. Since the balance arms of a good analytical balance seldom differ in length by more than one part in 20,000, W_1 is almost equal to W_2; thus the term $(W_2 - W_1)/W_1$ will certainly be small compared to unity, and we can use the approximation based on the binomial theorem to simplify Eq. (C–9):

$$(W_1W_2)^{1/2} \approx W_1\left[1 + \left(\frac{1}{2}\right)\frac{W_2 - W_1}{W_1}\right],$$
$$(W_1W_2)^{1/2} \approx \frac{(W_1 + W_2)}{2}. \tag{C–10}$$

This result may be substituted in (C–8) to give

$$M_0 \approx (W_1 + W_2)/2. \tag{C–11}$$

The actual ratio of the lengths of the balance arms during your test may be obtained by dividing Eq. (C–6) by Eq. (C–7):

$$M_0L_2/M_0L_1 = W_1L_1/W_2L_2,$$
$$L_2/L_1 = (W_1/W_2)^{1/2}. \tag{C–12}$$

Remember that this ratio is not a constant for your balance but is the ratio under the particular conditions of temperature, load, and balance position at which the test was made.

The transposition method of weighing must be used for very precise weighings (when an accuracy of one part in 1,000,000 is necessary). In your general analytical work it is not necessary to correct for the inequality of balance arms unless the test shows them to be much further off than one part in 20,000.

---

* Consult any intermediate algebra textbook.

Buoyancy

Any object suspended in a fluid medium is buoyed up in direct proportion to the mass of the fluid which it displaces. The sea of air which surrounds the weights and the object weighed on an analytical balance is a fluid medium which slightly counteracts the downward force of gravity on the weights and the object. The volume of an object times the density of the air is the mass of air displaced by the object; this must be subtracted from the true mass to give the apparent mass acted on by gravity. The volume of an object is given by its mass divided by its density,

$$\frac{M \text{ gm}}{\rho \text{ gm/cc}} = V \text{ cc.*}$$

Thus the condition for balance will be

$$M_0 - \frac{M_0}{\rho} \cdot \rho_a = W - \frac{W}{\rho_w} \cdot \rho_a, \qquad \text{(C-13)}$$

where M_0 is the true mass of the object *in vacuo*, W is the mass of the weights *in vacuo*, ρ is the density of the object, ρ_w is the density of the weights, and ρ_a is the density of the air. Equation (C-13) may be rearranged to

$$M_0 = W \left[\frac{1 - (\rho_a/\rho_w)}{1 - (\rho_a/\rho)} \right]. \qquad \text{(C-14)}$$

The ratio on the right-hand side of (C-14) can be simply divided out to give

$$M_0 \simeq W[1 + (\rho_a/\rho) - (\rho_a/\rho_w)], \qquad \text{(C-15)}$$

if terms of order greater than one in ρ_a/ρ and ρ_a/ρ_w are neglected, which is a valid approximation if the density ratios are small. [Although ρ_a varies with the exact composition of the air, temperature, and barometric pressure, it is usually sufficiently accurate to say that $\rho_a = 0.0012$ gm/cc. The density of solid or liquid objects to be weighed is almost never less than 0.5 gm/cc, and the density of the metals usually used for weights is about 8 gm/cc (brass, 8.4; chrome-nickel steel, 7.8). The density ratios are indeed very small in most cases, so the approximation is valid. If gases or vapors are weighed, the exact Eq. (C-14) must be used, since then ρ_a/ρ is not small compared with unity.]

Except when calibrating volumetric glassware, Section 1-11, and working with gases, you can neglect buoyancy corrections in routine laboratory work.

---

* The cubic centimeter is the conventional volume unit for density because it is an "absolute" volume, whereas the milliliter must always be related back to the volume of a gram of water at 3.98°C. See Section 1-11.

Inaccuracy of Weights

Probably the most common source of error in weighing is inaccuracy of the weights. For most purposes, it is not necessary to know the absolute values of the weights you use, but for quantitative work you must know the relative values of your weight pieces, i.e., whether the 2-gm weight is twice the mass of the 1-gm weight, and, if not, what the ratio is. To obtain accurate results you will have to calibrate your weight set and thus determine a correction for each weight.

The method of weight calibration presented here is that of T. W. Richards, who won the Nobel Prize for his research in determining exact atomic weights. The principle of the method is arbitrarily to assign to one of the weight pieces its exact nominal value and then to determine the masses of all the other weights relative to this standard. One of the 10-mg pieces is usually chosen as the standard for calibrating weights on the conventional double-pan balance. (This choice usually leads to rather large differences for the larger weights between their nominal values and their values relative to the standard. To make the corrections for the larger weights more manageable, after the relative values of the weights have been determined, a new standard, for example, one of the 10-gm pieces, may be chosen and all weight corrections made relative to this piece.) For weights on chainomatic balances, it is usual to choose the rider as the standard and to assume that the chain is accurate. The weights in a single-pan substitution-weighing balance usually do not suffer the same wear that external weights do and will retain their initial calibration longer. They may be calibrated relative to the optical scale if a set of tare weights is available. The optical scale itself can only be checked for accuracy if an absolutely calibrated 0.1 gm weight is available.

Calibration Procedure. The procedure will be outlined for calibrating the 1-, 1'-, 2-, 3-, and 5-gm weights of a set relative to the 1-gm piece. It should be evident how you would proceed if you were to begin with a 10-mg weight or a 1-gm rider.

1) Determine the sensitivity and rest point of your balance.

2) Place the "standard" 1-gm mass directly in the center of the right-hand pan and the other 1-gm piece, 1', in the center of the left-hand pan and determine the rest point.

3) Calculate the difference in mass, Δ, between the mass on the left-hand pan and that on the right,

$$\Delta = \text{mass}_{\text{left}} - \text{mass}_{\text{right}},$$

from the sensitivity of the balance and the difference in rest points.

4) Place the 1-gm and 1'-gm weights in the center of the right-hand pan and the 2-gm weight in the center of the left-hand pan and determine the rest point.

5) Once again determine the mass difference between the left-hand and right-hand pans.

6) Continue in this way for $1 + 2$ vs. 3 and $2 + 3$ vs. 5 and tabulate the results, as in Table C-1.

Table C-1
AN EXAMPLE OF WEIGHT CALIBRATION

Weights (right)	Weight (left)	Δ, mg	$Mass_{right}$, gm	$Mass_{left}$, gm	Correction to $weight_{left}$, mg
1	1'	−0.2	1	1 − 0.0002	−0.2
1 + 1'	2	0.0	2 − 0.0002	2 − 0.0002	−0.2
1 + 2	3	+0.3	3 − 0.0002	3 + 0.0001	+0.1
2 + 3	5	+0.7	5 − 0.0001	5 + 0.0006	+0.6

Study the construction of the table until you understand it clearly. The last column gives the correction in milligrams that must be added (algebraically) to the nominal mass marked on each weight to give its mass correctly, relative to the "standard" weight taken as 1.0000 gm. If an actual standard weight (one standardized by the National Bureau of Standards) is available, the weight in your set that has the nominal value of the standard may be compared with it to determine its true absolute mass. You can then calculate the absolute masses of all your weights, since the ratios of their masses relative to the newly established standard are known.

Illustrative Example: An object is exactly balanced by the 1-gm and 3-gm weights of the set whose calibration is given in Table C-1. What is the mass of the object?

The data recorded for this weighing should look like this:

$$\frac{\begin{array}{l} 1 + 0.0000 \\ 3 + 0.0001 \end{array}}{4 + 0.0001} = 4.0001 \text{ gm.}$$

The mass of the object is 4.0001 gm.

This example demonstrates two further weighing rules. The first is that the smallest possible number of weights should be used to balance the object. In this instance, it would also have been possible to balance the object (within 0.5 mg) using the 1-gm, 1'-gm, and 2-gm weights, but this would simply have increased the chance for error from inaccuracies in the weights (or weight calibration). The second rule is that the standard weight should always be used in preference to another of the same nominal mass.

Sample Changes during Weighing

Hygroscopic substances (those which readily absorb moisture) may gain in weight as they absorb moisture from the air if they are weighed in open vessels; the obvious cure is to weigh such substances in capped containers, such as weighing bottles, and to have these containers open in the atmosphere of the room for the minimum possible time. Volatile substances may lose weight by evaporation and should *never* be weighed in open vessels on an analytical balance. Aside from the obvious fact that the data will be useless, the vapors may damage the balance.

Temperature Effects

Objects to be weighed should be at the same temperature as the balance. It is impossible to predict the effects of the air currents and unequal heating or cooling of the balance parts except to say that they will be deleterious.

Electrification

Again it is impossible to predict the effects of static charges on the balance or balance case except that they will not improve the accuracy of your weighing. Avoid these effects by refraining from briskly rubbing glass vessels with cloth before they are weighed and from rubbing the outside of the balance case with a dry cloth.

C-9 AN ADMONITION

Analytical balances of all types are precision instruments. They are probably the most accurate instruments you will use in the laboratory. Although other instruments may look more pretentious, they usually will not match the balance for precision and accuracy. Treat your balance realizing it is capable of a precision of one part in 1,000,000 (0.1 mg in 100 gm). You will be rewarded with the best data you will obtain in the laboratory.

This admonition is often overlooked by the student using a single-pan balance. Its ease and speed of operation and the disarming simplicity of its exterior do not generate an appreciation for the exceedingly precise craftsmanship involved in its actual mechanism. A single-pan balance costs about twice as much as a conventional double-pan balance; to see why, ask your instructor to show you a single-pan balance with the case removed. To reiterate: *All analytical balances, double- and single-pan, are precision instruments and must be treated as such.*

C-10 THE CARE AND FEEDING OF THE BALANCE

Some of the most important points to remember in caring for your balance and in using good weighing procedure are as follows.

1) Know the capability of your balance and do not exceed its load limits (100–200 gm for most balances).

2) Before making a weighing, clean up around and in the balance case. Use a soft camel's-hair brush to brush off the balance pans and the inside of the case. After use leave the balance clean.

3) Make certain that the balance is level before you use it.

4) Keep the balance case closed as much as possible. On a single-pan balance, one of your worst enemies is dust on the weights, which causes inaccuracies. The only entrance for dust is through the opening into the weighing chamber for the sample pan, so it is especially important to keep the case closed as much as possible.

5) Be certain the beam is fully arrested whenever objects are placed on or removed from the pans.

6) Objects to be weighed and weights should be placed as near the center of the pans as possible to help ensure that the weight distribution along the knife edges is uniform.

7) Never place a chemical directly on the pans; use a container.

8) Do not weigh objects that are hotter or colder than the balance. This will not only give you poor results but may ruin the results of someone else who uses the balance before it returns to temperature equilibrium.

9) Always handle weights with ivory- or plastic-tipped forceps.

10) Avoid parallax in reading the scale by sitting directly in front of the balance. On some substitution-weighing balances the magnifying reader for the optical scale will force you to look straight at the scale.

11) Record weights directly in your notebook while you are at the balance. It is a temptation for you to take down weights on scrap paper, but it is an even greater temptation for instructors to confiscate and destroy these scraps. Beware.

12) When you have finished, clean up, close the balance case, and be sure the beam is arrested.

REFERENCES

Evans, W. D., "Fundamentals of the Analytical Balance," *J. Chem. Ed.* **32**, 419 (1955).

Kolthoff, I. M., and E. B. Sandell, *Textbook of Quantitative Inorganic Analysis*, 3rd ed., Macmillan, New York, 1952, Chapter 13.

Pierce, W. C., E. L. Haenisch, and D. T. Sawyer, *Quantitative Analysis*, 4th ed., John Wiley & Sons, New York, 1958, Chapter 3.

Skoog, D. A., and D. M. West, *Fundamentals of Analytical Chemistry*, Holt, Rinehart & Winston, New York, 1963, Chapter 5.

Waser, J., *Quantitative Chemistry*, revised ed., W. A. Benjamin, New York, 1964, Chapter 3 and Appendix II.

Instruction manuals prepared by the manufacturer of your balance are usually worthwhile for finding out what he thinks about the care and use of the instrument he makes.

PROBLEMS

1. Assuming that the ratio of the lengths of your balance arms remains constant, how can you use Eqs. (C–11) and (C–12) to correct the mass of an object without two weighings, once this ratio is known?

2. Show that Eq. (C–15) can be derived from Eq. (C–13) by using the approximation $W \approx M_0$. How is this approximation related to one used in the text to obtain Eq. (C–15)?

3. Show that Eq. (C–13) results from a consideration of the equality of moments about the fulcrum of the balance beam when the balance is balanced.

4. A sample with a density of 0.47 gm/cc weighed 0.5013 gm on a balance with chrome-nickel steel weights. What is the true mass of this sample? If the density was 0.0047 gm/cc, what would its true mass be?

5. If you were to calibrate the weight set listed on page 230, why would you begin with the 10-mg piece as the standard instead of, say, the 1-gm piece?

6. A 2.0000-gm weight calibrated by the National Bureau of Standards was compared with the 2-gm piece listed in Table C–1. The 2-gm piece was found to be 0.4 mg too heavy, i.e., it has a mass of 2.0004 gm. What are the true masses of the other weights in Table C–1?

7. Can you suggest how the chain in a chainomatic balance could be calibrated?

8. How would you go about calibrating the weights in a single-pan balance? Keep in mind that for each mass range controlled by a knob there are only four weights.

THE pH METER

D-1 THE ELECTRODE SYSTEM

For precise measurements of pH an electrometric determination is always used. Electrometric methods using the hydrogen and quinhydrone electrodes are outlined in Section 10–5, and the latter is used in Experiments 21 and 22. However, the hydrogen electrode is not very convenient and is potentially quite hazardous* and the quinhydrone electrode has a limited, although quite useful, range. The electrometric method used in pH meters depends instead on the convenient and accurate glass electrode.

When a thin conducting glass membrane is placed between solutions of different pH, a potential difference develops across it which can be detected by placing reference electrodes in the solutions on either side of the membrane.† The potential is a function of the two hydrogen-ion concentrations and at one time was thought to be due to actual transfer of hydrogen ions through the membrane. Labeling experiments now indicate that this is not the mechanism by which the potential is set up; the actual mechanism is not well understood. For our purposes we need to know only that the potential difference across such a membrane may be written (at 25°C) as

$$\Delta \mathcal{E}_{\mathrm{glass}} = k + 0.059(\mathrm{pH}_1 - \mathrm{pH}_2),$$

where the two pH's are those on opposite sides of the membrane and k is a constant.

The construction of a typical glass electrode is shown in Fig. D–1. On one side of the membrane, the reference

---

* The hydrogen electrode is, however, used in all very accurate work since pH is defined in terms of the potential of a hydrogen electrode.

† Developing glass for these electrodes is still more art than science and there are many formulations that are better for one purpose or another.

side, there is a solution of a known pH furnished by the HCl. The reference electrode in this solution is a silver-silver chloride electrode. The half-reaction for this electrode is

$$\mathrm{AgCl(s)} + \mathrm{e}^- = \mathrm{Ag(s)} + \mathrm{Cl}^-$$

and we see that the half-cell potential is a function only of the chloride concentration, since the activities of solid silver chloride and silver metal are constant so long as they are present. Since the chloride concentration, furnished by the HCl, is also constant, the half-cell potential is constant.

We must also have some reference electrode in the solution whose pH we wish to measure, preferably one whose potential is pH independent. The saturated

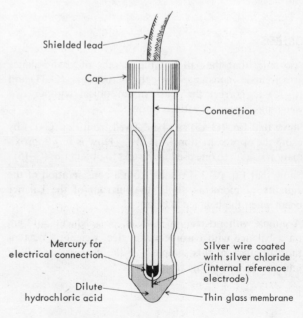

Shielded lead

Cap

Connection

Mercury for electrical connection

Dilute hydrochloric acid

Silver wire coated with silver chloride (internal reference electrode)

Thin glass membrane

Fig. D–1. The glass electrode.

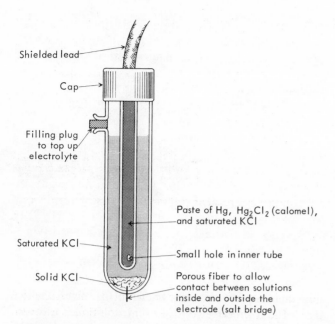

Fig. D–2. A commercial saturated calomel electrode.

Shielded lead

Cap

Filling plug
to top up
electrolyte

Saturated KCl

Solid KCl

Paste of Hg, Hg_2Cl_2 (calomel),
and saturated KCl

Small hole in inner tube

Porous fiber to allow
contact between solutions
inside and outside the
electrode (salt bridge)

D–2 THE INSTRUMENTATION USED WITH GLASS ELECTRODES

Measuring the potential difference in the glass electrode-SCE system must be done as nearly as possible in true potentiometric fashion. This means we must use a device that draws no current (or negligible current) from the electrode system while it performs the measurement. It might at first glance appear that a normal potentiometer would do, but it is not suitable: The internal resistance of the glass electrode is so very high that the input resistance of the measuring device must also be very high, as it never is in potentiometers.

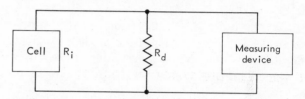

Fig. D–3. A potential measuring device.

Cell R_i R_d Measuring device

Let us show why the measuring device needs to have a very high input impedance. All potential measuring devices are basically like that shown in Fig. D–3; the cell generates the potential we wish to know, but the potential drop through the input resistance R_d, of the measuring device is what is really measured. Now let us consider two cases.

1) Suppose that the input resistance, R_d, is about the same as the internal resistance of the cell, R_i (at least 10^6 ohm for glass electrode systems). We shall also assume that the cell generates a potential of one volt, which is the correct order of magnitude for these systems. Now around any part of a circuit the sum of the potentials minus the sum of the current-resistance drops must be zero (Kirchhoff's Law), so

$$\Delta \mathcal{E}_{cell} - iR_i - iR_d = 0,$$

where i = current that flows in this part of the circuit:

$$1 \text{ volt} - i \times 10^6 \text{ ohm} - i \times 10^6 \text{ ohm} = 0,$$

$$i = \tfrac{1}{2} \times 10^{-6} \text{ amp}.$$

The potential we measure is $iR_d = \tfrac{1}{2} \times 10^{-6}$ amp $\times 10^6$ ohm $= \tfrac{1}{2}$ volt, but we know this is far from being correct, since $\Delta \mathcal{E}_{cell}$ is one volt.*

calomel electrode, SCE, is pH independent and can easily be made into a compact, convenient design as shown in Fig. D–2. The half-reaction at a calomel electrode is

$$Hg_2Cl_2(s) + 2e^- = 2Hg(l) + 2Cl^-,$$

which is only dependent on chloride-ion concentration, held constant by saturating the solution with KCl. The half-cell potential for the SCE is $\mathcal{E}_{SCE} = 0.246$ v (at 25°C.) and is independent of the pH of the solution being measured.

The potential of the cell created by placing both the glass electrode and the SCE into a solution in which we wish to determine $[H^+]$ is a combination of three terms: the potential for the AgCl | Ag half-cell, the potential of the SCE, and the potential difference across the glass membrane, $\Delta \mathcal{E}_{glass}$. We can combine these terms as

$$\Delta \mathcal{E} = \mathcal{E}_{AgCl|Ag} + \Delta \mathcal{E}_{glass} - \mathcal{E}_{SCE}$$
$$= \mathcal{E}_{AgCl|Ag} + k + 0.059(pH_1 - pH_2) - \mathcal{E}_{SCE},$$
$$\text{(D–1)}$$

where pH_1 is the pH to be determined and pH_2 is the pH on the reference side of the glass electrode. Both pH_2 and $\mathcal{E}_{AgCl|Ag}$ are constants because the fixed HCl concentration determines them and $\mathcal{E}_{SCE}$ is also a constant, so we can rewrite Eq. (D–1) as

$$\Delta \mathcal{E} = 0.059 pH + \text{const}, \qquad \text{(D–2)}$$

where the pH is that which we wish to determine. Thus a measurement of $\Delta \mathcal{E}$ can be translated into a value of pH.

---

* You might object that a potentiometer draws no current when it is nulled. To a first approximation this is correct, but potentiometers rarely have galvanometers capable of detecting currents much below 10^{-6} amp, so although we would detect no current flowing in this circuit, the potential reading would be incorrect, or at least it would not be sensitive to large changes in the slidewire setting.

2) Now suppose that the input resistance, R_d, is much greater than R_i. Let us take $R_d = 10^{13}$ ohm with all the other conditions the same as above:

$$\Delta\varepsilon_{\text{cell}} - iR_i - iR_d = 0,$$
$$1 \text{ volt} - i \times 10^6 \text{ ohm} - i \times 10^{13} \text{ ohm} = 0,$$
$$i = \frac{1}{(10^{13} + 10^6)} \text{ amp}.$$

We shall be making an error of only one part in ten million if we neglect the cell resistance (10^6) compared to the input impedance (10^{13}), so we can write

$$i = 10^{-13} \text{ amp}.$$

Thus we measure $iR_d = 10^{-13}$ amp $\times 10^{13}$ ohm = 1 volt, which is the potential of the cell. These examples demonstrate the necessity for a measuring device with a high input impedance if accurate potentials are to be obtained.

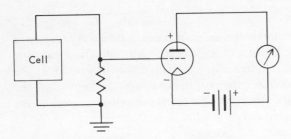

Fig. D–4. A representation of the essential parts of a VTVM.

The instrument usually used to measure the voltage of cells such as this is a vacuum tube voltmeter (VTVM). Although the actual electronics are not always easy to follow, the operation of the VTVM is easy to outline (Fig. D–4). The meter registers a current flow when current flows from the cathode to the anode of the vacuum tube. This current is controlled by the potential of the grid in the tube: if the grid becomes more negative, electrons from the cathode are repelled and less current flows. Conversely, when the grid becomes more positive more electrons are attracted and hence more current flows. Thus the potential of the cell controls the current flow. We can calibrate the meter in volts or in pH units; in the latter case it is called a pH meter.*

D–3 USING pH METERS

Since there are so many different kinds of pH meters available, we shall not attempt to outline the detailed operation of any one or all of them, but will simply discuss some features and precautions you should know

---

* Some pH meters are regular potentiometers with electronic amplification to boost the off-balance signal to detectable levels.

for all models. The operation of the instruments you actually have available will be explained by your instructor or the instruction manual with the instrument.

Let us think back to Eq. (D–2) and recall that the constant k, peculiar to the particular glass electrode you are using is hidden in the "constant"; in fact it varies with its age and the treatment it has had. Thus, before you can use a glass electrode with confidence you must standardize it with a solution of known pH. Usually, buffer solutions for standardization are kept handy near pH meters. If such a buffer solution is not available, you can use a saturated solution of potassium hydrogen tartrate, pH = 3.57 (at 25°C). Note that Eq. (D–2) is the equation of a straight line and standardizing is tantamount to adjusting the "intercept" of this line to a particular value so that the meter scale will accurately correspond to the pH of solutions. You do this by adjusting a dial on the instrument so the meter reading and the known pH of the standardizing buffer solution are the same.

The potentials of almost all cells are temperature dependent, and the glass electrode-SCE system is no exception. All pH meters have either a manual or automatic temperature compensator. If there is a manual compensator, you will have to turn a dial to read the temperature of the solution whose pH you are measuring. This compensation not only accounts for the changes in the "constant" of Eq. (D–2) with temperature, but also adjusts for the temperature dependence of the factor 0.059 (see Section 10–1).

Before you put electrodes from one solution into another you should rinse them copiously with water (or whatever solvent you are using) and then very carefully dab them dry with a soft laboratory tissue. They are quite fragile and must be handled with great care. The electrodes should *never* be allowed to dry out and must always be stored in water or a neutral buffer solution.

The membranes of glass electrodes seem to be harmed by prolonged contact with very basic solutions, although occasional use at high pH does not seem to hurt them. The usual all-purpose glass electrode is not accurate at high pH (above 12 or 13), so special high-pH glass electrodes are available. Usually ions other than H^+ do not affect the glass electrode, but at high ionic strengths, glass-electrode measurements become less accurate; sodium ion, in particular, causes bad measurements. (Special electrodes are available to alleviate this problem also).

Warning: Do not handle the glass-electrode receptacle insulation, the plug of the glass-electrode lead, and other parts of the input circuit. All insulation used in the high-impedance (glass-electrode) side of the input circuit of a pH meter is made of extremely low-electrical-loss material. Never handle such insulation with your bare hands, for they may leave dirt or perspiration salts on the surface of the insulation, thus forming leakage paths which will cause erroneous readings. These parts must always be kept clean and dry. If any insulating material becomes contaminated by handling, ask an instructor to take the necessary remedial measures. Avoid splashing solutions on the instrument and electrodes.

On most pH meters the scale is graduated in millivolts as well as pH units; a switch on the instrument converts to millivolt readings so that voltage readings from any pair of electrodes may be used. Consult your instructor or the instrument manual for directions on how to connect different electrodes and use the instrument as a vacuum tube millivoltmeter (or potentiometer, if that is the design).

REFERENCES

MALMSTADT, H. V., "Versatile and Inexpensive pH Recording Electrometer," *J. Chem. Ed.* **41,** 148 (1964) describes the instrumentation and indicates what can be done with it. "Inexpensive" in this case means under about five hundred dollars.

SLABAUGH, W. H., "Magnetic Stirrer," *J. Chem. Ed.* **40,** 641 (1963) describes a very inexpensive, home-made stirrer. Some form of continuous stirring is essential for good results in pH and other instrumental titrations.

SPECTROSCOPY AND SPECTROPHOTOMETERS

We need to understand something about the nature of light and the basic principles of its absorbance by matter to see how spectrophotometers are designed and used. In this appendix we will discuss both the theory underlying spectrophotometry (and the allied nomenclature) and the operation of the simple single-beam manual spectrophotometer, an instrument designed to work in the visible region of the electromagnetic radiation spectrum.

E–1 LIGHT

Nomenclature

Light seems to have a dual nature: in some connections it is useful to speak of light as waves (electromagnetic in nature); in other situations it is necessary to consider light as packets of energy, called photons. In fact, light has only one nature, but because the analogies we draw from the world are inadequate, we need to describe it in both these ways. The two descriptions of light are related according to the formula first postulated by Planck (and proved by him and his contemporaries at the beginning of the century, see Experiment 23):

$$\epsilon = h\nu, \tag{E–1}$$

where ϵ is energy of the photon, ν is the *frequency* of the light wave (discussed in the next paragraph), h is the proportionality constant, Planck's constant $= 6.62 \times 10^{-27}$ erg-sec. For example, the visible region of the electromagnetic radiation spectrum consists of waves with frequencies from about 3×10^{14} sec^{-1} (red) to about 7.5×10^{14} sec^{-1} (violet); these correspond to photon energies of 2×10^{-12} erg/photon (red) to 5×10^{-12} erg/photon (violet).

Before we go on, you should learn some of the common notations for light waves. The *frequency*, ν, is the number of cycles of the wave which pass a given point per second. The units are sec^{-1}. The length of each cycle, λ, is called the *wavelength* of the light. The units of wavelength are usually given as centimeters, angstroms, microns, or millimicrons.* You will sometimes see another unit of "frequency," the *wavenumber*, denoted $\bar{\nu}$, which is the number of waves per centimeter:

$$\bar{\nu} = 1/\lambda \quad (\lambda \text{ is expressed in cm}). \tag{E–2}$$

Since the light wave is of course traveling at the speed of light, $c = 3 \times 10^{10}$ cm/sec, we can divide its speed by the length of each cycle to find out how many cycles pass a point in one second:

$$\nu = c/\lambda \quad \text{or} \quad \lambda = c/\nu. \tag{E–3}$$

The relationship of ϵ, ν, λ, and $\bar{\nu}$ for a large part of the electromagnetic spectrum is shown in Fig. E–1.

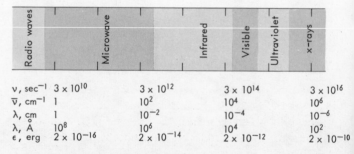

ν, sec^{-1}	3×10^{10}	3×10^{12}	3×10^{14}	3×10^{16}
$\bar{\nu}$, cm^{-1}	1	10^{2}	10^{4}	10^{6}
λ, cm	1	10^{-2}	10^{-4}	10^{-6}
λ, Å	10^{8}	10^{6}	10^{4}	10^{2}
ϵ, erg	2×10^{-16}	2×10^{-14}	2×10^{-12}	2×10^{-10}

Fig. E–1. Electromagnetic radiation regions and corresponding frequencies, wavelengths, and energies.

Although normally a beam of light includes waves of many frequencies, it is possible to separate light waves of a desired frequency from the rest. When light is

---

* 1 Å $= 10^{-8}$ cm; 1 micron (μ) $= 10^{-6}$ m $= 10^{-4}$ cm $= 10^{4}$ Å; 1 mμ $= 10^{-9}$ m $= 10^{-7}$ cm $= 10$ Å.

passed through a diffracting prism or "reflected" from a diffraction grating, the waves of different frequencies are deflected by different amounts so that the beam is "spread out" in space; see Fig. E–2. A narrow beam of "white light"* will be diffracted into a rectangle along which its frequencies will be spaced much as in Fig. E–1. If we intercept this broadened beam with an opaque barrier with a slit in it, then only the narrow band of frequencies that falls at this exit slit will pass through the barrier. By rotating the prism or the grating, one can vary the frequencies which will pass through the slit. This light can then be observed by a detector (usually, for wavelengths in the visible and ultraviolet, a photocell of some kind) placed in back of the exit slit.

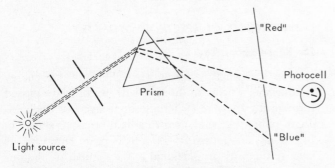

Fig. E–2. Dispersion of "white light" by a prism.

For convenience, we usually denote a band of light passing through the exit slit by its central frequency, saying, for instance, that the light coming through a slit has a frequency of 3×10^{14} sec^{-1} (or a wavelength of 10,000 Å), even though we know that other frequencies both greater and less than this value are also passing through. To describe our system precisely we must indicate its *band pass*, i.e., the actual range of frequencies (or wavelengths), $\Delta \nu$, around the central frequency, ν, which is passing through the exit slit.

The Interaction of Light and Matter

If a sample of some substance is placed between the exit slit and the detector, there will usually be certain frequencies at which light from the beam will be absorbed by the sample, i.e., at which fewer photons of this energy will reach the detector than when the sample is not there. Perhaps the most striking feature of the absorption of light by matter is the selectivity of the process. In the microwave and infrared regions of the electromagnetic spectrum, molecules absorb only very narrow bands of energy. In the visible and ultraviolet, the energy absorp-

tion bands are usually broader but can be shown to be overlapping packets of much narrower energy band absorptions. What is the mechanism of this structured light absorption?

Although we cannot present the details of the application of quantum and wave mechanics to the description of molecules here, we shall utilize the results of this description to "explain" energy absorption by molecules.† The theory predicts that molecules of any given compound exist only in certain energy states, or, to put it another way, only certain energy states are allowed to molecules of a particular compound. The energies are said to be *quantized*. This characteristic is confirmed by experiments in energy absorption. If a photon of a certain energy "collides" with a molecule, the photon's energy cannot be absorbed by the molecule unless the energy is exactly that required to raise the molecule from the energy state it is in when it encounters the photon to another of its energy states. The energy of the photon cannot be divided in this process; either it is absorbed *in toto* or it does not affect the molecule.

The energy state of a molecule is the result of a combination of three primary intramolecular motions: rotational, vibrational, and electronic. Since molecules are three-dimensional, they can rotate or tumble in space (although linear molecules rotate effectively in two dimensions only). The frequency of rotation is defined as the number of complete rotations per second around some molecular axis defined by the position of the atomic nuclei. Only certain frequencies, corresponding via Eq. (E–1) to certain energies, of rotation are allowed to the molecules of a particular compound. The spacing between rotational energy levels is small, so low-energy photons, in the microwave region, cause transitions between these rotational quantum levels to occur. (The concurrent absorbance of microwave energies is the basis of microwave spectroscopy.)

The atoms that make up molecules are in continuous motion, so the molecule is continuously vibrating. Again, only certain vibrational frequencies are allowed to any molecule, and hence only certain energies, corresponding to the energy spacings between vibrational quantum states, can be absorbed from radiation interacting with the molecule. These energy spacings are

---

* The term "white light" is used to refer to electromagnetic radiation which contains a wide range of frequencies; it does not necessarily refer to visible light.

† In fact, the arguments are a bit circular, since much of the necessity for the quantum theory was to explain the light emission and absorption properties of matter. The theory, however, goes a great deal further than simply rationalizing specific data; it is indeed heuristic, i.e., it predicts paths for investigation as yet unthought of and correctly predicts the results of these studies. This property of the theory gives us much more confidence that the description of matter it provides is a reasonable approximation to the truth.

larger than rotational energy spacings and the transitions require correspondingly higher photon energies; thus absorption of energy occurs in the higher-frequency infrared region of the electromagnetic spectrum.

A molecule, of course, is both vibrating and rotating at the same time, so one can add the energies and obtain a series of vibration-rotation energy levels for each vibrational state, as shown schematically in Fig. E–3. Also shown in the figure are the vibrational transitions allowed to the molecule. Due to the rotational "structure" of each vibrational level, these transitions often appear as an *absorption band* which is a combination of a number of closely-spaced energy transitions, see Experiment 24. (Quantum-mechanical calculations, verified by experiments, indicate that not all "possible" energy transitions are allowed to a molecule interacting with a photon, so many of these transitions will not be actually observed.*)

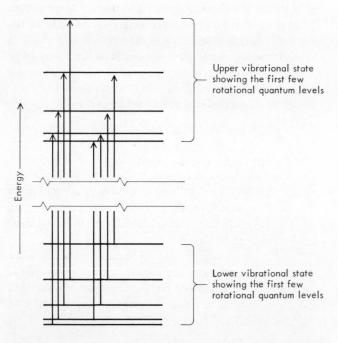

Fig. E–3. A schematic representation of vibration-rotation energy levels for two vibrational states of a molecule. Some of the allowed vibration-rotation transitions (in the infrared) for these levels are shown.

As we should expect from the discussion so far, the energies of the motions of the electrons in the molecule may also take only certain values. Thus only certain frequencies of light will excite an electron from one energy state to a higher one. The separation of electronic

---

* This does not mean that the molecule cannot exist in certain of its energy states, but that the molecule cannot go from one to the other of these states by absorption (or emission) of a photon. It is the transition, not the states, that is forbidden.

energy states is still greater than for vibrational states; these transitions are responsible for the absorption of energy in the visible and ultraviolet regions of the spectrum. Again superimposed on each electronic energy level are many vibrational levels and their concomitant rotational levels, so that the light absorption, especially absorption by molecules containing more than three or four atoms, usually appears as relatively wide bands. (Again, calculations indicate that certain transitions are not allowed, so that not all energy transitions are equally probable; this means that the percentage of the photons absorbed in any particular energy transition in a molecule is not the same as that for some other transition of the molecule at a different energy. This effect is observed experimentally, as we shall see below.)

E–2 PRINCIPLES OF SPECTROPHOTOMETRY

The Beer-Lambert Law

Let us see what happens when light of an energy (frequency) which can interact with a sample is passed through it. Imagine an infinitesimal layer, of thickness db, of sample perpendicular to a light beam, as shown in Fig. E–4. The *intensity* of the light beam entering this layer (a quantity proportional to the number of photons of a particular energy per second per unit area entering the layer) we shall call I. Since the photons can interact with the sample, some of them will not pass through the layer. Thus the intensity of the beam emerging from the layer will be $I - dI$, where dI represents the infinitesimal increment of light intensity absorbed by the layer (again proportional, with the same proportionality constant as above, to the number of photons of a particular energy per second per unit area that are absorbed in the layer.)

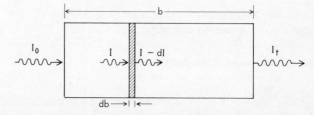

Fig. E–4. Relationship of the experimental quantities that enter the derivation of the Beer-Lambert law.

A number of factors determine how large a number of photons will be absorbed. First are the concentrations of the two interacting species: the more photons that enter the layer and/or the more sample molecules there are in the layer, the greater will be the number of photons that interact. It seems reasonable to assume that the number of photons absorbed is directly proportional to the number of photons entering the layer (or to the intensity, I), and to the concentration of absorbing molecules in the layer, c.* Second, we have seen in the preceding paragraphs that all energy absorptions are not equally probable, so there will have to be an energy- (frequency- or wavelength-)dependent parameter, a', introduced to account for the probability of photons of a particular energy being absorbed.† We can combine the concentration and probability factors into one equation that will allow us to compute the *decrease* in the number of photons caused by absorption of light in a layer of thickness db,

$$-\frac{dI}{db} = a'cI. \qquad (E-4)$$

If the concentration is uniform throughout the sample, then c may be taken as constant, and, for a given wavelength of light, a' is a constant, so we can integrate Eq. (E–4) over the entire length of the sample:

$$-\int_{I_0}^{I_t} \frac{dI}{I} = a'c \int_0^b db,$$

$$-\ln \frac{I_t}{I_0} = a'c(b - 0) = a'bc,$$

$$-\log \frac{I_t}{I_0} = abc, \qquad a = \frac{a'}{2.303}. \qquad (E-5)$$

Equation (E–5) is the integrated form of the Beer- Lambert Law for light absorption, sometimes referred to as Beer's Law. The symbol a represents the *absorptivity* (sometimes, when c is in moles/liter, it is called the *molar absorptivity*).‡ The units of a are liter/mole-cm if c is in moles/liter and b is in cm, the usual units for these quantities. The intensity of light transmitted by the sample is I_t. The ratio I_t/I_0, called the *transmittance*, T, of the sample, is always between 0 and 1, so the logarithm is a negative number and therefore the left- hand side of Eq. (E–5) is always positive (as we see it must be, since a, b, and c are all positive quantities or zero). Sometimes the *percent transmittance*, or *percent transmission* $T \times 100$, is given.

---

* This assumption, and indeed the statement preceding it, are by no means obvious; they can only be justified by experi- mentally verifying the conclusions to which they lead. If experiments contradict conclusions derived theoretically, then the assumptions on which the theory is based must be re-examined. In this case, experiments do confirm the theoretical predictions based on these assumptions.

† Although a' can in principle be calculated if the quantum- mechanical description of the system is complete, it is almost always defined in practice operationally as the proportionality factor, the absorptivity, that makes Eq. (E–5) valid for a particular compound.

‡ The older terminology called a the extinction coefficient and often gave it the symbol ϵ (Greek, lower-case epsilon).

The *absorbance*, A, of a sample (at a particular wave- length) is defined as

$$A \equiv -\log I_t/I_0 = -\log T = abc. \qquad (E-6)$$

The absorbance is very useful because it is directly proportional to the concentration of the absorbing molecules. We can use the absorbance to determine the absorptivity, a, for a particular compound by making up a sample, usually a solution of known concentration in some solvent that does not absorb light in the wave- length region of interest, and then measuring the ab- sorbance (see Section E–4) of a known path length of this sample. From A, c, and b the absorptivity, a, may be calculated. It is, however, more trustworthy to obtain a by making up a series of samples of known concentra- tions and obtaining the absorbance of a known path length of each sample. If the Beer-Lambert Law holds for these samples, then Eq. (E–6) predicts that a plot of A/b versus c will yield a straight line of slope a and intercept zero. The best evidence for the validity of the assumptions made in deriving Eqs. (E–4) and (E–5) is that such straight-line plots are obtained for a very large number of samples.

Apparent Deviations from the Beer-Lambert Law

There are, however, many samples which do not appear to obey Beer's Law. Most of these deviations result from two causes: neglecting the occurrence of chemical reac- tions by the species of interest and using polychromatic (many-colored, i.e., of many wavelengths) radiation instead of monochromatic (one-colored, i.e., of a single wavelength) radiation. These may be said to be *apparent deviations* from the law.§

If the compound of interest reacts with some other species in the solution, the actual concentration of the interesting compound will be reduced to an amount that is not, in general, a linear function of the quantity of compound initially introduced into the solution. Thus a plot of A/b vs. the apparent c (calculated without considering the reaction) will not be linear. Such a non- linear Beer's Law plot is an immediate clue that some unaccounted-for phenomenon, which we must try to identify, is taking place in the samples.‖

---

§ *Real deviations* from Beer's Law do exist. For example, the amount of light that passes through a sample and is not lost at the interfaces between the sample and the container or the air is determined largely by the sample's index of refraction. Since the index of refraction varies nonlinearly with the concentration of substances in a solution, the amount of light lost at the interfaces will also vary nonlinearly. Such effects are usually unimportant except for very concentrated solu- tions, and we shall treat them no further here.

‖ The occurrence of a linear Beer's Law plot is not, however, a guarantee that no reaction has occurred in the solution.

For example, we might make up a solution of a known quantity of iodine, I_2, and iodide ion, I^-, in water. If we then take aliquots of this solution and dilute them with varying amounts of water, we might expect the absorbance of the solution due to I_2 (which we know is strongly colored and hence must absorb some wavelengths in the visible region of the spectrum) to vary linearly with the calculated concentration of I_2 in these samples. Experiments show, however, that this is not the case. An equilibrium that consumes I_2 is set up in these solutions,

$$I_2(aq) + I^-(aq) \rightleftharpoons I_3^-(aq),$$

and when the ratio of the amount of I_2 to the amount of I^- (before any reaction occurs) is the same in each solution, as it is in the experiments we are imagining here, it is easy to show that the actual concentration of $I_2(aq)$ in the solutions will not be a linear function of the dilution and, hence, that the solutions will not obey Beer's Law. Show this for yourself.

Some of the most striking examples of reaction-caused deviations from Beer's Law in aqueous solutions occur in systems that are pH dependent, such as solutions of acid-base indicators. It is usually possible to obtain a great deal of information about the reactions and equilibria that occur in systems that do not obey Beer's Law by studying their deviations, as you will see when we examine some actual spectra in Section E–3.

Equations (E–4), (E–5), and (E–6) apply strictly to the absorption of monochromatic light. In general, any "monochromatic" beam of light will include a range of energies (which we try to keep small). If a sample's changes in absorptivity are small in a certain wavelength region, then the equations will hold quite well even if the spread of energies (*band pass*) in the light being absorbed is a moderately large fraction of this wavelength region. On the other hand, if the absorptivity changes very greatly within a wavelength region, then the equations will probably not hold at all if the band pass is a relatively large fraction of this wavelength region. These two cases are shown as cases *A* and *B*, respectively, in Fig. E–5. If Eq. (E–6) is not applicable, you will not obtain linear Beer's Law plots.

E–3 APPLICATIONS OF SPECTROPHOTOMETRY

Absorption Spectra

A plot of the absorbance, A, of a particular sample vs. wavelength (or frequency or energy) is called the *absorption spectrum* of the sample. Since the absorbance is a function of the concentration and the length of the sample in the light beam, whereas the absorptivity is independent of these quantities, it is also common to plot absorptivity, a, vs. wavelength and call this the absorption spectrum as well.* Such a plot is the one we would obtain if we plotted absorbance vs. wavelength for a sample of unit concentration and unit path length. Why?

One of the primary uses of absorption spectra is to identify unknown samples. Sometimes we can compare the absorption spectrum of an unknown with absorption spectra of known compounds to discover the identity of the unknown compounds. In many cases, however, this procedure is not feasible because the unknown compound may not exist anywhere else than in the vessel in which it was just synthesized. Fortunately, there are absorptions in various spectral regions, particularly in the infrared, that are characteristic of certain structural features of molecules. To a good approximation, certain vibrational motions of molecules are always found to absorb energy in the same infrared spectral region. For example, the absorption for stretching C—H bonds usually appears between 2800 to 3000 cm^{-1} and that for C=O bonds between 1600 to 1800 cm^{-1}, so if these absorptions are present in the absorption spectrum, we can probably infer that these features are present in the unknown molecule. Even more subtle features of its structure may often be inferred from the actual location of the absorptions within these limits.

The infrared spectra of a few very simple molecules are shown in Experiment 25.

Mixtures of Absorbing Compounds

Thus far we have examined samples in which only one light-absorbing species is present. What happens to the absorbance when there are two or more different kinds of molecules in the sample that absorb at the same wavelength? Since the interaction of a molecule with light is independent of the presence of other molecules (at least to a first approximation), we can simply add the effects of all the molecules to find the overall absorbance of the sample at this wavelength. For species 1 alone we would have $A_1 = a_1 b c_1$ and similarly for other species, so we can write the total absorption as a sum of such terms,

$$A = \sum_i A_i = \sum_i a_i b c_i. \tag{E–7}$$

Equation (E–7) is the basis for many analyses and experiments which are carried out spectrophotometrically (see Experiments 15 and 20).

Illustrative Example: Compounds X and Y both absorb light in the visible region of the spectrum. The absorbance of a solution containing unknown concentrations of X and Y

---

* The range of A or a can be very large for some samples, so sometimes log A or log a is plotted vs. wavelength.

in a cell with a sample path length of 5.02 cm is 0.292 at 5000 Å and 0.236 at 6000 Å. Given the data below, obtained from solutions of the pure compounds, compute the concentrations of X and Y in the mixture.

λ, Å	a_X, M^{-1} cm^{-1}	a_Y, M^{-1} cm^{-1}
5000	305	453
6000	590	227

We have two equations of the form (E-7):

$$0.292 = 305 \times 5.02 \times c_X + 453 \times 5.02 \times c_Y,$$
$$0.236 = 590 \times 5.02 \times c_X + 227 \times 5.02 \times c_Y.$$

These are two simultaneous equations in two unknowns, which may be solved to give $c_X = 8.65 \times 10^{-5}$ M and $c_Y = 7.03 \times 10^{-5}$ M.

It would appear from this example that a solution containing n absorbing compounds could be analyzed by measuring the absorbance at n different wavelengths and the absorptivities of each of the n compounds at each wavelength. In principle this method will work, but in practice errors begin to build up very rapidly as they propagate through the calculations, so the results are often not very accurate.

Figure E-5, showing absorption spectra of methyl red (an acid-base indicator) solutions of different pH's, illustrates several things we have observed about absorption spectra. The concentration of the indicator is the same in all three solutions, but the absorption spectra are quite different. At the lowest pH the acidic form of

the indicator, HIn, absorbs the light. The absorption is "centered" at about 520 mμ, which is in the green region of visible light, the central part of the visible spectrum, so that the HIn sample transmits wavelengths corresponding to the reds (longer wavelengths) and violets (shorter wavelengths) and appears red-violet to our eyes. We know that this absorption is due to a single species that is presumably HIn because the spectrum does not change with pH in the region below pH $\approx$ 3.5. Similarly, at the highest pH the basic form of the indicator, In$^-$, absorbs the light. This light absorption occurs in the violet and blue regions of the spectrum, so all colors except these are transmitted and the sample appears yellow. Again, the spectrum does not change in solutions of pH greater than about 6.5. Only in the pH range of about 3.5 to 6.5 does the spectrum vary with pH, presumably because in this region both the acidic and basic forms of the indicator are present in spectrophotometrically detectable amounts. Obviously, unless one holds the pH constant, the absorbance of a series of solutions of methyl red at different concentrations might not follow Beer's Law.

Careful study of the figure shows that there is one point where Beer's Law will be obeyed for methyl red solutions regardless of their pH, the point where all the curves intersect, at 462 mμ. Such a point is called an *isosbestic point*. Since both HIn (pH = 2) and In$^-$ (pH = 10) have the same absorbance at this wavelength and the concentrations and the cell path length are the same in both cases, the absorptivities of the two species must be the same, i.e., $a_{HIn} = a_{In^-}$ at 462 mμ. Thus, if both HIn and In$^-$ are present in the same solution at pH = 5.0 in the figure, we can write for the absorbance at 462 mμ

$$A_{462} = a_{HIn}b[\text{HIn}] + a_{In^-}b[\text{In}^-]$$
$$= a_{HIn}b([\text{HIn}] + [\text{In}^-]).$$

If ([HIn] + [In$^-$]) is constant for a series of solutions, i.e., if the total number of moles of the indicator per liter is constant, then the absorbance at 462 mμ will be a constant and an isosbestic point will be observed. The existence of an isosbestic point in this case is a good indication that the absorption spectrum for the pH = 5.0 solution is indeed made up only of contributions from the acidic and basic forms of the indicator.*

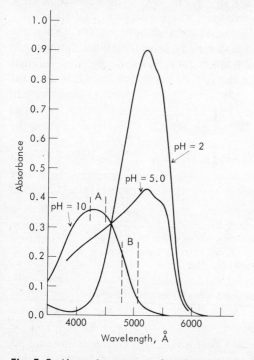

Fig. E-5. Absorption spectra of methyl red solutions at different pH's. The concentration of methyl red is 8.5×10^{-6} M in all three solutions. Cases A and B are discussed on page 248.

---

* A sufficient condition for the appearance of an isosbestic point (or points) is that the molar absorptivities of two absorbing species which are in equilibrium be the same at the wavelength of the isosbestic. Although the condition is sufficient for the possible existence of an isosbestic point, it is not a necessary condition. For an interesting and lucid discussion of isosbestic points see the article by M. D. Cohen and E. Fischer in *J. Chem. Soc.* (London) **1962**, 3044.

The apparent deviations from Beer's Law that are observed as a function of pH in a system such as this (at wavelengths other than isosbestic points) can be used to calculate equilibrium constants for the reactions that are occurring. For example, we can use the data from Fig. E–5 to calculate the pK_{In} for methyl red. The equilibrium constant we desire is

$$K_{In} = \frac{[H^+][In^-]}{[HIn]}.$$

Figure E–5 gives us the absorption spectra of methyl red at three pH's, so we know $[H^+]$ in the three solutions. We also know from the above discussion that essentially all the indicator is in the acidic form, HIn, at pH = 2 and in the basic form, In^-, at pH = 10. This statement is experimentally verified by the absorption spectrum's remaining the same as a function of pH in the region of these values and only beginning to change measurably at pH's within about one unit on either side of pH = 5.0. Thus it is only at pH = 5 that a measurable amount of the indicator is present in both the acidic and basic forms. We need only calculate the ratio $[In^-]/[HIn]$ at pH = 5 and multiply by $[H^+] = 10^{-5}$ to obtain K_{In}.

To make the calculations somewhat easier to follow, let us define a few terms:

A_a = absorbance (at 5200 Å in pH = 2 solution) = 0.905,

A = absorbance (at 5200 Å in pH = 5 solution) = 0.435,

A_b = absorbance (at 5200 Å in pH = 10 solution) = 0.030,

c = total concentration of indicator = [HIn] + [In$^-$] = 8.5×10^{-6} M.

(The wavelength 5200 Å is chosen because the largest change in absorbance is observed at this wavelength and these results will therefore be the most accurate. Why?) Now we can write

$A_a = a_{HIn}bc,$

$A_b = a_{In^-}bc,$

(Why?)

$A = a_{HIn}b[HIn] + a_{In^-}b[In^-].$

The last equation may be written

$A = a_{HIn}b(c - [In^-]) + a_{In^-}b[In^-]$

$= a_{HIn}bc - a_{HIn}b[In^-] + a_{In^-}b[In^-],$

and by substitution of the first two equations we obtain

$$A - A_a = (A_b - A_a)\frac{[In^-]}{c},$$

or

$$\frac{[In^-]}{c} = \frac{A - A_a}{A_b - A_a}. \tag{E–8}$$

In exactly the same fashion

$A = a_{HIn}b[HIn] + a_{In^-}b(c - [HIn])$

$\quad = a_{HIn}b[HIn] + a_{In^-}bc - a_{In^-}b[HIn],$

$$A - A_b = (A_a - A_b)\frac{[HIn]}{c}$$

$$\frac{[HIn]}{c} = \frac{A - A_b}{A_a - A_b} = \frac{A_b - A}{A_b - A_a}. \tag{E–9}$$

(What is the restriction on c in these three solutions such that the foregoing equations will be valid?) Now we combine Eqs. (E–8) and (E–9) to obtain

$$\frac{[In^-]}{[HIn]} = \frac{A - A_a}{A_b - A}. \tag{E–10}$$

Substitution of numerical values for these absorbances gives $[In^-]/[HIn] = 1.16$, and combination with $[H^+] = 10^{-5}$ yields $K_{In} = 1.2 \times 10^{-5}$ and $pK_{In} = 4.9$.

E–4 SPECTROPHOTOMETERS

Photoelectric Filter Colorimeters

The general design of photoelectric filter colorimeters is shown schematically in Fig. E–6. The wavelength filter is usually colored glass which passes only a certain band of wavelengths and absorbs all others. To investigate a wide range of wavelengths, one must use a number of such filters, each of different absorption character (color).

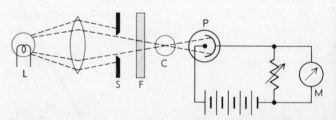

Fig. E–6. Schematic diagram of a photoelectric filter colorimeter showing light source, L, slit to define the light beam, S, removable wavelength filter, F, cell containing sample under investigation, C, photocell, P, meter, M.

There are two major disadvantages of this sort of colorimeter. Many filters are necessary to obtain an approximately continuous absorption spectrum, and the band pass of each filter is usually very broad, thus making good definition of an absorption spectrum almost impossible and increasing the chance of a given set of measurements' deviating from Beer's Law.

The general technique for handling cells and using a photoelectric filter colorimeter is very similar to that for manual spectrophotometers which is given in the next section.

Single-Beam Spectrophotometers

The essential difference between a spectrophotometer and a photoelectric filter colorimeter is that the spectrophotometer utilizes a prism or grating to resolve the light into its component wavelengths. With this kind of instrument, any wavelength may be chosen to be passed through the sample by simply turning the prism or grating with respect to the beam. One of the simplest and most popular of these instruments is the Bausch and Lomb Spectronic 20 (see the schematic diagram in Fig. E–7).*

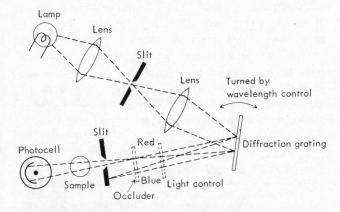

Fig. E–7. Schematic diagram of the Spectronic 20. (After C. N. Reilley and D. T. Sawyer, *Experiments for Instrumental Methods*, McGraw-Hill, New York, 1961.

The technique for determining the absorbance of a solution at a particular wavelength requires two sample cells. One cell, the sample, is filled about two-thirds full of the solution whose absorption is to be measured. The other cell, the blank or reference, is filled similarly with a compensating solution, usually identical to the sample solution in all respects except that the "colored" species is not present. There are a few rules to follow when handling your cells; they should be adhered to very strictly.

1) Always use the same two cells and do not interchange them in the course of an experiment.

* The optics and the detection system of the Spectronic 20 are purposely kept simple to keep the price of the instrument down. This, naturally, means some compromises in quality have been made, and indeed the band pass of this instrument is rather large, 30 Å. Thus the absorption spectra obtained from this instrument cannot be expected to be as good as those obtained with a higher resolution (lower band pass) instrument. Recognizing this, Bausch and Lomb calls the Spectronic 20 a "spectrocolorimeter."

2) Do not handle the lower portion of the cell. This is the portion through which light passes, and smudges, etc., on the surface will ruin an experiment.

3) Always rinse the cell with two or three *small* portions of the solution to be used before finally filling it.

4) Wipe any liquid drops or smudges off the cell with a clean Kimwipe® or other lens paper before placing it in the instrument. *Never* wipe cells with towels or handkerchiefs. Be certain no lint is on the outside of the cell and no small air bubbles are stuck to the inner walls.

5) The cells for some instruments (the Spectronic 20, for example) are test tubes especially made with very uniform wall thickness and careful attention to roundness. When you insert one of these cells into the sample compartment, you will avoid scratching the surface of the cell, which will be in the optical path, if you insert the cell with the etched index line on the cell turned 90° from the position of the index line on the cell compartment. After the cell is in place, rotate it so that the two index lines are aligned. Remove the cell by reversing this procedure (turning the cell to the left or right before removing it).

To measure the transmittance or absorbance at a particular wavelength, first adjust the wavelength control to the correct setting. With the sample compartment empty and its cover closed, adjust the "zero" control until the meter reads zero transmittance: infinite absorbance. (The reading should be zero under these circumstances because there will be some sort of occluder in the light path which prevents light from striking the photocell; hence, zero percent of the light is transmitted.) The "zero" knob controls the amplification factor of the phototube and may need to be readjusted at intervals, as the power from the lines varies. Check this adjustment often.

Insert the blank. Adjust the "100-%" control until the meter reads 100-% transmittance. (Most spectrophotometers of this sort read in percent transmittance and/or in absorbance. When the cell is inserted, the occluder will be removed from the light beam so that light passes through the blank to the photocell. In the Spectronic 20 the "100-%" control adjusts the position of a sheet of metal with a V-shaped hole cut in it. As the control is moved, more or less light passes through the blank, depending on the direction of motion. The adjustment is made until the amount of light striking the photocell gives a 100-% transmittance reading on the meter.) Remove the blank.

Insert the sample and read whichever scale of the meter (if you have a choice) is most accurate and convenient for your purposes. The 100-% adjustment made

® Kimwipe is a registered trademark of Kimberly-Clark.

with the blank has compensated for any light absorbed by the cell and the solvent (provided that the cells are as similar as possible; this is why they are to be treated with such care), so any absorption must be due to the solute of interest. Continue this process at all wavelengths of interest.*

Before using a spectrophotometer or any other instrument, chat with your instructor about how it works and the location of the important components within the "black box" that confronts you. It is very bad practice to use an instrument by simply following "cookbook" instructions. This will promote sloppy thinking and technique and discourage innovative use of the instrument.

Double-Beam Spectrophotometers

Almost all recording spectrophotometers used in the infrared, visible, and ultraviolet regions of electromagnetic radiation are double-beam instruments. This means that the light beam from the source is split into two separate beams. One of these beams is passed through the blank or reference cell and the other through a matched cell containing the sample under investigation. Before the cells are put in place, the instrument must be checked to be sure the light beams are being detected identically; then when the cells are in place, any *difference* in the intensities of light transmitted by the two cells is quickly detected. Any differences in amount of light transmitted are, of course, due to absorption of light by the sample. These differences are observed and analyzed electronically, and the final signal delivered by the detection system is proportional to the absorbance or transmittance of the sample. The motors which drive the recorder paper through the recorder and the wavelength changing mechanism are synchronized so that the signal which is recorded on the paper is recorded as a function of wavelength, i.e., the absorption spectrum is recorded directly without your having to plot points on another piece of paper. The infrared absorption spectra shown in Experiment 25 were recorded with such an instrument. Ask your instructor to demonstrate the uses of any double-beam spectrophotometers available in your laboratory.

---

* When you are using a manual spectrophotometer or colorimeter to obtain an absorption spectrum, it is a good idea to choose your wavelength settings randomly and repeat a few of them once or twice during the course of the experiment.

If something is changing (for example, if a chemical reaction is occurring), the first clue is often the irreproducibility of absorbances measured at the same wavelength at different times.

REFERENCES

BARROW, G. M., *The Structure of Molecules*, W. A. Benjamin, New York, 1963.

BELLAMY, L. J., *The Infrared Spectra of Complex Molecules*, John Wiley & Sons, New York, 1954.

PHILLIPS, J. P., and R. W. KEOWN, "Phototube Circuit with Transistors," *J. Chem. Ed.* **31,** 605 (1954) suggests a two transistor amplifier that boosts the signal from a phototube so that a microammeter rather than a galvanometer can be used.

PINKERTON, R. C., "Beer's Law Without Calculus," *J. Chem. Ed.* **41,** 366 (1964) is a wee bit of legerdemain which is in effect taking infinitesimals without saying so.

SWINEHART, D. F., "Beer-Lambert Laws," *J. Chem. Ed.* **39,** 333 (1962) is a good derivation and treatment with caveats about the usual loose use of the nomenclature.

RADIOACTIVITY AND RADIOISOTOPIC COUNTING

An immense variety of instrumentation is available for studying radioactivity; we shall limit ourselves here to general principles and refer you to your instructor and the instruction manual for specific directions for the instruments you have available.

F–1 RADIOACTIVITY

Many elements exist naturally or can be converted to isotopic forms that are unstable. The decay of these isotopes, called *radioisotopes*, to other more stable isotopes is accompanied by the emission of *radioactivity*, which carries off the energy released in the nuclear decay. Although we often talk about "radiation," the "radiation hazard," and "radiation damage" from these emissions, two of the three forms of radioactive emission are particles and only one form is actually electromagnetic radiation.

Alpha particles are helium nuclei ejected from a given radioisotope with a certain fixed energy (proportional to the energy difference between the product and reactant nuclei). They have a charge of $+2$ and a mass of about 4 atomic mass units (amu) and are abbreviated $_2\text{He}^4$. (The superscript is the mass number and is the sum of the protons and neutrons in the nucleus; the subscript is the atomic number, the number of protons in the nucleus.) Because they have such a high positive charge, alpha particles interact strongly with electrons and travel only a short distance through matter, even through air. They can be stopped (shielded) completely by a centimeter or two of lead and less effectively by lighter solid materials; the stopping effect per atom for a given alpha particle is about proportional to the square root of the atomic weight of the absorber. Examples of alpha decay are nicely demonstrated by the radioactive decay series (Mev = million electron volts):

$$_{94}\text{Pa}^{234} \rightarrow \ _{92}\text{U}^{230} + \ _2\text{He}^4, \quad 6.2 \quad \text{Mev} \quad \text{(energy of alpha particle),}$$
$$\downarrow$$
$$_{90}\text{Th}^{226} + \ _2\text{He}^4, \quad 5.86 \quad \text{Mev,}$$
$$\downarrow$$
$$_{88}\text{Ra}^{222} + \ _2\text{He}^4, \quad 6.30 \quad \text{Mev,}$$
$$\downarrow$$
$$_{86}\text{Rn}^{218} + \ _2\text{He}^4, \quad 6.51 \quad \text{Mev,}$$
$$\downarrow$$
$$_{84}\text{Po}^{214} + \ _2\text{He}^4, \quad 7.12 \quad \text{Mev,}$$
$$\downarrow$$
$$_{82}\text{Pb}^{210} + \ _2\text{He}^4, \quad 7.683 \ \text{Mev.}$$

Beta particles are negative or positive electrons (the latter are called *positrons*). They are emitted with a wide range of energies from a single isotopic species; different proportions of the nuclear decay energy are removed by beta emission depending on the state of the particular nucleus as it decays. High atomic weight absorbers are relatively effective as shielding materials. The range (maximum distance of travel) for beta particles is usually expressed in the odd unit, mg absorber/cm^2, indicating that the range depends on the mass of absorber through which the particle must pass. For example, a 1-Mev beta particle has a range of 400 mg/cm^2 in aluminum. Iodine 131, $_{53}\text{I}^{131}$, the radioisotope used in Experiment 32, emits beta particles of two maximum energies, 0.6 and 0.3 Mev. The decay series begun above continues

$$_{82}\text{Pb}^{210} \rightarrow \ _{83}\text{Bi}^{210} + \beta^-,$$
$$\downarrow$$
$$_{82}\text{Pb}^{206} + \ _2\text{He}^4 + \beta^-,$$
$$\text{(stable)}$$

where β^- is the negative electron. (Note how the product isotope can easily be written if the particles produced by the decay are known, and conversely.)

Gamma rays are electromagnetic radiation of wavelength about 10^{-11} cm (see Fig. E–1). Gamma rays (and their less energetic cousins, x-rays) have great penetrating power in matter because they are uncharged. For this same reason they cause much less ionization per centimeter traveled than do $_2$He^4, β^-, or β^+ particles, a difference that is important in the design of detectors for the three types of emissions. Gamma radiation often, but not invariably, accompanies beta particle emission; the emissions discussed above under beta emission also involve gamma ray emission, e.g., in the decay of $_{83}$Bi^{210} a 0.08-Mev gamma ray is also emitted:

$$_{83}\text{Bi}^{210} \rightarrow {}_{82}\text{Pb}^{206} + {}_2\text{He}^4 + \beta^- + \gamma.$$

F–2 DETECTING AND MEASURING RADIOACTIVITY

All detectors depend on the interaction of the "radiation" detected with the matter of the detector for their operation. The film badge, cloud chamber, and bubble chamber are examples of detectors which give a visual indication of this interaction. In these detectors, the ionization which the "radiation" causes is converted to a visible (or potentially visible) trail of particles (silver granules, "fog" droplets, or bubbles); the density of these particles is a measure of the extent of ionization caused by the "radiation." An early type of detector was the scintillation screen, a screen of specially prepared zinc sulfide. Alpha particles striking such a screen give discrete flashes of light (much like the electrons that impinge on the phosphor-coated surface of an oscilloscope or television tube). Rutherford and his assistants used such a screen in the alpha-particle scattering experiments that led to our present notions of atomic structure (Experiment 24). A modern adaptation of this device that avoids the need for a human observer to count and record the light flashes is called a *scintillation counter*. It usually consists of a crystal of sodium iodide, several centimeters on a side, lightly doped with thallous iodide (the foreign ions take the place of some of the sodium's lattice positions). A photoelectric multiplier tube is attached to one face of the crystal. The crystal gives off flashes of light when "radiation" passes through it; the photoelectric multiplier converts these to electrical pulses, and these are amplified and actuate a counter or a rate meter. Scintillation counters are most useful for gamma rays, since the detector is a solid with high stopping power. Gaseous counters (see below) often let 99% of the high-energy γ-rays pass through with no effect.

Other detectors collect the ions that are formed when the "radiation" strikes the detector. These are of two types: those in which the signal is dependent on the energy of the "radiation" (ionization chamber, *proportional counter*) and those in which it is not (*Geiger-Mueller counter*). Ionization chambers are little used now and will not be discussed in detail. Proportional counters and Geiger counters are physically the same, differing only in the voltage at which the detector is operated. The detector consists of a round tube, 2 to 3 cm in diameter, of metal or glass silvered on the inside, with a thin wire running down its axis which is insulated from the body of the tube or the silvered portion of it. The tube is filled with a suitable "counting gas" (often argon containing a small amount of a halogen or an organic vapor at a total pressure of about 100 torr) and is usually provided with a "window" of low density material through which the "radiation" can enter. The central wire is positively charged relative to the body of the tube and the tube is connected to an amplifier that amplifies and measures the current between the electrodes. At low applied voltages (about 100 volts) the primary ions formed in the tube will be drawn to the electrodes and a very small pulse will be produced in the tube. (This is the way an ionization chamber operates). As the voltage is increased to several hundred volts, the size of the pulse increases, even though the energy of the "radiation" remains the same. The increase results from a multiplication of ions in the strong electric field surrounding the small central wire. As the electrons which were produced by the "radiation" are accelerated to this wire through the strong field, they become energetic enough to cause further ionizations; these give rise to pulses as much as 100 times as large as those caused by the primary ions. Since the strength of the pulses is still proportional to the energy of the "radiation" producing them, the tube is now said to be a proportional counter. When the voltage reaches about 1000 volts, all the pulses become the same size, regardless of the energy of the "radiation." The electric field around the central wire is now so strong that even a small number of initial electrons is enough to promote a flood of secondary electrons all up and down the wire. At this voltage the tube is operating as a Geiger counter.

Electrons are produced inside the Geiger tube by ionizations and move rapidly to the central wire. The ionization process also, of course, produces heavy positive ions such as Ar^+ and Cl_2^+; these drift, much more slowly, to the outer, negatively-charged shell. (Their movement is slower because they are heavier and because the electric field is much smaller at the large electrode.) While the positive ions are drifting, the tube is insensitive to incoming "radiation"; this period is called the "dead time" of the tube and lasts 100 to 400 microseconds in typical Geiger tubes. The dead time must be considered when very active samples are being counted (see Section F–3).

If the voltage on a Geiger tube is increased much past 1150 volts or so, the electrons are accelerated to the central wire with so much energy that they knock other electrons out of the wire itself and the tube discharges continuously (arcs). This is harmful to the tube and care should always be taken not to increase the voltage beyond the "Geiger region" when operating a Geiger counter.

The electric pulses produced by a Geiger tube are sufficiently large that little amplification is needed before they can be used. The main auxiliary equipment needed is a high-voltage power supply to operate the tube and a scaler. The scaler registers the output pulses of the tube (or the amplified pulses from a scintillation counter), usually with a mechanical counting device and one or more electronic scaling circuits. The scaling circuits are used to reduce the speed at which the mechanical register must operate. They are composed of a series of binary circuit elements which produce an output of one pulse for every two pulses input. Placing these elements in series gives an output for every 4, 8, 16, . . . pulses; the final output is used to drive the register. By proper design, scaling circuits can also be made to count in the decimal system.

What are the results of these measurements? Can we, hopefully, relate them to chemically significant quantities? The result of a significant radioactivity counting measurement is the number of counts (or nuclear disintegrations), N, in a time period, t, or the rate, N/t, of nuclear decay. It is known from other measurements that the rate of nuclear decay for radioactive isotopes, I^*, follows a first-order rate law (see Chapter 13),

$$-\frac{d[I^*]}{dt} = k[I^*]. \qquad \text{(F–1)}$$

The rate of disappearance of I^* at any time is proportional to the amount of I^* still remaining. Our counting measurements, however, give a measurement that is proportional to the decay rate, i.e.,

$$\frac{N}{t} = -C'\frac{d[I^*]}{dt}, \qquad \text{(F–2)}$$

where C' is a constant that depends on sample size, geometry of the sample and detector, and counter efficiency, among other things. (If samples are carefully and reproducibly made, relative rates from one sample to the next may be determined.) Combining (F–1) and (F–2) we get

$$\frac{N}{t} = C[I^*], \qquad \text{(F–3)}$$

where $C = C'k$. This substitution is a very good approximation if t is small enough that $[I^*]$ does not change during the counting period. Counting times very much smaller than the half-life (time required for the one-half the nuclei originally present to disintegrate) adequately fulfill this requirement.

Thus radioisotopic counting can lead to at least relative measures of isotopic concentrations from differently treated samples and, hence, to conclusions about the effect the treatment had on the element in question. No chemical treatment has any effect on the nuclear decay processes so the radioactivity measurements serve as a very sensitive probe into a number of different kinds of problems. Because very tiny amounts of an element can be detected by radioisotopic counting, the usual experimental procedure is to use a trace of the radioactive isotope in a vast excess of a stable isotope of the same element to follow reactions. Examples of the use of radioisotopic tracers are found in Experiments 2 and 32.

F–3 ERRORS IN RADIOISOTOPIC COUNTING

In the past two decades, many uses have been found for radioisotopes. Radioactivity is definitely a valuable new tool for research and analysis; however, it must be used with a realization of the possible errors involved. If you do a radioisotopic-tracer experiment without considering possible errors, you may get a meaningless result even if the work is done very carefully. Three sources of error inherent in this sort of experiment are: background radiation, randomness of decay, and counter dead time.

Background radiation, produced mainly by cosmic radiation, is present in all laboratories. A common Geiger tube will usually register something of the order of 30 counts per minute (cpm) with no source of radiation in the laboratory. (Since the intensity of cosmic radiation increases with altitude, the background count may be several times as high in mountainous areas.) Background varies greatly from one type of detector to another. Naturally, any source of radioactivity in the laboratory will increase the background count. To correct for background radiation you should subtract the background count from each reading. The background count should be taken as closely as possible in time to the actual measurements since the factors that cause the background may change daily.

Although you can accurately determine the average rate of decay of any radioisotope, the rate at any instant is variable, i.e., there is a *randomness in the decay* of radioisotopes. Obviously, this randomness can cause large errors when one counts only a relatively small number of disintegrations. By taking longer counts, you can reduce the error to a very low value; by good design you can make the experiment give you the accuracy you desire (within certain limits). To provide a basis for experimental design we shall discuss a simple statistical formula for calculating the error expected due to randomness.

The *standard deviation*, σ, the commonest indicator of the reliability of a given determination, is given by the formula

$$\sigma = \pm\sqrt{N}, \tag{F–4}$$

where N is the number of counts. About 68% of the time, the "true" counting rate will lie within $\pm\sigma$ of the measured rate. About 95% of the time, it will be within $\pm2\sigma$. Usually the percent error in a reading is more important than the absolute error. Dividing by N and multiplying by 100, we obtain

$$\sigma = \pm(\sqrt{N}/N)100 = \pm100/\sqrt{N}\%. \tag{F–5}$$

Thus, if we wish to measure a count rate to 1-% accuracy, we will need $\sqrt{N} = 100/1$, $N = 10,000$, to accomplish our purpose. To obtain 0.1-% accuracy, 1,000,000 counts are necessary; because of the square-root relationship a hundred fold increase in count is required to increase the measuring accuracy tenfold. Because of the time required for high counts, the accuracy of all radiation experiments is limited. Errors less than 0.1% are rarely obtained.

As we noted above, the counting pulse of a Geiger tube temporarily inactivates the tube and leads to a *dead time* or resolving time after each count, usually between 100 to 400 microseconds. (The commonest tubes have a dead time of about 200 microseconds.) Scintillation counters also have a dead time, limited often by the electronics rather than the detector, but it is rarely longer than a few microseconds. At slow counting rates, the dead time is of little consequence, but the correction may be quite large when the counting rate is high. At a counting rate of N/t cpm the total dead time in one minute is $(N/t)\tau$ minutes, where τ is the dead time expressed in minutes. The total sensitive time is therefore $[1 - (N/t)\tau]$ minutes, and the actual or corrected count rate, N_c/t, is

$$\frac{N_c}{t} = \frac{N/t}{1 - (N/t)\tau} \text{ cpm.} \tag{F–6}$$

For example, if a count rate of 6000 cpm was observed with a counter with a 300-microsecond dead time we would have

$$\frac{N_c}{t} = \frac{6000}{1 - 6000 \times 300 \times 10^{-6}/60}$$

$$= \frac{60 \times 6000}{60 - 6 \times 3 \times 10^{-1}} = 6190 \text{ cpm,}$$

or an error of a bit over 3% without the correction.

To use Eq. (F–6) to make dead-time corrections you must know the dead time of your apparatus (such cor-

rections are probably only necessary for Geiger counters). In general, for rates below 5000 cpm, you will obtain sufficient accuracy by using the approximate value given by the manufacturer. At high rates you must often determine the dead time experimentally by using paired sources. By counting each source separately and then counting them together, you can calculate the dead time. How? Since dead time is impossible to determine exactly, extremely high count rates (100,000 cpm) should not be taken; dead time thus sets a practical limit on the counting rate if counts at different rates are to be compared with accuracy.

F–4 HEALTH AND SAFETY PRECAUTIONS

One of the dangers to beginners working with radioactive isotopes is that the senses do not give any indication that something may be amiss, as is common in ordinary chemical procedures. However, the use of radioisotopes in trace concentrations presents no health hazard from radiation *so long as the tracer remains off and out of the body.* You should develop an awareness of the problems of handling radioactive materials and the proper protective measures. Your primary concern will be to *do careful meticulous work;* neatness counts (it possibly may save your life). The biological danger of any radioisotope depends on the half-life of the isotope, the kind of radiation it produces, and what happens to it in the body. For example, I^{131} has a short half-life, 8 days, and emits only fairly weak β^- and γ radiation. However, the human body concentrates iodine in the thyroid gland so that the danger from the isotope is relatively high. (You are possibly aware that one treatment for goiter, enlarged thyroid, is to feed the patient radioactive iodide which concentrates in the thyroid and destroys the diseased tissue.) The situation with Sr^{90} or Sr^{89} is similar; if the body did not concentrate Sr in bones near where new red blood cells are being manufactured, it would be much less dangerous (in spite of the long, 25-year, half-life for Sr^{90}). Since almost all alpha emitters are heavy elements, their chemistry is such that many of them (like strontium) will deposit in the bones where they are capable of doing serious biological damage.*

To avoid serious over-exposure from beta and gamma activity, the survey instrument (which should always be available when radioisotopic experiments are being carried out) should be used to determine the level of activity in the experiment and the safe working time. If necessary, you should wear a film badge or other

---

* The detailed mechanism of the interaction that causes damage to living tissue is not known; presumably ionization of the complex biological molecules by the "radiation" from radioisotopes destroys or changes them in such a way that they can no longer carry on their functions.

personal dosage indicator to indicate the extent of your exposure to the "radiation."

Other precautions to be observed are as follows.

1) Never work with radioisotopes in an unsupervised laboratory.

2) Always wear a laboratory apron and disposable plastic gloves when working with *any* amount of tracer or with glassware that might be contaminated. Discard the gloves in the container provided at the end of *each* period.

3) Never bring any chemicals or glassware near your mouth. In particular, never fill a pipet by mouth.

4) If you should cut yourself in the laboratory, flush the wound immediately with copious amounts of running water and report the accident to your instructor.

5) Keep all operations except counting in the hood. Never take any liquid which may be radioactive out of the hood; it might be volatile. Perform all work over an enameled tray so that spills are contained. Plan your work as if you might spill things, prepare for the spills, and then *do not spill anything*. In case you do spill a radioactive substance, report the incident to your instructor at once. If possible, try to prevent the spreading of contamination; this will be automatically taken care of if you followed the preceding part of this precautionary measure.

6) Dispose of waste radioactive solutions and solids in the labeled covered containers provided for this purpose.

7) Above all, *do not hurry*. It is far better not to finish at all than to have a potentially dangerous accident.

REFERENCES

CHOPPIN, G. R., *Experimental Nuclear Chemistry*, Prentice-Hall, Englewood Cliffs, N.J., 1961.

CHOPPIN, G. R., *Nuclei and Radioactivity*, W. A. Benjamin, New York, 1964.

FRIEDLANDER, G., and J. W. KENNEDY, *Nuclear and Radiochemistry*, John Wiley & Sons, New York, 1955.

FRIEDLANDER, G., and J. W. KENNEDY, *Introduction to Radioactivity*, John Wiley & Sons, New York, 1949.

MYERS, R. T., "Dead Time of a Geiger Mueller Tube by the Double-Source Method," *J. Chem. Ed.* **33,** 395 (1956).

STEARNS, R. L., and J. F. MUCCI, "Using the Decay of Ba^{137} to Determine Resolving Time in G-M Counting," *J. Chem. Ed.* **38,** 29 (1961) shows some of the "defects" and limitations of counting equipment.

TABLES

In this appendix we have compiled tables of half-cell potentials (Table 1), solubility products (Table 2), acidity constants (Table 3), and complex instability constants (Table 4). These lists are not meant to be complete or entirely accurate but only useful for calculations you might wish to do in connection with the experiments in this text. The equilibrium constants for the ionic reactions presented are in most cases *not* thermodynamic constants for they have not been extrapolated to zero ionic strength (see Experiment 15). These constants may, however, be more valid in the actual solutions you use than the "correct" thermodynamic values. In like manner the half-cell potentials presented here may not, in some cases, represent true thermodynamic values, but again may be changed by ionic effects in the solutions of interest.

The sources for these tables are the books and compilations listed in the references. These sources contain much more information including many more equilibrium constants and references to original data so you can look up the conditions under which a particular constant was measured.

REFERENCES

BARD, A. J., *Chemical Equilibrium*, Harper and Row, New York, 1966, presents a discussion of the subject which is intermediate between the level of the two books by Butler. Also included are tables of equilibrium constants at the end of the book.

BJERRUM, J., G. SCHWARZENBACH, and L. G. SILLEN, *Stability Constants of Metal-Ion Complexes with Solubility Products of Inorganic Substances*, Part I: Organic Ligands, Part II: Inorganic Ligands, Chemical Society (London), Special Publication No. 6, 1957, No. 7, 1958.

BUTLER, J. N., *Ionic Equilibrium*, Addison-Wesley, Reading, Mass., 1964.

KORTÜM, G., W. VOGEL, and K. ANDRUSSOW, "Dissociation Constants of Organic Acids in Aqueous Solution," *Pure and Appl. Chem.* **1,** 187–536 (1961).

LATIMER, W. M., *Oxidation Potentials*, 2nd ed. Prentice-Hall, Englewood Cliffs, N. J., 1952.

YATSIMIRSKII, K. B., and V. P. VASIL'EV, *Instability Constants of Complex Compounds*, Consultants Bureau, New York, 1960.

Table 1

HALF–CELL POTENTIALS

Couple (Acidic solution)	$\mathcal{E}^0$
$Li^+ + e^- = Li$	-3.045
$K^+ + e^- = K$	-2.925
$Rb^+ + e^- = Rb$	-2.925
$Ba^{++} + 2e^- = Ba$	-2.90
$Sr^{++} + 2e^- = Sr$	-2.89
$Ca^{++} + 2e^- = Ca$	-2.87
$Na^+ + e^- = Na$	-2.714
$Al^{+3} + 3e^- = Al$	-1.66
$Mn^{++} + 2e^- = Mn$	-1.18
$Zn^{++} + 2e^- = Zn$	-0.763
$Cr^{+3} + 3e^- = Cr$	-0.74
$H_3PO_3 + 2H^+ + 2e^- = H_3PO_2 + H_2O$	-0.50
$Fe^{++} + 2e^- = Fe$	-0.440
$Cr^{+3} + e^- = Cr^{++}$	-0.41
$Cd^{+3} + 2e^- = Cd$	-0.403
$PbI_2 + 2e^- = Pb + 2I^-$	-0.365
$PbSO_4 + 2e^- = Pb + SO_4^=$	-0.356
$PbBr_2 + 2e^- = Pb + 2Br^-$	-0.280
$Co^{++} + 2e^- = Co$	-0.277
$Ni^{++} + 2e^- = Ni$	-0.250
$2SO_4^= + 4H^+ + 2e^- = S_2O_6^= + 2H_2O$	-0.22
$CuI + e^- = Cu + I^-$	-0.185
$AgI + e^- = Ag + I^-$	-0.151
$Sn^{++} + 2e^- = Sn$	-0.136
$Pb^{++} + 2e^- = Pb$	-0.126
$HgI_4^= + 2e^- = Hg + 4I^-$	-0.04
$2H^+ + 2e^- = H_2$	-0.00
$Ag(S_2O_3)_2^{-3} + e^- = Ag + 2S_2O_3^=$	$+0.01$
$CuBr + e^- = Cu + Br^-$	$+0.033$
$AgBr + e^- = Ag + Br^-$	$+0.095$
$CuCl + e^- = Cu + Cl^-$	$+0.137$
$Sn^{+4} + 2e^- = Sn^{++}$	$+0.15$
$Cu^{++} + e^- = Cu^+$	$+0.153$
$HgBr_4^= + 2e^- = Hg + 4Br^-$	$+0.21$
$AgCl + e^- = Ag + Cl^-$	$+0.222$
$Cu^{++} + 2e^- = Cu$	$+0.337$
$AgIO_3 + e^- = Ag + IO_3^-$	$+0.35$
$Fe(CN)_6^{-3} + e^- = Fe(CN)_6^{-4}$	$+0.36$
$2H_2SO_3 + 2H^+ + 4e^- = S_2O_3^= + 3H_2O$	$+0.40$
$Ag_2CrO_4 + 2e^- = 2Ag + CrO_4^=$	$+0.446$
$H_2SO_3 + 4H^+ + 4e^- = S + 3H_2O$	$+0.45$
$4H_2SO_3 + 4H^+ + 6e^- = S_4O_6^= + 6H_2O$	$+0.51$
$Cu^+ + e^- = Cu$	$+0.521$
$I_2 + 2e^- = 2I^-$	$+0.5355$
$I_3^- + 2e^- = 3I^-$	$+0.536$
$Cu^{++} + Cl^- + e^- = CuCl$	$+0.538$
$Cu^{++} + Br^- + e^- = CuBr$	$+0.640$
$Ag(CH_3COO) + e^- = Ag + CH_3COO^-$	$+0.643$
$Ag_2SO_4 + 2e^- = 2Ag + SO_4^=$	$+0.653$
$O_2 + 2H^+ + 2e^- = H_2O_2$	$+0.682$
$H_2O_2 + H^+ + e^- = OH + H_2O$	$+0.72$
$Fe^{+3} + e^- = Fe^{++}$	$+0.771$
$Hg_2^{++} + 2e^- = 2Hg$	$+0.789$
$Ag^+ + e^- = Ag$	$+0.7991$
$Cu^{++} + I^- + e^- = CuI$	$+0.86$
$2Hg^{++} + 2e^- = Hg_2^{++}$	$+0.920$
$NO_3^- + 3H^+ + 2e^- = HNO_2 + H_2O$	$+0.94$
$NO_3^- + 4H^+ + 4e^- = NO + 2H_2O$	$+0.96$
$HNO_2 + H^+ + e^- = NO + H_2O$	$+1.00$
$N_2O_4 + 4H^+ + 4e^- = NO + 2H_2O$	$+1.03$
$ICl_2^- + e^- = 2Cl^- + \frac{1}{2}I_2$	$+1.06$
$Br_2(l) + 2e^- = 2Br^-$	$+1.0652$
$N_2O_4 + 2H^+ + 2e^- = 2HNO_2$	$+1.07$

Table 1 (*Continued*)

HALF-CELL POTENTIALS

Couple (Acidic Solution)	$\mathcal{E}^0$
$ClO_4^- + 2H^+ + 2e^- = ClO_3^- + H_2O$	$+1.19$
$IO_3^- + 6H^+ + 5e^- = \frac{1}{2}I_2 + 3H_2O$	$+1.195$
$ClO_3^- + 3H^+ + 2e^- = HClO_2 + H_2O$	$+1.21$
$O_2 + 4H^+ + 4e^- = 2H_2O$	$+1.229$
$MnO_2 + 4H^+ + 2e^- = Mn^{++} + 2H_2O$	$+1.23$
$2HNO_2 + 4H^+ + 4e^- = N_2O + 3H_2O$	$+1.29$
$Cr_2O_7^= + 14H^+ + 6e^- = 2Cr^{+3} + 7H_2O$	$+1.33$
$Cl_2 + 2e^- = 2Cl^-$	$+1.3595$
$Mn^{+3} + e^- = Mn^{++}$	$+1.51$
$MnO_4^- + 8H^+ + 5e^- = Mn^{++} + 4H_2O$	$+1.51$
$BrO_3^- + 6H^+ + 5e^- = \frac{1}{2}Br_2 + 3H_2O$	$+1.52$
$MnO_4^- + 4H^+ + 3e^- = MnO_2 + 2H_2O$	$+1.695$
$H_2O_2 + 2H^+ + 2e^- = 2H_2O$	$+1.77$
$Co^{+3} + e^- = Co^{++}$	$+1.82$
$Ag^{++} + e^- = Ag^+$	$+1.98$
$F_2 + 2e^- = 2F^-$	$+2.87$

Couple (Basic solution)	$\mathcal{E}^0$
$Ca(OH)_2 + 2e^- = Ca + 2OH$	-3.03
$Sr(OH)_2 \cdot 8H_2O + 2e^- = Sr + 2OH^- + 8H_2O$	-2.99
$Ba(OH)_2 \cdot 8H_2O + 2e^- = Ba + 8H_2O + 2OH^-$	-2.97
$H_2AlO_3^- + H_2O + 3e^- = Al + 4OH^-$	-2.35
$Zn(OH)_2 + 2e^- = Zn + 2OH^-$	-1.245
$ZnO_2^= + 2H_2O + 2e^- = Zn + 4OH^-$	-1.216
$Zn(NH_3)_4^{++} + 2e^- = Zn + 4NH_3$	-1.03
$2H_2O + 2e^- = H_2 + 2OH^-$	-0.828
$Ag(NH_3)_2^+ + e^- = Ag + 2NH_3$	$+0.373$

Table 2

SOLUBILITY PRODUCTS

Compound	pK_{sp}	Compound	pK_{sp}
Barium		**Lead**	
BaC_2O_4	7.82	PbC_2O_4	11.08
$BaCO_3$	8.3	PbI_2	8.17
$BaCrO_4$	9.93	$Pb(IO_3)_2$	12.55
$Ba(IO_3)_2$	8.82	**Magnesium**	
$BaSO_4$	10.00	MgC_2O_4	4.07
Cadmium		$MgNH_4PO_4$	12.6
CdC_2O_4	7.75	**Mercury**	
CdS	28	Hg_2Cl_2	17.88
Calcium		$Hg_2(SCN)_2$	19.7
CaC_2O_4	8.89	**Silver**	
$CaCO_3$	8.32	$Ag(CH_3COO)$	2.64
$Ca(IO_3)_2$	6.15	$AgBr$	12.30
$Ca(OH)_2$	5.26	$AgBrO_3$	4.26
$CaSO_4$	5.0	$AgCl$	9.75
Copper		Ag_2CrO_4	11.72
$CuBr$	8.28	AgI	16.08
$CuCl$	6.73	$AgIO_3$	7.51
CuI	11.96	$AgSCN$	12.00
$CuSCN$	12.7	**Strontium**	
$Cu(IO_3)_2$	7.13	$SrCrO_4$	4.44
CuC_2O_4	7.54	SrC_2O_4	9.25
Iron		$Sr(IO_3)_2$	6.48
$Fe(OH)_2$	14.66	$SrSO_4$	6.49
FeS	17.2		
$Fe(OH)_3$	38.6		

Table 3

ACIDITY CONSTANTS

Acid	Reaction	pK_a
	INORGANIC ACIDS	
Ammonium	$NH_4^+ = H^+ + NH_3$	9.26
Carbonic [1]	$H_2CO_3 = H^+ + HCO_3^-$	6.35
[2]	$HCO_3^- = H^+ + CO_3^=$	10.33
Chromic [2]	$HCrO_4^- = H^+ + CrO_4^=$	6.50
Hydrocyanic	$HCN = H^+ + CN^-$	9.14
Hydrofluoric	$HF = H^+ + F^-$	3.17
Hydrosulfuric [1]	$H_2S = H^+ + HS^-$	6.96
[2]	$HS^- = H^+ + S^=$	14.0
Nitrous	$HNO_2 = H^+ + NO_2^-$	3.29
Phosphoric [1]	$H_3PO_4 = H^+ + H_2PO_4^-$	2.23
[2]	$H_2PO_4^- = H^+ + HPO_4^=$	7.21
[3]	$HPO_4^= = H^+ + PO_4^{-3}$	12.32
Sulfuric [2]	$HSO_4^- = H^+ + SO_4^=$	2.00
Sulfurous [1]	$H_2SO_3 = H^+ + HSO_3^-$	1.76
[2]	$HSO_3^- = H^+ + SO_3^=$	7.21
	ORGANIC ACIDS	
Acetic	$CH_3COOH = H^+ + CH_3COO^-$	4.74
Anilinium	$C_6H_5NH_3^+ = H^+ + C_6H_5NH_2$	4.61
Benzoic	C_6H_5COOH	
	$= H^+ + C_6H_5COO^-$	4.20
Ethylenediam- monium [1]	$C_2H_4(NH_3)_2^{++}$	
	$= H^+ + C_2H_4NH_2NH_3^+$	7.52
[2]	$C_2H_4NH_2NH_3^+$	
	$= H^+ + C_2H_4(NH_2)_2$	10.65
Ethylenediamine- tetra-acetic (EDTA)	$C_2H_4[N(CH_2COOH)_2]_2 = H_4Y$	
[1]	$H_4Y = H^+ + H_3Y^-$	1.99
[2]	$H_3Y^- = H^+ + H_2Y^=$	2.67
[3]	$H_2Y^= = H^+ + HY^{-3}$	6.16
[4]	$HY^{-3} = H^+ + Y^{-4}$	10.22
Oxalic [1]	$(COOH)_2 = H^+ + HOOCCOO^-$	1.25
[2]	$HOOCCOO^- = H^+ + (COO)_2^=$	4.28
Phthalic [1]	$C_6H_4(COOH)_2$	
	$= H^+ + C_6H_4COOH(COO)^-$	2.95
[2]	$C_6H_4COOH(COO)^-$	
	$= H^+ + C_6H_4(COO)_2^=$	5.41
Pyridinium	$C_5H_5NH^+ = H^+ + C_5H_5N$	5.17
Tartaric	$[CHOH(COOH)]_2 = H_2Tart$	
[1]	$H_2Tart = H^+ + HTart^-$	3.04
[2]	$HTart^- = H^+ + Tart^=$	4.37

Table 4

COMPLEX INSTABILITY CONSTANTS

$Ag(NH_3)_i^+ = Ag(NH_3)_{i-1}^+ + NH_3$ $pK_1 = 3.20$
$pK_2 = 3.83$

$Ag(SCN)_i^{+1-i} = Ag(SCN)_{i-1}^{+2-i} + SCN^-$
$pK_2 = 7.57$
$pK_3 = 2.51$
$pK_4 = 1.00$

$AgCl_i^{+1-i} = AgCl_{i-1}^{+2-i} + Cl^-$ $pK_1 = 2.69$
$pK_2 = 2.06$

$Ag(en)_i^+ = Ag(en)_{i-1}^+ + en$ $pK_1 = 5.0$
$pK_2 = 2.84$

$Ag(OAc)_i^{+1-i} = Ag(OAc)_{i-1}^{+2-i} + OAc^-$
$pK_1 = 0.74$
$pK_2 = 0.10$

$Co(en)_i^{++} = Co(en)_{i-1}^{++} + en$ $pK_1 = 5.89$
$pK_2 = 4.88$
$pK_3 = 3.10$

$Coen_3^{+3} = Co^{+3} + 3en$ $pK = 48.69$

$Cu(NH_3)_i^{++} = Cu(NH_3)_{i-1}^{++} + NH_3$ $pK_1 = 4.15$
$pK_2 = 3.50$
$pK_3 = 2.89$
$pK_4 = 2.13$
$pK_5 = -0.5$

$Cu(en)_i^{++} = Cu(en)_{i-1}^{++} + en$ $pK_1 = 10.55$
$pK_2 = 9.05$

$Fe(SCN)_i^{+3-i} = Fe(SCN)_{i-1}^{+4-i} + SCN^-$
$pK_1 = 2.06$
$pK_2 = 1.30$

$Fe(SO_4)_i^{+3-2i} = Fe(SO_4)_{i-1}^{+5-2i} + SO_4^=$
$pK_1 = 2.03$
$pK_2 = 0.95$

$FeHPO_4^+ = Fe^{+3} + HPO_4^+$ $pK_1 = 9.35$
$FeCl_i^{+3-i} = FeCl_{i-1}^{+4-i} + Cl^-$ $pK_1 = 0.62$
$pK_2 = 0.12$
$pK_3 = -1.40$

$FeSO_4 = Fe^{++} + SO_4^=$ $pK_1 = 2.30$

ANNOTATED BIBLIOGRAPHY

Many of the references cited at the end of the chapters in this text are of such general usefulness that they are gathered together here in a single annotated list. The annotations should help you to pick out suitable collateral reading so you can further pursue the topics that strike your fancy. A few books that are not cited at all in the rest of the text are also included here because they may be of value to you; these books are indicated by an asterisk. Also included, without annotation, are a number of analytical chemistry books that you may find useful in solving some of the problems you meet in the analytical procedures we have used.

BARROW, G. M., *The Structure of Molecules*, W. A. Benjamin, New York, 1963. Although the derivations leave a great deal to be desired for rigor, this little book is well worth reading as a first look at what molecular spectroscopy can tell us.

BASOLO, F., and R. C. JOHNSON, *Coordination Chemistry*, W. A. Benjamin, New York, 1964, is a fine introduction to the chemistry of metal complexes although slightly marred by a number of proofreading errors, which, fortunately, do not seriously impair understanding of the material.

BASOLO, F., and R. G. PEARSON, *Inorganic Reaction Mechanisms*, John Wiley & Sons, New York, 1958. A well-written book on an advanced level that is certainly worth looking into for tidbits of information and ideas for interesting experiments.

BEERS, Y., *Introduction to the Theory of Error*, Addison-Wesley, Reading, Mass., 1957, is a short book that presents some of the basis of error theory. The final chapter is concerned with the statistics of radiocounting.

*BREY, W. S., Jr., *Physical Methods for Determining Molecular Geometry*, Reinhold, New York, 1965 together with Barrow's book on structure constitutes a preliminary look at the power of physical methods for determining molecular structure.

*BROWN, G. I., *Modern Valency Theory*, Longmans, London, 1953 is an essentially nonmathematical introduction to molecular bonding. It is quite readable, but some of the nomenclature is a bit old fashioned, e.g., the classification of bond types.

BUTLER, J. N., *Ionic Equilibrium*, Addison-Wesley, Reading, Mass., 1964 is a fairly comprehensive introduction to the mathematical treatment of many common ionic-equilibrium problems. The approach taken is to set up each problem exactly and then make approximations (which are checked) to make the problem more easily solvable. One of the best features of the book is the fine set of annotated references at the end of each chapter.

BUTLER, J. N., *Solubility and pH Calculations*, Addison-Wesley, Reading, Mass., 1964 is a short introduction to ionic-equilibrium systems and the calculations required to understand them. The subject matter is simply a few selected topics from *Ionic Equilibrium*.

*BUTLER, J. N., and D. G. BOBROW, *The Calculus of Chemistry*, W. A. Benjamin, New York, 1965 emphasizes the usefulness of the mathematics it presents and in particular points out that mathematics should be used to make our work easier, not to becloud and confuse our problems.

*CAMPBELL, J. A., *Why Do Chemical Reactions Occur?*, Prentice-Hall, Englewood Cliffs, N. J., 1965, is a very nice introduction to the importance of the entropy concept based completely on directional and qualitative observations.

CHOPPIN, G. R., *Nuclei and Radioactivity*, W. A. Benjamin, New York, 1964 supplements nicely the standard textbook chapter on this topic and presents some interesting uses of radioactivity in chemistry.

CHOPPIN, G. R., *Experimental Nuclear Chemistry*, Prentice-Hall, Englewood Cliffs, N. J., 1961 is an introduction, with suggested experiments, to a number of aspects of radioactivity and the use of radioactive isotopes in chemistry.

CLIFFORD, A. F., *Inorganic Chemistry of Qualitative Analysis*, Prentice-Hall, Englewood Cliffs, N.J., 1961.

COMPANION, A., *Chemical Bonding*, McGraw-Hill, New York, 1964 is a well-written, short, nonmathematical introduction to our ideas on this subject.

COULSON, C., *Valence*, 2nd ed. Oxford University Press, New York, 1961 is a readable and exciting search into some of the mysteries of chemical bonding by one of the originators of many of the ideas that are presently used to describe the chemical bond.

DANIELS, F., J. H. MATHEWS, J. W. WILLIAMS, P. BENDER, and R. A. ALBERTY, *Experimental Physical Chemistry*, 5th ed. McGraw-Hill, New York, 1956 is a popular junior-senior level laboratory text from which ideas for special experiments may be gleaned. (Note: there is a sixth edition.)

* DENBIGH, K., *The Principles of Chemical Equilibrium*, Cambridge University Press, London, 1961 is an excellent junior-senior level text—definitely not an introduction, but a thorough treatment—that you will not have much difficulty with after a good calculus course. The final section on statistical thermodynamics is superb.

* DEWAR, M. J. S., *An Introduction to Modern Chemistry*, Oxford University Press, New York, 1965 is an "overview" of chemistry which gives a feeling for where you are going before you set out on the journey. Unfortunately, there is too much emphasis on the utility of quantum chemistry to the detriment of more classical material, which is reflected in the relative amount of space given to the two areas and in the somewhat careless treatment of the more classical topics.

* EDWARDS, J. O., *Inorganic Reaction Mechanisms*, W. A. Benjamin, New York, 1965 is at a somewhat advanced level, but anyone who becomes interested in the inorganic reactions in this book might find that Edwards' book would yield some valuable insights.

* EYRING, H., and E. M. EYRING, *Modern Chemical Kinetics*, Reinhold, New York, 1963 is not an introductory text like the others in this series of Reinhold books. Rather, this book presents one of the most prominent theoretical treatments of reaction kinetics, with no introduction to empirical kinetics but a brief chapter on the study of very fast reactions in aqueous solution. If your interest in kinetics is aroused, you might be interested in studying this book after you have digested one of the short introductory books.

* FLECK, G. M., *Equilibrium in Solution*, Holt, Rinehart & Winston, New York, 1966 although intended for use in a course beyond general chemistry, has a number of chapters that are applicable to the equilibria discussed in this laboratory textbook and could be good supplemental reading if you have difficulty with equilibrium problems.

FROST, A. A., and R. G. PEARSON, *Chemical Kinetics*, 2nd ed. John Wiley & Sons, New York, 1961 will not be at all difficult to tackle as a sequel to King's introductory text.

* GRAY, H. B., *Electrons and Chemical Bonding*, W. A. Benjamin, New York, 1964 presents a fairly pictorial introduction to chemical bonding. The molecular-orbital arguments, which are not well enough spelled out, are not completely clear but any confusion can usually be dispelled by your instructor.

* GREENBERG, D. A., *Mathematics for Introductory Science Courses: Calculus and Vectors*, W. A. Benjamin, New York, 1965 is an introduction to the subject that stresses use rather than proof and formalism.

* HARGREAVES, G., *Elementary Chemical Thermodynamics*, 2nd ed. Butterworth, London, 1963 is not as elementary as the short books by Nash or Mahan, but it might profitably be used as a follow-up book for anyone interested in pursuing the subject only a bit further.

HERZBERG, G., *Atomic Spectra and Atomic Structure*, Dover, New York, 1944 is a well-written introduction to atomic spectra. It is not a "nonmathematical" book nor does it stop with an analysis of simple atoms, but rather it introduces the whole complex range of the subject of atomic spectra.

* HILDEBRAND, J. H., *An Introduction to Molecular Kinetic Theory*, Reinhold, New York, 1963 is a lively introduction marred by a number of trivial, but annoying, proofreading errors.

* HOCHSTRASSER, R. M., *Behavior of Electrons in Atoms*, W. A. Benjamin, New York, 1964 would be a good introduction to atomic theory and spectra if it were not for the inordinate number of errors that make it virtually impossible for a neophyte to use the book independently.

HOLDEN, A., and P. SINGER, *Crystals and Crystal Growing*, Doubleday Anchor, Garden City, N.Y., 1960 is worth perusing for ideas for experiments and for a few insights into the behavior of crystals.

KING, E. L., *How Chemical Reactions Occur*, W. A. Benjamin, New York, 1963 is a short paperback that is a very worthwhile introduction to chemical kinetics.

KIEFFER, W., *The Mole Concept in Chemistry*, Reinhold, New York, 1962 introduces the subject in a very orderly manner with some carefully chosen examples and a refreshing point of view.

* KLEPPNER, D., and N. RAMSEY, *Quick Calculus*, John Wiley & Sons, New York, 1965 is an excellent little programmed manual for learning the fundamentals of calculus, albeit excluding rigorous proofs. This book teaches the usefulness of calculus.

* KLOTZ, I., *Introduction to Chemical Thermodynamics*, W. A. Benjamin, New York, 1964 is an "introduction" for those who are familiar with partial derivatives. This is an excellent textbook to delve into after you have exhausted the elementary thermodynamics books.

KOLTHOFF, I. M., and E. B. SANDELL, *Textbook of Quantitative Analysis*, 3rd ed. Macmillan, New York, 1952.

* LATHAM, J. L., *Elementary Reaction Kinetics*, Butterworth, London, 1964 is an introduction to chemical kinetics at the general chemistry level. The best part of the book is the use of many real chemical systems as examples of the points made.

* LATHAM, J. L., D. A. JENKINS, and G. R. H. JONES, *Selected Experiments in Physical Chemistry*, Butterworth, London, 1964 stresses the applications of physico-chemical methods to chemical analysis. You might find some good ideas for independent work in this series of experiments.

LATIMER, W., *Oxidation Potentials*, 2nd ed. Prentice-Hall, Englewood Cliffs, N.J., 1952 is a classic compendium of information gleaned from electrochemical cell measurements. Although some of this material is out of date and there is usually no indication whether a potential is an actual standard cell potential or a formal potential, this is still a most complete compilation and has had immense influence in electrochemistry. All half-reactions are written by Latimer as oxidations, so the signs of their potentials must be reversed if they are to be used as we discussed in Chapter 10.

LINNETT, J., *The Electronic Structure of Molecules*, John Wiley & Sons, New York, 1964 presents a well-written and lively account of an interesting and somewhat novel way to look at the "electron pairing" in molecules.

*LEWIN, S., *The Solubility Product Principle*, Pitman, London, 1960 stresses the activity concept and points out the myriad places one can go wrong if concentrations instead of activities are thoughtlessly plugged into equations.

*LIVINGSTON, R., *Physico-Chemical Experiments*, Revised ed. Macmillan, New York, 1948 is another book of physical chemistry experiments from which you might glean some interesting ideas for further experiments of your own.

LUDER, W. F., and S. ZUFFANTI, *The Electronic Theory of Acids and Bases*, 2nd ed. Dover, New York, 1961 is an excellent introduction to the Lewis theory of acids and bases. The book is filled with examples and suggestions for experiments to illustrate the ideas presented.

MAHAN, B. H., *Elementary Chemical Thermodynamics*, W. A. Benjamin, New York, 1963 is a straightforward introduction to thermodynamics using a minimum of calculus.

*MARTIN, D. F., and B. B. MARTIN, *Coordination Compounds*, McGraw-Hill, New York, 1964 is not nearly as good or as useful as the other short books on inorganic coordination chemistry that are available.

*MORRIS, K. B., *Principles of Chemical Equilibrium*, Reinhold, New York, 1965 stresses a thermodynamic approach to equilibrium problems although the phenomenological approach is not neglected. Applications of ionic equilibria to qualitative analysis make up a substantial and interesting portion of the book.

*MURMANN, R. K., *Inorganic Complex Compounds*, Reinhold, New York, 1964 is another introduction to this field, with an interesting chapter (not found in other books at this level) on the thermodynamics of inorganic coordination compounds.

NASH, L. K., *Elements of Chemical Thermodynamics*, Addison-Wesley, Reading, Mass., 1962 is an introduction to thermodynamics that is more classical and historical in approach than the other texts at this level. Again the use of calculus is minimized.

*NASH, L. K., *The Atomic-Molecular Theory*, Harvard University Press, Cambridge, Mass., 1950 is an historical survey of atomic-molecular theory from the inception of empirical atomic theory (Dalton) to the final resolution of the problem of determining atomic weights and molecular formulas (Cannizzaro).

NASH, L. K., *Stoichiometry*, Addison-Wesley, Reading, Mass., 1966 covers some of the same territory as Kieffer's *Mole Concept* but in much more detail with a much greater emphasis on the actual experimental observations that lead to our present understanding of atomic and molecular weights.

PAULING, L., *The Nature of the Chemical Bond*, 3rd ed. Cornell University Press, Ithaca, N.Y., 1960 is a classic compilation and interpretation of data on molecular structure by one of the pioneers in the field.

PAULING, L., and R. HAYWARD, *The Architecture of Molecules*, Freeman, San Francisco, 1965 is an exquisitely beautiful volume.

PIERCE, W. C., E. L. HAENISCH, and D. T. SAWYER, *Quantitative Analysis*, 4th ed. John Wiley & Sons, New York, 1958.

*RICH, R., *Periodic Correlations*, W. A. Benjamin, New York, 1965 is a peregrination through the periodic table that shows the similarities of scenery that recur throughout. This book goes well beyond the usual chapter on the subject in most general chemistry textbooks and yields a good glimpse of the awe-inspiring correlations one can make among the elements and their compounds.

*ROBERTS, J. D., *Notes on Molecular Orbital Calculations*, W. A. Benjamin, New York, 1962 presents the rudiments. Anyone who wants to understand (at least in a simple way) where some of the "fuzz-ball" pictures of molecules come from should study this book.

*ROMER, A., *The Restless Atom*, Doubleday Anchor, Garden City, N.Y., 1960 is the story of the experiments that led to our present level of understanding of the atom.

SEBERA, D. K., *Electronic Structure and Chemical Bonding*, Blaisdell, Waltham, Mass., 1964 is a well-conceived nonmathematical introduction to molecular structure which unfortunately contains many proofreading errors. If you read with care and keep your critical faculties alert, as they always should be, this is a rewarding book.

SHAMOS, M. H., ed., *Great Experiments in Physics*, Holt, Rinehart & Winston, New York, 1959 is an excellent compilation of the reports of some "break-through experiments" by the experimenters themselves from Galileo to Einstein.

*SHOEMAKER, D. P., and C. W. GARLAND, *Experiments in Physical Chemistry*, McGraw-Hill, New York, 1962 is a junior-senior level laboratory textbook that can provide a number of ideas for experiments. The format is much like this volume.

SHURCLIFF, W. A., and S. S. BALLARD, *Polarized Light*, D. Van Nostrand, Princeton, N.J., 1964.

*SISLER, H. H., *Chemistry in Non-Aqueous Solvents*, Reinhold, New York, 1961 is a good supplement to most textbooks which give only a small section to this area. Since the information gleaned by studying chemical interactions in nonaqueous media is often unattainable in any other way, an understanding of these systems is imperative.

SKOOG, D. A., and D. M. WEST, *Fundamentals of Analytical Chemistry*, Holt, Rinehart & Winston, New York, 1963.

*STRONG, L. E., and W. J. STRATTON, *Chemical Energy*, Reinhold, New York, 1965 is on an introductory level.

SWIFT, E. H., and W. P. SCHAEFER, *Qualitative Elemental Analysis*, Freeman, San Francisco, 1962.

*SYRKIN, V. K., and M. E. DYATKINA, *Structure of Molecules and the Chemical Bond*, Dover, New York, 1964 is loaded with experimental information as well as theoretical rationalization of the observed structures of molecules. Although some of this material is out of date (the original was published in Russian in 1946) the volume shows great insight into the development of ideas about chemical bonding.

*VANDERWERF, C. A., *Acids, Bases, and the Chemistry of the Covalent Bond*, Reinhold, New York, 1961 presents some of the same material as Luder and Zuffanti, but there is more in this book on the Brønsted acid-base concept. The two books are complementary rather than competitive.

VOGEL, A. I., *A Textbook of Micro and Semi-Micro Qualitative Inorganic Analysis*, 4th ed. Longmans Green, London, 1954.

WASER, J., *Quantitative Chemistry*, revised ed. W. A. Benjamin, New York, 1964 is a very fine laboratory textbook emphasizing experiments in quantitative analysis. The format is very much like that of this book and the material is presented at about the same level.

WASER, J., *Basic Chemical Thermodynamics*, W. A. Benjamin, New York, 1966 is an introductory thermodynamics text that is slightly more mathematically sophisticated than either Nash's or Mahan's books. The derivations requiring partial differentiation, etc., are, however, frosting on the cake; the text may be read and understood without delving into these sections.

*WEISKOPF, V. F., *Knowledge and Wonder*, Doubleday Anchor, Garden City, N.Y., 1963 should be read and wondered at every year or so by anyone interested in the sciences. A superb short account of what we think we know and don't know about the world about us.

WILSON, E. B., Jr., *An Introduction to Scientific Research*, McGraw-Hill, New York, 1952 is a superb book written in a lively style but not to be taken lightly. Become acquainted with it early to learn some of the pitfalls (and ways to avoid them) of experimental work.

YATSIMIRSKII, K. B., and V. P. VASIL'EV, *Instability Constants of Complex Compounds*, Consultants Bureau, New York, 1960 is most valuable as a compendium of equilibrium constants for dissociation of metal-ligand complexes. The book also contains a valuable introductory section in which the methods that are used to measure these equilibria are discussed.

*YOUNG, J. A., *Practice in Thinking*, Prentice-Hall, Englewood Cliffs, N.J., 1958 is a unique laboratory textbook in which questions are asked, but no directions for finding the answers are given. The present textbook is partially an attempt to translate the philosophy of Young's book into a somewhat different format.

INDEX

INDEX